DIFFUSION
IN SOLIDS, LIQUIDS, GASES

PHYSICAL CHEMISTRY
A Series of Monographs

Edited by

ERIC HUTCHINSON and P. VAN RYSSELBERGHE

Department of Chemistry, Stanford University, Stanford, California

ACADEMIC PRESS   New York and London

DIFFUSION
IN SOLIDS, LIQUIDS, GASES

By

W. JOST

PROFESSOR OF PHYSICAL CHEMISTRY
UNIVERSITÄT GÖTTINGEN
GÖTTINGEN, GERMANY

THIRD PRINTING
WITH ADDENDUM
1960

ACADEMIC PRESS INC., PUBLISHERS
NEW YORK

First Printing, 1952
Second Printing, 1955
Third Printing (with Addendum), 1960

Preface

Originally my intention was to write a second edition of "Diffusion und chemische Reaktion in festen Stoffen" (Leipzig-Dresden, 1937), but it soon became apparent that it would be better to treat diffusion processes on a broader basis and to neglect the subject of chemical reactions in solids entirely, except for such cases that could be described in terms of diffusion processes. This seems the more justified since several comprehensive articles on reactions in solids have appeared by G. Cohn, Fricke, Hüttig, and Hedvall, and because a monograph on reactions in solids will be published in this series.

Although the present monograph contains several theoretical chapters it is the work of an experimental physical chemist who time and again encountered diffusion problems. Its chief aim is to assist in planning, evaluating, and understanding diffusion experiments, at the same time giving a survey of the results obtained to date. There is no doubt that interest in, and the value of, research in diffusion will be greatly enhanced by the increased availability of radioactive isotopes.

No attempt has been made at completeness in the presentation of either theoretical or experimental material since I am convinced that selected examples presented in great detail are more valuable than many examples dealt with briefly.

I am deeply indebted to many colleagues; my special thanks are due to Professors Clusius and Eggert of Zürich, to Dr. Mörikofer of the Davos Meteorological Observatory for aid in obtaining literature, and to Dr. R. Haase, Professor F. Horst Müller, and Dr. A. Münster, who generously gave their support and criticism. My thanks are also due to Mr. E. Krücke who assisted in preparing lists of references and in the preparation of tables and to Mr. Eckhard who made the drawings for the figures. I wish also to express my gratitude to Professor E. Hutchinson, the editor of this series, for his valuable advice regarding the completion of the manuscript and for his suggestions in wording. Finally, my thanks are due to the publishers, Academic Press, for their liberal and understanding help during the preparation of this book.

Marburg, 1951.   W. Jost

PREFACE TO REVISED EDITION 1960

The friendly reception which the book has had since the first edition appeared in 1952 has encouraged the author to prepare a revised edition. It was decided that the most feasible plan would be to add appendices that would summarize recent developments.

In addition to the new textual material an annotated bibliography has been included as a guide to work published after the first edition. The field has grown to such an extent that it was necessary to be selective rather than to attempt to include all publications in the field.

The author is grateful for much valuable criticism he has had from friends and reviewers. In preparing the appendix to Chapters X—XII he had the cooperation of Dr. E. U. Franck of this laboratory.

Göttingen, 1960   W. JOST

Contents

APPENDIX TO 1960 EDITION
Supplement Summarizing Developments in the Field to 1959

CHAPTER I

THE FUNDAMENTAL LAWS OF DIFFUSION

I. Fundamental laws for isotropic substances

Diffusion is a process which leads to an equalization of concentrations within a single phase. The laws of diffusion connect the rate of flow of the diffusing substance with the concentration gradient responsible for this flow. Since in interdiffusion at least two substances are involved, there will be, in general, more than one diffusion equation, one referring to each of the different species present. In the case of two components we have two equations, expressing the fact that the rate of flow of the second component is of opposite direction, but of equal magnitude to that of the first one*. Hence we need not consider the second equation explicitly. In this chapter, generally, we shall write a single equation of diffusion only, without distinguishing magnitudes, referring to the single components by suffixes. It should be borne in mind, however, that generally there are at least two equations, one for each species present.

We define the diffusion flow or current J of a substance in a mixture with other substances as the amount of this substance passing perpendicularly through a reference surface of unit area during unit time.

The definition refers to any mixture, regardless of its state of aggregation. The dimension of J is: the quantity of substance per cm^2 per second, if we choose c.g.s. units for the measurement of length and time. The unit chosen for the quantity of substance is not specified since the formulae for diffusion are independent of the special choice. We therefore may choose mass (in grams or pounds or any other unit),

---

* Even here, there are exceptions. In the case of interstitial diffusion within a solid, as for instance carbon in iron, it seems reasonable to consider the iron lattice as frame of reference. Then we have a diffusion current of carbon, but no equivalent current of iron. Of course one could define diffusion in such a way that there are two currents of opposite sign and equal magnitude, but this hardly would be justified by the underlying physical process.

The reasonable physical picture might be to assume interdiffusion of empty interstitial sites and carbon atoms.

Cf. Onsager (111).

number of gram molecules (moles), number of molecules, cubic centimeters of gas at N.T.P. or whatever unit may seem most convenient in the case under consideration.

If x be the coordinate chosen perpendicular to the reference surface, and c the concentration of the diffusing substance, given as amount of substance per cubic centimeter, in the same units as those chosen for the diffusion current, Fick's (70) first law of diffusion may be stated in the form*

$$J = - D \, \partial c / \partial x ,\qquad\qquad [1.1]$$

where D is the coefficient of diffusion for the substance under consideration. D has the dimension $cm^2 \ sec^{-1}$ and, therefore changes correspondingly with a change of the units of length and time, but is independent of the unit by which the amount of substance in J and c is measured. The further assumption, usually implied by [1.1], that D be a constant for a given medium, temperature and pressure, is not necessary, and is usually only approximately true.

We can formulate [1.1] independently of a system of coordinates by using vector notation

$$\boldsymbol{J} = - D \ \text{grad} \ c .\qquad\qquad [1.2]$$

[1.2] states that the vector $\boldsymbol{J}$ of the diffusion current is in the opposite direction to the concentration gradient, grad c, being proportional to its absolute value. The surface of reference is to be chosen perpendicular to the direction of this vector. When we introduce a special rectangular coordinate system, the vector grad c has the components $\partial c / \partial x, \ \partial c / \partial y, \ \partial c / \partial z$.

If we wish to determine the diffusion coefficient by means of equation [1.1] we must find an arrangement in which both, J and $\partial c / \partial x$ are accessible to measurement. This is possible in special cases (cf. p. 8).

Generally, however, it is not possible to investigate diffusion under conditions of constant concentration gradient, which implies the establishment of a steady state. One, therefore, has to determine the change of concentration with time, caused by diffusion within a gas mixture, a liquid solution or a solid. When there is diffusion in the x-direction only, and when we observe the increase of the amount of

---

* The diffusion current J might also be given in the form

$$J = c \bar{v}$$

where c is the concentration of the diffusing substance, $\bar{v}$ its mean velocity, provided the system under consideration is at rest. Thus

$$\bar{v} = - D d \log c / d x .$$

The equation, corresponding to [1.2] is obvious.

substance within a volume element bounded by two parallel planes of unit area situated at x and $x + dx$, this increase is

$$(J)_x - (J)_{x+dx} = D [(\partial c/\partial x)_{x+dx} - (\partial c/\partial x)_x] = D (\partial^2 c/\partial x^2)_x dx + \dots \quad [1.3]$$

After dividing [1.3] by the volume $dx \cdot 1$ cm^2 of the element, we obtain for the increase of the concentration with time, in the limit $dx \to 0$

$$\partial c/\partial t = D \partial^2 c/\partial x^2 \quad [1.4]$$

which is Fick's (70) second law of diffusion, derived on the assumption that D is constant. If diffusion occurs in an arbitrary direction, we have to add to the right-hand side of [1.4] two corresponding expressions for the y and z coordinates, giving

$$\partial c/\partial t = D (\partial^2 c/\partial x^2 + \partial^2 c/\partial y^2 + \partial^2 c/\partial z^2) = D \Delta c = D \, \mathrm{div} \, \mathrm{grad} \, c \quad [1.5]$$

where Δ is Laplace's operator, $\partial^2/\partial x^2 + \partial^2/\partial y^2 + \partial^2/\partial z^2$. The last term in vector notation is independent of a special coordinate system. Equation [1.5] may be transformed to other systems of coordinates, in particular, to cylindrical or polar coordinates. Most important for practical purposes are the cases of cylindrical or spherical symmetry, where c depends on the radius r only, and is independent of the coordinate z (corresponding to the axis of the cylinder) and of the angle φ (in case of cylindrical coordinates) or independent of both angles Θ and φ (in case of spherical coordinates). For these special cases one obtains

$$\partial c/\partial t = D [\partial^2 c/\partial r^2 + (1/r) \partial c/\partial r] \quad \text{Axial Symmetry} \quad [1.6]$$

and

$$\partial c/\partial t = D [\partial^2 c/\partial r^2 + (2/r) \partial c/\partial r] \quad \text{Spherical Symmetry.} \quad [1.7]$$

It is not difficult to find solutions of [1.4], [1.5], [1.6] and [1.7] given adequate initial and boundary conditions.

As mentioned above (p. 2), the assumption that D is independent of the concentration and of the position coordinates, is a specialization, not generally valid. There is no difficulty in formulating the equations if D is not constant. [1.1] remains unchanged, but in deriving an expression for the change of concentration with time we must treat D as variable, thus obtaining

$$\partial c/\partial t = \partial/\partial x (D \, \partial c/\partial x) \quad [1.8]$$

instead of [1.4]. In the general case we obtain instead of [1.8]

$$\partial c/\partial t = \partial/\partial x (D \, \partial c/\partial x) + \partial/\partial y (D \, \partial c/\partial y) + \partial/\partial z (D \, \partial c/\partial z) \quad [1.9]$$

$$= \mathrm{div} (D \, \mathrm{grad} \, c) , \quad [1.10]$$

and corresponding expressions, if [1.9] is transformed to cylindrical or polar coordinates, Barrer (52). Again, we give only the equations for the special cases of axial or spherical symmetry

$$\partial c/\partial t = (1/r) \, \partial/\partial r \, (r \, D \partial c/\partial r) \qquad \text{Axial Symmetry} \qquad [1.11]$$

$$\partial c/\partial t = (1/r^2) \, \partial/\partial r \, (r^2 \, D \, \partial c/\partial r) \qquad \text{Spherical Symmetry} . \qquad [1.12]$$

Where the diffusion coefficient shows a marked dependence on the concentration, one is compelled to make use of one of the above relations, but it is usually very inconvenient to apply these equations. If D does not depend explicitly on the position coordinate, we may transform [1.8] to

$$\partial c/\partial t = D \, \partial^2 c/\partial x^2 + (\partial D/\partial c) \, (\partial c/\partial x)^2 . \qquad [1.13]$$

We repeat the argument which led to the equations [1.3] and [1.4]. The surplus of substance, entering into a volume element, bounded by two parallel faces of unit area and distant Δx, in unit time is:

$$(J)_x - (J)_{x+\Delta x} = - (D \partial c/\partial x)_x + (D \partial c/\partial x)_{x+\Delta x} \qquad [1.14]$$
$$= - (D \partial c/\partial x)_x + (D)_x \, (\partial c/\partial x)_{x+\Delta x} + (\partial D/\partial c)_x \Delta c \cdot (\partial c/\partial x)_{x+\Delta x} ,$$

where Δc is the concentration difference corresponding to the distance Δx. If, now, we reduce the concentration differences in our system sufficiently, keeping the average concentration constant in the volume element under consideration, then D and $\partial D/\partial c$ will remain unchanged, and the differential coefficients with respect to x will change by amounts approximately proportional to the change of the concentration differences. Hence with decreasing Δc the third term on the right will decrease as $(\Delta c)^2$, while the preceding terms decrease only as Δc. For sufficiently small concentration differences, therefore, the second term on the right-hand side of [1.13], containing $\partial D/\partial c$, may be neglected. Concentration differences will be sufficiently small, if the variation of D within the concentration range under consideration is small compared with D. It follows that the simplest way of dealing with variable D consists of determining differential diffusion coefficients within sufficiently narrow concentration ranges, employing the equations for constant average D.

II. Diffusion in anisotropic substances.

While gases and liquids are isotropic and diffusion of a substance is characterized by one single parameter, D, solid crystals, with the exception of those of the regular system, are generally anisotropic and diffusion is characterized by two or three independent magnitudes, the main diffusion coefficients. Therefore, in an anisotropic crystal, the diffusion current J has components J_x, J_y, J_z

$$
\begin{aligned}
J_x &= -D_{xx}\, \partial c/\partial x \\
J_y &= \qquad\qquad -D_{yy}\, \partial c/\partial y \\
J_z &= \qquad\qquad\qquad\qquad -D_{zz}\, \partial c/\partial z,
\end{aligned}
\qquad [1.15]
$$

where we have assumed that the axes x, y, z have been chosen properly as the main axes of diffusion (given by the symmetry properties of the crystal, cf. Voigt (42)). Then only the three main diffusion coefficients D_{xx}, D_{yy}, D_{zz} appear, the terms outside the main diagonal of the matrix scheme vanishing. It should be mentioned, however, that it is not immediately obvious, that the diffusion tensor (i. e., the scheme of coefficients on the right-hand side of [1.15]) must be symmetrical. Even if the equations refer to the main axes of diffusion, there might be antisymmetric components*

$$
\begin{aligned}
&- &D_{xy} &\quad D_{xz} \\
&-D_{xy} &- &\quad D_{yz} \\
&-D_{xz} &-D_{yz} &\quad -
\end{aligned}
\qquad [1.16]
$$

giving rise to additional components in the diffusion current

$$
\begin{aligned}
J'_x &= \qquad\qquad -D_{xy}\partial c/\partial y - D_{xz}\partial c/\partial z \\
J'_y &= +D_{xy}\partial c/\partial x \qquad\qquad -D_{yz}\partial c/\partial z \\
J'_z &= +D_{xz}\partial c/\partial x + D_{yz}\partial c/\partial z.
\end{aligned}
\qquad [1.17]
$$

This additional diffusion current J' (components J'_x, J'_y, J'_z), which should be added to [1.15] is of vanishing divergence, as is easily seen

$$
\begin{aligned}
\mathrm{div}\,J' &= \partial/\partial x\, J_x + \partial/\partial y\, J_y + \partial/\partial z\, J_z = \\
&= \qquad\quad -D_{xy}\partial^2 c/\partial y\partial x - D_{xz}\partial^2 c/\partial z\partial x \\
&+ D_{xy}\partial^2 c/\partial x\partial y \qquad\qquad -D_{yz}\partial^2 c/\partial z\partial y \\
&+ D_{xz}\partial^2 c/\partial x\partial z + D_{yz}\partial^2 c/\partial y\partial z \qquad\qquad = 0.
\end{aligned}
\qquad [1.18]
$$

Now the change of concentration with time is given by the divergence of the diffusion current, thus these additional flow components would not contribute to any change of concentrations. However startling this fact may be, it is not sufficient for the conclusion that such antisymmetric tensor components would not exist.

In crystal physics one can prove, (Voigt (42)), that for reversible processes the corresponding tensor must be symmetrical, as, for instance, for dielectric polarization. But these proofs fail with irreversible processes, like electric conduction and heat conduction, and, of course, diffusion as well.

* Provided we consider a crystal of sufficiently low symmetry.

But nevertheless the existence of such components is very improbable, Voigt (42), since all attempts to find rotatory components in heat conduction have failed. Finally Onsager (109, 110) (cf. also Meixner (104, 105)) succeeded in proving fundamental "reciprocity relations" for irreversible processes, by starting from the principle of microscopic reversibility. These reciprocity relations state that even in irreversible processes there must be symmetry of the corresponding tensors. If the components of any such tensor be denoted by a_{ik}, this means that $a_{ik} = a_{ki}$. Now in our special case we had chosen special axes, such that $D_{ik} = - D_{ki}$. This is compatible with Onsager's relations only if $D_{ik} = D_{ki} = 0$. It might be stressed again that this special form depends on the system of coordinates chosen. By transformation to other axes there will be terms outside the main diagonal, but symmetric ones, without rotatory components.

It therefore follows, that equation [1.15] is already the most general equation for anisotropic crystals, properly orientated, and of course with the restriction that either D does not vary considerably with concentration or that small concentration differences only are considered. In case of higher symmetry of the crystal two or all three of the main diffusion coefficients may become equal.

So far very little information is available on diffusion and electrolytic conduction in anisotropic crystals. We shall, therefore, refrain from discussing extensively the more complicated cases of diffusion in anisotropic bodies with diffusion coefficients depending on concentration. From [1.15] it can be seen that, except for the directions of the main axes of the diffusion tensor, the direction of the diffusion flow does not coincide with that of the concentration gradient. But, by choosing an adequate experimental arrangement, one can avoid serious difficulties in measuring diffusion in anisotropic substances. Instead of the single measurement required for an isotropic substance, however, one has to carry out two or three independent measurements with an anisotropic substance. When we cut a plate perpendicularly to one of the main axes (or a cylinder with an axis parallel to one of the main axes), diffusion through the plate (or parallel to the axis of the cylinder) will occur in exactly the same way as for an isotropic body. By two or three such measurements, therefore, we can determine the two or three main diffusion coefficients, which, for crystals, may differ by as much as 6 orders of magnitude (Seith (115)). Of course, in plates or cylinders cut in the above manner, we can determine concentration dependent coefficients of diffusion in exactly the same manner as with isotropic solids*.

---

* The problem becomes very complicated if the symmetry properties of the crystal change considerably with concentration, unless small concentration differences only are permitted.

Equation [1.15] is the analogue to Fick's first law of diffusion, generalized for anisotropic substances. Fick's second law for the one-dimensional case is to be substituted by one of the relations

$$\left.\begin{array}{l} \partial c/\partial t = D_{xx}\partial^2 c/\partial x^2 \\ \partial c/\partial t = D_{yy}\partial^2 c/\partial y^2 \\ \partial c/\partial t = D_{zz}\partial^2 c/\partial z^2 \end{array}\right\} \begin{array}{l} \text{for one-dimensional} \\ \text{diffusion in the direction of} \\ \text{one of the main axes} \end{array} \quad [1.19]$$

according to which direction has been chosen. In the three-dimensional case we have

$$\partial c/\partial t = D_{xx}\partial^2 c/\partial x^2 + D_{yy}\partial^2 c/\partial y^2 + D_{zz}\partial^2 c/\partial z^2 , \quad [1.20]$$

where now, in contrast to the formulation of p. 3, the x, y, z axes cannot be chosen arbitrarily but must coincide with the main axes of the diffusion tensor. Of course, by application of the laws of tensor transformation, equations [1.15], [1.19] and [1.20] might easily be transformed to arbitrary axes. But usually it is not worth while doing that, because the resulting equations would be more complicated than those we have chosen.

For a mathematical treatment of [1.20] it is possible to transform this equation into an expression identical with that for diffusion in an isotropic body. The substitution (cf. Carlslaw-Jaeger (3), Frank-Mises (22))

$$\xi = x\sqrt{D}/\sqrt{D_{xx}}, \quad \eta = y\sqrt{D}/\sqrt{D_{yy}}, \quad \zeta = z\sqrt{D}/\sqrt{D_{zz}} \quad [1.21]$$

gives

$$\partial c/\partial t = D \left(\partial^2 c/\partial \xi^2 + \partial^2 c/\partial \eta^2 + \partial^2 c/\partial \zeta^2\right) . \quad [1.22]$$

This equation has been employed in the case of heat conduction. Let us choose a plate perpendicular to the z-axis, of thickness small compared with the dimensions in the x- and y-directions. We now bring a point source of heat upon the centre 0 of the plate which we consider as of infinite extension. When the plate is isotropic, the isotherms are circles with centre 0. When the plate is anisotropic, these isotherms are transformed into ellipses with main axes coinciding with the x- and y-directions, for these have been chosen in accordance with the crystallographic symmetry. The ratio of the lengths of these axes, x_0 and y_0 follows from [1.21] and [1.22]

$$x_0 : y_0 = \sqrt{D_{xx}} : \sqrt{D_{yy}} . \quad [1.23]$$

In order to determine this ratio of the main heat conductivities de Sénarmont (116, 117, 118, 119) and Voigt (42, 137) covered the plate with a thin layer of a certain wax of a convenient melting point. During an experiment the wax melts, starting at the centre, up to an isotherm corresponding to the melting point of the wax. Therefore, the molten area will be bounded by an ellipse. This boundary line can easily be observed after the experiment has been stopped, and the lengths of the main axes of the ellipse can easily by measured. Therefore, in order to determine the two or three main heat conductivities of a crystal, one needs to carry out only one absolute measurement and one or two relative measurements by de Sénarmont's method.

It should be possible eventually to adapt this method to measurements of diffusion coefficients in anisotropic crystals, by using radioactive tracers.

III. Steady state in diffusion

In a steady state there is no change of concentration with time. The steady state, therefore, is characterized by the condition

$$\partial c/\partial t = 0 . \qquad [1.24]$$

According to the special case under consideration, this will lead to different stationary concentration distributions. For linear flow substitution of [1.24] into equation [1.4] p. 3 gives

$$D\partial^2 c/\partial x^2 = 0, \quad \partial c/\partial x = \text{const.}, \quad c = c_0 + c_1 x , \qquad [1.25]$$

consequently a constant concentration gradient and a linear distribution of concentration exist if the diffusion coefficient can be treated as constant. The case of varying D will be treated later. A steady state, as given by [1.25], may easily be realized experimentally; for instance in the case of a vapor diffusing through air or another gas (cf. Stefan (128, 129)). If we introduce some volatile substance, e.g. ether, into the lower part of a vertical cylinder, open at its upper end, ether vapor diffuses from the bottom to the free atmosphere above the open end of the cylinder. In order to avoid convection currents* one should choose a cylinder of not too large a cross section, q cm^2, and of sufficient length, l cm, measured from the surface of the ether to the open end of the cylinder. (During the course of evaporation this length l will increase slowly, but as long as the change of the length is small compared with the absolute value, this does not affect our argument.) After a certain time, the length of which may be estimated from the equations for non-stationary diffusion, the steady state will be established to a sufficient approximation. During this steady state ether will evaporate with constant velocity and diffuse with the same constant velocity through an air layer of height l. The equilibrium concentration c_e of the vapor just

---

* This means also that temperature differences within the cylinder must be kept sufficiently small.

above the ether surface is determined by the vapor pressure at the temperature of the experiment, and, therefore, is known. The amount of ether, s, evaporating during time t can easily be found. If, on the one hand convection currents within the cylinder are suppressed, while on the other hand, the ether, escaping at the upper end of the cylinder is carried away by slight convection currents, always present in the free atmosphere, then the ether concentration at the upper end of the cylinder can be considered as being zero. Thus the concentration gradient $\partial c/\partial x$, constant throughout the whole length of the cylinder is given by

$$\partial c/\partial x = \frac{c_0 - c_e}{l} = -c_e/l, \qquad [1.26]$$

if the x axis coincides with the axis of the cylinder. Then the quantity of ether which has evaporated and diffused, will be

$$s = Jq \cdot t = Dqtc_e/l \qquad [1.27]$$

and therefore

$$D = sl/qtc_e . \qquad [1.28]$$

D is the diffusion coefficient for ether vapor in air*.

* The above relations are approximately correct only, for the following reason. In diffusion equal amounts of either component (on a molar basis) must diffuse in opposite directions through a surface of reference. In our case, however, the lower end of the tube, i.e., the liquid surface, is impermeable toward air. Thus the air diffusing downward must cause an upward convection of the gas mixture of speed v. The diffusion equation for the stationary state in this case cf. p. 46) is

$$0 \approx \frac{\partial c}{\partial t} = D\frac{\partial^2 c}{\partial x^2} - v\frac{\partial c}{\partial x} \qquad [1.29]$$

$$0 \approx \frac{\partial C}{\partial t} = D\frac{\partial^2 C}{\partial x^2} - v\frac{\partial C}{\partial x} \qquad [1.30]$$

where c and C are the molecular concentrations of vapor and air respectively. The boundary conditions are

$$\text{at } x = 0: \quad c = 0, \ C = C_0$$

$$\text{at } x = -h: \quad C = C_0 - c_e; \quad c = c_e; \quad -D\frac{\partial C}{\partial x} + v(C_0 - c_e) = 0, \qquad [1.31]$$

the latter condition indicating impermeability of the ether surface towards the air. C_0 is the concentration of air in the open, c_e is the saturation concentration of the ether vapor. We further have, independent of x

$$c + C = C_0 . \qquad [1.32]$$

The methods of p. 46ff. give the solution

$$c = c_e \frac{1 - \exp\left(\frac{v}{D}x\right)}{1 - \exp\left(-\frac{v}{D}l\right)} . \qquad [1.33]$$

A steady state also can be obtained, even more easily than in the preceding example, in the case of diffusion through colloidal membranes or through solids*. If it is possible to determine the steady concentration at both sides of the membrane, then exactly the above considerations will hold. But the concentration of the diffusing substance within the surface of a membrane is not always given by the gas, or vapor, pressure of the substance, or its concentration in solution. For equilibrium at the interface membrane/gas or liquid will not be established in such cases where the transition gas (or liquid) → membrane is not a rapid process, compared with diffusion. In such cases, therefore, an absolute determination of the constant of diffusion is not possible without further measurements.

The passage of gases, or vapors, through membranes by diffusion is called permeation. If corresponding concentrations within the membrane are not available, one defines a permeability constant, Barrer (51), P, which is the value of the diffusion current under certain standard conditions. P is given in cm^3 of gas at N.T.P. diffusing per second through unit area (1 cm^2) of a membrane 1 mm thick, when there is 1 centimeter of mercury difference in pressure between its faces. Measurements of the permeation, therefore, do not give the diffusion coefficient itself, but only the product $D\partial c/\partial x$.

This, in connection with the last condition [1.31] and eq. [1.32] allows us to write down the equation determining v

$$-D\frac{\partial C}{\partial x} + v\left(C_o - c_e\right) = \frac{c_e v \exp\left(-\frac{v}{D}l\right)}{1 - \exp\left(-\frac{v}{D}l\right)} + v\left(C_o - c_e\right) = 0, \qquad [1.34]$$

giving

$$\frac{v}{D}l = \log\frac{C_0}{C_0 - c_e}. \qquad [1.35]$$

Thus we finally have for the total current of vapor at $x = 0$, where the convection current vanishes on account of $c = 0$,

$$J = -D\left(\frac{\partial c}{\partial x}\right)_o = C_o\frac{D}{l}\log\frac{C_o}{C_o - c_e} \qquad [1.36]$$

which is to replace the former relation [1.27].

For the limiting case $c_e \ll C_o$ this passes into the former expression

$$J = C_o\frac{D}{l}\log\left[\frac{1}{1 - \frac{c_e}{C_o}}\right] \approx \frac{c_e D}{l} \qquad [1.37]$$

which corresponds to the former equation [1.27]. For the above cf. A. Stefan (127, 129).

* As, for instance, diffusion of hydrogen through many metals, especially through palladium.

The concept of a "quasi-stationary state" plays an important role in kinetic phenomena, and we shall have to deal with quasi-stationary states in connection with several problems. In our first example, of the ether, evaporating in air, we were not actually dealing with a steady state in the strict sense of the word, but only a quasi-stationary state. For the height of the column of air and vapor in the cylinder was slowly increasing with time. Therefore, neither the concentrations themselves nor the concentration gradient were exactly constant (i.e., independent of time). We should have written instead of [1.24]

$$\partial c/\partial t \approx 0 \,, \qquad [1.38]$$

indicating that $\partial c/\partial t$ is not exactly zero, being so small, however, that no serious error is introduced if we replace [1.38] by [1.24]. Of course [1.24] must not be used if one is interested in the determination of the slow variation of the concentration distribution with time. All quasi-stationary states are characterized by similar relations. Of course, in every case one must make certain that the simplification thus introduced does not cause a serious error. In the following we shall treat one more example of a quasi-stationary state. A method, related to that of a constant concentration gradient, is that of quasi-stationary diffusion through a diaphragm, as employed for instance by Northrop and Anson (107) and by McBain (99), Gordon (74). A (usually aqueous) solution is kept above a diaphragm of sintered glass, the solute diffusing into an equal volume of solvent below the diaphragm. Since the highest concentration in each compartment, without stirring, would be at the top, the solutions are automatically stirred by convection and uniform concentrations are maintained. If q be the effective cross section of the diaphragm, δ its thickness, c and c' the concentrations of the solution above and below the diaphragm, we have

$$J = q \, (c - c') \, D/\delta \,. \qquad [1.39]$$

The assumption of a quasi-stationary state implies that the concentration gradient, within the diaphragm, may with sufficient accuracy be assumed to be constant, $\partial c/\partial x \approx \dfrac{c' - c}{\delta}$, while it is not independent of time. If V be the volume of either container*, the rate of change of concentrations due to the diffusion current, will be

$$dc'/dt = - \, dc/dt = J/V = q \, (c - c') \, D/V \delta \,. \qquad [1.40]$$

For integration we write

$$\frac{1}{c - c'} \frac{d (c - c')}{dt} = -2qD/V\delta; \quad c - c' = c_o \exp \, (-2qDt/V\delta), \qquad [1.41]$$

* The case of unequal volumes also has been treated, cf. (50), and Chap. XI.

and since $c + c' = c_o$, the initial concentration in the upper cell

a) $c = (c_o/2) [1 + \exp(-\beta D t)]$

b) $c' = (c_o/2) [1 - \exp(-\beta D t)]$, $\quad \beta = 2q/V\delta$. $\qquad$ [1.42]

Since q and δ cannot be measured directly, the cell constant β must be determined experimentally, by calibrating the cell with a solute of known D.

During the steady state in the one dimensional case we had a constant cross section for the diffusion stream, and consequently a constant concentration gradient. For other geometrical arrangements $\partial c/\partial x$ will vary with the position coordinate. A number of examples are easy to formulate and may be used in diffusion measurements, among these the spherical shell and the hollow cylinder.

The spherical shell. In this case the cross section for diffusion increases with the square of the radius r^2. Therefore for a substance, diffusing in the direction of increasing r, a steady state will be obtained if $\partial c/\partial r$ varies as $1/r^2$, consequently c varies as $1/r$. This leads to the following expressions for the steady state, if the shell extends from radius r_1 to r_2, and if at r_1 and r_2 the stationary concentrations c_1 and c_2 are maintained (cf. Barrer (52))

$$c = (c_1 r_1 - c_2 r_2)/(r_1 - r_2) + (c_1 - c_2)/[(1/r_1 - 1/r_2)r], \qquad [1.43]$$
$$\partial c/\partial r = (c_2 - c_1)/[(1/r_1 - 1/r_2)r^2].$$

Of course [1.43] could have been obtained by integration of [1.12]. In the limiting case, $r_2 - r_1 = \delta \ll r_1$, this passes into the former expression for a plane layer

$$\partial c/\partial r \approx (c_2 - c_1)/\delta.$$

Therefore, layers of any geometrical form, but of thickness small compared with the radius of curvature, can always be treated as plane to a sufficient degree of approximation.

The hollow cylinder. In this case the corresponding expressions are

$$c = \frac{c_1 \log r_2 - c_2 \log r_1}{\log r_2 - \log r_1} + \frac{(c_1 - c_2) \log r}{\log(r_1/r_2)}, \quad \frac{\partial c}{\partial r} = \frac{c_1 - c_2}{\log(r_1/r_2)} \; \frac{1}{r}. \quad [1.44]$$

As before, this gives in the limiting case, $r_2 - r_1 = \delta \ll r_1$,

$$\partial c/\partial r \approx (c_2 - c_1)/\delta.$$

Generally D will not be a constant, but will depend on concentration or position coordinate, or both. The kinetic theory shows, cf. Chapman and Cowling (5) and Chapter X, that for mixtures of gases the dependence of D on the concentration ratio is comparatively small. Therefore, for gases at constant pressure and constant temperature, it is usually safe to employ the approximation that D is constant. But consider an extreme example. The burning layer of a Bunsen burner, cf. Jost (30), Lewis-von Elbe (32), is of a thickness of about 10^{-2} cm or even less. Within this layer the temperature rises from room temperature to that of the burned gases somewhere between 1000° and 3000°C, depending on the gas mixture. Consequently, the diffusion coefficient for a component in this mixture may increase by a factor between 10 and 100 as one proceeds from the cold to the hot gas. In this case, therefore, the assumption of constant D would not be at all justified. However, a steady state still exists.

Practically, in any case it is safe to use sufficiently small concentration differences, and to calculate an average value of D. Where this is not possible, one has to apply the methods mentioned below.

For the geometrical conditions, treated above, it is possible to give the equations for the stationary state if D is not a constant, Barrer (52). From [1.8], [1.11] and [1.12] we obtain the equations for the stationary state

$$0 = \partial/\partial x \, (D \partial c/\partial x) \qquad \text{Plate} \qquad [1.45]$$
$$0 = \partial/\partial r \, (r D \partial c/\partial r) \qquad \text{Cylinder, axial symmetry} \qquad [1.46]$$
$$0 = \partial/\partial r \, (r^2 D \partial c/\partial r) \qquad \text{Spherical symmetry} \qquad [1.47]$$

and upon first integration

$$D \partial c/\partial x = A \qquad \text{Plate} \qquad [1.48]$$
$$r D \partial c/\partial r = B \qquad \text{Cylinder} \qquad [1.49]$$
$$r^2 D \partial c/\partial r = G \qquad \text{Sphere} \qquad [1.50]$$

Following Barrer, and excluding for the present the case where D depends explicitly on the position coordinate, we put

$$D = D_0 \, [1 + f(c)] \qquad [1.51]$$

where D_0 is the limiting value of D for vanishing c. A second integration yields

$$D_0 \int [1 + f(c)] \, dc = A x + a \qquad \text{Plate} \qquad [1.52]$$

$$D_0 \int [1 + f(c)] \, dc = B \log r + b \qquad \text{Cylinder} \qquad [1.53]$$

$$D_0 \int [1 + f(c)] \, dc = -G/r + g \qquad \text{Sphere} \qquad [1.54]$$

Each of these equations may be used for the determination of D_0 and of $f(c)$, see below.

As mentioned above, D may well depend explicitly on the position coordinate. If the temperature is not constant or if the properties of the medium vary with the position coordinate (for instance on account of unequal composition, not caused by differences in the concentration of the diffusing substance, presence of impurities etc.) then an explicit dependence of D on the position coordinate must be considered. In this case Barrer puts $D = D_0 [1 + f(x)]$ and obtains upon insertion into equations [1.48], [1.49] and [1.50] and integration one more set of equations, corresponding to [1.52], [1.53] and [1.54] which again may be used for the computation of D_0 and $f(x)$ or $f(r)$. While for a plate the steady-state concentration distribution is given by a straight line, as long as D is constant, typical deviations arise as soon as D is a function of c, x, or r. Some distributions as calculated by Barrer will be given below.

The equations obtained for the case of D depending explicitly on the position coordinate, are

$$D_0 c = A \int \frac{dx}{1 + f(x)} + a, \quad D_0 c = B \int \frac{dr}{r[1 + f(r)]} + b,$$
$$D_0 c = G \int \frac{dr}{r^2 [1 + f(r)]} + g, \tag{1.55}$$

again for plate, hollow cylinder and spherical shell respectively. In order to make use of the two sets of equations for the determination of D_0 and $f(c)$ or $f(x)$ or $f(r)$ Barrer proceeds as follows.

a) Plate. Boundary conditions $c = c_1$ at $x = 0$, $c = c_2$ at $x = l$, for all t. By integrating equation [1.52] between the limits 0 and x and 0 and 1 respectively, and by dividing the first result by the second one, we obtain

$$\frac{c - c_1 + F(c) - F(c_1)}{c_2 - c_1 + F(c_2) - F(c_1)} = x/l \tag{1.56}$$

if $c = c$ at $x = x$ and $\int_0^c f(\zeta) d\zeta = F(c)$.

If the concentration distribution for the steady state has been measured, $F(c_1)$, $F(c_2)$ and $F(c)$ can be determined by means of [1.56]. From a plot of $F(c)$ as function of c, $\partial F(c)/\partial c = f$ may be derived. $\partial c/\partial x$ is obtained from [1.56] by differentiation, for $c_2 = 0$

$$\partial c/\partial x = - [c_1 + F(c_1)]/(l[1 + f(c)]) . \tag{1.57}$$

In order to obtain D_0 Barrer starts from the equation for the steady flow

$$J = - [D\partial c/\partial x]_{x=0} = - [D\partial c/\partial x]_{x=l} . \tag{1.58}$$

The quantity of solute, passing during time t per unit area is

$$s = \int_0^t J dt = D_0[c_1 + F(c_1)]t/l \quad \text{for } c_2 = 0 \tag{1.59}$$

and

$$s = D_0 \left[c_1 + F(c_1) - c_2 - F(c_2)\right] \cdot t/l \quad \text{for } c_2 \neq 0 \, . \qquad [1.60]$$

Hence

$$D_0 = sl/\{[c_1 + F(c_1) - c_2 - F(c_2)] \, t\} \, . \qquad [1.61]$$

b) *Hollow cylinder and spherical shell.* The equations, corresponding to [1.60], for the quantity of solute, passing unit area of surface at $r = r_2$ are

$$s = D_0 t[c_1 + F(c_1) - c_2 - F(c_2)]/[(\log r_1 - \log r_2) r_2] \quad \text{Cylinder} \quad [1.62]$$

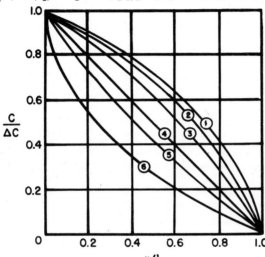

Fig. 1-1. Typical steady-state concentration distributions across a membrane when $D = D_0 (1 + f(c))$, after Barrer. Δc steady concentration difference across membrane of thickness l, Curve $1: f(c) = ac, a = 100$; $2: f(c) = ac, a = 10$; $3: f(c) = ac, a = 2$; $4: f(c) = 0$ (simple Fick law); $5: f(c) = -ac, a = 0.5$; $6: f(c) = -ac, a = 1.0$.

and

$$s = D_0 t r_1 [c_1 + F(c_1) - c_2 - F(c_2)]/[r_2(r_1 - r_2)] \quad \text{Sphere} \quad [1.63]$$

$f(c)$ and dc/dr for hollow cylinder and sphere must be determined from the equations analogous to [1.56], obtained by performing the integrations in the equations [1.55b] and [1.55c.] These relations are

$$[c_1 + F(c_1) - c - F(c)]/[c_1 + F(c_1) - c_2 - F(c_2)]$$
$$= [\log r_1 - \log r]/[\log r_1 - \log r_2] \quad \text{Cylinder} \qquad [1.64]$$

and

$$[c_1 + F(c_1) - c - F(c)]/[c_1 + F(c_1) - c_2 - F(c_2)]$$
$$= \frac{r_2}{r_1 - r_2} \cdot \frac{r_1 - r}{r_1} \qquad \text{Sphere} \, . \qquad [1.65]$$

For alternative ways of evaluation and for further details the reader is referred to Barrer, and also for the analogous evaluation in the case $D = D_0 [1 + f(r)]$. Barrer has calculated typical concentration curves for a series of laws, connecting D and c or x. In Figures 1-1 and 1-2 we reproduce some of Barrer's results.

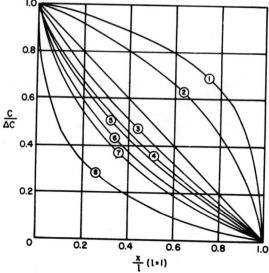

Fig. 1-2. Typical steady-state concentration distributions, $D = D_0 (1 + f(x))$, after Barrer. The straight line corresponds to the simple Fick law ($f(x) = 0$). Curve 1: $f(x) = -ax$, $a = 0.99$; 2: $f(x) = -ax$, $a = 0.90$; 3: $f(x) = ax$, $a = 1.0$; 4: $f(x) = ax$, $a = 2.0$; 5: $f(x) = bx + ax^2$, $a = 1$, $b = 2$; 6: $f(x) = bx + ax^2$, $a = 2.25$, $b = 3$; 7: $f(x) = ax$, $a = 9$; 8: $f(x) = ax$, $a = 99$.

IV. Solutions of the diffusion equations *

Since in many cases the coordinates x and t enter into the resulting expressions in the combination x^2/t only, one might be inclined to attempt a solution of the equation in the one-dimensional case

$$\partial c/\partial t = D \partial^2 c/\partial x^2 \qquad [1.66]$$

by putting $c = f(x^2/t)$, or more specifically $= \exp(-\lambda x^2/t)$. Insertion into [1.66] shows that the simplest possible solution is not of this form. A solution is obtained, however, in the form

$$c = (\alpha/\sqrt{t}) \exp(-x^2/4Dt), \qquad [1.67]$$

as may be verified by substitution into [1.66]**. [1.67] is symmetrical

---

* Cf. Carlslaw-Jaeger (3), Frank-Mises (22), Fürth (24), Sommerfeld (39).

** In a more direct way we might have found this solution by trying an expression for $c = g(x)h(t)\exp(-\lambda x^2/t)$, and requiring that the solution be the simplest one which remains finite at $x = 0$, except for $t = 0$. Upon substitution in [1.66] it is found that the solution satisfying these conditions, is the one mentioned above, i.e., $g(x) = \text{const.}$, $h(t) = 1/\sqrt{t}$, $\lambda = 1/4D$.

with respect to $x = 0$, and for $t = 0$ it is vanishing everywhere except for $x = 0$, where it becomes infinite. The integral $\int_{-\infty}^{+\infty} c\,dx$, however, remains finite even for $t = 0$, being an invariant independent of t. This is obvious for physical reasons. For if we consider a cylinder of infinite length and cross section 1 cm², of arbitrary shape, the total amount, s, of substance present, is given simply by this integral

$$s = (1 \text{ cm}^2) \int_{-\infty}^{+\infty} c\,dx . \qquad [1.68]$$

Therefore, the law of conservation of mass requires the invariance of this integral, which, of course, also follows from mathematical reasons. By performing* the integration in [1.68], we see that $\alpha = \dfrac{s}{2\sqrt{\pi D}}$ and consequently

$$c = \frac{s}{2\sqrt{\pi D t}} \exp(-x^2/4Dt). \qquad [1.69]$$

The solution, Fig. 1-3, refers to the following physical problem, if we agree to consider an infinite cylinder of unit cross section.

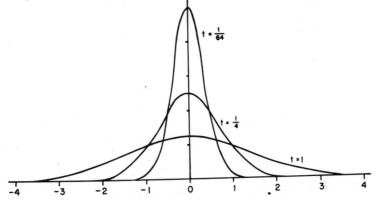

Fig. 1-3. The solution $c = \dfrac{s}{2\sqrt{\pi D t}} \exp\left(-\dfrac{x^2}{4Dt}\right)$ (ordinate) for values of $t = 1$, $^1/_4$, $^1/_{64}$ (x abscissa, arbitrary units).

At $t = 0$ the quantity s of the diffusing substance has been concentrated in the immediate vicinity of the plane $x = 0$, and for $t > 0$ [1.69] gives the resulting distribution of concentrations. The exponential is the Gauss' error curve (not to be confused with the error function or error integral, obtained by integration of the exponential). Our

* In integrations like this one substitutes $x^2/4Dt = \xi^2$, and one must know that $\int_{-\infty}^{+\infty} \exp(-\xi^2)\,d\xi = \sqrt{\pi}$.

solution, therefore, is that for an instantaneous source at $x = 0$ and $t = 0$, of unit area. Eq. [1.69] may be used for practical diffusion problems which conform sufficiently to the above conditions. As we shall see, eq. [1.69] can also be used for the case of the semi-infinite cylinder, bounded by a plane at $x = 0$, which is of greater practical importance than the infinite cylinder.

Solutions corresponding to [1.69] may easily be obtained also for the two and three dimensional problems, i. e., for the differential equations corresponding to axial and spherical symmetry

$$\partial c / \partial t = D \left[\partial^2 c / \partial r^2 + (1/r) \, \partial c / \partial r \right] \qquad [1.70]$$

$$\partial c / \partial t = D \left[\partial^2 c / \partial r^2 + (2/r) \, \partial c / \partial r \right] . \qquad [1.71]$$

If, in analogy to [1.67], we attempt to find a solution of the form

$$c = h \, (t) \exp \left(- r^2 / 4 \, Dt \right) \qquad [1.72]$$

we obtain, by inserting into [1.70] and [1.71], the differential equations for h

$$d \log h / dt = - \, 1/t \quad \text{and} \quad d \log h / dt = - \, 3/2t \qquad [1.73]$$

respectively, giving

$$h = \beta / t \quad \text{and} \quad h = \gamma / t^{3/2} \qquad [1.74]$$

for the two and three dimensional cases respectively. Thus in the case of axial symmetry we have

$$c = (\beta / t) \exp \left(- r^2 / 4 \, Dt \right) \qquad [1.75]$$

and for spherical symmetry

$$c = (\gamma / t^{3/2}) \exp \left(- r^2 / 4 \, Dt \right) . \qquad [1.76]$$

If we consider an infinite plate of thickness $1 \, \text{cm}$, [1.75] may be interpreted as the solution for an instantaneous linear source at $t = 0$ and $r = 0$, where the total amount s of substance had been concentrated in the immediate neighborhood of the axis $r = 0$ over a length of 1 cm. The constant β then must be determined from the condition

$$s = \beta / t \int_0^\infty \exp \left(- r^2 / 4Dt \right) 2\pi r dr . \qquad [1.77]$$

Correspondingly, in the three dimensional case, we have an instantaneous point source, the total s of the diffusing substance being concentrated at the origin, for $t = 0$, the constant γ being determined by

$$s = (\gamma / t^{3/2}) \int_0^\infty \exp \left(- r^2 / 4Dt \right) 4\pi r^2 dr . \qquad [1.78]$$

Since

$$\int_0^\infty \exp \left(- \, \xi^2 \right) \xi d \xi = \frac{1}{2} \quad \text{and} \quad \int_0^\infty \exp \left(- \, \xi^2 \right) \xi^2 d \xi = \frac{\sqrt{\pi}}{4} \qquad [1.79]$$

it follows

$$\beta = \frac{s}{4\pi D} \qquad \gamma = \frac{s}{(4\pi D)^{3/2}} \cdot \qquad [1.80]$$

Equation [1.69] is very valuable for obtaining further solutions in the problem of linear diffusion flow. We first note that it is legitimate to cut the infinite cylinder by a plane at $x = 0*$, perpendicular to the x axis, having the concentrations for negative x reflected by this plane. We thus arrive at a solution for the semi-infinite cylinder, bounded by an impermeable plane at $x = 0$

$$c = (s/\sqrt{\pi D t}) \exp(-x^2/4Dt) \qquad [1.81]$$

where again the amount s of the diffusing solute had been contained in the immediate vicinity of $x = 0$ at $t = 0$. The concentrations given by [1.81] are twice those given by [1.69], which is obvious for physical reasons. In the former case half the substance had been diffusing in the direction of negative x, the other half in that of positive x, while now the whole substance is diffusing in the direction of positive x.

It is also easily seen that the method (cf. 3, 22, 39) employed is mathematically sound. For reflection at $x = 0$ means superposition of two solutions of equation [1.66], which in our special case happen to be identical. Since the differential equation is linear, such a super-position is permissible. Furthermore, by the process of cutting off a boundary has been introduced into our system, which implies a certain boundary condition. The boundary being impermeable, this boundary condition is

$$\partial c/\partial x = 0, \quad \text{at} \quad x = 0 \qquad [1.82]$$

which states that there is no diffusion flow across the face at $x = 0$. In our example this condition is obeyed automatically, because for the original solution [1.69] $\partial c/\partial x$ already vanishes at $x = 0$, and this remains unchanged by reflection at $x = 0$, see Fig. 1-3. But even if we have an original solution with $\partial c/\partial x = \delta \neq 0$ at the boundary, reflection results in a concentration distribution with $\partial c/\partial x = 0$ at the boundary. For in this case we have superposition of two curves with slopes δ and $-\delta$, that of the resulting curve, therefore, being zero. Stefan (127) has made use of this method of reflection and superposition in the calculation of his tables, for the evaluation of diffusion measurements, which in the form given by Kawalki (90) have been, and are, widely applied (see below, p. 24). Solutions for the infinite system may be applied to actual experiments as long as concentration changes have not yet reached the boundaries.

* We might equally well cut by any other plane perpendicular to the x-axis and apply the principle of reflection. But the solutions thus obtained would be of less practical value.

V. Further solutions, derived from the basic source integral

If again we consider an infinite cylinder of unit cross section, not with an instantaneous plane source at $x = 0$, but with an initial distribution of concentration given by

$$c = c_0 \text{ for } x < 0, \text{ and } c = 0 \text{ for } x > 0, \text{ at } t = 0 \qquad [1.83]$$

we may proceed as follows. We start from our former equation [1.67] but treat the source as homogeneously distributed over a small volume element of height Δx and unit area, situated at $x = 0$. Consequently we replace α by $c' \Delta x$. The former solution represents the distribution caused by this volume source the better the smaller the value of Δx. We shall obtain the concentration distribution, resulting from the initial state [1.83], as a superposition of the effects of small volume sources, distributed along the negative x-axis. In the limiting case, $\Delta x \to 0$, equation [1.67], p. 16 will hold rigorously, and the sum will pass into an integral, giving

$$c(x, t) = (c'/\sqrt{t}) \int_x^\infty \exp(-\xi^2/4\,Dt)\,d\xi = c'' \int_{\frac{x}{2\sqrt{Dt}}}^\infty e^{-\eta^2} d\eta \qquad [1.84]$$

with $\eta = \xi/2\sqrt{Dt}$. By putting

$$erf\, x = (2/\sqrt{\pi}) \int_0^x e^{-\eta^2} d\eta, \quad erf(-x) = -erf(x), \quad erf(\infty) = 1, \qquad [1.85]$$

where $erf\,x$ is Gauss' error function, we may write instead of [1.84]

$$c(x, t) = c''' \left[erf(\infty) - erf(x/2\sqrt{Dt}) \right]. \qquad [1.86]$$

For $t = 0$, the right-hand side is either $2\,c'''\,erf(\infty)$ or 0 depending on whether x is < 0 or > 0. Therefore, since $erf(\infty) = 1$, we must put $c''' = c_0/2$ in order to conform with the initial condition [1.83], and we finally obtain, cf. Fig. 1-4

$$c(x, t) = (c_0/2) \left[1 - erf(x/2\sqrt{Dt}) \right]. \qquad [1.87]$$

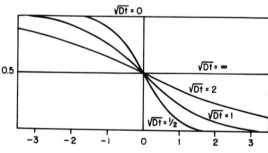

Tables of the error function are reproduced in the Appendix, p. 62. The integral [1.87] is valuable for many practical purposes, Fig. 1-4. We again emphasize that the equation for an infinite system may be applied to systems of finite

Fig. 1-4. The function $c = \frac{c_0}{2}\left[1 - erf\left(\frac{x}{2\sqrt{Dt}}\right)\right]$.

length as long as concentration changes near the boundaries are negligible. See also v. Göler's nomograph, Fig. 1-5. An experimental arrangement corresponding to the above conditions is possible for gases, liquids and solids. In the latter case one may simply bring into close contact

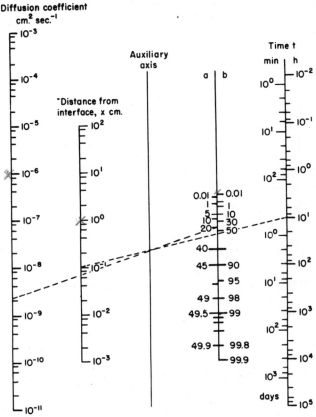

Fig. 1-5. Nomograph by v. Göler (after Seith) for the evalution of $c = \frac{c_0}{2}\left[1 - erf\left(\frac{x}{2\sqrt{Dt}}\right)\right]$. Connect the values of x and t on the corresponding axes and mark intersection with auxiliary axis. Then choose either $\frac{c \cdot 100}{c_0}$ on scale a (c_0 initial concentration) or $\frac{c \cdot 100}{C}$ on scale b (C concentration at interface) and connect with point on auxiliary axis. The intersection of this straight line with scale to the left gives D (cm².sec.$^{-1}$).

two cylinders of equal length, the one containing the diffusing "solute", the other one consisting of the "solvent", either a pure component, or a homogeneous mixture, differing in composition from that in the first cylinder. For gases the same is possible, using a tube of sufficient length, closed at both ends, and divided into two equal parts by a stopcock of bore equal in diameter to that of the tube. The two sides contain either two different gases or adequate mixtures, the beginning of an experiment being given by the opening of the stopcock, which is closed at the end. Then the mixtures at either side of the stopcock are analyzed. In earlier experiments it has been customary to use gun barrels for this purpose. Obviously the length of the tube ought to be large compared with the diameter, in order to avoid errors due to the influence of the stopcock. With liquids one uses a vertical cylinder, first filled with the component of lower density. At the beginning of an experiment the heavier component (usually the solution) is allowed to flow through a capillary underneath the solvent or the less concentrated solution. At the end of an experiment the two layers are analyzed. In all cases one must make certain that the concentration changes have not reached the boundaries.

Generally in experiments of the type mentioned, one does not measure the concentration distribution, as given by [1.87], but the total quantity of substance in two (or more) parts of the system. This quantity follows from [1.87] by a further integration. The amount of substance, contained in a cylinder of cross section q, bounded by the planes $x = x_1$ and $x = x_2$ is given by

$$s = q \int_{x_1}^{x_2} c \, dx = q \, (c_0/2) \left[x_2 - x_1 - \int_{x_1}^{x_2} erf \, (x/2 \sqrt{Dt}) \, dx \right]. \qquad [1.88]$$

The integration may be performed numerically, either by means of Simpson's rule or some other approximate formula or by means of tables of the integrated error function (Carlslaw, Jaeger (3)), cf. App., p. 62.

If only the total amount of substance for $x > 0$, and $x < 0$ has been determined, an evaluation is possible in an easier and quite rigorous way. Differentiation of [1.87] with respect to x gives for $x = 0$

$$(\partial c/\partial x)_{x=0} = -c_0/2 \sqrt{Dt\pi} \qquad [1.89]$$

Hence the diffusion flow at $x = 0$ is

$$J = -D \, (\partial c/\partial x)_{x=0} = c_0 \sqrt{D}/2 \sqrt{\pi t}. \qquad [1.90]$$

Now the total amount of substance, found for $x > 0$, has come there by diffusion across the plane $x = 0$ during the time t. Thus for a cylinder of cross section q this is

$$s = q \int_0^t J \, dt = \left(q c_0 \sqrt{D}/2 \sqrt{\pi} \right) \int_0^t \frac{d\vartheta}{\sqrt{\vartheta}} = q c_0 \sqrt{Dt/\pi}, \qquad D = \frac{s^2 \pi}{q^2 c_0^2 t}. \qquad [1.91]$$

Thus [1.91] gives an explicit expression for D.

It is possible to obtain solutions for a cylinder of finite length, starting from the integral for an instantaneous plane source. A solution, in a different form, can also be obtained by the general methods of integration, see below, p. 32. But here we shall follow Stefan's (127) derivation, making use of the principle of reflection, cf. (3, 39). Let us first consider an infinite system with the following initial distribution

$$c = c_0 \quad \text{for } -h < x < +h$$
$$c = 0 \quad \text{for } |x| > h .$$ [1.92]

As in the former case, we find for the resulting distribution by an integration over the solution for the plane source

$$c = \left(c_0 / \sqrt{\pi} \right) \int_{(x-h)/2\sqrt{Dt}}^{(x+h)/2\sqrt{Dt}} \exp\left(-\xi^2 \right) d\xi$$
$$= (c_0/2) \left[erf \left(\frac{h+x}{2\sqrt{Dt}} \right) + erf \left(\frac{h-x}{2\sqrt{Dt}} \right) \right].$$ [1.93]

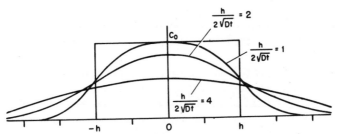

Fig. 1-6. The function $c = \frac{c_0}{2} \left[erf \left(\frac{h+x}{2\sqrt{Dt}} \right) + erf \left(\frac{h-x}{2\sqrt{Dt}} \right) \right]$ for diffusion out of a plate.

Since for $x = 0$ $\partial c / \partial x = 0$ for all t, as seen from [1.93] and from Fig. 1-6, we may cut the system in two by a plane at $x = 0$, without affecting the concentration distribution. Therefore [1.93] is also the solution for a semi-infinite cylinder with the initial distribution

$$c = c_0 \quad \text{for } 0 < x < h$$
$$c = 0 \quad \text{for } x > h \qquad \text{at } t = 0 .$$ [1.94]

This corresponds to actual experiments where in a vertical cylinder a "solution" extends from $x = 0$ to $x = h$, while a deep layer of "solvent" is contained above the solution, and care is taken that, during the time of an experiment, concentration changes do not reach the upper boundary of the solvent.

Now we may proceed further and introduce a second boundary, which might be situated at any height, but for which we choose the height $x = 4h$, in order to conform with a common experimental arrangement* and with the tables, calculated by Stefan (127) and modified by Kawalki (90), for the evaluation of these experiments.

We obtain the solution for the finite system from that for the semi-infinite system by first having reflected the concentration curve at $x = 4h$. The reflected curve is reflected again at $x = 0$, then at $x = 4h$ etc. We claim that by superposition of these curves we obtain the exact solution of our problem**. This can easily be seen. The solution, thus obtained, is an infinite series which, however, converges very rapidly, usually the first few members being sufficient. Since the differential equation is linear, the superposition is allowed (see p. 19) and the resulting expression is a solution of the original differential equation. Hence we must only make certain that the initial and the boundary conditions are fulfilled. For the initial conditions this is obvious at once, because the process of reflection does not affect these conditions at all. But the boundary conditions are obeyed, too, for by every reflection we superpose at the boundary two curves with differential coefficients of equal absolute magnitude but of opposite sign. Therefore at either boundary $\partial c/\partial x = 0$, which means vanishing of the diffusion current, as required by the presence of an impermeable boundary.

In this way we obtain the concentration distribution for our system of finite length $4h$. It is customary to divide the system into four parts of equal height after the experiment has been finished, and to analyze the single layers. The total amount of substance in a single layer, as determined experimentally, follows from the concentration curve by a further integration over the height of a layer. In App. p. 63 ff. we list the formulae referring to this problem and reproduce the tables, originally calculated by Stefan and by Kawalki. There, more details of the practical calculation are also given.

We shall deal with solutions for the cases of axial and spherical symmetry in connection with the general methods of integration, p. 45.

It is noteworthy that all solutions, given so far, hold only for homogeneous system (to be understood strictly in the sense of single-phase, systems***. The distribution of concentrations within the single phase, of course, is not homogeneous). In systems consisting of more than one phase, diffusion leads to an equalization of the chemical potential of the diffusing species, or of the absolute activities, but not to

---

* It may be emphasized that our notation differs from that used by Stefan and Kawalki.

** Equivalent to the method of images.

*** The usual definition of "phase" is restricted to a phase of uniform composition. It is obvious that we must use here a less rigorous definition.

an equalization of the concentrations, except within the single phases. We shall assume here that equilibria at phase boundary are always established, i.e., we shall exclude from our present consideration the case of rate determining reactions at phase boundaries. Then the ratio of the concentrations of the diffusing species at either side of an interface between two phases is given by Nernst's partition coefficient, $\varkappa$. For every phase a diffusion equation holds, with individual values for D. There are boundary conditions expressing the fact, that the substance, diffusing out of one phase, must be equal to that diffusing into the neighboring phase. In this case exact solutions for infinite cylinders are possible, Jost (29). Even much more general cases are tractable, cf. this Chapter, p. 69, where unpublished results of C. Wagner have been used, and p. 75, after Jost (88a). Characteristic concentration curves for different values of $\varkappa$ and different ratios of the diffusion coefficients in the two phases are given in the following Figures 1-7 to 1-10, computed by the author.

VI. Mean displacement of diffusing particle. Brownian movement

Eq. [1.69], p. 17 and Fig. 1-3 give the concentration distribution in a cylinder of infinite length, when for $t = 0$ all the diffusing substance is contained at $x = 0$. Now we may ask, what distance will a single diffusing particle travel during time t? Obviously, the question in this form is meaningless, because in a single experiment a molecule may have travelled any distance between zero and very great values. But we may repeat our observation many times and try to find the average distance, travelled by a molecule during time t, Einstein (19, 66), Smoluchowki (122), cf. also (4, 18, 23, 31).

In the case of a single particle the above mentioned equation does not give the resulting concentration distribution, but the probability $p(x)$ dx for a certain displacement between x and $x + dx$ during time t

$$p(x)\,dx = \left[\frac{\alpha}{\sqrt{t}} \exp\left(-\frac{x^2}{4Dt} \right) dx \right] \Big/ \int_{-\infty}^{+\infty} \frac{\alpha}{\sqrt{t}} \exp\left(-\frac{x^2}{4Dt} \right) dx. \quad [1.95]$$

The denominator must be inserted, in order to obtain absolute probabilities. Thus the probability for finding the particle anywhere between $-\infty$ and $+\infty$ becomes 1, as it has to be. We calculate the mean square of the displacement $\overline{\Delta x^2}$, the mean displacement itself being zero, since positive and negative displacements are equally probable. For the mean square displacement we obtain

$$\overline{\Delta x^2} = \int_{-\infty}^{+\infty} x^2 p(x)\,dx = 2Dt \quad [1.96]$$

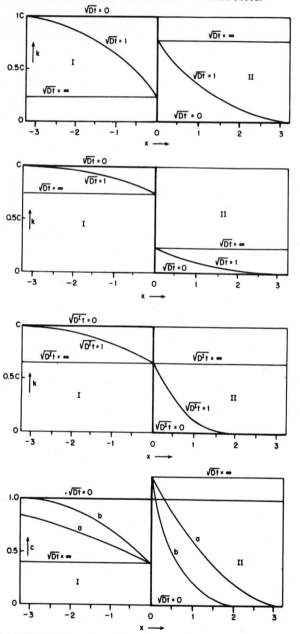

Fig. 1-7 to 1-10. Diffusion in a two-phase system, after Jost (cf. p. 68). 1-7: Distribution coefficient: $\varkappa = 3$, $D_I = D_{II}$; 1-8: $\varkappa = 1/3$, $D_I = D_{II}$; 1-9: $\varkappa = 1$, $D_I = 4\,D_{II}$; 1-10: $\varkappa = 3$, $D_I = 4\,D_{II}$; a) $\sqrt{D_I t} = 2$, b) $\sqrt{D_I t} = 1$.

where the substitution has been made $\xi^2 = \frac{x^2}{4Dt}$, and use has been made of the formulae

$$\int_{-\infty}^{+\infty} \exp\left(-\xi^2\right) d\xi = \sqrt{\pi}, \qquad \int_{-\infty}^{+\infty} \xi^2 \exp\left(-\xi^2\right) d\xi = \frac{\sqrt{\pi}}{2} . \quad [1.97]$$

In the case of Bownian movement it is possible to observe the displacement of single particles and to calculate $\overline{\varDelta x^2}$ as the average of many observations. This, therefore, is a straightforward method for the determination of diffusion coefficients of suspended particles. But formula [1.96] is very useful in many cases, other than those where single particles are concerned. For the distance $\sqrt{\overline{\varDelta x^2}}$ is comparable with the half width of the error curve [1.69]. If, therefore, we want to know to what depth a diffusing substance will have penetrated into a given medium during time t, then equation [1.96] will yield a very satisfactory estimate of this depth. We note that only the product Dt is of importance, and that $\sqrt{\overline{\varDelta x^2}}$ increases only as the square root of this expression.

We consider a few characteristic examples. Diffusion coefficients of gases at N.T.P. are of the order of magnitude of 0.1 to 1 cm.^{2} sec.$^{-1}$. For liquids at room temperature many values lie in the range 0.1 to 1 cm.^{2} day$^{-1} \approx 10^{-6}$ to 10^{-5} cm.^{2} sec.$^{-1}$. For solids, at temperatures where diffusion is observable, values between those for liquids and about 10^{-20} cm.^{2} sec.$^{-1}$ have been determined. Consequently, to cover an average distance of 1 cm. takes a time of the order of magnitude of some seconds for molecules in gases at N.T.P., of some days for liquid solutions at room temperature, and of between a day and 10^{12} years for such solids and temperatures where measurements have been possible. Therefore one sees that for the measurement of diffusion coefficients it will be advisable to work with distances of the order of magnitude of decimeters for gases, of centimeters or less for liquids, and of between a few centimeters and some 10^{-7} cm. for solids.

The equation for the mean square displacement is related to the expression we derived on p. 22 for the concentration gradient at $x = 0$ for a system, where at $t = 0$ the concentration was constant for negative x, being zero for positive x. If a tangent is drawn to the concentration curve at $x = 0$, it intersects the abscissa at $x = \mathfrak{x}_0$, where

$$x_0 = \sqrt{\pi Dt}, \qquad x_0^2 = \pi Dt, \qquad D = \frac{x_0^2}{\pi t} . \qquad [1.98]$$

If the concentration curve is known from experiments, [1.98] also may be used for evaluation, giving directly a value for D.

In treating Brownian movement we might equally well have adopted the opposite method, namely by first deriving an expression for the mean square displacement from considerations of probability, and then showing that the results thus derived are in agreement with the diffusion equations (cf. Fürth (23)).

Let us consider a single particle, undergoing consecutive displacements δ_1, δ_2, $\delta_3 \ldots$ in the $+ x$ or $- x$ directions, all displacements being of the same absolute magnitude, $|\delta_1| = |\delta_2| = \ldots$, but completely independent and at random. Then the mean displacement, caused by n elementary displacements, will be

$$\overline{\Delta x} = \sum_1^n \delta_i = 0 \qquad [1.99]$$

since positive and negative displacements are of equal probability. The mean square displacement, however, will not vanish, though it will be small compared with the square of the sum of the absolute amounts of the single displacements $\overline{\Delta x^2} \ll \left(\sum_1^n |\delta_i|^2 \right)$, provided n is large. One obtains

$$\overline{\Delta x^2} = \overline{\left(\sum_1^n \delta_i \right)^2} = \overline{\sum_1^n \delta_i^2} \doteq n \, \delta^2, \qquad [1.100]$$

because the sum of the double products, $\delta_i \cdot \delta_k$, vanishes on taking averages, since δ_i and δ_k are independent of each other, and positive and negative values are equally probable, thus $\sum_{i \neq k} \delta_i \cdot \delta_k = 0$.

From [1.100]

$$\sqrt{\overline{\Delta x^2}} = \delta \sqrt{n} \, . \qquad [1.101]$$

If t be the time necessary for a displacement the average square of which is $\overline{\Delta x^2}$, and if further, τ be the time, necessary for one single displacement δ, then $n \tau = t$, $n = \dfrac{t}{\tau}$, hence

$$\sqrt{\overline{\Delta x^2}} = \frac{\delta}{\sqrt{\tau}} \sqrt{t} = \sqrt{2 \, D t} \qquad [1.102]$$

i.e., the expression derived earlier is obtained if we identify $\dfrac{\delta^2}{2 \, \tau}$ with the diffusion coefficient D.

The actual total displacement, x, after n single displacements δ may have any value between 0 and $\pm n \delta$. The probability for a displacement $x = \nu \delta : W(x) = W(\nu \delta)$ may be calculated by the standard methods of the theory of probabilities, cf. (8, 9, 11, 20, 33, 41). Since we shall always assume that the numbers involved are large compared with unity, we may as well assume that ν be even. Then, if n be the total number of displacements, a positive displacement $x = \nu \delta$ must be the resultant of $\frac{n+\nu}{2}$ positive and $\frac{n-\nu}{2}$ negative displacements. Now the probability of a single positive displacement, is equal to that of a negative one, namely $^1/_2$. The probability for $\frac{n+\nu}{2}$ positive and $\frac{n-\nu}{2}$ negative displacements in a definite given order, therefore, is $(^1/_2)^n$. The resultant displacement, however, may be obtained by $\frac{n+\nu}{2}$ positive and $\frac{n-\nu}{2}$ negative displacements, irrespective of the order in which they are carried out. The above probability, therefore, must be multiplied by the number of distinguishable arrangements of $\frac{n+\nu}{2}$ positive and $\frac{n-\nu}{2}$ negative displacements, which is $\dfrac{n!}{\left(\dfrac{n+\nu}{2}\right)!\left(\dfrac{n-\nu}{2}\right)!}$. Consequently

$$W(\nu\delta) = \frac{n!}{\left(\dfrac{n+\nu}{2}\right)!\left(\dfrac{n-\nu}{2}\right)!}\left(\frac{1}{2}\right)^n. \qquad [1.103]$$

If n and ν are large numbers, and $\nu\delta = x$, this is approximately given by

$$W(\nu\delta) \approx \sqrt{\frac{2\tau}{\pi t}} \exp\left(-\frac{x^2\tau}{2\,\delta^2 t}\right) \qquad [1.104]$$

on account of Stirling's formula.

Since we had assumed ν to be even, in order to have to deal with integers only, we may assume that [1.104] represents the probability of a displacement between $x = \nu\,\delta$ and $x = (\nu + 2)\delta$. Hence the probability for a displacement between x and $x + dx$ will be

$$W(x)\,dx = W(\nu\delta)\,\frac{dx}{2\delta} \qquad [1.105]$$

If again we put $D = \dfrac{\delta^2}{2\,\tau}$, we finally obtain

$$W(x)\,dx = \frac{1}{2\sqrt{\pi D t}} \exp\left(-\frac{x^2}{4Dt}\right)dx \qquad [1.106]$$

which is identical with the integral [1.69], obtained on p. 17 for the diffusion equation in one dimension. Thus, either from this agreement, or by differentiating [1.106] with respect to time and twice with respect to x, we may convince ourselves that this probability obeys the diffusion equation.

If instead of the mean square displacement in one coordinate only the mean square displacement $\overline{\varDelta r^2}$, in a plane, irrespective of the direction is observed, we may compute this value in the following way. Let x and y be rectangular coordinates in the plane. Then we have a probability function $W(y)$ wholly analogous to [1.106], and since displacements in the x and y directions are to be considered as independent, we have a total probability for a displacement x, y ($x^2 + y^2 = r^2$) (i.e., between x and $x + dx$ and y and $y + dy$)

$$W(x)W(y)dxdy = \frac{1}{4\pi Dt} \exp\left(-\frac{r^2}{4Dt}\right)dxdy \qquad [1.107]$$

and for the probability of a displacement between r and $r + dr$

$$W(r)dr = \frac{r}{2Dt} \exp\left(-\frac{r^2}{4Dt}\right)dr \qquad [1.108]$$

which gives for the mean square displacement, irrespective of direction, $\overline{\Delta r^2}$

$$\overline{\Delta r^2} = \int_0^\infty r^2 W(r)dr \Big/ \int_0^\infty W(r)dr = 4Dt. \qquad [1.109]$$

The following table taken from Fürth (23), based upon Perrin's (35, 36) measurements with gamboge particles, shows observed and calculated values for the mean square displacements, $\overline{\Delta x^2}$ and $\overline{\Delta r^2}$.

Table I

Relative abundancies of displacements x and r, observed and calculated.

Interval for x	Abundance obs.	calc.	Interval for r	Abundance obs.	calc.
0.0 to 1.7	86	92	0 to 1	32	34
1.7 ,, 3.4	82	83	1 ,, 2	83	78
3.4 ,, 5.1	79	75	2 ,, 3	107	106
5.1 ,, 6.8	62	58	3 ,, 4	105	103
6.8 ,, 8.5	51	44	4 ,, 5	75	75
8.5 ,, 10.2	26	31	5 ,, 6	50	49
10.2 ,, 11.9	22	21	6 ,, 7	27	30
11.9 ,, 13.6	13	11	7 ,, 8	14	17
13.6 ,, 15.3	9	8	8 ,, 9	7	9
15.3 ,, 17.0	6	4			

Table I shows a remarkable agreement between observed and calculated displacements. In addition, it shows, just as in the case of the Maxwellian velocity distribution, that, while the probabilities for displacements in one direction decrease monotonously with increasing distance, this probability for a displacement in a plane irrespective of direction, has a maximum value for a certain finite displacement. The same would hold for a displacement in three dimensions, where $\overline{\Delta r^2} = 6Dt$.

It need scarcely be mentioned that our foregoing derivation for the Brownian movement is not yet quite rigorous, because we assumed all elementary displacements to be of equal length.

VII. Diffusion in a linear infinite system, with D depending on concentration. Boltzmann's method of treatment*

The differential equation for diffusion in the x-direction with diffusion coefficient depending on concentration was (eq. [1.13] p. 4)

$$\frac{\partial c}{\partial t} = D(c)\frac{\partial^2 c}{\partial x^2} + \frac{dD(c)}{dc}\left(\frac{\partial c}{\partial x}\right)^2. \qquad [1.110]$$

Boltzmann (56) has treated this equation for the following initial conditions: $c = c_0$ for $x<0$ and $t = 0$, $c = 0$ for $x>0$ and $t = 0$. The system is supposed to be infinite in the x direction. Upon the substitution $y = \frac{x}{\sqrt{t}}$, Boltzmann obtains the ordinary differential equation

$$\frac{d^2 c}{dy^2} + \frac{y}{2D}\frac{dc}{dy} + \frac{D'}{D}\left(\frac{dc}{dy}\right)^2 = 0, \qquad D' = \frac{dD}{dc}. \qquad [1.111]$$

This equation, however, for c as function of y, defining D arbitrarily as function of c, cannot be integrated either. But for practical purposes one may proceed as follows. Usually the task consists in the determination of $D(c)$, if c has been obtained from direct experiments, as function of y. [1.111] may then be rewritten

$$\frac{d}{dy}\left(D\frac{dc}{dy}\right) = -\frac{y}{2}\frac{dc}{dy} \qquad [1.112]$$

and upon a first integration

$$D(c) = -\frac{1}{2}\frac{dy}{dc}\int_{c_0}^{c} y\,dc. \qquad [1.113]$$

Since the right-hand side is supposed to be given experimentally, it is always possible to carry through the integration by means of numerical or graphical methods, and thus to evaluate $D(c)$.

Eq. [1.113] has been used in a number of cases for the evaluation of experiments. It should be emphasized that [1.113] refers to an infinite system. Therefore, if [1.113] shall be applicable, concentration changes must not have reached the boundaries of the system, consisting of two layers of equal height of "solvent" and "solution".

Besides it must be remembered that at the beginning all the diffusing substance had been contained in the region $x<0$. Therefore, at the end of an experiment, all diffusing substance, found at $x>0$, has arrived there by diffusion from regions $x<0$, and, therefore, must be equal to the deficit of substance, found for $x<0$. This seems trivial, but, except with gases, this condition is not always fulfilled, if one chooses as $x = 0$ simply the original geometrical boundary. Whereas in such cases for D independent of c, the plane $x = 0$ is

* Cf. Boltzmann (56), Matano (101), Fürth (24), Mehl (114), Seitz (38), Jost (88a).

determined by the condition $c = c_0/2$, if we consider an infinite system, we now must determine this plane from the condition

$$\int_0^{c_0} y\,dc = 0 \qquad [1.114]$$

which expresses the equality of the two shaded areas in Fig. 1-11 and is equivalent to the above-formulated condition. Fig. 1-11 has been taken from Rhines' and Mehl's (114) experiments on diffusion in metals (the copper-aluminium system).

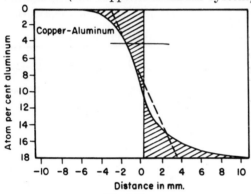

Fig. 1-11.
Boltzmann method (after Mehl and Rhines).

Since equation [1.113] is applied to diffusion systems which have been analyzed after the end of an experiment, it always refers to $t = $ const, and therefore may be transformed into

$$D = \frac{1}{2t} \frac{dx}{dc} \int_c^{c_0} x\,dc,$$

for $t = $ const. [1.115]

Therefore, as it has been done in Fig. 1-11, for $t = $ const., the condition $\int y\,dc = 0$, may be replaced by

$$\int_0^{c_0} x\,dc = 0, \quad \text{for} \quad t = \text{const}. \qquad [1.116]$$

The practical method of evaluation is obvious. After diffusion has been allowed to proceed for a time t, the system under consideration is analyzed and c determined as function of x. Then a graph of c versus x is plotted, and from this dx/dc and $\int_c^{c_0} x\,dc$ are determined.

In experiments of Jedele (87), there is a variation of D with concentration of about $1 : 8$, which, therefore, necessitates the employment of Boltzmann's method (first applied by Matano (101)).

VIII. The general methods for the evaluation of the diffusion equations for constant D*

1. Infinite system

In the preceding paragraphs we have treated a number of special cases by elementary methods, including those of the conventional

* Cf. (3, 22, 26).

arrangements, for the determination of diffusion coefficients. These methods, however, are not sufficient for all cases of practical importance.

It is, generally, quite easy to find particular integrals of the diffusion equation by means of the method of the separation of the variables. Thus, for instance, in the linear case

$$\partial c / \partial t = D \partial^2 c / \partial x^2 \qquad [1.117]$$

we may attempt to find a solution by putting

$$c = X(x) \cdot T(t) \qquad [1.118]$$

where X and T are functions of x and t respectively. On substituting in [1.117] we obtain

$$\text{a) } XT' = DTX'', \quad \text{b) } T'/T = DX''/X \qquad [1.119]$$

where dashes refer to differentiation with respect to the corresponding variables. In [1.119 b] we have on the left-hand side an expression depending on t only, while that on the right hand side depends on x only. They can be equal only, if either one is equal to the same constant, independent of x and t, which, for convenience, we shall choose equal to $-\lambda^2 D$. Thus we obtain the ordinary differential equations

$$T'/T = -\lambda^2 D, \quad X''/X = -\lambda^2 \qquad [1.120]$$

with the solutions

$$T \approx \exp(-\lambda^2 Dt), \quad X = A \cos \lambda x + B \sin \lambda x. \qquad [1.121]$$

Obviously $\lambda^2 > 0$, if the solution is to remain finite for all values of t. There are no further restrictions on λ, as long as no boundary conditions are introduced. We obtain the most general solution for the unbounded linear system from [1.121], by considering A and B as functions of λ and by integrating the expression, thus obtained for c, with respect to λ over its range of variation

$$c = \int_0^\infty [A(\lambda) \cos \lambda x + B(\lambda) \sin \lambda x] \exp(-\lambda^2 Dt) d\lambda. \qquad [1.122]$$

Using Fourier's integral theorem, [1.122] may be adapted to given initial conditions. If the initial distribution of concentrations is given by $c = \varphi(x)$ at $t = 0$, the solution satisfying this condition is

$$c = \frac{1}{\pi} \int_{-\infty}^{+\infty} \varphi(\alpha) d\alpha \int_0^\infty \exp(-\lambda^2 Dt) \cos \lambda(\alpha - x) d\lambda \qquad [1.123]$$

where α is an integration variable.

Integrating with respect to λ* we obtain the general formula

$$c = \frac{1}{2\sqrt{\pi Dt}} \int_{-\infty}^{+\infty} \varphi(\alpha) \exp\left[-\frac{(\alpha - x)^2}{4 Dt}\right] d\alpha \qquad [1.124]$$

---

* The integration of $\int_0^\infty e^{-\lambda^2 Dt} \cos \lambda(\alpha - x) d\lambda$ may be performed as follows, cf. (22).

which allows us to prove some of the results of the first part of this chapter in a mathematically more rigorous fashion.

First we note that [1.124] gives the integral for a plane source at $x = 0$ (cf. p. 17), if we put $\alpha = 0$ and pass to the limit $d\alpha \to 0$, with the condition $\int \varphi(\alpha)d\alpha = $ const.

Further, we at once obtain from [1.124] the solution for the infinite system, cf. p. 20, with $c = c_0 = \varphi(\alpha)$ for $\alpha < 0$ at $t = 0$, and $\varphi(\alpha) = c = 0$ for $\alpha > 0$ at $t = 0$. With the substitution $\xi = \dfrac{\alpha - x}{2\sqrt{Dt}}, d\alpha = 2\sqrt{Dt}\,d\xi$, we have

$$c = (c_0/\sqrt{\pi}) \int_{-\infty}^{-x/2\sqrt{Dt}} e^{-\xi^2}d\xi = \frac{c_0}{2}\left[1 - erf\left(x/2\sqrt{Dt}\right)\right]. \quad [1.125]$$

If $\varphi(\alpha) = c_0$ for $-h < x < +h$, $\varphi(\alpha) = 0$ for $|x| > h$ and $t = 0$, we obtain, cf. p. 23, using the same substitution as in the preceding example

$$c = (c_0/\sqrt{\pi}) \int_{(-h-x)/2\sqrt{Dt}}^{(h-x)/2\sqrt{Dt}} e^{-\xi^2}d\xi$$

$$= (c_0/2)\left[erf\left(\frac{h-x}{2\sqrt{Dt}}\right) + erf\left(\frac{h+x}{2\sqrt{Dt}}\right)\right]. \quad [1.126]$$

On account of the symmetry of this solution with respect to $x = 0$, the system may be cut in two at $x = 0$, and [1.126] also represents the

---

Continued from p. 33

Putting $\lambda^2 Dt = \eta^2$, and $\dfrac{\alpha - x}{\sqrt{Dt}} = \xi$, we obtain

$$\frac{1}{\sqrt{Dt}}\int_0^\infty e^{-\eta^2}\cos\eta\xi\,d\eta \equiv I(\xi).$$

Hence

$$I'(\xi) = dI/d\xi = -\frac{1}{\sqrt{Dt}}\int_0^\infty -e^{-\eta^2}\eta\sin\eta\xi\,d\eta$$

$$= \frac{1}{2\sqrt{Dt}}\left\{\left[e^{-\eta^2}\sin\eta\xi\right]_0^\infty - \xi\int_0^\infty e^{-\eta^2}\cos\eta\xi\,d\eta\right\} = -\frac{\xi}{2}I(\xi),$$

after integrating by parts with $v' = e^{-\eta^2}\eta$. Thus

$$d\log I/d\xi = -\frac{\xi}{2}, \qquad I = \text{const.}\exp(-\xi^2/4).$$

Since for $\xi = 0$, $\quad I = \dfrac{1}{2}\sqrt{\dfrac{\pi}{Dt}}$, we finally obtain

$$I = \frac{1}{2}\sqrt{\frac{\pi}{Dt}}\exp(-\xi^2/4) = \frac{1}{2}\sqrt{\frac{\pi}{Dt}}\exp\left(-\frac{(\alpha-x)^2}{4Dt}\right).$$

It is remarkable that by this integration an expression, containing $\exp(-\lambda^2 Dt)$ is finally transformed into an exponential with D in the nominator of the exponent.

solution for the semi-infinite system, bounded by an impermeable plane at $x = 0$, with the initial and boundary conditions $c = c_0$ for $0 < x < h$, $c = 0$ for $h < x < \infty$ at $t = 0$, and $\partial c / \partial x = 0$ at $x = o$ for all t.

By the same methods we also could obtain the general solutions for the unbounded two- and three-dimensional systems. These solutions, however, are not of as great practical value as those for the one-dimensional case, and for these we, therefore, refer the reader to the literature (3, 22, 24). The general solution for the two-dimensional case is

$$c = \int_{-\infty}^{+\infty} \int_{-\infty}^{+\infty} (B(\xi, \eta) / t) \exp\left[-\frac{(x - \xi)^2 + (y - \eta)^2}{4 D t} \right] d\xi \, d\eta \qquad [1.127]$$

where $B(\xi, \eta)$ must be chosen according to the initial conditions.

For the three-dimensional case, we mention a special solution, with the initial condition of spherical symmetry:

$$c = c_0 \quad \text{for } r < r_0, \quad c = 0 \quad \text{for } r > r_0, \text{ at } t = 0$$

$$c = (c_0/2)\left[erf\left[\frac{r_0 - r}{2\sqrt{Dt}} \right] + erf\left[\frac{r_0 + r}{2\sqrt{Dt}} \right] \right.$$

$$\left. + \frac{2\sqrt{Dt}}{r\sqrt{\pi}} \left\{ \exp\left[-\frac{(r + r_0)^2}{4 D t} \right] - \exp\left[-\frac{(r_0 - r)^2}{4 D t} \right] \right\} \right]. \qquad [1.128]$$

2. Finite system. Linear case

We shall consider a system bounded by two planes perpendicular to the x-axis, either of infinite dimensions perpendicular to the x-axis, or bounded by an impermeable surface of arbitrary shape, but parallel to the x-axis, initial and boundary conditions depending on x only.

To obtain a particular integral of the diffusion equation

$$\partial c / \partial t = D \partial^2 c / \partial x^2 \qquad [1.129]$$

we proceed exactly as in the preceding example for the infinite system. The solution thus obtained, again is

$$c = X(x) T(t) = [A \sin \lambda x + B \cos \lambda x] \exp(-\lambda^2 Dt). \qquad [1.130]$$

But while in the former example no further conditions were imposed upon the constant, except, $\lambda^2 > 0$, the values of λ now will be restricted to an infinite set of discrete positive values. Therefore the most general integral will now be represented by an infinite sum over the discrete values of λ instead, as before, by an integral over the continuously varying values of λ.

We shall treat several examples of practical importance.

Diffusion out of a slab. System with constant initial concentration, the concentrations at its faces being kept at zero for $t > 0$.

$$c = c_0 \text{ for } 0 < x < h \quad \text{at } t = 0$$
$$c = 0 \text{ for } x = 0 \text{ and } x = h \text{ at } t > 0.$$

We see from [1.130] that the boundary conditions are fulfilled for

$$B = 0, \quad \lambda = n\pi/h .$$ [1.131]

Therefore the most general solution is of the form

$$c = \sum_{n=1}^{\infty} A_n \exp\left[-\frac{n^2 \pi^2 D t}{h^2}\right] \sin\frac{n\pi x}{h} .$$ [1.132]

The arbitrary constants A_n, now, must be determined in such a way as to conform with the initial conditions, i.e., we must have

$$c_0 = \sum_{1}^{\infty} A_n \sin\frac{n\pi x}{h}, \text{ for } 0 < x < h \text{ at } t = 0.$$ [1.133]

A solution may be obtained by using Fourier's theorem. Putting, more generally, for the initial distribution $\varphi(x)$ instead of c_0, we obtain after multiplying [1.133] by $\sin\frac{n\pi x}{h}$ and integrating with respect to x from 0 to h

$$A_n = \frac{2}{n} \int_0^h \varphi(x) \sin\frac{n\pi x}{h} dx .$$ [1.134]

In our special case, $\varphi(x) = c_0$, it follows

$$A_n = 4c_0 /[2\nu + 1)]\pi , \quad \nu = 0, 1, 2 \ldots$$ [1.135]

and

$$c = \frac{4 c_0}{\pi} \sum_{\nu = 0}^{\infty} \frac{1}{2\nu+1} \times \sin\frac{(2\nu+1)\pi x}{h} \times \exp\left[-\left(\frac{(2\nu+1)\pi}{h}\right)^2 Dt\right],$$ [1.136]

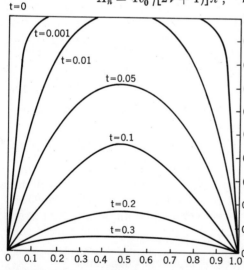

Fig. 1-12.

The above problem refers to the diffusion out of a slab, when the concentrations at its faces are kept at zero. From [1.136] we may obtain, as well, the solution of the reverse problem, diffusion into a slab, with initial concentration zero, the concentrations at

Fig. 1-12. Integral eq. [1.136] for diffusion out of a plate, the concentration at the boundaries being kept at zero.

its boundaries being kept at $c = c_0$ for $t > 0$. For, if [1.136] is a solution of the diffusion equation [1.129], the negative of it also is a solution. Therefore, with c given by [1.136], $c_0 - c$ is the solution of our problem giving the initial concentration $c = 0$ for $0 < x < h$, and $c = c_0$ for $x = 0$ and $x = h$ for $t > 0$. This solution for diffusion into a slab, therefore is

$$c = c_0 \left\{ 1 - \frac{4}{\pi} \sum_{\nu = 0}^{\infty} \frac{1}{2\nu + 1} \sin \frac{(2\nu + 1)\pi x}{h} \exp\left[-\left(\frac{(2\nu + 1)\pi}{h} \right)^2 Dt \right] \right\}. \quad [1.137]$$

Equations [1.136] and [1.137] give the local concentrations as functions of time for the above stated conditions. Now, in practical experiments one often does not measure local concentrations, but the total amount of substance which has been given off or taken up by the slab. From such measurements the average concentration c may be derived at once. We obtain for this value from [1.136] and [1.137]

$$\bar{c} = \frac{1}{h} \int_0^h c \, dx = \frac{8 c_0}{\pi^2} \sum_{\nu = 0}^{\infty} \frac{1}{(2\nu + 1)^2} \exp\left[-\left(\frac{(2\nu + 1)\pi}{h} \right)^2 Dt \right] \quad [1.138]$$

for diffusion out of a slab, and

$$\bar{c} = c_0 \left\{ 1 - \frac{8}{\pi^2} \sum_{\nu = 0}^{\infty} \frac{1}{(2\nu + 1)^2} \exp\left[-\left(\frac{(2\nu + 1)\pi}{h} \right)^2 Dt \right] \right\} \quad [1.139]$$

for diffusion into a slab.

We may obtain a slight simplification of these formulae, by calculating the relative change in concentration $(\bar{c} - c_f)/(c_i - c_f)$ were c_f is the final, c_i the initial concentration within the slab. The expressions thus resulting for diffusion into or out of a slab are identical, namely

$$\frac{\bar{c} - c_f}{c_i - c_f} = \frac{8}{\pi^2} \sum_{\nu = 0}^{\infty} \frac{1}{(2\nu + 1)^2} \exp\left[-\left(\frac{(2\nu + 1)\pi}{h} \right)^2 Dt \right] \quad [1.140]$$

for diffusion either into, or out of, a slab.

For t sufficiently large, the first term in the series [1.140] gives a good approximation

$$\frac{\bar{c} - c_f}{c_i - c_f} \approx \frac{8}{\pi^2} \exp\left[-t/\tau \right], \qquad \tau = \frac{h^2}{\pi^2 D} \quad [1.141]$$

The function [1.140] is represented graphically in Fig. 1-13, taken from Dünwald and Wagner (65). One has approximately, from [1.141]

$$\log \left[\frac{\bar{c} - c_f}{c_i - c_f} \right] \approx \text{const} - t/\tau. \quad [1.142]$$

Consequently, τ and D may be obtained from the slope of the straight part of the curve in Fig. 1-13.

Instead of the above solution, in the form of a trigonometric series, we may obtain as well a solution as a series of error functions. In the

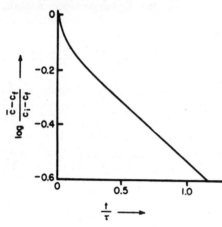

first part of this chapter, p. 23, we have constructed solutions of this type, by applying the principle of reflection. We shall give here explicitly the series of error functions for the above boundary and initial conditions, first, because for practical calculations this solution is often advantageous, second because Liebhafsky (96) has published certain semi-empirical results of practical value, which thus may be derived rigorously.

Fig. 1-13. Diffusion out of a plate, eq. [1.140] p. 37, after Dünwald and Wagner.

Obviously, we may obtain a solution for the semi-infinite system, $x > 0$, with the initial and boundary conditions

$$c = c_0 \quad \text{for} \quad 0 < x < \infty \quad \text{at} \quad t = 0,$$
$$c = 0 \quad \text{for} \quad \quad x = 0 \quad \text{at} \quad t > 0, \qquad [1.143]$$

by adapting initial conditions outside the region under consideration in such a way as to fulfill the boundary conditions automatically. This is easily achieved in our case by putting

$$c = -c_0 \quad \text{for} \quad -\infty < x < 0 \quad \text{at} \quad t = 0. \qquad [1.144]$$

For, the initial distribution is now antisymmetric with respect to $x = 0$, consequently the solution, too, will be antisymmetric with respect to $x = 0$, giving $c = 0$ for $x = 0$ at all $t > 0$. This may be verified at once by means of the following formulae.

The general formula [1.124], p. 33 gives the solution for this case

$$c = \frac{c_0}{2\sqrt{\pi Dt}} \left\{ \int_0^\infty \exp\left[-\frac{(\alpha - x)^2}{4Dt}\right] d\alpha - \int_{-\infty}^0 \exp\left[-\frac{(\alpha - x)^2}{4Dt}\right] d\alpha \right\}$$
$$= c_0 \, erf \, (x/2\sqrt{Dt}) \qquad [1.145]$$

It is seen at once, that [1.145] satisfies initial and boundary conditions. In our former examples, p. 23, we simply had the concentration distribution reflected at the boundaries, and thus satisfied the boundary conditions $\partial c/\partial x = 0$. To satisfy the boundary condition

$c = 0$, one must reflect the concentration at the boundary and change its sign at the same time, i.e., produce a concentration distribution antisymmetric with respect to the boundary instead of the symmetrical distribution, employed formerly.

For our finite systems, with initial and boundary conditions of p. 23

$$c = c_0 \quad \text{for} \quad 0 < x < h \qquad \text{at} \quad t = 0,$$
$$c = 0 \quad \text{for} \quad x = 0 \text{ and } x = h \text{ at} \quad t > 0 \qquad \text{[1.145]}$$

we may choose a periodic initial state, corresponding to the method of images, cf. (3, 39), where every reflection is combined with a change of sign, obtaining, Fig. 1-14

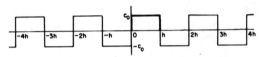

Fig. 1-14. Method of images, concentration distribution corresponding to the problem of Liebhafsky.

$$c = c_0 \quad \text{for} \quad 2nh < x < (2n+1)h \quad \text{at } t = 0, \qquad \text{[1.146]}$$
$$c = -c_0 \quad \text{for } (2n-1)h < x < 2nh \quad \text{at } t = 0,$$
$$n = \ldots -3, \, -2, \, -1, \, 0, \, 1, \, 2, \, 3 \ldots$$

Now, for reasons of symmetry, the boundary conditions are fulfilled automatically

$$c = 0 \quad \text{for} \quad x = nh \quad \text{and} \quad t > 0, \text{ } n \text{ as above}. \qquad \text{[1.147]}$$

Then the solution, obtained from the general formula [1.124] p. 33, corresponding to [1.145], is

$$c = \frac{c_0}{\sqrt{\pi}} \sum_{n=-\infty}^{+\infty} \left\{ \int_{[2nh-x]/2\sqrt{Dt}}^{[(2n+1)h-x]/2\sqrt{Dt}} e^{-\xi^2} d\xi - \int_{[(2n-1)h-x]/2\sqrt{Dt}}^{[2nh-x]/2\sqrt{Dt}} e^{-\xi^2} d\xi \right\}. \qquad \text{[1.148]}$$

[1.148] is a series converging very rapidly for sufficiently large values of $h/2\sqrt{Dt}$. In order to make use of tabulated values of the error function, we may write [1.148] in the form

$$c = \frac{c_0}{2} \sum_{-\infty}^{+\infty} \left\{ \left[erf\left(\frac{(2n+1)h-x}{2\sqrt{Dt}} \right) - erf\left(\frac{2nh-x}{2\sqrt{Dt}} \right) \right] \right.$$
$$\left. - \left[erf\left(\frac{2nh-x}{2\sqrt{Dt}} \right) - erf\left(\frac{(2n-1)h-x}{2\sqrt{Dt}} \right) \right] \right\}. \qquad \text{[1.149]}$$

In applying [1.149], it must be borne in mind that every integral of [1.148] now is expressed as a difference of two integrals which, for large values of n are not small, being approximately equal to unity. The series [1.149], therefore, does not converge absolutely, if the single error functions in the brackets are treated as its members.

Consequently, it is not permissible to rearrange the terms of this series for summation.

We now apply [1.149] to the problem of Liebhafsky (96), retaining only the terms with $n = 0$ and $n = \pm 1$. This corresponds to an

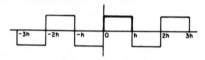

initial distribution as shown in Fig. 1-15. Actually, we shall have more terms then necessary for our purpose; it would be sufficient to consider the region $-2h$ to $+2h$ in Fig. 1-15.

Fig. 1-15. Approximate distribution used for eq. [1.150].

We first obtain

$$c = (c_0/2) \left\{ \begin{array}{l} \left[erf\left(\dfrac{h-x}{2\sqrt{Dt}}\right) + erf\left(\dfrac{x}{2\sqrt{Dt}}\right) \right] + \left[erf\left(\dfrac{x}{2\sqrt{Dt}}\right) - erf\left(\dfrac{h+x}{2\sqrt{Dt}}\right) \right] \\ + \left[erf\left(\dfrac{3h-x}{2\sqrt{Dt}}\right) - erf\left(\dfrac{2h-x}{2\sqrt{Dt}}\right) \right] - \left[erf\left(\dfrac{2h-x}{2\sqrt{Dt}}\right) - erf\left(\dfrac{h-x}{2\sqrt{Dt}}\right) \right] \\ - \left[erf\left(\dfrac{h+x}{2\sqrt{Dt}}\right) - erf\left(\dfrac{2h+x}{2\sqrt{Dt}}\right) \right] + \left[erf\left(\dfrac{2h+x}{2\sqrt{Dt}}\right) - erf\left(\dfrac{3h+x}{2\sqrt{Dt}}\right) \right] \end{array} \right\} \quad [1.150]$$

For the range of values, discussed by Liebhafsky, i.e., $h/2\sqrt{Dt} > 2.24$, the terms in the third and sixth brackets may be neglected, as is easily seen from tables of the error function. Thus we finally obtain

$$\frac{c}{c_0} = \left\{ \begin{array}{l} \left[erf\left(\dfrac{x}{2\sqrt{Dt}}\right) + erf\left(\dfrac{h-x}{2\sqrt{Dt}}\right) - erf\left(\dfrac{h+x}{2\sqrt{Dt}}\right) \right] \\ \qquad + 1/2\left[erf\left(\dfrac{2h+x}{2\sqrt{Dt}}\right) - erf\left(\dfrac{2h-x}{2\sqrt{Dt}}\right) \right] \end{array} \right\} \quad [1.151]$$

Since for reasons of symmetry, we need consider only the region $0 < x < h/2$, we have, to a very good approximation,

$$erf\left(\frac{2h+x}{2\sqrt{Dt}}\right) \approx erf\left(\frac{2h-x}{2\sqrt{Dt}}\right) \approx 1 \,.$$

It is, therefore, sufficient to retain the first three terms of [1.151]. The first term is the solution for the infinite system. The second one, giving a distribution symmetrical to that of the first term with respect to $x = h/2$, would be the solution for an infinite system, with $c = c_0$ for $x < h$ at $t = 0$, and $c = 0$ at $x = h$ and $t > 0$, Fig. 1-16, curve 2. The third term is almost constant, equal to 1. The resulting distribution of c/c_0 for $0 < x < h/2$, therefore, may be described as follows. The relative concentration is given, to a first approximation, by the error function 1. To a second approximation, the values of 1 must be reduced by the difference $\left[erf\left(\dfrac{h+x}{2\sqrt{Dt}}\right) - erf\left(\dfrac{h-x}{2\sqrt{Dt}}\right) \right]$ i.e., approximately by the difference between the horizontal line $c/c_0 = 1$ and curve 2. This difference is equal to the difference between $c/c_0 = 1$ and curve 1, at a point situated symmetrically with respect to $x = h/2$.

Now, Liebhafsky arrived empirically at the result that the shaded areas in Fig. 1-16, between error curve 1 and the correct curve 3 on the left, and between the error curve 1 and the horizontal $c/c_0 = 1$ on the right, must be equal. From the above, not only the equality of these areas follows, but it also follows that the vertical distance between every point of curve 1 at the left and curve 3 is equal to the distance between $c/c_0 = 1$ and curve 1 on the right, for symmetrical values of the abscissae.

For $x = 0$, c is exactly given by $erf\left(\dfrac{x}{2\sqrt{Dt}}\right)$ and $\dfrac{\partial c}{\partial x}$ is given, to a very good approximation, by the derivative of $erf\left(\dfrac{x}{2\sqrt{Dt}}\right)$ the contributions of the second and third terms in eq. [1.151] cancelling.

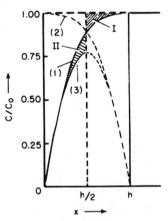

Fig. 1-16.
Problem of Liebhafsky, see text.

The amount of material lost from unit area in the time interval $t = 0$ to $t = t$ is

$$\Delta s = \int_0^t D(\partial c/\partial x)_{x=0}\, dt = c_0\, 2\pi^{-1/2} (Dt)^{1/2}, \text{ from the above.} \qquad [1.152]$$

For the slab the average concentration is, eq. [1.138], p. 37

$$\frac{\bar{c}}{c_0} = r = \frac{1}{h}\int_0^h (c/c_0)\, dx = \frac{8}{\pi^2}\sum_{n=0}^{\infty}\frac{1}{(2n+1)^2}\exp\left(-[2n+1]^2 y\right),$$

$$y = \frac{D\pi^2 t}{h^2}. \qquad [1.153]$$

Since, for a slab of volume V, the total content of diffusing substance at times 0 and t respectively is

$$s_0 = c_0 V, \quad s_t = \bar{c} V, \quad \text{we have } r = \frac{s_t}{s_0} = 1 - \frac{\Delta s}{s_0}. \qquad [1.154]$$

From [1.151] we obtain

$$r = 1 - \Delta s/s_0 = 1 - (2/\pi^{1/2})(Dt)^{1/2}/(h/2) \qquad [1.155]$$

as discussed above.

Values of r from equation [1.153] and from [1.154] are listed in the following table II.

Table II

Calculated values for relative losses r for the slab [Liebhafsky (96)]

$y \cdot 4/\pi^2$	r		
	From equation [1.153]	From equation [1.155]	
0.01	0.88 717	0.88 716	
0.02	0.84 041	0.84 042	
0.04	0.77 432	0.77 432	
0.06	0.72 360	0.72 361	$y = \dfrac{\pi^2 D t}{h^2}$
0.08	0.68 084	0.68 085	
0.10	0.64 318	0.64 318	
0.12	0.60 913	0.60 912	
0.16	0.54 876	0.54 865	
0.20	0.49 591	0.49 537	

As is seen from the table, the agreement between both sets of values is very good for $y < 0.2$. The reason for this, as we know, is that either solution is correct, the series of error functions converging more rapidly in the region under consideration, giving for small y an approximation equivalent to that of several members of the trigonometric series.

The present calculation had been carried through for the evaluation of measured losses of plasticizers from polyvinyl chloride plastics (97, 106, 121).

3. Diffusion through membranes

The solution [1.132], p. 36, for the finite, one dimensional system, may easily be generalized to obtain an integral for the permeation of gases through membranes.

Let h be the thickness of the membrane, then we have the diffusion equation

$$\partial c/\partial t = D \partial^2 c/\partial x^2 \qquad [1.156]$$

with the initial and boundary conditions

$$c = \varphi(x) \quad \text{for} \quad 0 < x < h \quad \text{and} \quad t = 0$$
$$c = 0 \quad \text{for} \quad x = 0 \text{ and } c = c_1 \text{ for } x = h \text{ and } t > 0^*. \qquad [1.157]$$

We can solve the problem by putting [cf. Frank-Mises (22)]

$$c = \zeta_1 + \zeta_2$$

where ζ_1 and ζ_2 are to be chosen in such a way as to conform with the above conditions

$$\zeta_1 = \varphi(x) \quad \text{for } 0 < x < h \quad \text{and} \quad t = 0$$
$$\zeta_1 = 0 \quad \text{for } x = 0 \text{ and } x = h \text{ at } t > 0 , \qquad [1.158]$$

___

* The more general case, with $c = c_{00} \neq 0$ at $x = 0$ for $t > 0$ is reduced to the above by the substitution $c' = c - c_{00}$. Of course, this substitution is also to be applied to the boundary conditions, giving $c' = 0$ for $x = 0$ and $c' = c_1 - c_{00}$ for $x = h$, and $\varphi(x) - c_{00}$ instead of $\varphi(x)$.

and

$$\zeta_2 = 0 \quad \text{for } 0 < x < h \text{ and } t = 0 ,$$
$$\zeta_2 = 0 \quad \text{for } x = 0, \ \zeta_2 = c_1 \text{ for } x = h, \ t > 0 . \quad [1.159]$$

The solution for ζ_1 is that given previously, eq. [1,132], [1,134] p. 36. It therefore only remains to determine $\zeta_2{}^*$.

For t sufficiently large, the solution must be $(c_1/h) x$, giving a linear concentration distribution for the stationary state. To this a time dependent concentration distribution must be added, vanishing for $t \to \infty$, and equal to $-(c_1/h)x$ for $t = 0$. The general equation [1.132] of p. 36 gives for this function

$$\frac{2 c_1}{h^2} \sum_1^\infty \exp\left[-\left(\frac{n\pi}{h}\right)^2 Dt\right] \sin\frac{n\pi x}{h} \int_0^h \xi \sin\frac{n\pi \xi}{h} d\xi. \quad [1.160]$$

We obtain for ζ_2, by evaluating the integral in [1.160] and adding $c_1 x / h$

$$\zeta_2 = c_1\left[x/h + \frac{2}{\pi} \sum_1^\infty (-1)^n \frac{1}{n} \exp\left[-\left(\frac{n\pi}{h}\right)^2 Dt\right] \sin\frac{n\pi x}{h} \right] \quad [1.161]$$

and finally

$$c = \zeta_1 + \zeta_2 = \frac{c_1 x}{h} + 2 \sum_1^\infty \left\{ \exp\left[-\left(\frac{n\pi}{h}\right)^2 Dt\right] \sin\frac{n\pi x}{h} \left[\frac{(-1)^n c_1}{n\pi} + \right.\right.$$
$$\left.\left. + \frac{1}{h} \int_0^h \varphi(\xi) \sin\frac{n\pi \xi}{h} d\xi \right] \right\} \quad [1.162]$$

We shall make use of this solution in treating a problem of permeation, first dealt with by Daynes (59) and Barrer (51), cf. Jaeger (86). Our formulae are slightly simplified, compared with those of Barrer. To obtain Barrer's results, we must make the substitutions, indicated in the preceding footnote. Putting $\varphi(\xi) = c_0$, we obtain

$$c = \frac{c_1 x}{h} + \frac{2 c_1}{\pi} \sum_1^\infty \frac{(-1)^n}{n} \sin\frac{n\pi x}{h} \exp\left[-\left(\frac{n\pi}{h}\right)^2 Dt\right]$$
$$+ \frac{4 c_0}{\pi} \sum_0^\infty \frac{1}{2n+1} \sin\frac{(2n+1)\pi x}{h} \exp\left[-\left(\frac{(2n+1)\pi}{n}\right)^2 Dt\right]. \quad [1.163]$$

From this the expression for $\partial c/\partial x$ at $x = 0$ is derived

$$(\partial c/\partial x)_{x=0} = \frac{c_1}{h} + \frac{2 c_1}{h} \sum_1^\infty (-1)^n \exp\left[-\left(\frac{n\pi}{h}\right)^2 Dt\right] +$$
$$+ \frac{4 c_0}{h} \sum_0^\infty \exp\left[-\left(\frac{(2n+1)\pi}{h}\right)^2 Dt\right]. \quad [1.164]$$

* Footnote cf. p. 42

We now assume that the face $x = 0$ of the membrane is connected with a gas volume V, the rate of flow of the gas through the membrane being measured by the change of gas concentration, c_g, in this volume V. It is assumed, however, that this change is sufficiently small and does not affect the equilibrium concentration at the face $x = 0$ of the membrane. We thus obtain

$$V \frac{dc_g}{dt} = D \left(\frac{\partial c}{\partial x} \right)_{x=0}. \qquad [1.165]$$

Upon substitution of the above value [1.164] for $\partial c / \partial x$ and integration we have

$$c_g = \frac{D}{V} \int_0^t \left(\frac{\partial c}{\partial x} \right)_{x=0} dt = \frac{Dc_1 t}{Vh} + \frac{2c_1 h}{V \pi^2} \sum_1^\infty \frac{(-1)^n}{n^2} \left[1 - \exp\left[-\left(\frac{n\pi}{h} \right)^2 Dt \right] \right] +$$

$$+ \frac{4c_0 h}{V \pi^2} \sum_0^\infty \frac{1}{(2n+1)^2} \left[1 - \exp\left[-\left(\frac{(2n+1)\pi}{h} \right)^2 Dt \right] \right] \qquad [1.166]$$

the limiting expression of which, for t sufficiently large, is

$$c_g = \frac{Dc_1 t}{Vh} - \frac{c_1 h}{6 V} + \frac{c_0 h}{2 V}, \qquad [1.167]*$$

with $\sum_1^\infty (-1)^n / n^2 = -\pi^2/12, \ \sum_1^\infty 1/n^2 = \pi^2/6, \ \sum_0^\infty 1/(2n+1)^2 = \frac{\pi^2}{8}.$

Without time lag, the total gas flow would have been

$$c_g \, V = Dc_1 \, t/h, \qquad c_g = Dc_1 \, t/h V . \qquad [1.168]$$

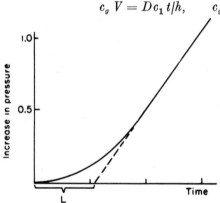

Fig. 1-17. Establishment of a steady state in diffusion through a membrane, after Barrer. Time lag defined by L.

Thus it is seen, that the time lag L, as defined by Fig. 1-17, is given by

$$L = h^2/6D - c_0 h^2/2 Dc_1. \quad [1.169]$$

For the more general case, as stated in footnote p. 42, where at $x = 0$ $c = c_{\infty}$, we have to replace the above concentrations by $c - c_{\infty}$ and obtain

$$L = \frac{h^2}{D(c_1 - c_{\infty})} \left[\frac{c_1}{6} + \frac{c_{\infty}}{3} - \frac{c_0}{2} \right], \qquad [1.170]$$

Barrer's equation with slightly different notation.

* The right-hand side of eqs. [1.167] etc. must be multiplied by 1 cm.^{2} in order to obtain the correct dimensions. In the general case a factor q cm.^{2} would have to be inserted.

If especially $c_o = c_{oo} = 0$, we have the simple expression $L = \dfrac{h^2}{6D}$.

Hence D can be calculated directly from permeation measurements, if these cover the preliminary period, necessary for the establishment of the stationary state, while normal permeation measurements during the stationary state give only $P = D \partial c / \partial x$. In Chap. VII use will be made of these relations.

4. Diffusion into or out of a cylinder or sphere (65)

We shall not treat here the general case, but give the formulae corresponding to those for a plate, cf. p. 37.

In the case of a cylinder it is assumed that we either have to deal with a cylinder of infinite length, or with a finite cylinder with sealed end faces, diffusion, in either case, occuring in a radial direction only. The formula to be given, refers to the average concentration, $\bar{c}$, in the cylinder of radius r_0, whose initial uniform concentration had been c_i while its final concentration is c_f. This includes the following special cases.

$$\begin{aligned}c &= 0 &&\text{for} \quad 0 < r < r_0 \quad \text{and} \quad t = 0 \\ c &= c_f \neq 0 &&\text{for} \quad r = r_0 \quad\quad\; \text{and} \quad t > 0,\end{aligned} \qquad [1.171]$$

$$\begin{aligned}c &= c_i \neq 0 &&\text{for} \quad 0 < r < r_0 \quad \text{and} \quad t = 0 \\ c &= c_f = 0 &&\text{for} \quad r = r_0 \quad\quad\; \text{and} \quad t > 0,\end{aligned} \qquad [1.172]$$

and the general case

$$\begin{aligned}c &= c_i \neq 0 &&\text{for} \quad 0 < r < r_0 \quad \text{and} \quad t = 0, \\ c &= c_f \neq 0 &&\text{for} \quad r = r_0 \quad\quad\; \text{and} \quad t > 0\end{aligned} \qquad [1.173]$$

where c_i may be larger or smaller than c_f.

The solution, analogous to equation [1.140] of p. 37, is

$$\frac{\bar{c} - c_f}{c_i - c_f} = \sum_1^\infty \frac{4}{\xi_\nu^2} \exp\left[-\frac{\xi_\nu^2 D t}{r_0^2} \right]. \qquad [1.174]$$

Here the ξ_ν are the roots of the equation $J_0(x) = 0$, where $J_0(x)$ is the Bessel-function of zero order ($\xi_\nu = 2.405,\ 5.520,\ 8.654,\ 11.792,\ 14.931,\ 18.071 \ldots$). For t sufficiently large, the first term of the series is a good approximation

$$\frac{\bar{c} - c_f}{c_i - c_f} \approx \frac{4}{(2.405)^2} \exp\left[-t/\tau \right] \qquad [1.175]$$

with

$$\tau = \frac{r_0^2}{(2.405)^2 D}.$$

The corresponding solution for a sphere, with the same initial and boundary conditions, is

$$\frac{\bar{c}-c_f}{c_i-c_f} = \frac{6}{\pi^2} \sum_1^\infty \frac{1}{\nu^2} \exp\left[-\nu^2\pi^2 Dt/r_0^2\right] \approx \frac{6}{\pi^2} \exp\left[-t/\tau\right] \qquad [1.176]$$

where

$$\tau = r_0^2/\pi^2 D \ .$$

If, for the above initial and boundary conditions, c is measured as function of r, solutions also are available, which may be found in the monographs quoted (3, 22). For the cylindrical case see also p. 51 ff.

In cases with complicated boundary conditions where explicit solutions of Fick's law are impossible the method of the electrical analogue (113, 48) may be valuable, as suggested by Mehl (103).

IX. Diffusion and convection
Diffusion under the influence of external forces
1. Diffusion and convection *.

In many diffusion problems of practical importance, with liquids or gases, the medium under consideration is not at rest. Then, besides concentration changes due to diffusion, concentration changes caused by convection must be considered, too. Let us first consider the one dimensional problem, with flow in the x-direction only. If v be the convection velocity, c the concentration of the diffusing substance the concentration change, due to convection, in a volume element of unit cross section, bounded by two planes at x and $x + \Delta x$, during time Δt will be

$$\Delta c = -\frac{1}{\Delta x}\left[(vc)_{x+\Delta x} - (vc)_x\right]\Delta t = -\frac{\partial}{\partial x}(vc)\Delta t + \cdots. \qquad [1.177]$$

Consequently, the differential equation for the rate of change of concentration, due to both, diffusion and convection, now is

$$\partial c/\partial t = D\,\partial^2 c/\partial x^2 - \partial/\partial x\,(vc) \ . \qquad [1.178]$$

The generalization for three dimensions is obvious

$$\partial c/\partial t = D\left[\partial^2 c/\partial x^2 + \partial^2 c/\partial y^2 + \partial^2 c/\partial z^2\right] - \frac{\partial}{\partial x}v_x c - \frac{\partial}{\partial y}v_y c - \frac{\partial}{\partial z}v_z c$$
$$= D\Delta c - \text{div}\,(\boldsymbol{v}c) , \qquad [1.179]$$

where Δ is Laplace's operator.

When $\boldsymbol{v}$ is constant [1.178] and [1.179] are reduced to

$$\partial c/\partial t = D\,\partial^2 c/\partial x^2 - v\,\partial c/\partial x \qquad [1.180]$$

* Cf. (3), (22), (24).

and

$$\partial c/\partial t = D\,\Delta c - v_x \partial c/\partial x - v_y \partial c/\partial y - v_z \partial c/\partial z$$
$$= D\ \mathrm{div\ grad}\ c - (v\ \mathrm{grad}\ c) \qquad\qquad [1.181]$$

where v_x, v_y, v_z are the rectangular components of the flow vector v.

2. Diffusion under the influence of external forces *

If we restrict our consideration to the one-dimensional case, diffusion alone causes a flow of matter

$$J' = - D\partial c/\partial x\ . \qquad\qquad [1.182]$$

If there is an external force, F, acting in the x-direction upon the dissolved molecules or colloidal particles, or upon gas molecules of a certain kind, and if u be the mobility of the particles under consideration (i.e., the steady velocity, acquired under the action of unit force), the steady velocity of these particles will be $F \cdot u$, and the resulting flux of matter

$$J'' = cFu = cv\ . \qquad\qquad [1.183]$$

Consequently, the total current, J, due to diffusion and the action of the external force, will be

$$J = J' + J'' = - D\partial c/\partial x + cv\ , \quad v = Fu \qquad [1.184]$$

and the rate of change of concentration with time, due to this current

$$\partial c/\partial t = D\partial^2 c/\partial x^2 - \partial/\partial x(cv)\ . \qquad\qquad [1.185]$$

If the force F and, consequently, the steady velocity, v, are independent of x, [1.185] is reduced to

$$\partial c/\partial t = D\partial^2 c/\partial x^2 - v\partial c/\partial x \qquad\qquad [1.186]$$

which is identical with the equation derived in the preceding section for diffusion, coupled with convection.

It is even possible to reduce the problem of equation [1.186] to that of ordinary diffusion, by means of the following transformation, cf. Fürth (24),

$$c = c^* \exp\left[\frac{v}{2D}(x - x_0) - \frac{v^2 t}{4D}\right]. \qquad\qquad [1.187]$$

Substitution in [1.186] gives the differential equation for c^*

$$\partial c^*/\partial t = D\partial^2 c^*/\partial x^2\ . \qquad\qquad [1.188]$$

Hence, there are no difficulties in treating problems of this type.

* Cf. (3), (22), (24).

3. Stationary state in diffusion under the influence of external forces, or in presence of uniform convection

Let us first consider the steady state in the case of diffusion under the influence of an external field of force or in the presence of uniform convection. From [1.186] we have

$$0 = D \frac{d^2 c}{dx^2} - v \frac{dc}{dx}.$$
[1.189]

Let the diffusing substance be contained in a vertical cylinder of infinite height, $v = Fu$ being the stationary velocity in the direction of negative x, due to gravity, then

$$c = c_0 \exp\left[-(v/D)x\right]$$
[1.190]

if at the bottom of the cylinder $x = 0$, $c = c_0$. If we use $v = Fu$, $D = uRT/N$, cf. p. 139, which in the case of a gas may be considered as definition of u, it follows from [1.190]

$$c = c_0 \exp\left[-\frac{FNx}{RT}\right].$$
[1.191]

If we deal with a gas, FN, the force acting upon N gas molecules, is gM, where M is the molecular mass (molecular "weight"), g the acceleration in the gravitational field. Hence

$$c = c_0 \exp\left[-Mgx/RT\right]$$
[1.192]

the well known formula of the decrease with height of the concentration of a gas in the atmosphere.

In the case of a centrifuge* with angular speed ω ($\omega = 2\pi n$, if n be the number of revolutions per second), the force acting upon a single particle is $+ mx\omega^2$, if we identify x with the direction of the radius. Then equation [1.186], being derived for a force independent of x, is no longer applicable. If, instead, we use [1.185], we may write at once for the stationary state

$$D \frac{dc}{dx} - mx\omega^2 uc = 0,$$
[1.193]

since, due to the boundary condition, that of a cylinder closed at the bottom, the resulting current of matter, J, must not only be constant, but even vanish. From [1.193] follows immediately

$$c = c_0 \exp\left(+\frac{Nm\omega^2}{2RT}[x^2 - x_0^2]\right)$$
[1.194]

where for the bottom of the diffusion cylinder, at a distance $x = x_0$ from the axis of rotation, $c = c_0$. Again it has been supposed that the cylinder is sufficiently high (or the concentration gradient sufficiently large) that we may treat the cylinder as having infinite length, the presence of the upper boundary being without influence upon the

* Cf. Svedberg (40), Archibald (46, 47).

resulting distribution of concentrations. If in [1.194] c differs appreciably from zero only for a distance $\xi = x_0 - x$ from x_0, which is very small compared with x_0, then [1.194] may be transformed to

$$c = c_0 \exp\left[-\frac{M\omega^2 x_0}{RT}\xi\right] \qquad [1.195]$$

where $\xi \ll x_0$, $\xi = 0$ for $x = x_0$ and ξ is directed towards the axis of rotation. [1.195] is in complete agreement with [1.192], the acceleration g of the gravitational field of force being replaced by the centrifugal acceleration $\omega^2 x_0$.

If we are not dealing with a gas, the hydrostatic buoyancy has to be taken into account. The force, acting upon N molecules of solute, then will be (if ϱ be the density of the solute, ϱ_0 that of the solution),

$$Mg\frac{\varrho - \varrho_0}{\varrho_0}.$$

This expression is to replace Mg in the exponent of equation [1.192], for solutions and accordingly a factor $\frac{\varrho - \varrho_0}{\varrho_0}$ is to be inserted in [1.193], [1.94], [1.195] etc., if these equations are applied to solutions.

4. Sedimentation

Now it is easy to obtain the time dependent equation for sedimentation (22, 24). In a cylinder of infinite length, the only boundary condition refers to the impermeability of the bottom at $x = 0$. Since the total stream of matter is $-D\partial c/\partial x + vc$, where v is the velocity under the influence of the force, the boundary condition for $x = 0$ becomes

$$-D\partial c/\partial x + vc = 0 \qquad [1.196]$$

or transformed to the function c^*, by means of [1.187]

$$D\partial c^*/\partial x - vc^*/2 = 0, \qquad [1.197]$$

or if we replace v by $-V$, where V is the velocity toward the bottom of the cylinder, due to gravity, then we have, finally,

$$D\partial c^*/\partial x + Vc^*/2 = 0 \qquad [1.198]$$

Without going into details we shall give the solution of [1.185], with the boundary condition [1.198], if for $t = 0$ all the substance, of amount 1 per cm² cross section, had been contained in the immediate neighborhood of $x = x_0$, Smoluchowski (123), Fürth (24).

$$c = \frac{1}{2\sqrt{\pi Dt}}\left\{\exp\left[-\frac{(x-x_0)^2}{4Dt}\right] + \exp\left[-\frac{(x+x_0)^2}{4Dt}\right]\right\}\exp\left[-\frac{V}{2D}(x-x_0)-\frac{V^2 t}{4D}\right] +$$
$$+ \frac{V}{2D}\exp\left[-\frac{V}{D}x\right]\left\{1-erf\left[\frac{x+x_0-Vt}{2\sqrt{Dt}}\right]\right\} \qquad [1.199]$$

If for $t = 0$ the concentration in a cylinder of infinite height is c_0 for $0 \leq x \leq h$, and 0 for $x > h$, then the following solution is obtained (72, 73). It may be derived from [1.199] by integration with respect to x from $x = 0$ to $x = h$, and by multiplication by c_0.

$$c/c_0 = \frac{1}{2}\left\{ erf\left[\frac{x+Vt}{2\sqrt{Dt}}\right] - erf\left[\frac{x-h+Vt}{2\sqrt{Dt}}\right]\right\} + \frac{1}{2}\exp\left[-\frac{Vx}{D}\right].$$
$$\left\{erf\left[\frac{x-h-Vt}{2\sqrt{Dt}}\right] - erf\left[\frac{x-Vt}{2\sqrt{Dt}}\right]\right\} + \frac{V\sqrt{t}}{\sqrt{\pi D}}\exp\left[-\frac{Vx}{D}\right].$$
$$\left\{\exp\left[-\frac{(x-Vt)^2}{4Dt}\right] - \exp\left[-\frac{(x+h-Vt)^2}{4Dt}\right]\right\} + \frac{V}{2D}\exp\left[-\frac{Vx}{D}\right].$$
$$\left\{(x-Vt)\,erf\left[\frac{x-Vt}{2\sqrt{Dt}}\right] - (x+h-Vt)\,erf\left[\frac{x+h-Vt}{2\sqrt{Dt}}\right]\right\} + \frac{Vh}{2D}\exp\left[-\frac{Vx}{D}\right]. \quad [1.200]$$

The problem also can be solved for a cylinder of finite height h, filled at $t = 0$ with a solution of concentration c_0. The integral, thus obtained by Fürth (72, 73), is

$$c/c_0 = 32 D^3 \pi^2 h\, V \exp\left[-\frac{Vx}{2D} - \frac{V^2 t}{4D}\right] \sum_{n=t}^{\infty} \left(\frac{n}{V^2 h^2 + 4\pi^2 D^2 n^2}\right)^2 \exp\left[-\frac{\pi^2 D t n^2}{h^2}\right]$$
$$\left[(-1)^n \exp\left(\frac{Vh}{2D}\right) - 1\right]\left[\cos\frac{n\pi x}{h} - \frac{Vh}{2\pi nD}\sin\frac{n\pi x}{h}\right] + \quad [1.201]$$
$$+ \frac{Vh}{D}\frac{1}{1-\exp(-Vh/D)}\exp[-Vx/D].$$

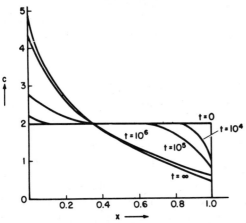

Fig. 1-18.
Sedimentation, after Fürth. Infinite cylinder.

A graphical representation of the integral [1.200] is to be found in the Fig. 1-18, taken from Fürth.

5. Diffusion and convection. Flow between parallel plates.

For a gas or liquid, streaming in the x-direction between two parallel plates, the equation for the stationary state is

$$D(\partial^2 c/\partial x^2 + \partial^2 c/\partial y^2) - v\partial c/\partial x = 0 \quad [1.202]$$

if the origin of our coordinate system be chosen in the center of the planes, the y-direction being perpendicular to these planes and where, further, it has been assumed that the velocity of flow, v, is constant. We shall treat this problem, with the boundary conditions

$$c = c_0 \quad \text{at} \quad x = 0$$
$$c = 0 \quad \text{at} \quad y = \pm a \quad \text{and} \quad x > 0 \qquad [1.203]$$

corresponding to the diffusion of a component, present in concentration c, which is either destroyed or removed at the planes $x = \pm a$, its concentration, there, being kept zero.

A particular integral of [1.202] is obtained by the usual procedure, putting $c = X(x)\, Y(y)$ and substituting in [1.202]. Denoting the separation constant by $\lambda^2 D$, we obtain the two ordinary differential equations

$$D\, d^2 X/d x^2 - v\, dX/d x = \lambda^2 D X \qquad [1.204]$$

and

$$D\, d^2 Y/d y^2 + \lambda^2 D Y = 0 \ . \qquad [1.205]$$

From [1.205] we find the particular integral for Y

$$Y = \left.\begin{matrix} \sin \\ \cos \end{matrix}\right\} \lambda y \ . \qquad [1.206]$$

The boundary condition $c = 0$ at $y = \pm a$ for $x > 0$ requires

$$Y = \cos \frac{(2n + 1)\, \pi y}{2 a}, \quad \lambda^2 = (2n + 1)^2\, \pi^2/4a^2. \qquad [1.207]$$

Consequently from [1.204]

$$d^2 X/d x^2 - (v/D)\, d X/d x = \frac{(2n + 1)^2\, \pi^2}{4\, a^2} X \ , \qquad [1.208]$$

giving

$$X = \exp\left[\left(\frac{v}{2 D} - \sqrt{\frac{(2n + 1)^2 \pi^2}{4\, a^2} + \frac{v^2}{4\, D^2}}\right) x\right] = \exp(\beta_n x). \qquad [1.209]$$

The general solution, therefore, is of the form

$$c = \sum_{n=0}^{\infty} a_n \cos \frac{(2n + 1)\, \pi y}{2 a} \exp(\beta_n x). \qquad [1.210]$$

By using the boundary condition $c = c_0$ at $x = 0$, we finally obtain

$$[1.211]$$

$$c = \frac{4 c_0}{\pi} \sum_{n=0}^{\infty} \frac{(-1)^n}{2n + 1} \cos \frac{(2n + 1)\pi y}{2 a} \exp\left[\left(\frac{v}{2 D} - \sqrt{\frac{(2n + 1)^2 \pi^2}{4\, a^2} + \frac{v^2}{4 D^2}}\right) x\right].$$

6. Flow in a tube.

We also may solve the corresponding problem for a gas or a liquid streaming in a tube. By first neglecting the diffusion in the direction of the axis of the tube, we have the differential equation

$$D(\partial^2 c/\partial r^2 + (1/r)\, \partial c/\partial r) - v\, \partial c/\partial x = 0 \qquad [1.212]$$

if again the direction of flow is supposed to coincide with the x-axis which now is the axis of our cylindrical tube. The boundary conditions are

$$c = c_0 \quad \text{at} \quad x = 0$$
$$c = 0 \quad \text{at} \quad r = r_0 \quad \text{and} \quad x > 0 \,. \qquad [1.213]$$

Putting $c = R(r)X(x)$, we find the ordinary differential equations, $\lambda^2 D$ being the separation constant

$$d^2 R/dr^2 + (1/r)d\,R/dr + \lambda^2 R = 0 \qquad [1.214]$$

and

$$dX/dx + (\lambda^2 D/v)X = 0 \qquad [1.215]$$

From [1.215] we at once obtain

$$X = \exp\left(-\lambda^2 D x/v\right) \,. \qquad [1.216]$$

[1.214] may be slightly simplified by the substitution

$$\rho = \lambda r \qquad [1.217]$$

yielding

$$d^2 R/d\rho^2 + (1/\rho)d\,R/d\rho + R = 0 \qquad [1.218]$$

which is the differential equation of the Bessel-function of zero-order, $J_0(\rho)$. We therefore have the particular integral

$$c = J_0(\lambda r) \exp\left(-\lambda^2 D x/v\right) \,. \qquad [1.219]$$

To satisfy the boundary condition $c = 0$ for $r = r_0$, we must choose

$$\lambda = \xi_\nu/r_0 \qquad \nu = 1, 2 \dots \qquad [1.220]$$

where the ξ_ν are the roots of the equation $J_0(x) = 0$, cf. p. 45, infinite in number. Then the general solution is

$$c = \sum_1^\infty A_\nu J_0(\xi_\nu r/r_0) \exp\left[(- \xi_\nu^2 D/v r_0^2) x\right] \,. \qquad [1.221]$$

The coefficients A_ν are to be determined in a way analogous to that used for a Fourier series cf. (3, 22, 39), giving, with the boundary condition $c = c_0$ at $x = 0$

$$c = 2 c_0 \sum_{\nu=1}^\infty \frac{1}{\xi_\nu J_1(\xi_\nu)} J_0(\xi_\nu r/r_0) \exp\left[(- \xi_\nu^2 D/v r_0^2) x\right] \,. \qquad [1.222]$$

$J_1(x)$ is the Bessel function of first order; the numbers $J_1(\xi_\nu)$ must be taken from tables for the Bessel functions (27), as well as the values of the function $J_0(x)$. For most practical purposes, it is possible to get rid of the Bessel functions by calculating c, the average concentration in a cross section $x = $ const. Since $c(r)$ is the concentration for the value r, the average concentration for constant x is

$$\bar{c} = \frac{2}{r_0^2} \int_0^{r_0} c(r)\,r\,dr \qquad [1.223]$$

where $c(r)$ from (1.222) must be substituted. We, therefore, must evaluate the integral

$$\int_0^{r_0} J_0(\xi_\nu\, r/r_0)\,r\,dr \qquad [1.224]$$

which we transform to

$$\frac{r_0^2}{\xi_\nu^2} \int_0^{\xi_\nu} J_0(y)\,y\,dy \qquad [1.225]$$

by means of the substitution $\dfrac{\xi_\nu r}{r_0} = y$. From the theory of Bessel-functions it is known that

$$\int J_0(y)\,y\,dy = y\,J_1(x) . \qquad [1.226]$$

Consequently

$$\frac{r_0^2}{\xi_\nu^2} \int_0^{\xi_\nu} J_0(y)\,y\,dy = \frac{r_0^2}{\xi_\nu}\, J_1(\xi_\nu). \qquad [1.227]$$

By substituting in [1.223] we finally obtain

$$\bar{c} = 4\,c_0 \sum_{\nu=1}^{\infty} (1/\xi_\nu^2) \exp\left[-(\xi_\nu^2\, D/r_0^2 v)\, x\right] \qquad [1.228]$$

where for ξ_ν the values of p. 45 must be used.

If we consider that the fluid takes a time $t = x/v$ to travel from $x = 0$ to $x = x$, [1.228] becomes identical with the equation for diffusion out of or into a cylinder, as given without proof on p. 45. It might be emphasized that the solution for the stationary state in the system with flow is identical with that for the time dependent state in a system without flow.

We have neglected, so far, diffusion in the direction of flow, which, as we shall see below, is justified under special conditions only. We did this, because thus we obtained formulae which, at once, could be used for a proof of the former equation [1.174], p. 45.

If this factor is not neglected, we have the equation for the stationary state

$$D(\partial^2 c/\partial r^2 + [1/r]\partial c/\partial r + \partial^2 c/\partial x^2) - v\,\partial c/\partial x = 0 \qquad [1.229]$$

where again the variables can be separated by the substitution $c = R(r)X(x)$, giving the ordinary differential equations

a) $d^2 R/dr^2 + (1/r)d R/dr + \lambda^2 R = 0$

b) $d^2 X/dx^2 - (v/D)dX/dx - \lambda^2 X = 0 .$ $\qquad [1.230]$

Thus, the solution for R remains unchanged, while for X we obtain

$$X \sim \exp\left[\frac{v}{2D}\left(1 - \sqrt{1 + \frac{4\,D^2\,\lambda^2}{v^2}}\right)x\right] \qquad [1.231]$$

which only for

$$D^2\lambda^2/v^2 \ll 1 \qquad [1.232]$$

passes into the former expression, i.e., for sufficiently high values of the streaming velocity v,

$$X \approx \exp\left(-\frac{D\lambda^2}{v}\,x\right) \qquad [1.233]$$

7. Separation of gas mixtures by diffusion in a streaming system (83,84)

The equation, obtained for the one dimensional problem, of a gas streaming in the x-direction, to which at $x = 0$ another component of concentration c_0 has been added, had been [1.190], p. 48

$$c = c_0 \exp\left(- vx/D\right). \qquad [1.234]$$

Now, if two components distinguished by dashes are mixed, their concentrations at $x = 0$ being c_0' and c_0'', it follows for the ratio of their concentrations at $x = x$, from [1.234]

$$c'/c'' = (c_0'/c_0'') \exp\left[- vx\,(1/D' - 1/D'')\right]. \qquad [1.235]$$

In order to make use of this effect for the separation of the two components, Hertz (83, 84), the gas must be pumped off at some point, say $x = l$. The separation, thus obtained, is given by

$$(c'/c'')/(c_0'/c_0'') = \exp\left[- vl\,(1/D' - 1/D'')\right]. \qquad [1.236]$$

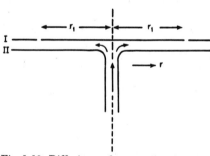

Fig. 1-19. Diffusion and convection in space bounded by two parallel plates with axial symmetry. Cross section.

In order to obtain high yields, one will take l as small as possible and v rather high, since the effect depends on the product vl only.

A solution can also be given for the problem analogous to the above treated one, with radial flow of the gas. Consider the following boundary conditions. A gas (or liquid) is streaming radially between two parallel circular plates I and II, a second component being added through a circular slit at $r = r_1$, Fig. 1-19. This component will diffuse against the flowing gas, supposed to flow outward from the centre. The differential equation for the steady state is

$$D\left[\partial^2 c/\partial r^2 + (1/r)\partial c/\partial r\right] - (v_0 r_0/r)\partial c/\partial r = 0, \qquad [1.237]$$

where v_0 is the radial gas velocity at some fixed value of $r = r_0$. As in the former examples, it is supposed that the pressure of the streaming gas is uniform. [1.237] can be integrated by means of a simple power expression, $c = \beta r^\alpha$ which, on substitution in [1.237], leads to the equation

$$\alpha^2 - \frac{v_0 r_0 \alpha}{D} = 0 \qquad [1.238]$$

giving

$$\alpha = \frac{v_0 r_0}{D} \qquad [1.239]$$

8. Diffusion out of a streaming gas into a solid

Wagner (140) has treated the following diffusion problem of some technical importance. For surface treatment of metals, one may pass over the surface of the metal a stream of gas, containing a component which is to diffuse into the metal. For instance, a surface layer of chromium can be produced by passing a mixture of $CrCl_2 + H_2 + HCl$ over iron at elevated temperatures (cf. Chap. V, p. 223). In the gas the concentration of the diffusing component decreases as the

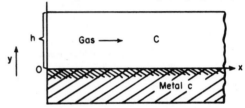

Fig. 1-20. Diffusion out of a streaming gas into a metal, after Wagner.

gas passes over the metal. We want to know the distribution of the diffusing component in the metal as a function of the space coordinates and of time. Fig. 1-20 gives a schematic drawing of the experimental set up. The flow of gas coincides with the x-direction, y is the coordinate perpendicular to the metal surface, c is the concentration in the metal, C that in the gas phase. For the sake of simplicity we assume equilibrium to be established at the metal-gas interface, the ratio of the concentrations in the metal and in the gas being given by a distribution coefficient $\varkappa$, i.e.,

$$c = \varkappa C \qquad [1.240]$$

for $y = 0$ and all values of x and of t. In the gas phase the concentration is assumed to be independent of y, diffusion being considered in the metal only,

$$\partial c/\partial t = D \partial^2 c/\partial y^2 . \qquad [1.241]$$

We further assume, as will practically always be the case, that the depth of the diffusion layer in the metal is small compared with the thickness of the metal, which implies that diffusion in the x-direction is negligible compared with that in the y-direction. The flow of matter into the metal at a point x is $-D(\partial c/\partial y)_{y=0}$. In the quasi-stationary state, this must be equal to the decrease of the content of the gas which, if h be the height of the gas stream, is given by

$$-vh\,\frac{\partial C}{\partial x}$$

where v is the velocity of flow, supposed to be independent of x and y, as an approximation sufficiently accurate for our present purpose. Hence, with [1.240]

$$\left(\frac{\partial c}{\partial y}\right)_{y=0} = \frac{hv}{D}\,\frac{\partial C}{\partial x} = \frac{hv}{\varkappa D}\left(\frac{\partial c}{\partial x}\right)_{y=0} \qquad [1.242]$$

The gas, entering at $x=0$, is of the concentration C_0, thus $c_0 = \varkappa C_0$ at $x=0$ and $y=0$, for all $t>0$. We further assume $c=0$ at $t=0$. We attempt to obtain a solution by putting

$$\xi = (\varkappa D/hv)x/2\sqrt{Dt}\,, \quad \eta = y/2\sqrt{Dt}\,. \qquad [1.243]$$

By means of this substitution, [1.241] is transformed to

$$\partial^2 c/\partial\eta^2 + 2\,(\xi\partial c/\partial\xi + \eta\partial c/\partial\eta) = 0\,. \qquad [1.244]$$

The boundary conditions in the new coordinates are

$$c = c_0 \quad \text{at} \quad \xi = 0,\ \eta = 0, \quad c = 0 \quad \text{at} \quad \xi = \infty,\ \eta = \infty\,,$$
$$\partial c/\partial\xi = \partial c/\partial\eta \quad \text{at} \quad \eta = 0\,. \qquad [1.245]$$

A solution of [1.244], satisfying the boundary conditions [1.245], may be obtained by assuming $c(\xi,\eta) = c(\sigma)$, $\sigma = \xi + \eta$. On substituting this in [1.244], we obtain the ordinary differential equation

$$d^2 c/d\sigma^2 + 2\sigma dc/d\sigma = 0\,, \qquad [1.246]$$

which is solved by the error function

$$c = c_0\,[-erf\,\sigma] = c_0\,[1 - erf\,(\xi + \eta)]$$
$$= c_0\left[1 - erf\left\{([\varkappa D/vh]\,x + y)\,\frac{1}{2\sqrt{Dt}}\right\}\right] \qquad [1.247]$$

satisfying the boundary conditions. The relative decrease of C in the gas with increasing x is given approximately by (cf. p. 55)

$$\frac{C(x,t)}{C_0} = \frac{c(x,y=0,t)}{c_0} \approx 1 + x\left(\frac{\partial c}{\partial x}\right)_{x=0,\,y=0} = 1 - \frac{2}{\sqrt{\pi}}\,\frac{\varkappa D}{hv}\,\frac{x}{2\sqrt{Dt}}\,. \qquad [1.248]$$

Thus the decrease in the gas phase is most marked for small values of t. A graphical representation of the solution is to be found in Wagner's paper.

X. Diffusion, convection and chemical reaction*

1. Diffusion and chemical reaction, one-dimensional case

If we consider the rate of change of concentration of a single component, partly due to diffusion and partly due to chemical reaction, we obtain in the one dimensional case

$$D\partial^2 c/\partial x^2 + f(c) = \partial c/\partial t \qquad [1.249]$$

if $f(c)$ is the law of reaction rate, giving the increase of the concentration c with time, due to chemical reaction. $f(c)$ may depend on the concentrations of other components and on external influences, for instance illumination. The problem, thus stated, is closely related to that of heat conduction, coupled with heat production, cf. (3, 22). We shall treat the special case, where all other influences are independent of the space coordinates and of time, and $f(c)$ is proportional to c, i.e., reaction of the first order. Then, putting $f(c) = -kc$, we have

$$D\partial^2 c/\partial x^2 - kc = \partial c/\partial t . \qquad [1.250]$$

This equation may be integrated by separation of the variables, if we put $c(x, t) = X(x)T(t)$. Upon insertion into [1.250] we obtain

$$Dd^2X/dx^2 \cdot T - kXT = XdT/dt . \qquad [1.251]$$

From [1.251]

$$(Dd^2X/dx^2)/X - k = (dT/dt)/T = \lambda \qquad [1.252]$$

where λ is a constant.

We shall consider the two cases, with boundary conditions

a) $\partial c/\partial x = 0$ for $x = \pm a$ (impermeable walls)
b) $c = 0$ for $x = \pm a$ and $t > 0$,

with $c = c_0$ at $t = 0$ for all x, in either case.

a) leads to the trivial result, namely that c is independent of x

$$c = c_0 \exp(-kt) .$$

In case b) we obtain

$$d^2X/dx^2 - (k+\lambda)/D \cdot X = 0, \qquad X = \left.\begin{matrix}\cos\\\sin\end{matrix}\right\} \sqrt{-\frac{k+\lambda}{D}}\, x , \qquad [1.253]$$

$$T = \exp(\lambda t) . \qquad [1.254]$$

Hence λ must be < 0, and [1.253] gives imaginary, and not real exponentials. From the boundary condition $c = 0$ for $x = \pm a$, we obtain

$$\sqrt{-\frac{k+\lambda}{D}} = \frac{n\pi}{2a} , \qquad \lambda = -\frac{n^2\pi^2 D}{4a^2} - k \qquad [1.255]$$

$$T = \exp(-kt)\exp\left(-\frac{n^2\pi^2 D}{4a^2}t\right) . \qquad [1.256]$$

* Cf. Förster und Geib (71), Damköhler (12), (13), (14), (15).

Therefore the time dependence is given by a product of the normal time law for a first-order reaction, multiplied by a time dependent factor due to diffusion.

With the initial condition $c = c_0$, for all values of x, we obtain for X, as before (cf. p. 36, 51)

$$X = \frac{4c_0}{\pi} \sum_{n=0}^{\infty} \frac{(-1)^n}{2n+1} \cos \frac{(2n+1)\pi x}{2a} \qquad [1.257]$$

and thus finally

$$c = \frac{4c_0}{\pi} \exp(-kt) \sum_{n=0}^{\infty} \frac{(-1)^n}{2n+1} \cos \frac{(2n+1)\pi x}{2a} \exp\left(-\left[\frac{(2n+1)\pi}{2a}\right]^2 Dt\right) \qquad [1.258]$$

2. Diffusion and chemical reaction. Three-dimensional case

On exactly similar lines a solution can be found for the three-dimensional case

$$D \Delta c - f(c) = \partial c / \partial t . \qquad [1.259]$$

Putting $c = X(x)Y(y)Z(z)T(t)$, in the case of rectangular coordinates, we obtain

$$D[(d^2X/dx^2)/X + (d^2Y/dy^2)/Y + (d^2Z/dz^2)/Z] - k$$
$$= (dT/dt)/T = \delta \qquad [1.260]$$

where δ is a constant and where the special value $f(c) = kc$ has been chosen. Again

$$T = \exp(\delta t) \qquad [1.261]$$

and

$$d^2X/dx^2 = \alpha X , \quad d^2Y/dy^2 = \beta Y , \quad d^2Z/dz^2 = \gamma Z \qquad [1.262]$$

where

$$\alpha + \beta + \gamma = (\delta + k)/D . \qquad [1.263]$$

The further treatment is quite analogous to that in the preceding example.

The cases of cylindrical and spherical symmetry also can be treated. Here the first term of [1.259] would be

$$D(\partial^2 c/\partial r^2 + (1/r)\partial c/\partial r) \quad \text{and} \quad D(\partial^2 c/\partial r^2 + (2/r)\partial c/\partial r) \qquad [1.264]$$

respectively.

3. Diffusion, convection and chemical reaction. One-dimensional case

The equation for the one-dimensional case, with reaction of first order, is

$$D\partial^2 c/\partial x^2 - v\partial c/\partial x - kc = \partial c/\partial t . \qquad [1.265]$$

Again the substitution $c = X(x) \cdot T(t)$, leads to a separation of the variables. We shall only treat the stationary state, given by

$$D \partial^2 c / \partial x^2 - v \partial c / \partial x - kc = 0 . \qquad [1.266]$$

This equation may be integrated by putting $c \sim \exp(\beta x)$, giving

$$c = c_0 \exp\left\{ \frac{v}{2D} \left(1 - \sqrt{1 + \frac{4kD}{v^2}} \right) x \right\} \qquad [1.267]$$

if $c = c_0$ at $x = 0$. We have the limiting case: $k = 0$, $c = c_0$, independent of x.

4. A special two-dimensional problem

For a gas or liquid, streaming in the z-direction between parallel plates of distance $2a$, this distance being small compared with the two other dimensions, b and l, we may solve the following diffusion problem. Diffusion in the x- and z-directions, besides chemical reaction of first order, giving a term $- kc$, and convection in the z-direction. The equation resulting for the steady state, is

$$D (\partial^2 c / \partial x^2 + \partial^2 c / \partial z^2) - kc - v \partial c / \partial z = 0. \qquad [1.268]$$

With $c = X(x) Z(z)$ we obtain the ordinary differential equations

$$d^2 X / dx^2 - \left(\frac{k + \lambda}{D} \right) X = 0 , \quad d^2 Z / dz^2 - (v/D) dZ/dz + (\lambda/D) Z = 0 \qquad [1.269]$$

where the separation constant λ is to be determined in accordance with the boundary conditions. We obtain

$$X = \left.\begin{matrix} \cos \\ \sin \end{matrix}\right\} \sqrt{- \frac{k + \lambda}{D}} \, x , \qquad [1.270]$$

and with the initial and boundary conditions

$$c = c_0 \text{ at } t = 0 \text{ independent of } x \text{ and } z$$
$$c = 0 \quad \text{at } x = \pm a \text{ and } t > 0$$

we find the solution in the form previously given.

For λ we have

$$\lambda = - \frac{(2n + 1)^2 \pi^2 D}{4 a^2} - k .$$

Thus finally, from the second equation [1.269]

$$Z = \exp(\gamma z) \qquad [1.271]$$

with

$$\gamma^2 - \frac{v}{D} \gamma + \frac{\lambda}{D} = 0 , \qquad [1.272]$$

$$\gamma = \frac{v}{2D} - \sqrt{\frac{v^2}{4D^2} + \frac{(2n + 1)^2 \pi^2}{4 a^2} + \frac{k}{D}} .$$

5. A further example of diffusion and chemical reaction

For a gas at rest between plane parallel plates, the distance of the plates being small compared with the other linear dimensions, the following diffusion problem can be solved for the stationary state. The rate of chemical reaction be given by a quite general function of c, diffusion occuring in the x-direction, the concentration c being kept at zero at the walls, situated at $x = \pm \delta$. The differential equation for the stationary state is

$$D\,d^2c/d\,x^2 - f(c) = 0 . \qquad [1.273]$$

Since $\dfrac{d^2 c}{d\,x^2} \dfrac{d\,c}{d\,x} = \dfrac{1}{2} \dfrac{d}{d\,x} \left(\dfrac{d\,c}{d\,x}\right)^2$, [1.273] yields upon multiplication by dc/dx

$$\frac{D}{2}\left(\frac{d\,c}{d\,x}\right)^2 = \int f(c)\,d\,c = F_1 + C , \sqrt{\frac{2}{D}}\,(x_2 - x_1) = \int_1^2 \frac{d c}{\sqrt{F_1 + C}} . \qquad [1.274]$$

The integrations being quadratures, the solution of [1.273] is always possible, if necessary by numerical or graphical methods. Since, however, in reaction kinetics the problem usually consists in the determination of the law of reaction velocity, $f(c)$, the practical solution in most cases is rather laborious, and can only be accomplished by trial and error.

In the special case, cf. (88), where c is the concentration of one kind of atom, being produced photochemically at a constant rate a, from dissociation of a diatomic molecule, disappearing by recombination, with speed bc^2, and by diffusion to the wall, the resulting expression $-f(c)$ is $a - bc^2$, and equation [1.273] becomes

$$D\,d^2c/d\,x^2 + a - b c^2 = 0 , \qquad [1.275]$$

giving as solution the elliptic integral

$$\sqrt{\frac{2}{D}}\,(x_2 - x_1) = \int_1^2 \frac{d c}{\sqrt{-b c^3/3 + a c + C}} . \qquad [1.276]$$

In the limiting case $|b c^2| \ll |D d^2 c/d\,x^2|$, we have the simple result

$$D\,d^2c/d\,x + a = 0, \qquad d\,c/d\,x = -\frac{a x}{D} \qquad [1.277]$$

and finally

$$c = \frac{a}{2 D}\,(\delta^2 - x^2), \qquad \bar{c} = \frac{1}{3}\frac{a \delta^2}{D} , \qquad [1.278]$$

where $\bar{c}$ is the average concentration.

APPENDIX

I. Error function

Many integrals of the diffusion equation lead to the error function. Therefore we reproduce a table of the error function. Using the notation of Carlslaw and Jaeger (3) we have

$$erf\ x = \frac{2}{\sqrt{\pi}} \int_0^x \exp{(-\xi^2)}d\xi,\ erf\ (\infty) = 1,\ erf\ (-x) = -erf\ (x).\quad [1.279]$$

Sometimes it is convenient to introduce the function

$$erf\ c\ x = 1 - erf\ x = \frac{2}{\sqrt{\pi}} \int_x^\infty \exp{(-\xi^2)}d\xi,\quad [1.280]$$

The first two derivatives of the error function are

$$\frac{d}{dx}(erf\ x) = \frac{2}{\sqrt{\pi}}\exp{(-x^2)},\quad \frac{d^2}{dx^2}(erf\ x) = -\frac{4}{\sqrt{\pi}}x\exp{(-x^2)}.\quad [1.281]$$

The integrals of the diffusion equation usually give the concentration as function of time and position coordinates. Experimental determinations, however, often give the content of diffusing substance within a finite volume. To obtain this from the integral of the diffusion equation involves a second integration. Consequently, the integrated error function is of importance for the evaluation of such experiments. Using again the notation of Carlslaw and Jaeger (3), we have

$$i^n\ erf\ cx = \int_x^\infty i^{n-1}erf\ c\,\xi\,d\xi,\qquad n = 1, 2\cdots,\quad [1.282]$$

and for the first two integrals of the error function

$$i\ erf\ cx = \frac{1}{\sqrt{\pi}}\exp{(-x^2)} - x\ erf\ cx\quad [1.283]$$

and

$$i^2\ erf\ cx = \frac{1}{4}\left[erf\ cx - 2\ xi\ erf\ cx\right].\quad [1.284]$$

Therefore, it is possible to express these integrals by means of the error function and of the function $\exp{(-x^2)}$. For the sake of convenience we reproduce below a table of the integrated error function, taken from Carlslaw-Jaeger, cf. Hartree (82), together with the function $erf\ c\ x$.

Table III

Error function, $erf(x)$

x	0	1	2	3	4	5	6	7	8	9
0.0	0.0000	0.0113	0.0226	0.0338	0.0451	0.0564	0.0676	0.0789	0.0901	0.1013
0.1	0.1125	0.1236	0.1348	0.1459	0.1569	0.1680	0.1790	0.1900	0.2009	0.2118
0.2	0.2227	0.2335	0.2443	0.2550	0.2657	0.2763	0.2869	0.2974	0.3079	0.3183
0.3	0.3286	0.3389	0.3491	0.3593	0.3694	0.3794	0.3893	0.3992	0.4090	0.4187
0.4	0.4284	0.4380	0.4475	0.4569	0.4662	0.4755	0.4847	0.4937	0.5027	0.5117
0.5	0.5205	0.5292	0.5379	0.5465	0.5549	0.5633	0.5716	0.5798	0.5879	0.5959
0.6	0.6039	0.6117	0.6194	0.6270	0.6346	0.6420	0.6494	0.6566	0.6638	0.6708
0.7	0.6778	0.6847	0.6914	0.6981	0.7047	0.7112	0.7175	0.7238	0.7300	0.7361
0.8	0.7421	0.7480	0.7538	0.7595	0.7651	0.7707	0.7761	0.7814	0.7867	0.7918
0.9	0.7969	0.8019	0.8068	0.8116	0.8163	0.8209	0.8254	0.8299	0.8342	0.8385
1.0	0.8427	0.8468	0.8508	0.8548	0.8586	0.8624	0.8661	0.8698	0.8733	0.8768
1.1	0.8802	0.8835	0.8868	0.8900	0.8931	0.8961	0.8991	0.9020	0.9048	0.9076
1.2	0.9103	0.9130	0.9155	0.9181	0.9205	0.9229	0.9252	0.9275	0.9297	0.9319
1.3	0.9340	0.9361	0.9381	0.9400	0.9419	0.9438	0.9456	0.9473	0.9490	0.9507
1.4	0.9523	0.9539	0.9554	0.9569	0.9583	0.9597	0.9611	0.9624	0.9637	0.9649
1.5	0.9661	0.9662	0.9663	0.9665	0.9666	0.9667	0.9668	0.9669	0.9670	0.9672

1.55	1.6	1.65	1.7	1.75	1.8	1.9	2.0	2.1	2.2
0.9716	0.9763	0.9804	0.9838	0.9867	0.9891	0.9928	0.9953	0.9970	0.9981

Table IV

$$erf\,c\,x = 1 - erf\,x \quad \text{and} \quad \int_{x}^{\infty} erf\,c\,\xi\,d\xi = i\,erf\,c\,x$$

x	$erf\,c\,x$	$2i\,erf\,c\,x$	x	$erf\,c\,x$	$2i\,erf\,c\,x$
0	1.00000	1.1284	1.00	0.15730	0.1005
0.05	0.94363	1.0312	1.1	0.11980	0.0729
0.10	0.88754	0.9396	1.2	0.08969	0.0521
0.15	0.83200	0.8537	1.3	0.06599	0.0366
0.20	0.77730	0.7732	1.4	0.04772	0.0253
0.25	0.72367	0.6982	1.5	0.03390	0.0172
0.30	0.67137	0.6284	1.6	0.02365	0.0115
0.35	0.62062	0.5639	1.7	0.01621	0.0076
0.40	0.57161	0.5043	1.8	0.01091	0.0049
0.45	0.52452	0.4495	1.9	0.00721	0.0031
0.50	0.47950	0.3993	2.0	0.00468	0.0020
0.55	0.43668	0.3535	2.1	0.00298	0.0012
0.60	0.39614	0.3119	2.2	0.00186	0.0007
0.65	0.35797	0.2742	2.3	0.00114	0.0004
0.70	0.32220	0.2402	2.4	0.000689	0.0002
0.75	0.28884	0.2097	2.5	0.000407	0.0001
0.80	0.25790	0.1823	2.6	0.000236	0.0001
0.85	0.22933	0.1580	2.7	0.000134	
0.90	0.20309	0.1364	2.8	0.000075	
0.95	0.17911	0.1173	2.9	0.000041	

II. Stefan and Kawalki's tables

Stefan (128) has computed tables for the evaluation of diffusion measurements, adapted to experimental conditions chosen by Graham (75) in the earliest diffusion measurements of quantitative value. Though these tables were drawn up for special conditions, they may be adapted to other experimental conditions by the method of reflection (cf. 38), as has been done by Kawalki (90) in a special case.

Stefan used the error function integral of the one-dimensional diffusion equation and tabulated the concentration distribution for a semi-infinite system as well as for a finite system, derived from the former one by the method of reflection. A solution is also possible by means of a Fourier series for the finite system (cf. p. 35). This solution has already been given by Stefan himself who used it to obtain certain relations between the contents of the diffusing substance in different layers which may be of value for control of experiments (cf. Stefan's original papers). Later Lederer (93, 94) attempted to recalculate Stefan's and Kawalki's tables by means of the trigonometric series for a finite system. His results, however, contain a serious error, and therefore must not be used for the evaluation of experiments. It might be worth while to stress this point because publications on diffusion experiments have appeared in print which were evaluated by means of these erroneous tables. Stefan does not actually give the concentrations but the contents of diffusing substance in consecutive layers of equal height. These can be obtained exactly by means of the integrated error function (see above). Since tables of this function were not available at Stefan's time he carried through the integration numerically by means of the approximate formula

$$\int_{x}^{x+\Delta x} c\, dx = \frac{c_i + 4c_m + c_f}{6}\, \Delta x \,. \qquad [1.285]$$

c_i, c_m, c_f being concentrations at the beginning, middle and end of the interval which is of sufficient accuracy except in regions with high values of the second derivative of the error function. For evaluation of precision measurements it might be worth while to make certain that Stefan's tables in the region of interest are of sufficient accuracy.

In table V we reproduce Stefan's tables for an infinite system. They refer to the following experimental conditions. In a semi-infinite cylinder the quantity 10,000 of diffusing substance had been contained at $t = 0$ in a layer of height $2h$ above the boundary at $x = 0$. The content of diffusing substance in consecutive layers of height h is listed as function of $h/2\sqrt{Dt}$. We might stress the fact that this h is only one half the height of the layer which had contained the diffusing substance at $t = 0$. There are numerous errors in the literature due to overlooking this fact (which causes an error by a factor 4 in the diffusion coefficients thus determined).

Table V

Distribution of substance in a semi-infinite cylinder, if for $t = 0$ the quantity 10 000 had been contained in a layer of height $2h$. Listed is the content in consecutive layers of height h as function of the argument $h/2\sqrt{Dt}$

$h/2\sqrt{Dt} =$	0.10	0.11	0.12	0.13	0.14	0.15	0.16	0.17	0.18	0.19
Number of layer										
1	1110	1217	1322	1427	1530	1631	1732	1829	1927	2023
2	1089	1188	1286	1381	1474	1564	1651	1736	1817	1895
3	1046	1134	1217	1295	1369	1437	1501	1560	1614	1664
4	988	1057	1120	1176	1225	1266	1301	1331	1352	1368
5	914	963	1003	1034	1056	1069	1075	1074	1067	1054
6	829	857	873	880	877	866	847	823	793	760
7	738	743	740	725	704	672	638	597	556	513
8	644	631	609	579	541	500	456	411	367	324
9	551	524	489	447	402	356	311	268	228	192
10	463	425	381	334	288	244	202	164	133	106
11	381	336	289	242	199	159	125	97	74	55
12	308	260	213	170	132	100	74	54	38	27
13	244	196	153	115	84	60	42	28	19	12
14	189	145	108	76	52	35	22	15	9	5
15	144	104	72	48	31	20	11	7	4	2
16	108	73	48	30	18	10	6	3	2	1
17	79	50	31	18	10	5	3	1	1	
18	57	34	19	10	5	3	1			
19	40	22	12	6	3	1				
20	28	14	7	3	2					
21	19	9	4	2	1					
22	13	6	2	1						
23	8	3	1							
24	5	2	1							
25	3	1								
26	2	1								
27	1									
28	1									

Table V. Continued

$h/2\sqrt{Dt}$	0.20	0.22	0.24	0.26	0.28	0.30	0.32	0.34	0.36	0.38
No.										
1	2117	2299	2473	2640	2799	2950	3093	3228	3355	3475
2	1970	2112	2243	2361	2468	2566	2653	2732	2802	2866
3	1708	1784	1843	1888	1918	1938	1948	1949	1944	1934
4	1378	1384	1373	1348	1312	1263	1218	1165	1110	1056
5	1035	986	926	858	787	715	646	579	517	459
6	723	645	565	486	413	347	289	238	193	157
7	470	387	311	245	190	144	110	80	59	42
8	284	213	155	109	76	51	35	22	14	9
9	159	106	69	43	26	15	9	5	3	1
10	83	49	28	15	8	4	2	1		
11	40	21	10	5	2	1				
12	18	8	3	1	1					
13	8	3	1							
14	3	1								
15	1									

Table V. Continued

$h/2\sqrt{Dt}$	0.40	0.42	0.44	0.46	0.48	0.50	0.52	0.54	0.56	0.58	0.60
No.											
1	3587	3692	3790	3881	3966	4045	4118	4186	4249	4307	4361
2	2923	2974	3021	3064	3103	3139	3173	3204	3234	3262	3289
3	1920	1903	1882	1863	1841	1820	1795	1771	1747	1724	1700
4	1000	946	894	843	794	746	701	658	617	578	541
5	406	358	314	275	240	208	180	156	134	115	98
6	127	101	80	63	49	38	30	23	17	13	10
7	30	21	15	10	7	4	3	2	1	1	
8	5	3	2	1	1						
9	1										

For values of $h/2\sqrt{Dt} < 0.19$ Stefan has reduced the table for the semi-infinite cylinder to that for 16 layers, by the method of reflection, cf. p. 23 ff. The practical procedure is obvious from the following scheme which shows the reduction from 28 to 8 layers

		1	2	3	4	5	6	7	8	9	10	11	···
18	17	16	15	14	13	12	11	10	9				
		17	18	19	20	21	22	23	24	25	26	···	
						28	27	26	25				

By a threefold reflection the scheme between the vertical lines has been obtained, meaning that the content of the first layer of the finite cylinder is equal to the sum of the contents of the first, 16th and 17th layers of the semi-infinite cylinder, etc. Thus Stefan's original table may be adapted to a great variety of experimental conditions. In the following table VI Stefan's table for 16 layers is reproduced. For values of the argument $h/2\sqrt{Dt} > 0.18$ table V should be used.

Table VI
Stefan's table for a finite cylinder of height $16\,h$

$h/2\sqrt{Dt}=$	0.10	0.11	0.12	0.13	0.14	0.15	0.16	0.17	0.18
No.									
1	1110	1217	1322	1427	1530	1631	1732	1829	1927
2	1089	1188	1286	1381	1474	1564	1651	1736	1817
3	1046	1134	1217	1295	1369	1437	1501	1560	1614
4	988	1057	1120	1176	1225	1266	1301	1331	1352
5	915	963	1003	1034	1056	1069	1075	1074	1067
6	830	857	873	880	877	866	847	823	793
7	740	744	740	725	704	672	638	597	556
8	647	632	609	579	541	500	456	411	367
9	556	526	490	447	402	356	311	268	228
10	471	428	382	334	288	244	202	164	133
11	394	342	291	243	199	159	125	97	74
12	327	269	217	172	133	100	74	54	38
13	272	210	160	118	86	60	42	28	19
14	229	167	120	82	55	36	22	15	9
15	201	138	91	58	36	23	12	7	4
16	187	123	79	48	28	15	9	4	3

Table VII

Kawalki's table. Initial conditions as in the case treated by Stefan: Diffusing substance of amount 10,000 in layer of height $2h$, finite system of height $8h$. Tabulated is the content of diffusing substance in four consecutive layers of height $2\,h$ each as function of the argument $h/\sqrt{2Dt}$

$h/2\sqrt{Dt}$	0.10	0.12	0.14	0.16	0.18	0.20	0.22	0.24	0.26	0.28
layer no.										
1	2587	2778	3068	3404	3751	4088	4411	4716	5001	5267
2	2535	2617	2735	2866	2994	3097	3172	3217	3236	3230
3	2466	2384	2265	2121	1972	1816	1660	1504	1350	1203
4	2414	2221	1935	1607	1284	996	755	563	412	300

$h/2\sqrt{Dt}$	0.30	0.32	0.34	0.36	0.38	0.40	0.44	0.48	0.52	0.56
1	5516	5746	5960	6157	6341	6510	6811	7069	7291	7483
2	3201	3166	3114	3054	2990	2920	2776	2635	2496	2364
3	1063	935	817	710	616	533	394	289	210	151
4	214	156	108	76	52	36	17	8	3	1

$h/2\sqrt{Dt}$	0.60	0.70	0.80	1.00
1	7650	7985	8238	8593
2	2241	1968	1744	1406
3	108	45	18	3
4				

Table VIII e^{-x^2}

x	0	1	2	3	4	5	6	7	8	9
0.0	1.0000	0.9999	0.9996	0.9991	0.9984	0.9975	0.9964	0.9951	0.9936	0.9919
0.1	0.9900	0.9880	0.9857	0.9832	0.9806	0.9778	0.9747	0.9715	0.9681	0.9645
0.2	0.9608	0.9569	0.9528	0.9485	0.9440	0.9394	0.9346	0.9297	0.9246	0.9193
0.3	0.9139	0.9084	0.9027	0.8968	0.8908	0.8847	0.8785	0.8721	0.8655	0.8589
0.4	0.8521	0.8453	0.8384	0.8312	0.8240	0.8167	0.8093	0.8018	0.7942	0.7866
0.5	0.7788									

x	0	2	4	6	8		x	
0.5	0.7788	0.7631	0.7471	0.7308	0.7143		2.20	0.0079
0.6	0.6977	0.6809	0.6639	0.6469	0.6298		2.25	0.0063
0.7	0.6126	0.5955	0.5783	0.5613	0.5442		2.30	0.0050
0.8	0.5273	0.5105	0.4938	0.4773	0.4610		2.35	0.0040
0.9	0.4449	0.4290	0.4133	0.3979	0.3827		2.40	0.0032
1.0	0.3679	0.3533	0.3391	0.3251	0.3115		2.45	0.0025
1.1	0.2982	0.2853	0.2726	0.2604	0.2485		2.50	0.0019
1.2	0.2369	0.2257	0.2149	0.2044	0.1943		2.55	0.0015
1.3	0.1845	0.1751	0.1660	0.1573	0.1489		2.6	0.0012
1.4	0.1409	0.1331	0.1257	0.1187	0.1119		2.7	0.0007
1.5	0.1054	0.0992	0.0933	0.0877	0.0824		2.8	0.0004
1.6	0.0773	0.0725	0.0679	0.0636	0.0595		2.9	0.0002
1.7	0.0556	0.0519	0.0484	0.0452	0.0421		3.0	0.0001
1.8	0.0392	0.0364	0.0339	0.0314	0.0292		3.1	0.0001
1.9	0.0271	0.0251	0.0232	0.0215	0.0198		3.2	0.0000
2.0	0.0183	0.0169	0.0156	0.0144	0.0132			
2.1	0.0122	0.0112	0.0103	0.0094	0.0086			

Table IX

First derivative of error function $= (2/\sqrt{\pi})\, e^{-x^2}$

x	0	1	2	3	4	5	6	7	8	9
0.0	1.1284	1.1283	1.1279	1.1274	1.1266	1.1256	1.1243	1.1229	1.1212	1.1193
0.1	1.1172	1.1148	1.1122	1.1095	1.1065	1.1033	1.0999	1.0962	1.0924	1.0884
0.2	1.0841	1.0797	1.0751	1.0702	1.0652	1.0600	1.0546	1.0490	1.0433	1.0374
0.3	1.0313	1.0250	1.0186	1.0120	1.0052	0.9983	0.9912	0.9840	0.9767	0.9692
0.4	0.9615	0.9538	0.9459	0.9379	0.9298	0.9215	0.9132	0.9047	0.8962	0.8875
0.5	0.8788	0.8700	0.8610	0.8520	0.8430	0.8338	0.8246	0.8154	0.8060	0.7967
0.6	0.7872	0.7778	0.7683	0.7587	0.7491	0.7395	0.7299	0.7203	0.7106	0.7010
0.7	0.6913	0.6816	0.6719	0.6622	0.6526	0.6429	0.6333	0.6237	0.6141	0.6045
0.8	0.5950	0.5855	0.5760	0.5666	0.5572	0.5479	0.5386	0.5293	0.5202	0.5110
0.9	0.5020	0.4930	0.4840	0.4752	0.4664	0.4576	0.4490	0.4404	0.4319	0.4235
1.0	0.4151	0.4068	0.3987	0.3906	0.3826	0.3747	0.3668	0.3591	0.3515	0.3439
1.1	0.3365	0.3291	0.3219	0.3147	0.3076	0.3007	0.2938	0.2870	0.2804	0.2738
1.2	0.2673	0.2610	0.2547	0.2485	0.2425	0.2365	0.2307	0.2249	0.2192	0.2137
1.3	0.2082	0.2028	0.1976	0.1924	0.1873	0.1824	0.1775	0.1727	0.1680	0.1634
1.4	0.1589	0.1545	0.1502	0.1460	0.1419	0.1378	0.1339	0.1300	0.1262	0.1225

Table IX Continued

x	0	1	2	3	4	5	6	7	8	9
1.5	0.1189	0.1154	0.1120	0.1086	0.1053	0.1021	0.0990	0.0959	0.0930	0.0901
1.6	0.0872	0.0845	0.0818	0.0792	0.0766	0.0741	0.0717	0.0694	0.0671	0.0649
1.7	0.0627	0.0606	0.0586	0.0566	0.0546	0.0528	0.0510	0.0492	0.0475	0.0458
1.8	0.0442	0.0426	0.0411	0.0396	0.0382	0.0368	0.0355	0.0342	0.0329	0.0317
1.9	0.0305	0.0294	0.0283	0.0272	0.0262	0.0252	0.0242	0.0233	0.0224	0.0215
2.0	0.0207	0.0199	0.0191	0.0183	0.0176	0.0169	0.0162	0.0155	0.0149	0.0143
2.1	0.0137	0.0132	0.0126	0.0121	0.0116	0.0111	0.0106	0.0102	0.0097	0.0093
2.2	0.0089	0.0085	0.0082	0.0078	0.0075	0.0071	0.0068	0.0065	0.0062	0.0060
2.3	0.0057	0.0054	0.0052	0.0050	0.0047	0.0045	0.0043	0.0041	0.0039	0.0037
2.4	0.0036	0.0034	0.0032	0.0031	0.0029	0.0028	0.0027	0.0025	0.0024	0.0023
2.5	0.0022	0.0021	0.0020	0.0019	0.0018	0.0017	0.0016	0.0015	0.0015	0.0014
2.6	0.0013	0.0012	0.0012	0.0011	0.0011	0.0010	0.0010	0.0009	0.0009	0.0008
2.7	0.0008	0.0007	0.0007	0.0007	0.0006	0.0006	0.0006	0.0005	0.0005	0.0005
2.8	0.0004	0.0004	0.0004	0.0004	0.0004	0.0003	0.0003	0.0003	0.0003	0.0003
2.9	0.0003	0.0002	0.0002	0.0002	0.0002	0.0002	0.0002	0.0002	0.0002	0.0001
3.0	0.0001									

III. Diffusion in a system consisting of two phases

If one component is diffusing in a two-phase medium, and if we suppose that equilibrium is established at the interface of the two phases, we have the condition at this interface,

$$\mu^{\mathrm{I}} = \mu^{\mathrm{II}} \qquad [1.286]$$

where μ is the chemical potential of the diffusing particles, assumed to be electrically neutral, and the superscript refers to the phases I and II, respectively. Within the range of validity of the laws of ideal solutions [1.286] is equivalent to Nernst's distribution law

$$c^{\mathrm{I}}/c^{\mathrm{II}} = \varkappa . \qquad [1.287]$$

We shall treat now the linear problem, the phases I and II being of infinite extension in the $-x$- and $+x$- directions, respectively, and of constant cross section, the common boundary being situated at $x = 0$. If we denote the diffusion coefficients within the phases I and II by D^{I} and D^{II}, we have the following differential equations, and boundary and initial conditions,

$$\partial c/\partial t = D^{\mathrm{I}} \partial^2 c/\partial x^2 \text{ for } x < 0, \quad \partial c/\partial t = D^{\mathrm{II}} \partial^2 c/\partial x^2 \text{ for } x > 0 \qquad [1.288]$$

$$c = c_0 \text{ for } x < 0, \quad c = 0 \text{ for } x > 0 \text{ and } t = 0, \qquad [1.289]$$

$$(c^{\mathrm{I}})_{x=0}/(c^{\mathrm{II}})_{x=0} = \varkappa, \quad D^{\mathrm{I}} (\partial c/\partial x)^{\mathrm{I}}_{x=0} = D^{\mathrm{II}} (\partial c/\partial x)^{\mathrm{II}}_{x=0} .$$

The last equation expresses the continuity of flow through the plane $x = 0$.

The general solution of our problem is (Jost (29))

$$c = c_0\left\{1 - \frac{\varkappa\sqrt{D^{II}}}{\varkappa\sqrt{D^{II}} + \sqrt{D^{I}}}\left[1 + erf\left(\frac{x}{2\sqrt{D^{I}t}}\right)\right]\right\} \quad \text{for} \quad x < 0,$$

$$c = c_0 \frac{\varkappa\sqrt{D^{I}}}{\varkappa\sqrt{D^{II}} + \sqrt{D^{I}}}\left[1 - erf\left(\frac{x}{2\sqrt{D^{II}t}}\right)\right] \quad \text{for} \quad x > 0,$$

[1.290]

$erf\ x$ denoting the error function (cf. p. 61). For $D^{I} = D^{II} = D$ this reduces to

$$c = c_0\left\{\frac{\varkappa}{1 + \varkappa}\left[1 - erf\left(\frac{x}{2\sqrt{Dt}}\right)\right] + \frac{1 - \varkappa}{1 + \varkappa}\right\} \quad \text{for } x < 0,$$

$$c = c_0 \frac{\varkappa}{1 + \varkappa}\left[1 - erf\left(\frac{x}{2\sqrt{Dt}}\right)\right] \quad \text{for } x > 0.$$

[1.291]

Solutions of [1.290] and [1.291] are shown graphically in Figs. 1-7 to 1-10 p. 26, cf. (124)

IV. Further integrals for systems consisting of more than one phase

C. Wagner* has treated diffusion problems in binary systems consisting of more than one phase. In the following we give a survey of some of his results which may be valuable for practical purposes.

1. Diffusion from a surface into a heterogeneous system of given overall concentration, Fig. 1-21

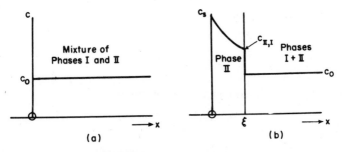

Fig. 1-21. Diffusion in two-phase system, after Wagner. a) Distribution of overall concentration of phases I and II, at $t = 0$. b) Distribution of concentration at $t > 0$. Phase II for $x < \xi$, conglomerate of phases I and II for $x > \xi$.

Given a conglomerate of phases I and II, with average concentration c_0 at $t = 0$, of infinite extension in the x-direction, Fig. 1-21. At the surface, $x = 0$, conditions shall be imposed such that phase II

* C. Wagner, unpublished results. The author is indebted to Wagner for permission to reproduce his calculations, cf. also Bückle (57).

with surface concentration c_s is obtained*. Then diffusion will proceed from the surface, in the homogeneous phase II, and at time t the region of phase II will extend from $x = 0$ to $x = \xi$, Fig. 1-21.

The diffusion process will be governed by the equation

$$\frac{\partial c}{\partial t} = D \frac{\partial^2 c}{\partial x^2} \qquad [1.292]$$

where a concentration independent diffusion coefficient has been assumed. The boundary condition is

$$c = c_s \quad \text{at } x = 0 \quad \text{and} \quad t > 0 . \qquad [1.293]$$

At the plane of discontinuity, $x = \xi$, the concentration of the diffusing species in phase II is that corresponding to equilibrium between phases I and II, thus

$$c = c_{II,I} \quad \text{at } x = \xi . \qquad [1.294]$$

While the interface between the homogeneous and heterogeneous region is displaced by $d\xi$ within time dt, the amount $[c_{II,I} - c_0]d\xi$ of diffusing substance must be supplied per unit area from the region $x < \xi$, thus (approximately)

$$[c_{II,\,I} - c_0] \, d\xi = - D \, dt \left(\frac{\partial c}{\partial x}\right)_{\xi - 0} \qquad [1.295]$$

A particular integral of equation [1.292] is

$$c = c_s - B \; erf\left(\frac{x}{2\sqrt{Dt}}\right), \quad \text{for } 0 < x < \xi . \qquad [1.296]$$

Wagner assumes tentatively that the plane of discontinuity is shifted proportionally with $\sqrt{t}$, i.e.,

$$\xi = \gamma 2\sqrt{Dt} \qquad [1.297]$$

where γ is a dimensionless parameter. Substituting [1.296] and [1.297] in equations [1.294] and [1.295] one obtains

$$c_s - c_{II,\,I} = B \; erf\,(\gamma) \qquad [1.298]$$

and

$$c_{II,\,I} - c_0 = \frac{B}{\sqrt{\pi}\,\gamma} \exp\,(-\gamma^2), \qquad [1.299]$$

and by eliminating B

$$\frac{c_s - c_{II,I}}{c_{II,I} - c_0} = \sqrt{\pi}\,\gamma e^{\gamma^2} erf\,(\gamma) . \qquad [1.300]$$

Equation [1.300] permits of a determination of the parameter γ. Then B may be determined from equations [1.298] and [1.299]. Thus

---

* The phases I and II, for instance, might be ferrite and austenite at 850° C, the surface being in contact with a carburizing gas of definite partial pressure, e. g. $CO + CO_2$ or $CH_4 + H_2$.

with D known, the rate of displacement of the plane of discontinuity and the concentration distribution within phase II may be calculated from the above equations. On the other hand D may be determined from the observed displacement of the plane of discontinuity by means of equation [1.297] which gives

$$D = \xi^2/4\gamma t .$$ [1.301]

2. Diffusion into a homogeneous phase, a second phase developing from the surface, fig. 1-22

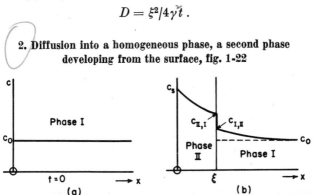

Fig. 1-22. Diffusion in two-phase system, after Wagner. a) Concentration in phase I for $t = 0$. b) Concentration in phase II $(x < \xi)$ and in phase I $(x > \xi)$ at $t > 0$.

The notation used is seen from Fig. 1-22. We now have the two differential equations

$$\frac{\partial c}{\partial t} = D_{II} \frac{\partial^2 c}{\partial x^2} \text{ for } 0 < x < \xi$$ [1.302]

and

$$\frac{\partial c}{\partial t} = D_I \frac{\partial^2 c}{\partial x^2} \text{ for } x > \xi$$ [1.303]

where D_I and D_{II} are the (concentration independent) diffusion coefficients within phases I and II, and ξ is again the locus of the plane of discontinuity.
The initial condition is

$$c = c_0 \quad \text{at} \quad x > 0 \quad \text{and} \quad t = 0$$ [1.304]

and the boundary conditions are

$$c = c_s \quad \text{at} \quad x = 0 \quad \text{and} \quad t > 0$$ [1.305]

$$c = c_{II,I} \quad \text{at} \quad x = \xi - 0 \text{ (phase II)}$$ [1.306]

and

$$c = c_{I,II} \quad \text{at} \quad x = \xi + 0 \text{ (phase I)}.$$ [1.307]

Again we have the approximate relation for the amount of diffusing substance, needed at $x = \xi$ for a displacement $d\xi$ of the phase boundary during time dt

$$[c_{II,I} - c_{I,II}] d\xi ,$$

referred to unit cross-section. This amount is the surplus of substance reaching the phase boundary by diffusion in phase II over that entering into phase I by diffusion, thus

$$[c_{II,I} - c_{I,II}]d\,\xi = -D_{II}\left(\frac{\partial c}{\partial x}\right)_{\xi - 0} + D_{I}\left(\frac{\partial c}{\partial x}\right)_{\xi + 0}. \qquad [1.308]$$

As above, a particular integral for phase II, satisfying the boundary condition [1.305] is

$$c = c_s - B_{II}\,erf\left(\frac{x}{2\sqrt{D_{II}\,t}}\right) \quad \text{for } 0 < x < \xi. \qquad [1.309]$$

A particular integral for phase I, satisfying the initial condition is

$$c = c_0 + B_{I}\left[1 - erf\left(\frac{x}{2\sqrt{D_{I}t}}\right)\right] \quad \text{for } x > \xi. \qquad [1.310]$$

Assuming again a relation

$$\xi = \gamma\,2\sqrt{D_{II}\,t} \qquad [1.311]$$

for the displacement ξ of the phase boundary with time, we obtain by substituting equations [1.309], [1.310] and [1.311] in equations [1.306], [1.307] and [1.308]

$$c_{II,I} = c_s - B_{II}\,erf\,(\gamma) \qquad [1.312]$$
$$c_{I,II} = c_0 - B_{I}\,[1 - erf\,(\gamma\sqrt{\varphi})] \qquad [1.313]$$

and

$$c_{II,I} - c_{I,II} = \frac{B_{II}}{\sqrt{\pi}\,\gamma}\exp\,(-\gamma^2) - \frac{B_{I}}{\gamma\sqrt{\pi}\,\sqrt{\varphi}}\exp\,(-\gamma^2\varphi) \qquad [1.314]$$

where

$$\varphi = D_{II}\,/\,D_{I}.$$

Finally, by eliminating B_{I} and B_{II} from equations [1.312], [1.313] and [1.314]

$$c_{II,I} - c_{I,II} = \frac{c_s - c_{II,I}}{\sqrt{\pi}\,\gamma\,erf\,\gamma}\exp\,(-\gamma^2) - \frac{(c_{I,II} - c_0)\exp\,(-\gamma^2\varphi)}{\sqrt{\pi\varphi}\,\gamma\,[1 - erf\,(\gamma\sqrt{\varphi})]} \qquad [1.315]$$

Again, γ can be evaluated from [1.315] by numerical or graphical methods, if D_{I}, D_{II} and $c_{I,II}$ and $c_{II,i}$ are known, and, thus, the rate of displacement of the phase boundary can be calculated from [1.315]. However, it is not possible to determine the two diffusion coefficients D_{I} and D_{II} from one observation of the variation of ξ with time.

3. Diffusion from phase II into a conglomerate of phases I and II, fig. 1-23

The problem is similar to case 1. We have the differential equation

$$\frac{\partial c}{\partial t} = D_{II}\frac{\partial^2 c}{\partial x^2} \quad \text{for } x < \xi, \qquad [1.316]$$

diffusion proceeding in phase II only, with the initial condition

$$c = c_{II,0} \quad \text{at } x < 0 \quad \text{and } t = 0 \qquad [1.317]$$

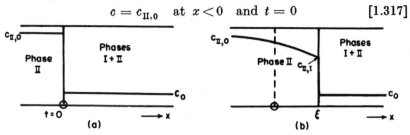

Fig. 1-23. Diffusion in two-phase system, after Wagner. a) Concentration in phase II ($x < 0$) and in conglomerate of phases I and II ($x > 0$) for $t = 0$. b) Concentration in phase II ($x < \xi$) and in conglomerate of phases I and II ($x > \xi$) at $t > 0$.

and

$$c = c_0 \quad \text{at } x > 0 \quad \text{and } t = 0. \qquad [1.318]$$

Again putting

$$\xi = \gamma 2 \sqrt{D_{II} t} \qquad [1.319]$$

and using the particular integral

$$c = c_{II,0} - B \left\{ 1 + erf \left(\frac{x}{2 \sqrt{D_{II} t}} \right) \right\} \qquad \text{for } x < \xi \quad [1.320]$$

one obtains from the preceding equations, as in the previous examples

$$\frac{c_{II,0} - c_{II,I}}{c_{II,I} - c_0} = \sqrt{\pi} \, \gamma \exp(\gamma^2) [1 + erf(\gamma)]. \qquad [1.321]$$

From [1.321] γ may be calculated, and by means of this value of γ we may either determine ξ as function of the known value of D_{II}, or we may determine D_{II} from observed values of ξ as function of time.

4. Diffusion from phase II into phase I, with resulting transformation of phase I into phase II and corresponding displacement of the interface, Fig. 1-24

With the previous notation one obtains for the constant γ, defined as above

$$\frac{c_{II,I} - c_{II,0}}{\sqrt{\pi} \, \gamma [1 + erf(\gamma)]} - \frac{c_{I,II} - c_0}{\sqrt{\pi \varphi} \, \gamma [1 - erf(\gamma \sqrt{\varphi})]} = c_{II,I} - c_{I,II}, \qquad [1.322]$$

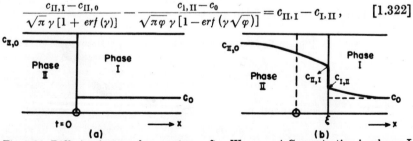

Fig. 1-24. Diffusion in two-phase system, after Wagner. a) Concentration in phases I and II at $t = 0$; b) Concentration in phase II ($x < \xi$) and in phase I ($x > \xi$) at $t > 0$.

and again the displacement ξ of the phase boundary with time may be determined with the value of γ, thus calculated, by means of

$$\xi = \gamma \, 2\sqrt{D_{\text{II}} \, t} \, . \qquad [1.323]$$

5. Diffusion from a conglomerate of phases II and III into a conglomerate of phases I and II, Fig. 1-25

Initial conditions

$$c = c_0'' \text{ for } x < 0$$
$$c = c_0' \text{ for } x > 0.$$

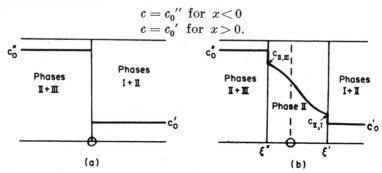

Fig. 1-25. Diffusion in three-phase system, after Wagner. a) Concentration in conglomerates of phases II and III ($x < 0$) and of phases I and II ($x > 0$) at $t = 0$; b) Concentration in conglomerate of phases II and III ($x < \xi''$), in phase II ($\xi'' < x < \xi'$) and in conglomerate of phases I and II ($x > \xi'$) at $t > 0$.

After a time t a homogeneous region of phase II extends from ξ'' to ξ', diffusion in this phase obeying the differential equation

$$\frac{\partial c}{\partial t} = D_{\text{II}} \frac{\partial^2 c}{\partial x^2} , \qquad \text{for } \xi'' < x < \xi' \, . \qquad [1.324]$$

We have the boundary conditions, in accordance with previous examples,

$$c_{\xi'-0} = c_{\text{II, I}} \qquad [1.325]$$

phase II in equilibrium with phase III, and

$$c_{\xi''+0} = c_{\text{II, III}} \qquad [1.326]$$

phase II in equilibrium with phase I, and

$$[c_{\text{II, I}} - c_0'] \, d\xi' = -D_{\text{II}} \, dt \left(\frac{\partial c}{\partial x} \right)_{\xi'-0} , \qquad [1.327]$$

and

$$[c_0'' - c_{\text{II, III}}] \, d\xi'' = D_{\text{II}} \, dt \left(\frac{\partial c}{\partial x} \right)_{\xi''+0} \, . \qquad [1.328]$$

Again the assumption is introduced

$$\xi' = \gamma' \, 2\sqrt{D_{\text{II}} t} \qquad [1.329]$$

$$\xi'' = \gamma'' \, 2\sqrt{D_{\text{II}} t} \, . \qquad [1.330]$$

A particular solution of [1.324] is

$$c = A - B \; erf \left[\frac{x}{2\sqrt{D_{II} t}} \right] \quad \text{for } \xi'' < x < \xi' . \qquad [1.331]$$

By substituting equations [1.329], [1.330] and [1.331] in equations [1.325], [1.326], [1.327] and [1.328], we obtain the equations for γ' and γ''

$$\frac{c_{II,III} - c_{II,I}}{c_{II,I} - c_0'} = \sqrt{\pi} \; \gamma' \; \exp \; (\gamma'^2) \left[erf \; (\gamma') + erf \; (\gamma'') \right] \qquad [1.332]$$

and

$$\frac{c_{II,III} - c_{II,I}}{c_0'' - c_{II,III}} = \sqrt{\pi} \; \gamma'' \; \exp \; (\gamma''^2) \left[erf \; (\gamma') + erf \; (\gamma'') \right] \qquad [1.333]$$

which may be solved graphically or numerically if c_0', c_0'', $c_{II,I}$ and $c_{II,III}$ are given. Further, it is possible to determine the diffusion coefficient D_{II} from the observed rate of displacement of the boundaries by means of the equations [1.329] and [1.330]

$$D_{II} = (\xi')^2 / 4\gamma' t \qquad [1.334]$$

or

$$D_{II} = (\xi'')^2 / 4\gamma'' t . \qquad [1.335]$$

V. Diffusion in systems, consisting of more than one phase, with diffusion coefficients depending on concentration

Diffusion within a single phase, where the diffusion coefficient varies with concentration, is usually treated by Boltzmann's (56) method (cf. p. 31). From the equation [1.13], p. 4

$$\frac{\partial c}{\partial t} = D \frac{\partial^2 c}{\partial x^2} + \frac{dD}{dc} \left(\frac{\partial c}{\partial x} \right)^2 \qquad [1.336]$$

one obtains for the diffusion coefficient

$$D = -2 \frac{dy}{dc} \int_{c_0}^{c} y \, dc$$

$$= +2 \frac{dy}{dc} \int_{c_1}^{c} y \, dc . \qquad [1.337]$$

Here the substitution has been introduced

$$c = c \; (x,t) = c \left(\frac{x}{\sqrt{t}} \right) = c \; (y), \quad y = \frac{x}{\sqrt{t}} .$$

Equation [1.337] holds for the initial conditions, depending on y only

$c = c_0$ for $x < 0$ and $t = 0$ (i.e., for $y = -\infty$), and

$c = c_1$ for $x > 0$ and $t = 0$ (i.e., for $y = +\infty$). \qquad [1.338]

In our former treatment we had put $c_1 = 0$. Equation [1.337] permits the evaluation of $D(c)$ from experimental concentration distributions. Actually, the range of validity of eq. [1.337] is wider than so far has been noticed. It is not necessary that our system be continuous at $x = 0$. We may have a boundary condition at $y = 0$, i.e. $x = 0$, $t > 0$, of the form

$$f(c_+, c_-) = 0 ,$$ [1.339]

where c_+ and c_- are the concentrations at the sides of positive and negative y, respectively. Then, generally, c and D will be discontinuous at $x = 0$. This, however, does not prevent the application of Boltzmann's method, Jost (88a). The integral in eq. [1.337] remains continuous at the locus of the discontinuity. The discontinuity in D arises due to a discontinuity in $\frac{dy}{dc}$. It is seen at once that the correct change in D is obtained, in accordance with the condition of continuity at $x = 0$, namely

$$-D_-\left(\frac{\partial c}{\partial x}\right)_- = -D_+\left(\frac{\partial c}{\partial x}\right)_+ .$$ [1.340]

[1.340] remains of the same form in the system of the y, since it refers to constant t.

In our former case (p. 68) we had

$$f(c_+, c_-) = \frac{c_+}{c_-} - \varkappa = 0 ,$$ [1.341]

Nernst's partition law, and

$$D_-, D_+ \text{ independent of } c.$$

Now this restriction is no longer necessary. Instead of [1.341] we may even have a non-linear boundary condition, as for instance

$$f(c_+, c_-) = \frac{c^2_+}{c_-} - \varkappa = 0 ,$$ Nernst's partition law for equilibrium between single and double molecules. [1.342]

Therefore, even such cases as the interdiffusion in the system $Cu_2S + 2\,AgI = Ag_2S + 2\,CuI$, investigated by Tubandt and Reinhold (136a), become tractable, provided that the system under consideration is sufficiently long.

It is a necessary condition, however, that the boundary condition does not contain the time explicitly, as seen from the following example. It would be of interest to treat a two-phase problem, as above, but without equilibrium being established at the interface, according to eq. [1.339]. If the speed of transition from one phase to the other is inhibited, we have a condition at $x = 0$

$$J = \varphi(c_+, c_-)$$ [1.343]

where J is the current of diffusing substance through the interface. For reasons of continuity we then must have

$$J = - D_- \left(\frac{\partial c}{\partial x}\right)_- = - D_+ \left(\frac{\partial c}{\partial x}\right)_+ = \varphi\,(c_+, c_-) \, . \qquad [1.344]$$

In the system of the y this condition becomes, however,

$$- D_- \left(\frac{dc}{dy}\right)_- = - D_+ \left(\frac{dc}{dy}\right)_+ = \varphi\,(c_+, c_-)\,\sqrt{t} \qquad [1.345]$$

containing the time explicitly. This is not compatible with Boltzmann's assumption.

If a concentration curve, referring to this case, is determined experimentally, eq. [1.345] gives the correct ratio of the diffusion coefficients at either side of the discontinuity. Also, it is seen that a condition of the type [1.343] is valid. Application of eq. [1.337], however, will no longer yield the correct diffusion coefficients. However in general it will give the right order of magnitude and qualitatively the correct dependence on concentration.

Since c depends on $\frac{x}{\sqrt{t}}$ only, it follows that from a concentration curve for one finite time t_1 the curves for other times t can be obtained by distorting the abscissa in the ratio $\sqrt{\frac{t}{t_1}}$. As a consequence, it is seen that the concentrations c_+ and c_- at $x = 0$ must be independent of time. We finally mention that the method may be extended to a system consisting of more than two phases if the additional phase boundaries are located at $y = $ const., i.e., are moving according to $x = x_0 \sqrt{t}$, as sometimes is the case, cf. Chap. IX.

VI. Thermal convection. Eddy diffusion

In this book we are treating exclusively true diffusion processes. It might be worth while mentioning, however, that in fluid media a mixing by thermal convection and by eddy diffusion may become of importance or may even prevail. For these problems we must refer to the literature on hydrodynamics and aerodynamics (Durand (65a), Prandtl (113b), Prandtl-Tietjens (113a)). Though a quantitative theoretical treatment of these processes, comparable to that of true diffusion processes, is generally not possible, considerations of similarity may lead to results of great practical value (cf. books on Chemical Engineering).

We mention here one problem, generally treated in text books of physical chemistry, but usually not correlated to modern hydrodynamic theory. This is the Nernst-Brunner (56a) theory of dissolution. The dissolution of many substances (as for instance of MgO in an acid) can be treated quantitively on the assumption that in a stirred solution there is a layer adherent to the solid, of thickness δ, through which diffusion occurs. This layer, turns out to be much thicker than adsorbed films. It can be identified, however, with the boundary layer in hydrodynamic theory. This theory gives the correct order of magnitude for the adherent layer. One obtains for δ [cf. Prandtl (113a, 113b)]

$$\delta \approx \sqrt{\frac{\eta \xi}{\varrho v}}$$

where δ thickness of layer, η viscosity of medium, ρ density, ξ linear dimension of surface of solid, v velocity of liquid (or gas), due to stirring.

For water we have $\nu = \dfrac{\eta}{\varrho} \approx 0.01$; with $\xi = 1$ cm and an assumed value 10^2 cm sec^{-1} for v we obtain

$$\delta \approx 0.1 \text{ mm},$$

which is of the correct order of magnitude [for the rate of dissolution cf. Wagner (138); for further problems see Bakhmeteff (49a), Dryden (64a), Sherwood (121, 121a)].

REFERENCES

Monographs and Review Articles

1. Barrer, R. M., Diffusion in and through solids. Cambridge, University Press, 1941.
2. Carlslaw, H. S., and Jaeger, J. C., Operational Methods in Applied Mathematics. Oxford 1941.
3. Carlslaw, H. S., and Jaeger, J. C., Conduction of heat in solids. Oxford, Clarendon Press, 1947.
4. Chandrasekhar, S., *Rev. mod. Phys.* **15**, 20 (1943).
5. Chapman, S., and Cowling, T. G., The Mathematical Theory of Non-Uniform Gases. Cambridge, University Press, 1939.
6. Churchill, R. V., Fourier Series and Boundary value problems. McGraw Hill, New York 1941.
7. Churchill, R. V., Modern Operational Mathematics in Engineering. McGraw Hill, New York 1944.
8. Coolidge, J. L., An Introduction to mathematical Probability. New York 1937.
9. Coolidge, J. L., Einführung in die Wahrscheinlichkeitsrechnung. Leipzig 1927.
10. Courant, R., and Hilbert, D., Methoden der mathematischen Physik, Vol. 1. Berlin 1931.
11. Czuber, E., Wahrscheinlichkeitsrechnung. Leipzig 1924.

12. Damkoehler, G., Z. *Elektrochem.* **42**, 846 (1936).
13. Damkoehler, G., Z. *Elektrochem.* **43**, 1, 8 (1937).
14. Damkoehler, G., Z. *Elektrochem.* **44**, 193, 228 (1938).
15. Damkoehler, G., Der Chemieingenieur Vol. III, 1. Leipzig 1937.
16. Doetsch, G., Theorie und Anwendung der Laplace-Transformation. Springer, Berlin 1937.
17. Doetsch, G., Tabellen zur Laplace-Transformation u. Anleitung zum Gebrauch. Springer, Berlin 1947.
18. Duclaux, J., Mouvement Brownien. *Actualités scientifiques* Nr. 529 and 700. Herman, Paris 1937/38.
19. Einstein, A., Investigation of the Theory of the Brownian Movement, edited by R. Fürth, Methuen, London 1926.
20. Fisher, A., The mathematical Theory of Probabilities and its Application to Frequency Curves and Statistical Methods. New York 1930.
21. Fourier, J. B., Théorie analytique de la chaleur. Paris 1822.
22. Frank, Ph., and v. Mises, R., Die Differential- u. Integralgleichungen der Mechanik und Physik, Vol. II. Braunschweig 1935.
23. Fuerth, R., Article Brownian Movement in F. Auerbach, and W. Hort: Handbuch physik. techn. Mechanik Vol. 7. Leipzig 1931, p. 198ff.
24. Fuerth, R., Article Diffusion in F. Auerbach, and W. Hort: Handbuch physik. techn. Mechanik, Vol. 7. Leipzig 1931, p. 635ff.
25. de Groot, S. R., Dissertation. Amsterdam 1945.
26. Harned, H. S., *Chem. Rev.* **40**, 461 (1947).
27. Jahnke, F., and Emde, E., Funktionentafeln 3rd edition. Leipzig 1938.
28. Jeffreys, H., and Jeffreys, B. S., Methods of mathematical Physics. Cambridge 1946.
29. Jost, W., Diffusion und chemische Reaktion in festen Stoffen. Dresden und Leipzig 1937.
30. Jost, W., Explosions- und Verbrennungsvorgänge. Berlin 1939.
31. Kappler, E., *FIAT Review of German Science*, Vol. Physics of Liquids and Gases, 1948.
32. Lewis, B., and von Elbe, G., Combustion, Flames and Explosions of Gases. Cambridge 1938, p. 13, 214, 220.
33. von Mises, R., Wahrscheinlichkeitsrechnung. Leipzig 1931.
34. von Mueffling, L., Article wall recombination of free atoms and radicals, in G. M. Schwab: Handbuch der Katalyse, Vol. 6, p. 116ff. Springer, Wien 1943.
35. Perrin, J., Die Atome, edited by A. Lottermoser. Leipzig und Dresden 1920.
36. Perrin, J., Atoms, translated by D. L. Hammick. London 1920.
37. Seith, W., Diffusion in Metallen (Platzwechselreaktionen). Springer, Berlin 1939.
38. Seitz, F., Fundamental Aspects of Diffusion in Solids. Pittsburgh (1948).
39. Sommerfeld, A., Partial Differential Equations in Physics. Academic Press, New York 1949.
40. Svedberg, T., and Pedersen, K. O., The Ultracentrifuge. Oxford (1940).
40a Tables of Probability Functions, W. P. A. New York 1941/42
41. Uspensky, J. V., Introduction to mathematical probability. New York 1937.
42. Voigt, W., Lehrbuch der Kristallphysik. Leipzig (1928).
43. Zernike, F., Wahrscheinlichkeitsrechnung und mathematische Statistik; in H. Geiger, and K. Scheel, Handbuch der Physik, Vol. III. Berlin 1928.

General Bibliography

44. Amdur, J., and Robinson, A. L., *J. Am. Chem. Soc.* **55**, 1395 (1933).
45. Amdur, J., *J. Am. Chem. Soc.* **60**, 2347 (1938). (Diffusion and chemical reaction.)
46. Archibald, W. J., *Phys. Rev.* **53**, 746 (1938); **54**, 371 (1938).
47. Archibald, W. J., *J. Applied Phys.* **18**, 362 (1947).
48. Avrami, M., and Paschkis, V., *Trans. Amer. Soc. Chem. Engrs.* **38**, 631 (1942).
49. Awbery, J. H., *Proc. Phys. Soc. (London)* **48**, 118 (1936).
49a. Bakhmeteff, B. A., Mechanics of turbulent Flow, Princeton 1936.
50. Barnes, C., *Physics* **5**, 4 (1934).
51. Barrer, R. M., *Trans. Faraday Soc.* **35**, 628 (1939).
52. Barrer, R. M., *Proc. Phys. Soc. (London)* **58**, 321 (1946).
52a. Barrer, R. M., *Trans. Faraday Soc.* **36**, 1235 (1940)
52b. Barrer, R. M. and Skirrow, G., *J. Polymer Sci.* **3**, 549 (1948) (Time-lag method)
53. Beckmann, Ch. O., and Rosenberg, J. L., *Ann. N. Y. Acad. Sci.* **46**, 329 (1945).
54. Bevilacqua, E. M., Bevilacqua E. B., Bender, M. M., and Williams, J.W., *Ann. N. Y., Acad. Sci.* **46**, 309 (1945). (Diffusion of high polymers.)
55. Bodenstein, M., Lenher, S., and Wagner, C., *Z. physik. Chem.* **B 3**, 459 (1929). (Diffusion and chemical reaction.)
56. Boltzmann, L., *Wied. Ann.* **53**, 959 (1894).
56a. Brunner, E., *Z. physik. Chem.* **47**, 56 (1904).
57. Bueckle, H., *Metallforschung* **1**, 175 (1946).
58. Bursian, V., and Sorokin, V., *Z. physik. Chem.* **B 12**, 247 (1931). (Diffusion and chemical reaction.)
58a. Crank, J., *Phil. Mag.* **39**, 140 (1948) (cf. (141c)).
58b. Crank. J. and Henry, M. E., *Trans. Faraday Soc:* **45**, 636, 1119 (1949) (Diffusion in media with variable properties).
58c. Crank, J., *Phil. Mag.* **39**, 362 (1948).
58d. Crank J., *Soc. Dyers* **66**, 366 (1950).
59. Daynes, H., *Proc. Roy. Soc. (London)* **A 97**, 286 (1920).
60. Damköhler, G., *VDI-Beiheft Verfahrenstechnik* **2**, 7 (1936).
61. Damköhler, G., *Die Chem. Fabrik* **12**, 469 (1939).
62. Damköhler, G., *Z. physik. Chem.* **A 193**, 16 (1943).
62a. Danckwerts, P. V., *Trans. Faraday Soc.* **46**, 701 (1950) (Unsteady-state diffusion with moving boundary).
63. Dobrowsky, A., *Kolloid-Z.* **104**, 87 (1943).
64. Dobrowsky, A., *Kolloid-Z.* **105**, 56 (1943).
64a. Dryden, H. L., *Ind. Eng. Chem.* **31**, 416 (1939).
65. Dünwald, H., and Wagner, C., *Z. physik. Chem.* **B 24**, 53 (1934).
65a. Durand, W. F., Aerodynamic Theory, Springer, Berlin 1934—1937.
66. Einstein, A., *Ann. Physik* **17**, 549 (1905).
67. v. Elbe, G., and Lewis, B., *J. Am. Chem. Soc.* **59**, 970 (1937).
68. Ellickson, R. T., and Serin, B., *Phys. Rev.* **59**, 922 (1941).
69. Eversole, W. G., Peterson, J. D., and Kindsvater, H. M., *J. phys. Chem.* **45**, 1398 (1941).
70. Fick, A., *Pogg. Ann.* **94**, 59 (1855).
71. Förster, Th., and Geib, K. H., *Ann. Physik* (5) **20**, 250 (1934).
71a. Frank, F. C., *Proc. Roy. Soc. (London)* **A 201**, 586 (1950) (Radially symmetric phase growth controlled by diffusion).
72. Fürth, R., *Z. Physik* **40**, 351 (1926).
73. Fürth, R., *Z. Physik* **45**, 83 (1927).

74. Gordon, A. R., *Ann. N. Y. Acad. Sci.* **46**, 285 (1945).
75. Graham, Th., *Phil. Trans. Roy. Soc. (London)* **1861**, 138—224
76. Gralén, N., *Kolloid-Z.* **95**, 188 (1941). (Diffusion of high polymers.)
77. Gralén, N., Dissertation, Uppsala 1944.
78. de Groot, S. R., *Proc. Nederl. Akad. Wetensch.* Amsterdam **45**, 820 (1942).
79. de Groot, S. R., *Proc. Nederl. Akad. Wetensch.* Amsterdam **45**, 643 (1942).
80. Grube, G., and Jedele, A., *Z. Elektrochem.* **38**, 799 (1932).
81. von Hartel, H., and Polanyi, M., *Z. physik. Chem.* **B 11**, 97 (1931). (Diffusion and chemical reaction.)
82. Hartree, D. R., *Mem. Proc. Manchester Lit. & Phil. Soc.* **80**, 85 (1935).
82a. Hermans, J. J., *J. Colloid Sci.* **2**, 387 (1947). (Diffusion with discontinuous boundary.)
83. Hertz, G., *Physik. Z.* **23**, 433 (1922).
84. Hertz, G., *Z. Physik* **19**, 35 (1923).
85. Hopkins, M. R., *Proc. Phys. Soc. (London)* **50**, 703 (1938).
86. Jaeger, J. C., *Trans. Faraday Soc.* **42**, 615 (1946). (Diffusion through hollow cylinder.)
87. Jedele, A., *Z. Elektrochem.* **39**, 691 (1933).
88. Jost, W., *Z. physik. Chem.* **B 3**, 95 (1929).
88a. Jost, W., *Z. Physik* **127**, 163 (1950).
89. Kassel, L. S., and Storch, H. H., *J. Am. Chem. Soc.* **57**, 672 (1935). (Diffusion and chemical reaction.)
90. Kawalki, W., *Wied. Ann.* **52**, 166 (1894).
91. Lamm, O., *Nova Acta Regiae Soc. Scient. Upsaliensis.* Ser. IV **10**, Nr. 6 (1937).
92. Langer, R. E., *Tôhoku Mathem. Journal* **35**, Pt. II, 260 (1932).
93. Lederer, E. L., *Kolloid-Z.* **44**, 108 (1928).
94. Lederer, E. L., *Kolloid-Z.* **46**, 169 (1928).
95. Lewis, B., and von Elbe, G., *J. Chem. Phys.* **2**, 537 (1934). (Diffusion and chemical reaction.)
96. Liebhafsky, H. A., *J. Applied Phys.* **12**, 707 (1941).
97. Liebhafsky, H. A., Marshall, A. L., and Verhoek, F. H., *Ind. Eng. Chem.* **34**, 704 (1942)
98. Linderstrom-Lang, K., *Compt. rend. trav. lab. Carlsberg* (Sér. chim.) **24**, 249 (1942).
99. McBain, J. W., and Dawson, C. R., *Proc. Roy. Soc. (London)* **A 148**, 32 (1935).
99a. McCarter, R. J., Stutzman, L. F. and Koch Jr., H. A., *Ind. Eng. Chem.* **41**, 1290 (1949) (Eddy diffusivities in turbulent fluid flow).
100. March, H. M., and Weaver, W., *Phys. Rev.* **31**, 1072 (1928).
101. Matano, C., *Japan. J. Physics* **8**, 109 (1933).
102. Matano, C., *Proc. Phys. Math. Soc. Japan* **15**, 405 (1933).
103. Mehl, R. F., *Metals Technol. Tech. Publ.*, 1658 (1943).
104. Meixner, J., *Ann. Physik* **39**, 333 (1941).
105. Meixner, J., *Ann. Physik* **40**, 165 (1941).
106. Newman, A. B., *Trans. Am. Inst. Chem. Engrs.* **27**, 310 (1931).
107. Northrop, J. H., and Anson, M. L., *J. Gen. Physiol.* **12**, 543 (1929).
108. von Obermayer, A., *Sitzungsber. Wiener Akad. Wissensch.* IIa **81**, 1102 (1880).
109. Onsager, L., *Phys. Rev.* **37**, 405 (1931).
110. Onsager, L., *Phys. Rev.* **38**, 2265 (1931).
111. Onsager, L., and Fuoss, R. M., *J. Phys. Chem.* **36**, 2759 (1932).

112. Paneth, F., and Herzfeld, K. F., *Z. Elektrochem.* **37**, 577 (1931).
113. Paschkis, V., and Baker, H. D., *Trans. Amer. Soc. Mech. Engrs.* **64**, 105 (1942).
113a. Prandtl, L., and Tietjens, O., Hydro- und Aerodynamik. Berlin 1929, 1931.
113b. Prandtl, L., Führer durch die Strömungslehre. Braunschweig 1944.
113c. Reiss, H. and La Mer, V. K., *J. Chem. Phys.* **18**, 1 (1950) (Diffusional boundary value problem involving moving boundaries)
114. Rhines, F. N., and Mehl, R. F., *Trans. Am. Inst. Mining Met. Engrs.* **128**, 185 (1938).
115. Seith, W., *Z. Elektrochem.* **39**, 538 (1933).
116. de Sénarmont, H., *Compt. rend. Paris* **21**, 457 (1847).
117. de Sénarmont, H., *Compt. rend. Paris* **22**, 179 (1848).
118. de Sénarmont, H., *Compt. rend. Paris* **23**, 257 (1848).
119. de Sénarmont, H., *Compt. rend. Paris* **28**, 279 (1850).
120. Serin, B., and Ellickson, R. T., *J. Chem. Phys.* **9**, 742 (1941).
121. Sherwood, T. K., *Ind. Eng. Chem.* **21**, 12 (1929).
121a. Sherwood, T. K., and Woertz, B. B., *Ind. Eng. Chem.* **31**, 1034 (1939).
122. v. Smoluchowski, M., *Ann. Physik* **21**, 756 (1906).
123. v. Smoluchowski, M., *Ann. Physik* **48**, 1103 (1915).
124. Smoluchowski, R., *Phys. Rev.* **62**, 539 (1942).
125. Soret, Ch., *Arch. de Genève* **29**, 355 (1893).
126. Soret, Ch., *Arch. de Genève* **32**, 631 (1894).
127. Stefan, A., *Sitzungsber. Wiener Akad. Wissensch.* II **68**, 385 (1873).
128. Stefan, A., *Sitzungsber. Wiener Akad. Wissensch.* II **79**, 161 (1879)
129. Stefan, A., *Sitzungsber. Wiener Akad. Wissensch.* II **98**, 1418 (1889).
130. Stefan, A., *Ann. Physik* (3), **41**, 725 (1890).
131. Stefan, A., *Sitzungsber. Wiener Akad. Wissensch.* II **77**, 371 (1879).
132. Steiner, W., and Wicke, F. W., *Z. physik. Chem.* Bodenstein-Festbd. **1931**, 817.
133. Steiner, W., *Trans. Faraday Soc.* **31**, 962 (1935).
134. Steiner, W., *Trans. Faraday Soc.* **31**, 623 (1935). (Diffusion and chemical reaction.)
135. Thovert, J., *Ann. chim. phys.* (7) **26**, 366 (1902).
136. Thovert, J., *Ann. chim. phys.* (9) **2**, 369 (1914).
136a. Tubandt, C., and Reinhold, H., *Z. physik. Chem.* **140**, 291 (1929).
136b. Vreedenberg, H. A., *Rec. trav. chim.* **67**, 839 (1948). (Cylindrical diffusion with discontinuous boundary.)
137. Voigt, W., *Nachr. Ges. Wiss. Göttingen Math. Phys. Kl.* p. 87 (1903).
138. Wagner, C., *J. Phys. & Colloid Chem.* **53**, 1030 (1950).
139. Wagner, C., unpublished.
140. Wagner, C., *Z. physik. Chem.* A **192**, 157 (1943).
141. Wagner, C., *Z. physik. Chem.* A **193**, 1 (1943).
141a. Wagner, C., *J. Colloid Sci.* **5**, 85 (1950). (Mathematical analysis of the formation of periodic precipitation.)
141b. Weinbaum, S., *J. Applied Phys.* **19**, 867 (1948). (Alloying of metal powders by diffusion, mathematical theory.)
141c. Wilson, A. H., *Phil. Mag.* **39**, 48 (1948). (A diffusion problem in which the amount of diffusing substance is finite I, II cf. Crank. (58a)).
142. Wiener, O., *Wied. Ann.* **49**, 105 (1893).
143. Zuber, R., *Z. Physik* **79**, 291 (1932).

CHAPTER II

DISORDER IN CRYSTALS *

I. Introduction. Experimental Evidence of Disorder in Crystals

The most stable state of a crystal at the absolute zero of temperature is that of complete order. At finite temperatures the structure of a crystal still approaches very closely a regular lattice, but deviations from this regular structure are possible. Though the regular lattice structure is favored energetically, configurations with deviations from complete order have a higher entropy, and therefore structures with a certain degree of disorder might be observable at not too low temperatures.

There are several conceivable types of disorder in a crystal lattice. Lattice sites may be unoccupied which, in case of complete order, are occupied, atoms or ions may be found on lattice sites which, in case of complete order, are unoccupied, i. e., in interstices between normal lattice sites; finally, in a lattice built up by more than one constituent, particles of different kinds may have been exchanged.

There is ample evidence for the existence of all these types of disorder in real crystals. This is most obvious, perhaps, for crystals containing some impurity in small concentrations, for instance, iron with small additions of carbon, nitrogen, or hydrogen. These components, not being present in a stoichiometric ratio, cannot fill the sites of a regular sublattice. Even if for some concentrations of the addition one could find a sublattice of sufficiently high lattice constants all sites of which would be occupied by the component under consideration, this would not be possible even with only slightly altered concentration. Further, many compounds are known exhibiting deviations from an exact stoichiometric composition, which, in a crystal, must be connected with deviations from a perfect lattice structure. From investigations of phase equilibria in the system Fe-O it is known that the phase FeO (Wüstite) is stable within a finite range of concentrations, corresponding to Fe-contents below that for the stoichiometric compound FeO. X-ray analysis (Jette and Foote (96))

* Cf. the monographs and comprehensive articles quoted on p. 129.

revealed a sodium chloride type of lattice, with continuously varying
lattice parameter. The values observed, as shown in Table I, indicate

TABLE I
Lattice distance, density, and composition of ferrous oxide
(after Jette and Foote)

Atom % Fe	Lattice Distance Å	Density	Composition
47.68	4.282	5.613	$Fe_{0.91}O$
47.85	4.285	5.624	$Fe_{0.92}O$
48.23	4.292	5.658	$Fe_{0.93}O$
48.56	4.301	5.728	$Fe_{0.945}O$

that with increasing surplus of oxygen (deficit of iron) the density decreases. This would not be reconcilable with the assumption that oxygen
is taken up by the interstices of the lattice. The explanation given
by the authors is quite conclusive: oxygen excess corresponds to
vacancies in the iron lattice. To compensate the loss of positive electric
charge two Fe^{++} ions must be transformed into Fe^{+++} ions for every
vacancy created, in complete agreement with the chemical explanation
that an excess of oxygen corresponds to the formation of Fe_2O_3. The
process might be described equally well as the formation of mixed
crystals of FeO and Fe_2O_3, three Fe^{++} ions being substituted for two
Fe^{+++} ions, leaving one vacancy in the iron lattice. As a first approximation, the Fe^{+++} ions and vacancies may be considered as being
distributed at random.

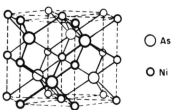

O As

O Ni

Fig. 2-1. Ni-As lattice.

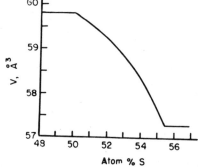

Fig. 2-2. Dependence of volume of unit
cell of FeS on composition (after Hägg
and Sucksdorff).

Ferrous sulfide, FeS, and FeSe crystallize in the nickel arsenide
type of lattice (Fig. 2-1). FeS is stable within a range of concentrations from 50 to > 55.5 atom per cent of sulfur. With increasing
sulfur content the lattice distance decreases (Hägg and Sucksdorff
(83)), while at the same time the density decreases, Fig. 2-2. Within

he limits of error the density agrees with that calculated for a struc-
ure with vacancies in the iron lattice. For the highest sulfur content
•bserved, approximately 20% of the sites in the Fe^{++} lattice are
ınoccupied.

FeSe behaves similarly, though there exists a second phase of te-
ragonal structure at the composition of 50 atom per cent of selenium.
\t elevated temperatures the hexagonal phase of the nickel arsenide
ype is stable, its range of stability extending to room temperature
·or a selenium content above that of the stoichiometric compound,
Hägg and Kindström (84). For selenium contents above 53 atom
per cent, the hexagonal structure is deformed, giving monoclinic
ıymmetry. Up to about 57 atom per cent of Se, the volume of the
·lementary cell decreases continuously with increasing selenium
:ontent. Observed densities are compatible with the presence of
·acancies in the iron lattice. At the limiting concentration of this
phase, 26 per cent of the Fe-sites in the lattice are unoccupied.

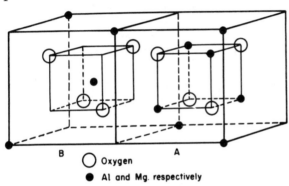

B   O Oxygen
A
● Al and Mg. respectively

Fig. 2-3. Spinel structure, after Verwey.

The group of the spinels crystallizes in a complicated cubic lattice
Fig. 2-3. Magnesium aluminum spinel ($MgO \cdot Al_2O_3$) dissolves an
excess of aluminum oxide. Hägg and Söderholm (85) have shown
that this surplus is dissolved by substitution of Mg^{++} ions by Al^{+++}
ions and formation of a corresponding number of holes in the lattice
of the cations. The homogeneous spinel phase ranges from 50 to about
67 mol per cent of Al_2O_3. There further exists a γ-phase of Al_2O_3
which may be considered as an unstable limiting phase of the spinel.
The lattice parameter of γ-Al_2O_3 agrees with the value extrapolated
·rom the spinel phase for the composition 100% Al_2O_3. Again, from
the determination of lattice parameters and of densities it is seen that
only the above mechanism accounts for the formation of the mixed
crystals. In γ-Al_2O_3 one-ninth of the cation sites of the normal spinel

lattice are unoccupied. γ-Fe_2O_3 is related to Fe_3O_4 in the same way as γ-Al_2O_3 to the spinels. Fe_3O_4 crystallizes in the spinel lattice. With increasing ratio of O:Fe the lattice distance decreases continuously. Combination of x-ray data and density measurements again decides in favor of a vacancy type of crystal, Hägg (86), Verwey (163) .

The structure of $MgCl_2$—LiCl mixed crystals may be described as a substitution of a lithium ion by Mg^{++} in the lattice of lithium chloride accompanied by the formation of a vacancy in the Li^+-lattice, or as a substitution of a Mg^{++} ion and of a vacancy in the $MgCl_2$ lattice by two Li^+ ions, Bruni (37).

A different mechanism is involved in the formation of mixed crystals in the system $CaF_2 + YF_3$, Ketelaar and Willems (110) (within the range from O to 25 % of YF_3), and in the case of SrF_2 and LaF_3 and CaF_2 and ThF_4. In the case of $CaF_2 + YF_3$ Ca^{++} ions in the CaF_2 lattice are substituted by Y^{+++} ions. The surplus charge, however, is not compensated by formation of holes in the cation lattice, but a corresponding number of F^- ions is placed into the interstices, Zintl and Udgard (183).

In the system $CeO_2 + La_2O_3$ Zintl and Croatto (182) found mixed crystals with up to 44 mole per cent of La_2O_3. Here, again, Ce^{4+} ions in the fluorite type of lattice are substituted by La^{3+} ions, but vacancies in the lattice of the anions are left, as seen from x-ray measurements and from pycnometric density measurements. Croatto and co-workers (56, 57) also investigated a number of analogous oxide systems.

Mixed crystals of CdO with Bi_2O_3 seem to exhibit vacancies in the lattice of the anions, too (Sillén and Sillén (149, 150, 151)). In the system $ZrO_2 + MgO$, however, a mixed crystal of fluorite structure is formed, with part of the cations on interstitial sites (Ruff and Ebert (145), Ebert and Cohn (61), Buessem, Schusterius, and Ungewiß (39)).

By treating a Ni_2Al_3 alloy with NaOH, Taylor and Weiss (160) were able to dissolve the major part of the aluminum without destroying the trigonal structure of the original alloy. Thus they finally obtained a mixed crystal still exhibiting the unchanged Ni_2Al_3 lattice though it contained more than 95 % of nickel. Since x-ray patterns continued to be sharp, it may be assumed that the particles remained comparatively large, of linear dimensions of about 1000 Å. The so-called Raney nickel, used as a hydrogenation catalyst, is similarly treated. Defect lattices of ternary alloys have been investigated by Lipson and Taylor (122).

In the system Ni-Al there exists a phase NiAl, crystallizing in a cubic, body-centered lattice. A transition from this phase to the δ-phase Ni_2Al_3 may be described as follows: one-third of the Ni-sites in the NiAl lattice remain unoccupied. Thus the cubic symmetry is lost and a transition to the trigonal system occurs. This phase is stable within a range of concentrations from 37.3 to 41.35 atom per cent of Ni (Bradley and Taylor (34)).

The examples, given so far, refer to compounds of non-stoichiometric composition. The disorder present in these crystals, would still exist after cooling down to the absolute zero of temperature. These crystals, however, would not represent the most stable state at absolute zero, but only a metastable one, comparable with that of an supercooled liquid.

In crystals of exactly stoichiometric composition, too, there may be deviations from a state of complete order, even disorder necessarily connected with the special type of lattice.

Early investigations of the crystal structure of α-AgI, stable between 145° and 555° C, met' with considerable difficulties though the compound crystallizes in the regular system. Its structure is indeed quite unusual, the anions occupying a regular lattice while the cations are distributed at random, over a great number of interstitial sites, as found by Strock (154, 155), Fig. 2-4. Tubandt (162) had suggested many years before that in substances like α-AgI and α-Ag$_2$S only the anions should occupy a regular lattice while the lattice of the cations should be practically "molten," these being not bound to definite positions, for, measurements of electric conductivity (cf. p. 188)

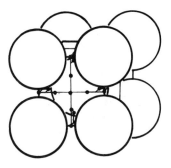

Fig. 2-4. Structure of α-AgI. Cubic body-centered lattice of I$^-$-ions; random occupation of 42 interstitial sites (of which a fraction is shown (●)) by Ag$^+$-ions.

and of transference numbers had shown that the cations possess an abnormally high mobility, equal to that of ions in aqueous solution, while the anions are practically immobile. The essential correctness of this picture has been borne out by the x-ray analysis. The iodide ions occupy the sites of a cubic body-centered lattice while the observed intensities of the x-ray patterns are best explained by the assumption that the silver ions are distributed at random among the 42 interstitial sites of an elementary cell. α-CuI, stable above 440° C, is completely miscible with α-AgI and should, therefore, have the same structure.

The compounds α-Ag$_2$S, α-Ag$_2$Se, α-Ag$_2$Te, α-Cu$_{1.8}$S, and α-Cu$_2$Se, all of which are stable between a transformation point, situated above room temperature, and the melting point, and which show an abnormally high onic conductivity, are built similarly, as proved by Rahlfs (141).

α-Ag$_2$S, with transformation point at 179°C, is essentially of the same structure as α-AgI: the sulfur ions form a cubic body-centered lattice, where now twice as many silver ions as in the former example 4 per elementary cell, are to be distributed at random among 42 interstitial sites.

α-Ag$_2$Se, transformation point 133°C, is of analogous structure, though a better agreement between observed and calculated intensities is obtained if, in the distribution of the cations, the larger interstices are somewhat favored.

In α-Cu$_2$Se, stable above 110°C, there is a cubic face-centered lattice for the anions. The lattice may be described as of the zinc blende type where once more the same number of cations has been distributed among the interstices.

The structure of α-Ag$_2$Te, above 149.5°C, is essentially analogous to that of α-Cu$_2$Se, though again, as in the case of α-Ag$_2$Se, there seems to be a preference for the occupation of the larger interstices by the cations.

With the α phase of Cu$_2$S, above 91°C, a regular structure could only be obtained in the presence of an excess of sulfur, for instance for the composition Cu$_{1.8}$ S. The structure is probably analogous to that of α-Cu$_2$Se. To account for the sulfur surplus, there seems to be hardly any other possibility than to assume a deficiency of copper, where the lack of electrical charge would have to be compensated by the presence of an equivalent number of Cu^{++} ions.

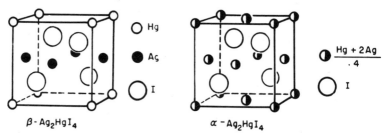

Fig. 2-5. Structure of β-Ag$_2$HgI$_4$.   Fig. 2-6. Structure of α-Ag$_2$HgI$_4$.

The compound Ag$_2$HgI$_4$ shows especially interesting features, Ketelaar (106, 107, 108, 109). At room temperature, a tetragonal modification is stable, the structure of which is shown in Fig. 2-5. In the cubic α-phase, stable above 50°C, the lattice of the anions is the same as in the β-phase, while the three cations now occupy the four sites of a face-centered cubic lattice, every site, therefore, is occupied, on the average, by (1 Hg + 2 Ag)/4 ions, one-quarter of the sites being unoccupied, Fig. 2-6. As in the former examples, this structure is connected with a rather high electrolytic conductivity. A further remarkable feature is the fact that the transition from the β-phase into the α-phase becomes observable within a finite temperature range below the transformation point. This transition shows all the characteristics of order-disorder transformations in alloys, and we shall further deal with it in connection with these phenomena, Ketelaar (loc. cit.).

One fact might be emphasized in connection with these compounds of a crystal structure of inherent disorder and anomalous mobility of ions. None of these phases is stable at the absolute zero of temperature where a state of complete order should prevail, the stability in all cases being limited toward lower temperatures by the occurrence of a transformation point.

So far we have met with the following types of lattice imperfections:

A A A A A A
$\quad B$
A A A A A A
$\quad\quad\quad\quad B$
A A A A A A
$\quad B$
A A A A A A

Fig. 2-7. Mixed crystal of interstitial type

A B A B A B A B A B

B A B $\quad$ B A B A B A

A B A B A B A B A B

B A B A B A B $\quad$ B A

A B A B A B A B A B

Fig. 2-8. Compound AB, with a surplus of B, due to A-vacancies

A X A X A X A X A X
$\quad X$
X A X A X B X A X A
$\quad\quad\quad\quad\quad X$
A X B X A X A X A X
$\quad X$
X A X A X A X B X A
$\quad\quad\quad\quad X$
A X B X A X A X A X

Fig. 2-9. Mixed crystals $AX_n + BX_{n+1}$ with occupation of interstitial sites

A A B A B A A B B B

B A B A A B A A B A

A B B A B A B B A A

B B A B A B B A B A

A B A B B A A B A B

Fig. 2-10. Substitution type of mixed crystal, complete disorder

(a) mixed crystals of the interstitial type, Fig. 2-7, (b) compounds with an excess of one component, due to vacancies in the lattice of the other component, Fig. 2-8, (c) mixed crystals with occupation of interstitial sites, Fig. 2-9. As a fourth type we add, (d) normal mixed crystals of the substitution type, Fig. 2-10, (e) averaged structures, Fig. 2-4, 2-6. These different cases may be reduced to three types of disorder, namely, (1) vacancies, (2) occupation of interstitial lattice sites, and (3 exchange between different types of atoms or molecules in the lattice

In a binary mixed crystal of components A and B we may have several limiting cases. On the one hand complete disorder (Fig. 2-10) state of maximum entropy, and on the other hand either complete order, Fig. 2-11, in so far as the ratio of the concentrations of the components does permit ordering, or a splitting into two separate phases, of A-rich and of B-rich mixed crystals. Which of these cases may be observed at low temperatures depends on the sign of the energy of mixing for the components. If ΔH for mixing is positive, i. e., heat is absorbed during mixing, we may have a splitting into

A B A B A B A B A B

B A B A B A B A B A

A B A B A B A B A B

B A B A B A B A B A

A B A B A B A B A B

Fig. 2-11. Mixed crystal $A\,B$ with complete order

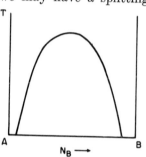

Fig. 2-12. Partial miscibility of A and B, as function of T.

two phases below a certain temperature, depending on the concentration of the original mixed crystal, Fig. 2-12. With decreasing temperature the compositions of the two coexisting phases approach more and more those of the two pure components. Alternatively, for $\Delta H < 0$, heat being liberated on mixing, an ordered phase of the mixture may be formed below a certain temperature, as shown in Fig. 2-11, for the composition $A\,B$ in the plane case. This ordered structure will disappear above a certain critical temperature. The theory of these order-disorder transformations in mixed crystals, especially in alloys, will be treated in a separate paragraph.

Now we may have more complicated types of disorder in a crystal, arising from a combination of the above-mentioned simple types. Thus, for instance, we may have interstitial sites occupied and vacancies left in the original lattice, Fig. 2-13.

In principle it should be possible to distinguish experimentally the different types, shown in Fig. 2-13. The pycnometric density in case (a) lies above that derived from an x-ray determination of the lattice constant, in (b) the pycnometric density lies below this value, whereas in (c) agreement or deviations in either direction are dependent on whether the number of occupied interstitial sites is equal to that of vacancies or not. As far as the author is aware, however, no case is known so far where for a simple compound this method has been applied with success. It would be of interest, for instance, to find out whether there are holes present in the lattices of metals. The effects to be expected, usually, are too small to be detected.

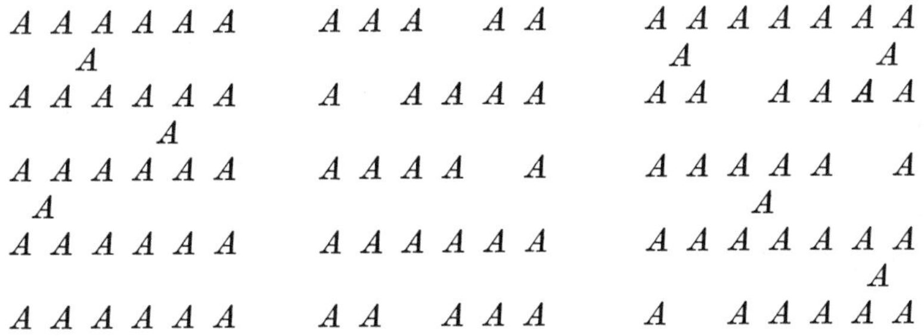

```
A A A A A A        A A A     A A        A A A A A A A A
      A                                 A           A
A A A A A A        A   A A A A           A A     A A A A
          A
A A A A A A        A A A A     A         A A A A A     A
  A                                            A
A A A A A A        A A A A A A           A A A A A A A A
                                                      A
A A A A A A        A A     A A A         A     A A A A A
```

(a) Interstitial disorder   (b) Vacancy disorder   (c) Interstices occupied and
                                                               vacancies left
                                  Fig. 2-13

In binary compounds a combination of the types of disorder, as discussed for pure components, is possible. For ionic compounds, for instance of type AB, the variety of combinations is limited by the condition of electric neutrality. Thus in case of disorder in the lattice of component B only, Fig. 2-14, there must be equal numbers of holes and occupied interstitial sites, Frenkel type of disorder (67).

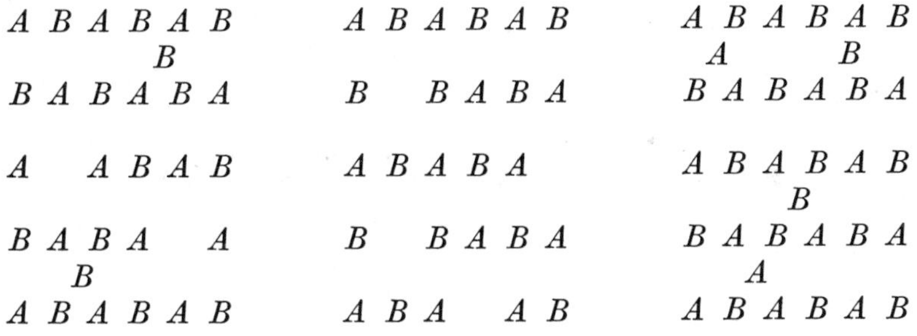

```
A B A B A B        A B A B A B          A B A B A B
      B                                 A     B
B A B A B A        B   B A B A           B A B A B A

A   A B A B        A B A B A           A B A B A B
                                              B
B A B A   A        B   B A B A          B A B A B A
    B                                     A
A B A B A B        A B A   A B          A B A B A B
```

(a) Frenkel type of   (b) Schottky type of   (c) Disorder with
    disorder for com-   disorder   occupied interstices
        ponent B
                             Fig. 2-14

In the case of vacancies only, Fig. 2-14 (b), the numbers of A and of B vacancies must be equal, a case first treated by Schottky (158). If interstices only are occupied, their numbers must be equal for either component, Fig. 2-14 (c).

An accurate treatment of disorder will be given below. Generally, one obtains the correct formal expressions by applying the simple law of mass action to the different types of particles, vacancies being treated as one type of particles. If, for instance, in a crystal of a single constituent there are formed vacancies of number n_v per cubic centimeter, n_L being the total number of particles per cubic centimeter, equal to the number of lattice positions if n_v is sufficiently small, then the law of mass action gives

$$n_v/n_L = K_v \qquad [2.1]$$

and for the occupation of interstitial sites only, of number n_i per cubic centimeter,

$$n_i/n_L = K_i \qquad [2.2]$$

where the equilibrium constants, K_v and K_i, will depend exponentially on temperature. We may formally write reaction equations, leading to the mass action equations [2.1] and [2.2]. For instance,

Particle in the lattice + Unoccupied lattice site at the surface of crystal = Vacancy in the lattice + Particle on   [2.3] a new lattice site.

Since there are new lattice sites available of unlimited constant concentration and since the number of lattice sites for small degrees of disorder, (which we shall always assume), remains practically constant, equation [2.1] follows from [2.3]. In the other example we should have to write

Particle in the lattice + Unoccupied interstitial site = Particle in an interstice + Vacancy at the surface. [2.4]

Again, the number of unoccupied interstitial sites and the number of vacant lattice points outside the boundary of the crystal can be considered constant, and [2.2] follows from [2.4].

For the case of Frenkel disorder, equal number of vacancies of one type of ion and interstitial ions of the same type, Fig. 2-14 (a), we should have to write

Particle on lattice site + Unoccupied interstitial site = Vacancy + Particle on interstitial site   [2.5]

from which it follows, if we retain in the final expression the numbers n_L of normal lattice sites per cubic centimeter and of βn_L interstitial sites per cubic centimeter, β being a small integer, that,

$$n_v n_i = \beta n_L^2 K \qquad [2.6]$$

and since for a pure crystal both types of lattice defects must be equal in number

$$n_v = n_i = n_L \sqrt{K\beta}. \qquad [2.7]$$

Of course, we might have included the constant term βn_L^2 in [2.6] in the equilibrium constant K, but from the way we have written the equation it is apparent at once that the number of each type of defects must be proportional to the number of lattice points. For the Schottky case we should have the analogous formula, cf. Fig. 2-14 (b)

Particle A on lattice site + Particle B on lattice site
+ 2 new lattice sites at the surface of the crystal   [2.8]
    = Vacancy of A + vacancy of B + Particle A on
    new lattice site + Particle B on new lattice site

from which it follows in analogy to the preceding example, that

$$n_{va} n_{vb} = n_L^2 K. \qquad [2.9]$$

While in the examples discussed first, like solid solutions of carbon or hydrogen in metals, in compounds with deviations from stoichiometric composition, like FeO, FeS, etc., there was the possibility of a direct experimental proof of the presence of disorder and of the special type prevailing, the evidence in the cases treated later is of a more indirect nature. Where ionic conduction and diffusion is found in crystals, one may conclude that some disorder of the lattice is responsible for the observed motion of particles. Ions on interstitial sites can move, reaching equivalent neighboring positions after having surmounted a certain potential barrier; or ions on normal lattice sites may move into neighboring vacancies, which is equivalent to a movement of vacancies, also connected with surmounting of a potential barrier, and both mechanisms may work simultaneously. Of course interstitial ions may move occasionally into a vacancy and new lattice ions may pass into interstitial sites. Strong support to this view is given by the fact that compounds with extreme disorder due to the special type of lattice structure, like the above-mentioned salts α-AgI, etc., α-Ag$_2$S, etc., show extremely high ionic conduction, and correspondingly high diffusion constants, as for instance is observed with copper ions in α-AgI and α-Ag$_2$S. Which type of disorder prevails in a definite case may sometimes be estimated from theoretical considerations; sometimes indirect experimental evidence can be adduced. Thus, for instance, in the case of AgBr, which, just below its melting point, should exhibit a high degree of disorder, of the order of magnitude of several per cent, Wagner and Beyer (168) were able to show that there is agreement between pycnometric density and density derived from x-ray analysis, thus almost ruling out the possibility of Schottky disorder, in accordance with other observations; see, however, Lawson (119a).

Some salts form anomalous mixed crystals with other compounds not belonging to the same type of composition; for instance, silver chloride, which dissolves $CdCl_2$ or $PbCl_2$ in small concentrations, or silver bromide, which, correspondingly, dissolves $CdBr_2$ and $PbBr_2$, etc. In such cases, one must imagine that formation of mixed crystals occurs by substitution of silver ions by cadmium or lead ions. Since these ions carry twice the charge of a silver ion, and since nothing is changed in the lattice of the anions, there must arise vacancies in the lattice of the silver ions, equal in number to that of the substituting bivalent ions, Fig. 2-15, cf. the examples of p. 84ff.

$$
\begin{array}{cccccc}
Ag^+ & Cl^- & Ag^+ & Cl^- & Ag^+ & Cl^- \\
Cl^- & Ag^+ & Cl^- & Cd^{++} & Cl^- & Ag^+ \\
Ag^+ & Cl^- & Ag^+ & Cl^- & Ag^+ & Cl^- \\
Cl^- & & Cl^- & Ag^+ & Cl^- & Ag^+ \\
Ag^+ & Cl^- & Ag^+ & Cl^- & Ag^+ & Cl^-
\end{array}
$$

Fig. 2-15. Anomalous mixed crystals of AgCl with $CdCl_2$.

Now, if the assumption were correct that diffusion and electrolytic conduction are due to the presence of disorder, then addition of those salts with bivalent cations should influence the conductivity in a predictable way. This is, in fact, the case, cf. p. 192, and gives strong support to the picture assumed. If new vacancies are created in the lattice of AgCl by addition of $CdCl_2$, and if there had been before a certain disorder in thermal equilibrium, then, on account of the law of mass action [eq. [2.6] p. 92, cf. the rigorous proof below], the concentration of interstitial ions must be diminished, the product of the concentrations of interstitial ions and of vacancies remaining constant. A thorough investigation by Wagner and Koch (115) confirmed all the effects thus predicted, which may be considered as proof of the assumed mode of disorder, cf. p. 192ff.

As may be presumed from the application of the law of mass action to disorder, and as will be proved below, the degree of disorder varies exponentially with temperature. In the case of Frenkel disorder or of Schottky disorder of an ionic crystal of the same type as NaCl, we shall obtain for the degree of disorder, α, the fraction of normal lattice ions which have been removed from their ordinary sites

$$\alpha \approx \exp(-E/2RT) \tag{2.10}$$

where E is the energy necessary to remove one mole of ions from their normal position and either to bring them into interstitial positions (Frenkel type), or to build up a new crystal lattice outside the original structure (Schottky type, ions of either sign must be removed, while in the Frenkel type only cations have been removed). This disorder, depending strongly on temperature, must give a certain contribution to the specific heat. From the preceding equation one obtains for the contribution to the molar heat capacity

$$c = \frac{dE_c}{d\alpha} \frac{d\alpha}{dT} \qquad [2.11]$$

where E_c is the energy of a crystal consisting of $2N$ particles, and consequently, since $dE_c = E d\alpha$

$$c = E \frac{d\alpha}{dT} = \frac{E^2}{2RT^2} \exp\left(-E/2RT\right) \qquad [2.12]$$

an expression which might be slightly improved, taking into account the results of a more accurate theory (cf. p. 114ff.).

This contribution to specific heat, though normally very small, may reach the order of magnitude of 1 cal/degree centigrade just below the melting point, for substances with a high degree of disorder. This should be observable, though accurate measurements of the specific heat close to the melting point are not easy. For instance, in the example of silver chloride and silver bromide, Wagner (115) gives the following values for the energies of disorder

	AgCl	AgBr
E	25 000	20 200 cal/mol

from which, for AgBr immediately below the melting point, $422°\,C$, a contribution to specific heat is derived equal to

$$c \approx 0.14 \text{ cal/mol deg} .$$

With the empirical formula, derived by Wagner and Koch (115)

$$\alpha = 10^{1.46} \exp\left(-20,200/2\,RT\right) \qquad [2.13]$$

however, the specific heat turns out to be larger by a factor $10^{1.46}$, giving

$$c \approx 4.1 \text{ cal/mol deg} ,$$

which should be well outside the limits of possible errors in measurements of specific heats. For a theoretical explanation of an equation such as [2.13], cf. p. 114ff.

II. Frenkel's Theory of Disorder

Frenkel (67) derives an equation for the degree of disorder in a simple substance, due to transitions of atoms from their normal lattice sites to interstitial positions and vice versa, Fig. 2-16. Let n_L be the number of lattice sites, equal to the total number of atoms, $n'_i = \beta n_L$

be the number of interstitial sites, which may differ from the number of normal lattice sites by a factor β, equal to a small integer, n_i be the number of particles on interstitial sites and n_v be the number of vacancies. In the case of a pure substance, there is, of course, the identity $n_i = n_v$. Now the probability for a transition of a particle from a normal lattice site to an interstitial position will be proportional to

$$\exp\left(-[E + U]/RT\right) \qquad [2.14]$$

if E is the difference in energy per mole for an interstitial site and a normal one, and U is the height of an additional potential barrier,

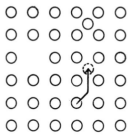

Fig. 2-16. Frenkel disorder of simple lattice. Transition from normal lattice site to interstitial site.

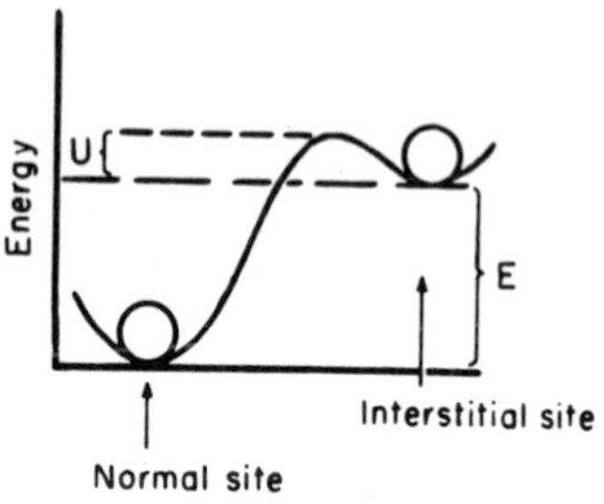

Fig. 2-17. Change in potential energy connected with transition of Fig. 2-16.

to be surmounted by a particle moving from its original position into an interstitial one, Fig. 2-16, 2-17. The total number of transitions, $\dot{n}$, per unit time and cubic centimeter, will be proportional to

$$\dot{n} \sim n_L \exp\left(-[E + U]/RT\right), \qquad [2.15]$$

where we have dropped a factor of proportionality of the order of magnitude of the frequency of an oscillation of a particle in the lattice. A similar factor, of almost equal magnitude, would occur again in the expression for the reverse transitions and, therefore, cancel in the final result. Also, in [2.15] use has been made of the fact that the degree of disorder, α, is small compared with unity, for otherwise a factor would have had to be introduced providing for the probability that a particle, leaving its original site, will hit upon an unoccupied interstitial position.

Now the number of reverse transition per unit time, $\dot{n}'$, will be proportional to the number n_i of particles, present on interstitial sites, to an exponential term $\exp\left(-U/RT\right)$, where U is the same as above, cf. Fig. 2-17, and to the probability of meeting an unoccupied lattice point, $n_v/n_L = n_i/n_L$. Here, this factor cannot be neglected, being very small compared with unity. Consequently

$$\dot{n}' \sim n_i \left(n_i/n_L\right) \cdot \exp\left(-U/RT\right) \qquad [2.16]$$

where again, as in [2.15], a frequency factor of the order of magnitude of the frequency of the lattice vibrations has been neglected. In equilibrium, the number of transitions $\dot{n}$ [2.15] and $\dot{n}'$ [2.16] must be equal, and consequently

$$n_L \cdot \exp\left(-[E + U]/RT\right) = (n_i^2/n_L)\exp\left(-U/RT\right) \qquad [2.17]$$

and

$$n_i^2 = n_L^2 \exp\left(-E/RT\right); \quad n_i = n_L \exp\left(-E/2RT\right). \qquad [2.18]$$

This process of disordering may be considered, in Frenkel's terminology, as a dissociation of normal lattice particles into equal numbers of vacancies and interstitial particles. In analogy to such dissociation phenomena, we obtain the concentration of "dissociated" particles proportional to the square root of an exponential factor, containing the heat of dissociation, here the energy of disorder. Hence the number of disordered particles and the degree of disorder become proportional to an exponential, containing only half of the energy of disorder. Since $n_i = n_v$, we may write instead of [2.18]

$$n_i n_v = n_L^2 \exp\left(-E/RT\right) \qquad [2.19]$$

in accordance with our equation [2.6] of p. 92, derived from the elementary law of mass action. Beyond the result of p. 92, we now obtain, to a first approximation, the value of the equilibrium constant K. From measured values of electrolytic conductivity and of diffusion, one may conclude that E is often of the order of magnitude of 20 to 50 kcal. In table II degrees of disorder, α, of the Frenkel type, have been listed for several temperatures and several values of E. Frenkel's result, of course, is only an approximation, because the frequency factors, occurring in [2.15] and [2.16] have been assumed to be equal and because the simple exponentials are a first approximation only to the fraction of particles with sufficient energy. Since the oscillation frequencies of particles surrounding a hole, of particles on interstitial positions, and of particles surrounding an occupied interstitial position may be considerably changed, compared with those of particles on normal lattice sites, there might eventually arise factors, differing appreciably from unity.

TABLE II

Degree of disorder, $\alpha \approx \exp\left(-E/2RT\right)$ for varying temperature and several values of E

E kcal $\overline{\text{mol}}$	100 373	200 473	300 573	400 673	500 773	800 1073	1000 1273	1500°C. 1773°K.
20	$1.5 \cdot 10^{-6}$	$3 \cdot 10^{-5}$	$2 \cdot 10^{-4}$	$6 \cdot 10^{-4}$	$2 \cdot 10^{-3}$	$9 \cdot 10^{-3}$	$2 \cdot 10^{-2}$	$6 \cdot 10^{-2}$
30	$2 \cdot 10^{-9}$	10^{-7}	$2 \cdot 10^{-6}$	10^{-5}	$6 \cdot 10^{-5}$	$9 \cdot 10^{-4}$	$3 \cdot 10^{-3}$	10^{-2}
40	$2 \cdot 10^{-12}$	$5 \cdot 10^{-10}$	$2 \cdot 10^{-8}$	$3 \cdot 10^{-7}$	$2 \cdot 10^{-6}$	$8 \cdot 10^{-5}$	$4 \cdot 10^{-4}$	$3 \cdot 10^{-3}$
50	$2 \cdot 10^{-15}$	$3 \cdot 10^{-12}$	$3 \cdot 10^{-10}$	$8 \cdot 10^{-9}$	$9 \cdot 10^{-8}$	$8 \cdot 10^{-6}$	$5 \cdot 10^{-5}$	$8 \cdot 10^{-4}$
80	$3 \cdot 10^{-24}$	$3 \cdot 10^{-19}$	$5 \cdot 10^{-16}$	10^{-13}	$5 \cdot 10^{-12}$	$7 \cdot 10^{-9}$	10^{-7}	10^{-5}

III. Schottky and Wagner's Statistical-Thermodynamic Theory of Disorder

Schottky and Wagner (22) treat a rather general case of disorder, considering the occurrence of vacancies, of interstitial particles, and of an exchange of particles of different kinds. The main limitation, still retained, is that of small disorder, i.e., degree of disorder small compared with unity. They proceed by calculating the Gibbs free energy G of the disordered crystal, deriving all quantities of interest from it. We shall follow their mode of treatment in this paragraph. The following notation will be used. The two types of particles 1 and 2 are distinguished by subscripts 1 and 2, subscripts L, v, and i referring to lattice, vacancy, and interstices. Hence

n_L = total number of lattice sites

n_{L1}, n_{L2} = number of lattice sites for particles 1 and 2

n_1 and n_2 = number of particles 1 and 2

$n_i = \beta n_L$, number of interstitial sites (there may be different types of interstitial sites, a refinement which we shall not deal with)

n_{1i} and n_{2i} = numbers of particles 1 and 2 on interstitial sites

n_{1v} and n_{2v} = number of vacancies (holes) of type 1 and 2.

The thermodynamic symbols used are in accordance with the notation in Guggenheim's (7) Modern Thermodynamics.

G = Gibbs free energy per mol

E = energy

S = entropy

V = volume

P = pressure

μ = chemical potential

R = gas constant per mol

$k = R/N$ Boltzmann's constant

N = Avogadro's number

In this chapter it will generally be assumed that the degree of disorder is small compared with unity. Consequently, since n_L, n_{L1}, n_{L2}, n_i are all of the same order of magnitude,

$$n_{1i} \ll n_L, \quad n_{1i} \ll n_{L1}, \quad n_{1i} \ll n_{L2}, \quad n_{1i} \ll n_i \qquad [2.20]$$

and corresponding relations for n_{2i}, n_{1v}, n_{2v}. We have, with sufficient accuracy,

$$E = \{n_L\,\varepsilon_L + n_{1i}\,\varepsilon_{1i} + n_{2i}\,\varepsilon_{2i} + n_{1v}\,\varepsilon_{1v} + n_{2v}\,\varepsilon_{2v}\} \qquad [2.21]$$

where ε_L is the lattice energy per particle (not, as is usual, for a pair of particles 1 and 2), equal to the energy gained per particle when equal numbers of particles 1 and 2, originally at infinite distance, form a lattice. ε_{1i}, ε_{2i}, correspondingly, are the energies supplied when a particle 1 or 2 is brought on to an interstitial site, whereas ε_{1v}, ε_{2v}, are the energies to be supplied for the removal of a particle 1 or 2 from a normal lattice site to an infinite distance*.

The entropy S_v, due to vibrations of the lattice, may be written

$$S_v = \{n_L s_L + n_{1i} s_{1i} + n_{2i} s_{2i} + n_{1v} s_{1v} + n_{2v} s_{2v}\} \qquad [2.22]$$

where the meaning of the symbols used is to be understood in accordance with the preceding remarks. It will actually be difficult to determine the different terms in this equation, and Schottky and Wagner made no attempt in this direction. A refined treatment of this contribution leads to a marked improvement of the theory (cf. Mott and Gurney (13)). The essential term in the expression for the entropy, of course, is that due to the permutation of the different kinds of particles, distinguishable by their localization. For the number W of distinguishable arrangements one thus obtains

$$W = \frac{n_{L1}!}{n_{1v}!\,(n_{L1}-n_{1v})!} \cdot \frac{n_{L2}!}{n_{2v}!\,(n_{L2}-n_{2v})!} \cdot \frac{n_i!}{n_{1i}!\,n_{2i}!\,(n_i-n_{1i}-n_{2i})!} \cdot \qquad [2.23]$$

The number of distinguishable arrangements has been written as the product of three terms, the first gives the number of different ways of choosing n_{1v} vacancies among n_{L1} lattice sites 1, accordingly the second one gives this number for sites 2, while the third term gives the number of distinguishable arrangements of n_{1i} particles 1 and of n_{2i} particles 2 on n_i interstitial sites. We did not consider an exchange of particles 1 and 2, which, while for positive and negative ions completely negligible, in other cases may become of importance (cf. below p. 100). Making use of Stirling's formula, we finally obtain from [2.23]

$$k \log W = -k \left\{ n_{1i} \log \frac{n_{1i}}{n_i} + n_{2i} \log \frac{n_{2i}}{n_i} + n_{1v} \log \frac{n_{1v}}{n_{L1}} + n_{2v} \log \frac{n_{2v}}{n_{L2}} \right.$$

$$+ (n_{L1} - n_{1v}) \log \frac{n_{L1} - n_{1v}}{n_{L1}} + (n_{L2} - n_{2v}) \log \frac{n_{L2} - n_{2v}}{n_{L2}}$$

$$\left. + (n_i - n_{1i} - n_{2i}) \log \frac{n_i - n_{1i} - n_{2i}}{n_i} \right\}. \qquad [2.24]$$

Using for V an expression, analogous to that for E and S_v,

$$V = \{n_L v_L + n_{1i} v_{1i} + n_{2i} v_{2i} + n_{1v} v_{1v} + n_{2v} v_{2v}\} \qquad [2.25]$$

---

* Here, in contrast to the usual definition of lattice energy, ε_i has a negative sign.

we may finally write for the Gibbs free energy

$$G = \{n_L \mu_L + n_{1i}\,\mu_{1i} + n_{2i}\,\mu_{2i} + n_{1v}\mu_{1v} + n_{2v}\mu_{2v}\}$$
$$+ kT\left\{n_{1i}\log\frac{n_{1i}}{n_i} + n_{2i}\log\frac{n_{2i}}{n_i} + n_{1v}\log\frac{n_{1v}}{n_{L1}} + n_{2v}\log\frac{n_{2v}}{n_{L2}}\right.$$
$$+ (n_{L1} - n_{1v})\log\frac{n_{L1} - n_{1v}}{n_{L1}} + (n_{L2} - n_{2v})\log\frac{n_{L2} - n_{2v}}{n_{L2}}$$
$$\left. + (n_i - n_{1i} - n_{2i})\log\frac{n_i - n_{1i} - n_{2i}}{n_i}\right\} \qquad [2.26]$$

where we have put

$$\mu_L = \varepsilon_L - Ts_L + Pv_L, \qquad [2.27]$$
$$\mu_{1i} = \varepsilon_{1i} - Ts_{1i} + Pv_{1i} \quad \text{etc.}$$

We give in the following, without derivation, the expression which would have to be added to [2.26] if disorder due to exchange of particles 1 and 2 were also present

$$n_{1d}\,\mu_{1d} + n_{2d}\,\mu_{2d} + kT\left\{n_{1d}\log\frac{n_{1d}}{n_{L2}} + n_{2d}\log\frac{n_{2d}}{n_{L1}}\right\}. \quad [2.28]\,{}^*$$

The second and third terms from the end in equation [2.26] must now be replaced by

$$kT\left[\{n_{L1} - n_{1v} - n_{2d}\}\log\left(\frac{n_{L1} - n_{1v} - n_{2d}}{n_{L1}}\right) + \right.$$
$$\left. + \{n_{L2} - n_{2v} - n_{1d}\}\log\left(\frac{n_{L2} - n_{1v} - n_{2d}}{n_{L2}}\right)\right] \qquad [2.29]$$

Equilibrium is determined by the condition

$$(\delta G)_{p,\,T,\,n_1,\,n_2} = 0\,. \qquad [2.30]$$

We shall treat, as an example, the equilibrium disorder in a binary ionic crystal, of type AB. As mentioned before, an exchange of positive and negative ions is quite negligible, therefore, the additional terms of equation [2.28] and [2.29] need not be considered. From [2.26] we derive for the chemical potentials of the different kinds of particles, referred to one particle as unit (a vacancy is to be considered an independent unit, too)

a. $\partial G/\partial n_L = \mu_L$

b. $\partial G/\partial n_{1i} = \mu_{1i}^\circ + kT\log\left[\dfrac{n_{1i}}{n_i - n_{1i} - n_{2i}}\right] \approx \mu_{1i}^\circ + kT\log\dfrac{n_{1i}}{n_i}$

c. $\partial G/\partial n_{2i} = \mu_{2i}^\circ + kT\log\left[\dfrac{n_{2i}}{n_i - n_{1i} - n_{2i}}\right] \approx \mu_{2i}^\circ + kT\log\dfrac{n_{2i}}{n_i}$

d. $\partial G/\partial n_{1v} = \mu_{1v}^\circ + kT\log\left[\dfrac{n_{1v}}{n_{L1} - n_{1v}}\right] \approx \mu_{1v}^\circ + kT\log\dfrac{n_{1v}}{n_{L1}}$

e. $\partial G/\partial n_{2v} = \mu_{2v}^\circ + kT\log\left[\dfrac{n_{2v}}{n_{L2} - n_{2v}}\right] \approx \mu_{2v}^\circ + kT\log\dfrac{n_{2v}}{n_{L2}}$ [2.31]

* Where n_{1d} is the number of particles 1, on sites 2, and correspondingly n_{2d} the number of particles 2, on sites 1. μ_{1d} and μ_{2d} have analogous significance.

By inserting the "lattice" concentrations

$$x_{1i} = n_{1i}/n_L, \quad x_{2i} = n_{2i}/n_L, \quad x_{1v} = n_{1v}/n_L, \quad x_{2v} = n_{2v}/n_L \qquad [2.32]$$

and using $n_i = \beta n_L$, where β is a factor of the order unity, we obtain

$$(a) \ \mu_{1i} = \mu_{1i}^\circ + kT \log x_{1i} - kT \log \beta$$
$$(b) \ \mu_{2i} = \mu_{2i}^\circ + kT \log x_{2i} - kT \log \beta$$
$$(c) \ \mu_{1v} = \mu_{1v}^\circ + kT \log x_{1v} + kT \log \beta_1'$$
$$(d) \ \mu_{2v} = \mu_{2v}^\circ + kT \log x_{2v} + kT \log \beta_2' \qquad [2.33]$$

the term $kT \log \beta$ entering into the last two equations because

$$n_L = \beta_1' \, n_{L1} = \beta_2' \, n_{L2} \,.$$

In the case of the sodium chloride type of lattice $\beta_1' = \beta_2' = 2$. The quantities μ° are of the form

$$N \, \mu^\circ = E - TS + PV \,.$$

Now estimates show, cf. p. 107, that E is usually of the order of magnitude of 1 electron volt. In comparison to this value PV may be neglected, as long as we do not consider the influence of pressure on disorder, cf. p. 114. Also, for the approximation aimed at momentarily, we may use for ε the value referring to absolute zero, and neglect TS, the entropy term due to lattice vibrations. With these approximations, equations [2.33] become

$$\mu_{1i} \approx \varepsilon_{1i} + kT \log x_{1i} - kT \log \beta \quad \mu_{1v} \approx \varepsilon_{1v} + kT \log x_{1v} + kT \log \beta_1', \quad [2.34]$$
$$\mu_{2i} \approx \varepsilon_{2i} + kT \log x_{2i} - kT \log \beta \quad \mu_{2v} \approx \varepsilon_{2v} + kT \log x_{2v} + kT \log \beta_2',$$

and if we also drop the terms with β, β_1', β_2'

$$\mu_{1i} \approx \varepsilon_{1i} + kT \log x_{1i} \qquad \mu_{1v} \approx \varepsilon_{1v} + kT \log x_{1v}$$
$$\mu_{2i} \approx \varepsilon_{2i} + kT \log x_{2i} \qquad \mu_{2v} \approx \varepsilon_{2v} + kT \log x_{2v} \,. \qquad [2.35]$$

In equilibrium, the value μ for one kind of particle must be the same on whatever type of site it may be. Since μ_v is the potential corresponding to the production of a vacancy, the potential, for instance, of a particle 1, brought from infinite distance into a vacancy of type 1 is $-\mu_{1v}$. Therefore, we have the set of equilibrium conditions

$$\mu_{1i} = -\mu_{1v}, \quad \mu_{2i} = -\mu_{2v} \qquad [2.36]$$
$$\mu_{1i} + \mu_{2i} = \mu_{12} = 2\,\mu_L \approx 2\,\varepsilon_L \qquad [2.37]$$
$$-\mu_{1v} - \mu_{2v} = \mu_{12} = 2\,\mu_L \approx 2\,\varepsilon_L \qquad [2.38]$$

to which the condition for electrical neutrality must be added, which for anions and cations of equal valency is

$$x_{1i} - x_{1v} = x_{2i} - x_{2v} \qquad [2.39]$$

The equations [2.37] and [2.38] have the following meaning. The potentials must be equal not only for a particle brought to an interstitial position and a vacancy, but also for a particle on a normal lattice site. Since the potential for one pair of particles 1 and 2, on normal lattice sites, is $\mu_{12} = 2\mu_L \approx 2\varepsilon_L$ (cf. p. 98), one obtains the equations [2.37] and [2.38]. On account of [2.36], the equations [2.37] and [2.38] are not independent of each other, and we consequently have four relations, from which the following equations may be derived

$$
\begin{aligned}
&(a) \quad x_{1i}\, x_{1v} = \exp\left(-\,[\varepsilon_{1i} + \varepsilon_{1v}]/kT\right) \\
&(b) \quad x_{2i}\, x_{2v} = \exp\left(-\,[\varepsilon_{2i} + \varepsilon_{2v}]/kT\right) \\
&(c) \quad x_{1i}\, x_{2i} = \exp\left(-\,[\varepsilon_{1i} + \varepsilon_{2i} - 2\,\varepsilon_L]/kT\right) \\
&(d) \quad x_{1v}\, x_{2v} = \exp\left(-\,[2\,\varepsilon_L + \varepsilon_{1v} + \varepsilon_{2v}]/kT\right)
\end{aligned}
\qquad [2.40]
$$

with the additional relation [2.39] for the x's. If we use the following abbreviations, introduced by Schottky

$$
\begin{aligned}
K &= \exp\left(-\,[2\,\varepsilon_L + \varepsilon_{1v} + \varepsilon_{2v}]/kT\right) \\
k_1 &= \exp\left(-\,[\varepsilon_{1i} - \varepsilon_{2v} - 2\,\varepsilon_L]/kT\right) \\
k_2 &= \exp\left(-\,[\varepsilon_{2i} - \varepsilon_{1v} - 2\,\varepsilon_L]/kT\right)
\end{aligned}
\qquad [2.41]
$$

we finally obtain the formulae for the concentrations x

$$
\begin{aligned}
x_{1v} &= K^{1/2}\left(\frac{1+k_1}{1+k_2}\right)^{1/2} & x_{2v} &= K^{1/2}\left(\frac{1+k_2}{1+k_1}\right)^{1/2} \\
x_{1i} &= K^{1/2}\,k_1\left(\frac{1+k_2}{1+k_1}\right)^{1/2} & x_{2i} &= K^{1/2}\,k_2\left(\frac{1+k_1}{1+k_2}\right)^{1/2}.
\end{aligned}
\qquad [2.42]
$$

Before we further discuss these equations, we should convince ourselves that the special equations, derived above (p. 97) by more primitive methods, follow from these general equations. For instance, it follows from [2.40], under the assumption that disorder is due to one component only, 1, e.g., silver ions in silver chloride or silver bromide, giving equal numbers of interstitial ions and vacancies

$$
\begin{aligned}
x_{1i} \cdot x_{1v} = x_{1v}{}^2 &= \exp\left(-\,\Delta\,\varepsilon/kT\right) \\
x_{1i} &= \exp\left(-\,\Delta\varepsilon/2\,kT\right)
\end{aligned}
\qquad [2.43]
$$

which is the result of p. 97, formula [2.18].

The array of equations [2.42] shows that the ratio for the different types of disorder depends only upon the constants k_1 and k_2 (constant only for $T = \text{const.}$), these being determined by the energy expressions

$$
\Delta' = \varepsilon_{1i} - \varepsilon_{2v} - 2\,\varepsilon_L \qquad \Delta'' = \varepsilon_{2i} - \varepsilon_{1v} - 2\,\varepsilon_L. \qquad [2.44]
$$

Δ' and Δ'' are the energies to be supplied for the removal of one pair of ions from their normal lattice sites, and their transfer upon either an interstitial site 1 and a vacancy 2 or an interstitial site 2 and a vacancy 1. There are four limiting cases

$$k_1 \gg 1, \; k_2 \ll 1 \qquad k_2 \gg 1, \; k_1 \ll 1$$
$$k_1 \gg 1, \; k_2 \gg 1 \qquad k_1 \ll 1, \; k_2 \ll 1 \; . \qquad [2.45]$$

The types of disorder, corresponding to these limiting cases for an ionic compound of type AB, are given in Table III.

Types 1 and 2 are identical with the Frenkel type of disorder, either for particles 1 or for particles 2; type 4 may be termed Schottky disorder, having been first discussed in Schottky's paper (158) and being present, with great probability, in the case of alkali halides. Type 3 disorder, consisting of the occupation of interstitial sites only of either type, no holes being present, so far has not yet been observed. For intermetallic compounds this type has recently been observed by Brauer and Tiesler (36a).

TABLE III*

Types of disorder for simple ionic compound AB (after Schottky)

Type	k_1	k_2	$x_{1v}/\sqrt{K}$	$x_{2v}/\sqrt{K}$	$x_{1i}/\sqrt{K}$	$x_{2i}/\sqrt{K}$
1	$\gg 1$	$\ll 1$	$(\sqrt{k_1})$	$1/\sqrt{k_1}$	$(\sqrt{k_1})$	$k_2\sqrt{k_1}$
2	$\ll 1$	$\gg 1$	$1/\sqrt{k_2}$	$(\sqrt{k_2})$	$k_1\sqrt{k_2}$	$(\sqrt{k_2})$
3	$\gg 1$	$\gg 1$	$\sqrt{k_1/k_2}$	$\sqrt{k_2/k_1}$	$(\sqrt{k_1 k_2})$	$(\sqrt{k_1 k_2})$
4	$\ll 1$	$\ll 1$	(1)	(1)	$\sqrt{k_1}$	$\sqrt{k_2}$

IV. Energy of Disorder

If only electrostatic interactions between rigid ions are taken into account, energies of disorder are calculated which are of the order of magnitude of the lattice energy** (7 to 9 electron volts, correspond-

* In this table the magnitudes of the terms in parentheses are large compared with other terms.

** In a lattice consisting of one type of particles, the lattice energy is given by $-\Phi = \dfrac{1}{2} \sum_i \sum_k \varphi_{ik}$, $i \neq k$, if φ_{ik} is the energy of interaction of two particles. If the crystal is sufficiently large to allow surface influences to be neglected, we may write instead $-\Phi = \dfrac{N}{2} \sum_k \varphi_{ik}$, if we are considering a crystal composed of N particles. The factor $1/2$ arises, because otherwise every term would be counted twice. If, however, one particle from the interior of the crystal is removed to an infinite distance, the energy required is just twice the lattice energy per particle $\dfrac{2\Phi}{N} = -\sum_k \varphi_{ik}$, as is seen at once. On the other hand, the energy required for the creation of a single hole in the crystal is again equal

ing to 160 to 200 kcal. per mole for alkali halides). Consequently, at accessible temperatures, the degree of disorder would be so small as not to give rise to any observable effects.

Now it was been pointed out by the author, (100, 101, 102, 103), that on account of the polarization in the dielectric surrounding a position of disorder (either an interstitial ion or a vacancy) there will be a second term in the energy which may be of the same order of magnitude as the lattice energy but of opposite sign. Thus the resulting energy of disorder, instead of being of the order of almost 10 electron volts, may be as low as 1 to 2 electron volts, in extreme cases perhaps even less. Though the results, thus obtained, are not of great accuracy, being differences of two terms of equal order of magnitude, they prove that energies of disorder may be sufficiently small to allow of an explanation of observed effects of diffusion and electrolytic conduction in solids. Further, if these calculations are carried through for substances of similar type, for instance, alkali halides and silver halides, crystallizing in the sodium chloride type of lattice, some of the errors involved are similar in all cases. Therefore, the order of magnitude and the sense of differences of energies of disorder for these substances may be obtained with much less uncertainty. Thus, Schottky (158), using the method of the author, was able to show that in the case of alkali halides the type 4 of Table III should prevail, now called Schottky type of disorder. In this case vacancies are present in equal numbers in the lattices of anions and of cations, the number of interstitial ions being quite negligible. In

to the lattice energy $\frac{\Phi}{N} = -\frac{1}{2} \sum \varphi_{ik}$. For, if the particles, which formerly had been situated at the position of newly formed holes, are first removed into infinite distance and then are added again to the crystal, forming new crystalline structure outside the limits of the original crystal, energy equal to the lattice energy is gained for every particle, leaving as difference an energy just equal to the lattice energy.

φ_{ik} in $\Phi = \frac{-1}{2} \sum_i \sum_k \varphi_{ik\,(i\,\neq\,k)}$ is of negative sign. Therefore, Φ, the lattice energy (without consideration of the zero point energy) is positive in accordance with the usual definition. We have for an ionic crystal consisting of N particles A and N particles B

$$\Phi = -\frac{1}{2} \sum_{i=1}^{2N} \sum_{k=1}^{2N} \varphi_{ik} = -N \sum_{k=1}^{2N} \varphi_{ik}, \qquad i \neq k \,.$$

The energy per particle in the crystal, ε_g, as used in paragraph III, is in this case

$$\varepsilon_g = -\frac{1}{2} \sum_{k=1}^{2N} \varphi_{ik} = -\frac{\Phi}{2N} \,.$$

the case of silver halides, however, though they crystallize in the sodium chloride type of lattice, the Frenkel type of disorder, for cations only, should prevail, as shown theoretically by Jost (loc. cit.) and proved experimentally by Wagner and co-workers (115, 168). Here, equal numbers of interstitial cations and vacancies in the lattice of the cations are present, disorder in the lattice of the anions being negligible (cf. however Mitchell (127a)).

The effect of polarization on energies of disorder and on the degree of disorder is readily understood because there is complete analogy between the processes of disordering in a crystal lattice and that of dissolution of an ionic crystal in water.

A. Theory of dissolution of a crystal. Hydration of ions. In order to separate completely the ions of a crystal in dissolution, the lattice energy must be supplied. However, if this were the only energy change involved in the process of dissolution of an ionic crystal in water, the solubility of crystals like sodium chloride in water would be quite negligible, for the heat of dissolution would be of the order of magnitude of 180 kcal/mol, the separation being a highly endothermic process. The rather high solubility of, for instance, sodium chloride, is due to the following fact. In the neighborhood of each dissolved ion the dielectric, in this case water with its high dielectric constant, is strongly polarized. The lattice energy of 1 mol of an alkali halide, crystallizing in the sodium chloride type of lattice, is

$$1.746 \frac{Ne^2}{a}\left(1 - \frac{1}{n}\right) \qquad [2.46]$$

where a is the lattice distance (distance between neighboring anions and cations), e the elementary charge and n is of the order of magnitude of 10. It is customary to take this positive energy Φ as the lattice energy, being the energy necessary to separate the ions and to remove them to an infinite distance.

The energy of the electric field, surrounding a spherical charge e, the radius of the sphere being r, is

$$\varphi_i = \frac{1}{2}\frac{e^2}{r} \qquad [2.47]$$

provided the charge is *in vacuo*. If we bring the charged sphere into a dielectric of dielectric constant $\varkappa$, field strength and energy of the field decrease to $1/\varkappa$ times their original value

$$\varphi_i' = \frac{1}{2}\frac{e^2}{\varkappa r}. \qquad [2.48]$$

Hence the change of energy, which we shall call polarization energy, denoted by ε_{pol}, is

$$\varepsilon_{pol} = -\frac{1}{2}\frac{e^2}{r}\left(1 - \frac{1}{\varkappa}\right). \qquad [2.49]$$

Now, since 1 mol of an alkali halide consists of $2N$ ions, the polarization energy per mol encountered in the process of dissolution is

$$E_{pol} = -N\frac{e^2}{2}\left(1-\frac{1}{\varkappa}\right)\left(\frac{1}{r_a}+\frac{1}{r_c}\right) \qquad [2.50]$$

where r_a and r_c are the radii of the anions and of the cations respectively. If we are only interested in the order of magnitude of this term, we may put $r_a = r_c = a/2$, because $r_a + r_c = a$, the lattice distance. A comparison of the expression, thus obtained

$$E_{pol} \approx -\frac{Ne^2}{a}\left(1-\frac{1}{\varkappa}\right) \qquad [2.51]$$

with equation [2.46] for the lattice energy, shows that, with $\varkappa = 81$, [2.51] would be more than sufficient to compensate for the lattice energy. Therefore, energy may even be gained in the process of dissolution, accounting for the high solubilities observed in many cases. Of course, the accuracy of the result, thus obtained, must not be overestimated. Equation [2.51] involves the assumptions first that the ions may be treated as charged spheres of a well-defined radius, and secondly that the dielectric is a continuum with a definite dielectric constant. It is certainly not permissible to treat the dielectric in the vicinity of small ions as a continuum; also in the immediate neighborhood of a small ion, due to saturation effects, the dielectric constant would drop below its normal value. But, notwithstanding such objections, the order of magnitude of the resul tsobtained is essentially correct, unless the theory is applied to ions of very small radius, for instance, lithium or even to the proton. The theory, as outlined above, is Fajans' (63) and Born's (33) theory of hydration of ions, accounting for the observed order of magnitude of heats of hydration. Several attempts to improve this theory have been reported (1,117,173).

B. Elementary theory of Energy of Disorder. If, now, we consider the process of disordering in a crystal, the same energy terms arise as in the preceding discussion, and the energy of disorder is obtained as difference of lattice energy and energy of polarization(100). Let us first consider Schottky disorder. We suppose the disordering process to be carried through in several steps. First N anions and N cations are removed from lattice positions and transferred to infinite distance, assuming that no changes occur in the surrounding of the vacancies, thus created. The energy to be supplied for this process is twice the lattice energy, cf. p. 103. Then we use the removed ions to build up a new lattice structure outside the limits of the original crystal. In doing this once the lattice energy is gained, leaving just the lattice energy as energy of disorder, so far. Now we must consider the changes occurring in the neighborhood of the newly created vacancies. Creating a vacancy, i. e., removing an elementary charge of one sign, is, as far as effects at some distance are concerned, equivalent to bringing a charge of opposite sign into the position of the removed ion. Thus, we have to consider the polarization of the surrounding dielectric caused by this charge. This is a process completely analogous to the polarization of the dielectric in the neighborhood of a dissolved ion, giving rise to an energy term of the same order of magnitude. Due to the smaller dielectric constant of the medium under consideration, the energy of polarization will be smaller than the energy of hydration of an ion. The difference in dielectric constants, however, 81 for water and ≤ 10 for most salts, does not affect the order of magnitude of the resulting expression, because $1 - 1/\varkappa$ only changes from 0.9 to 1 even if $\varkappa$ increases from 10 to infinity. Besides, effects of saturation become important with high dielectric constants. The result, therefore, that energies of disorder, like energies of dissolution, are of lower order of magnitude than the lattice energies, is quite general. There arise, however, characteristic differences in energies of disorder, due to differences in dielectric constant. In the above example we have

$$E_{dis} = E_L + E_{pol\,a} + E_{pol\,c} = E_L + \frac{Ne^2}{2}\left(1 - \frac{1}{\varkappa}\right)(1/_{ra} + 1/_{rc}) \qquad [2.52]$$

where r_a and r_c are the effective radii of an anion and of a cation hole. If we only want to obtain a first estimate of the order of magnitude of the energy of disorder, we may put $r_a = r_c$ (which is approximately the case with K F), and obtain

$$E_{dis} \approx \left[\frac{1 \cdot 746\,e^2}{a}\left(1 - \frac{1}{n}\right) - \frac{2\,e^2}{a}\left(1 - \frac{1}{\varkappa}\right)\right]N \qquad [2.53]$$

which shows that the contributions of the lattice energy and of the energy of polarization almost cancel. The relative error in the energy of disorder, if calculated by this crude method of approximation, of course, is very large. It is, however, quite certain that the energy of disorder is small compared with the lattice energy. Equation [2.52] is quite correct of course, because it contains the effective radii of the vacancies as available parameters which should be determined in such a way as to give correct results. As a first approximation, one may attempt to use as the effective radii those of the ions which formerly had occupied the sites of the vacancies. For an improvement of the calculations see below, p. 118ff, and especially Mott and Little-ton (129).

If, instead of Schottky disorder, we had considered Frenkel disorder, we should have arrived at the same equation [2.52]. The different steps, involved in the process of disordering, here are: first removal of N ions of one type (normally the smaller cations), energy to be supplied equal to the lattice energy. Creation of $2N$ centers of disorder, N vacancies left behind by the removed ions, and further N centers arising after the N ions have been brought onto interstitial sites. Therefore twice the energy of polarization for N charges enters into the result, r_v and r_i being now the effective radii of a vacancy and of an interstitial ion. In most cases the ion, brought into an interstice, will be larger than the space normally available, and it will be necessary to displace the surrounding ions in order to provide sufficient space for the interstitial ion. This process requires a supply of energy, and, therefore, makes Frenkel disorder less probable. If, however, in a crystal of high dielectric constant Frenkel disorder of the small cations is produced, the energy of polarization is also higher than in case of Schottky disorder, and this, together with the additional influence of van der Waals energy, may lead to the prevalence of the Frenkel type of disorder.

C. Disorder of Crystals of Alkali Halides. Schottky (158) has discussed the conditions for disorder in crystals of alkali halides, and has been able to show that one may conclude with sufficient certainty, that Schottky disorder should be found, while the author, with Nehlep (104), was able to show that in the case of the silver halides, crystallizing in the sodium chloride type of lattice, Frenkel disorder should prevail. If by α we denote the fraction of disordered particles, either interstitial ions or vacancies, then we obtain for the Schottky cases 1 and 4 (α is proportional to the lattice concentration, as introduced on p. 101), 1 is Frenkel disorder, 4 is Schottky disorder

$$\alpha_1 \approx \exp[(-\varepsilon_{1i} - \varepsilon_{1v})/2\,kT] \qquad [2.54]$$

and

$$\alpha_4 \approx \exp[-(\varepsilon_L + \varepsilon_{1v} + \varepsilon_{2v})/2\,kT] \qquad [2.55]$$

where the subscripts refer to Schottky's cases 1 and 4.

For the present we shall consider potassium fluoride, as a concrete example, with ions of rather similar radii which, as an approximation, will be assumed to be equal. We obtain for the ratio

$$\alpha_4/\alpha_1 = \exp\left[-(\varepsilon_L + \varepsilon_{2v} + \varepsilon_{1i})/2\,kT\right]. \qquad [2.56]$$

For our present purpose it is sufficient to use the Born expression for the lattice energy $-1.74\dfrac{e^2}{a}\left(1-\dfrac{1}{n}\right)$, which, with opposite sign, is equal to the coulomb energy and energy of repulsive forces in ε_{2v}. The coulomb energy, entering into ε_{1i} is zero because an interstitial site in the sodium chloride type of lattice is surrounded symmetrically by positive and negative ions. If displacements of the ions surrounding a position of disorder are neglected, the contribution of repulsive energy to that of an interstitial ion will be increased by a factor $(2/\sqrt{3})^n$ compared with the term in the normal lattice energy. For on an interstitial site the distance to the neighboring ions is only $\sqrt{3}/2$ of the lattice distance. In both, ε_{2v} and ε_{1i} a term corresponding to [2.49], p. 105 will arise due to the energy of polarization,

$$\varepsilon_{pol} = \frac{e^2}{2r}\left(1 - \frac{1}{\varkappa}\right)$$

where it seems reasonable to choose for r half the distance to the neighboring particle (measured from center to center), i. e., $a/2$ for a vacancy and $r = a\sqrt{3}/4$ for an interstitial ion. Thus finally we have

$$\varepsilon_L = -1.74\left(1 - \frac{1}{n}\right)\frac{e^2}{a}$$

$$\varepsilon_{2v} = +1.74\left(1 - \frac{1}{n}\right)\frac{e^2}{a} - \left(1 - \frac{1}{\varkappa}\right)\frac{e^2}{a} \qquad [2.57]$$

$$\varepsilon_{1i} = +1.74\frac{e^2}{na}\left(\frac{2}{\sqrt{3}}\right)^n - 2\left(1 - \frac{1}{\varkappa}\right)\frac{e^2}{a\sqrt{3}}$$

and

$$\alpha_4/\alpha_1 = \exp\left[\frac{e^2}{a}\left\{\frac{1{,}74}{n}\left(\frac{2}{\sqrt{3}}\right)^n - \left(1 - \frac{1}{\varkappa}\right)\left(\frac{2}{\sqrt{3}} - 1\right)\right\}\bigg/ 2\,kT\right] \qquad [2.58]$$

With numerical values, $n \approx 9$, $\varepsilon \to \infty$, chosen in such a way as to give the most favorable estimate for Frenkel disorder, we obtain

$$\alpha_4/\alpha_1 = \exp\left[\frac{1{,}74e^2}{2\,a} \cdot \frac{0{,}64}{2\,kT}\right] \approx \exp\left[+\,50\,\text{kcal}/2\,R\,T\right] \qquad [2.59]$$

where use has been made of the known lattice energy for KF:

$$N\frac{e^2}{a}\frac{1{,}74}{}\left(1 - \frac{1}{n}\right) = 8{,}41\,\text{e volt} \approx 194\,\text{kcal/mol}\,.$$

Even for $T = 1000°$ K we find from [2.59]

$$\alpha_4/\alpha_1 \approx 10^{5.5}\,. \qquad [2.60]$$

Consequently, at all accessible temperatures there is an overwhelming probability for the Schottky type of disorder. Considering that we made the most favorable assumptions for Frenkel disorder, i. e., $\varepsilon \to \infty$, we safely may assume that in spite of the coarseness of our approximations (i. e., treating the crystal as a continuum in calculating polarization, displacements of ions around points of disorder neglected, etc.) Schottky disorder should prevail in crystals of alkali halides, with the exception, perhaps, of extreme cases, like LiI.

Nehlep and Jost (104) extended Schottky's calculations and confirmed Schottky's qualitative conclusions viz., that vacancy disorder should prevail in most alkali halides. For silver halides, crystallizing in the alkali halide type of lattice, the result, however, may be different. Here van der Waals forces cause a rather large contribution to the lattice energy, raising it above the values of the alkali halides. This contribution, which is responsible for the low solubility of the silver halides in water, favors the occurrence of interstitial cations compared with the occurrence of anion holes. Therefore, Frenkel disorder might occur in these compounds. This is suggested by experiments of Wagner and Beyer (168) who measured densities and lattice distances of AgBr near its melting point. Since the degree of disorder of AgBr immediately below its melting point must be very high, of the order of 10 %, Schottky disorder would produce a marked drop of density below the value calculated from x-ray data. Since such a difference was not found, Schottky disorder should be ruled out; see, however, Lawson (119a).

In ionic crystals, two types of disorder always occur simultaneously, vacancies of either sign, or vacancies and interstitial ions. The two types are equivalent to electric charges of opposite sign. With respect to total electric charge, creation of a vacancy in the lattice of the cations is equivalent to bringing a negative charge of equal magnitude to the site of a cation, and vice versa. Consequently, there must be an electrostatic interaction between these centers and a refined theory analogous to the Debye-Hückel-Onsager theory of liquid electrolytes would be required. Moreover, in the case of vacancies, an association of vacancies of opposite sign is possible, which might give rise to certain observable effects, Seitz (19), Dienes (59), Rittner (143), Stern and Leivo (153), though perhaps not noticeable in electrolytic conduction, because an associated pair of vacancies is electrically neutral. This question will be discussed below, see p. 113.

In the case of vacancies and of interstitial ions of the same type, again the centers are equivalent to electric charges of opposite sign, a cation on an interstitial site being equivalent to a positive charge, and a cation vacancy being equivalent to a negative charge.

D. *Disorder in Molecular Lattices.* A rough estimate may be made for disorder in molecular lattices. Here, it is a priori highly probable that the vacancy type of disorder will prevail. Now, defining the negative lattice energy, $-\Phi$, as the potential energy of the lattice, neglecting the contribution of residual energy of lattice vibrations at absolute zero*, we have (see p. 103).

$$-\Phi = \frac{1}{2} \sum_{1}^{N} \sum_{1}^{N} \varphi_{ik} = \frac{N}{2} \sum \varphi_{ik} \qquad i \neq k \qquad [2.61]$$

* We shall apply the following considerations to solid hydrogen where the residual energy plays an important role. An analogous argument, of course, is valid for ionic crystals, where we have neglected the zero point energy. For refined calculations, however, it should be taken into account.

where Φ is the lattice energy, in the restricted sense, as defined above, φ_{ik} is the energy of interaction of the ith and the kth particle, and N Avogadro's number.

If no zero point energy were present, Φ would be approximately equal to the energy of sublimation, $\Lambda - RT$, where Λ is the heat of sublimation. Where the zero point energy, E_0, is not negligible we have

$$\Phi - E_0 = \Lambda - RT . \qquad [2.62]$$

On the other hand, the energy necessary for the creation of N elementary holes is, if the removed particle is transferred to infinite distance (see p. 103)

$$2\Phi - E_0 . \qquad [2.63]$$

For N particles brought back from infinity to build up new crystal structure, we gain energy

$$\Phi - E_0 . \qquad [2.64]$$

Consequently, the energy necessary for the creation of N vacancies is

$$E_v = (2\Phi - E_0) - (\Phi - E_0) \qquad [2.65]$$

and with [2.62]

$$E_v = \Lambda + E_0 - RT . \qquad [2.66]$$

We have dealt in some detail with this question, because the sign with which the zero point energy enters into the final result is unexpected, increasing the energy of disorder above the value of the energy of evaporation. This is due to the fact that by the process of disordering the total zero point energy of the crystal remains approximately unchanged since the number of lattice particles remains unchanged; only an energy of disorder equal to the change in potential energy must be supplied.

The above considerations are accurate to the approximation involved in neglecting the temperature dependence of Φ and Λ, and changes in position and in vibration frequencies of particles surrounding a vacancy. Numerical results, derived from [2.66], seem reasonable, as far as can be judged from the experimental data of the only compound investigated so far.

The rate of self diffusion in solid hydrogen (Cremer (53)) can be represented by an expression

$$D = A \exp\left(-E/RT\right) = A \exp\left(-[790 \pm 130]/RT\right) . \qquad [2.67]$$

The energy in the exponent of [2.67] should be equal to the sum of E_v and of an energy barrier, U, to be surmounted by a neighboring particle which moves into a vacancy,

$$E = E_v + U = 790 \pm 130 \text{ cal/mol} . \qquad [2.68]$$

Now the heat of sublimation of solid hydrogen is 183 cal (Clusius (50)), and the zero point energy $E_0 = 305$ cal, which is by no means negligible, thus,

$$E_v \approx 488 - (\sim 25) = 463 \text{ cal/mol}. \qquad [2.69]$$

This leaves for U a value, using [2.68],

$$U = 325 \pm 130 \text{ cal/mol}. \qquad [2.70]$$

This is reasonable, for, where calculations or direct determinations have been possible, Koch and Wagner (115), U turns out to be smaller than E_v, but of equal order of magnitude.

Frenkel (6) has attempted to calculate the energy necessary for the widening of an interstice, to take up an interstitial ion, by treating the crystal as an isotropic elastic continuum. An original spherical cavity of radius r_0 is assumed which is extended to one of radius $r_1 > r_0$. He calculates the energy due to the elastic strain of the continuum. If displacements in the crystal are referred to cartesian coordinates, x, y, z, with origin at the center of the sphere, and if r is the distance from the center of the sphere, $r^2 = x^2 + y^2 + z^2$, then the components of a displacement u at a point x, y, z, are

$$u_x = \frac{\alpha x}{r^3}, \qquad u_y = \frac{\alpha y}{r^3}, \qquad u_z = \frac{\alpha z}{r^3} \qquad [2.71]$$

For the elastic energy the result is

$$E = 8\pi\mu \, \alpha^2/r_0^3, \quad \alpha = r_0^2(r_1 - r_0) \qquad E = 8\pi\mu r_0 (r_1 - r_0)^2 \qquad [2.72]$$

Taking a value of 10^{11} dynes/cm². for μ, the following values for the energy involved in the widening of a hole are found:

$r_0 = 10^{-8}$ cm	1.5×10^{-8} cm
$r_1 = 2\, r_0$	$1.2\, r_0$
$E = 2.4 \times 10^{-12}$ erg	3.24×10^{-13} erg
$\sim 30,000$ cal/mole	4000 cal/mole.

These are to be compared with values calculated for the displacement of ions in the neighborhood of an interstitial ion (104, 129).

E. Refined Treatment of Energies of Disorder. The calculation of energies of disorder has been improved considerably by Mott and Littleton (129), by a refined treatment of the energy of polarization. If the result obtained is written, again, in the form

$$E_{pol} = \frac{e^2}{2r}\left(1 - \frac{1}{\varkappa}\right) \qquad [2.73]$$

as used by Jost and by Schottky for the polarization energy of a continuum, the calculations of Mott and Littleton amount to an exact calculation of the effective radii r_c and r_a, cf. p. 113.

TABLE IV
(from Mott and Littleton)

Crystal	r/a
$\alpha_1 = \alpha_2$, $\varkappa_0 - 1 \ll 1$	0.76
$\alpha_1 = \alpha_2$, $\varkappa_0 = 4$	0.68

	Positive Ion	Negative Ion
NaCl	0.58	0.95
KCl	0.61	0.85
RbCl	0.635	—
KBr	—	0.88

Table IV contains values of r/a thus calculated. Here α_1 and α_2 are the polarizabilities of cations and anions, $\varkappa_0$ is the dielectric constant for alternating fields of frequency great compared with that of the residual waves $(5 \times 10^{12}\,\mathrm{sec}^{-1})$, equal to the square of the index of refraction in the near infrared, a is the lattice constant.

Energies, calculated by Mott and Littleton, and believed to be correct to within 5 or 10 per cent, are reproduced in Table V.

TABLE V
Energies in electron volts (taken from Mott and Littleton)

	NaCl	KCl	KBr
Work to remove positive ion, E_+	4.62	4.47	4.23
Work to remove negative ion, E_-	5.18	4.79	4.60
Lattice energy per ion pair, Φ........	7.94	7.18	6.91
$1/2\,E = \dfrac{1}{2}\,(E_+ + E_- - \Phi)$............	0.93	1.04	0.96

Mott and Littleton's refined calculations confirm the earlier conclusions of Schottky (158) and of Jost and Nehlep (104) that in the case of alkali halides the Schottky mechanism by far outweighs the Frenkel type of disorder. Their calculations, however, do not refer to the case of silver halides.

Seitz (18) has shown that the energy of combination of positive and negative vacancies in KCl is about 0.93 ev, and analogous results are to be expected for the other alkali halides. Therefore, especially at low temperatures, the relative concentration of neutral pairs of vacancies should be high, see Chapter III, p. 164.

The calculation of the polarization energy has recently been improved by Rittner, Hutner, and du Pré (143). Results for sodium chloride are seen in Table VI, which shows that the Mott-Littleton approximation is already very satisfactory.

TABLE VI

Polarization work in NaCl calculated by various methods, electron volts
(taken from Rittner, Hutner, and Du Pré)

Removal of	Landshoff appr.	Jost $r=a/2$	Jost-Nehlep	$M—L$ 0 order	$M—L$ 1st ord.	$M—L$ 4th ord.	$R—H—DP$ I	II
Na$^+$	3.73	2.90	3.20	2.31	2.53	2.50	2.51	2.52
Cl$^-$	2.43	2.90	1.66	1.50	1.53		1.57	1.56
Sum	6.16	5.80	4.86	3.81	4.06		4.08	4.08

The calculation around two adjacent charges in NaCl and RbCl has recently been calculated to a high degree of approximation by Hutner, Rittner, and du Pré (93a). Results are seen in Table VII.

TABLE VII

Polarization work in electron volts for different degrees of approximation

	Klemm-Born (113a)	Zero order	First order
NaCl	1.51	0.94	1.11
RbCl	1.20	0.77	0.92

F. Disorder in metals. For metals, Frenkel or Schottky type of disorder is conceivable. A first rough estimate suggests that the Schottky type should be favored. Huntington and Seitz (91, 92, 93) carried through a more detailed calculation, cf. also Zener (180c), Seitz (147a). This gave, in case of copper, an energy of activation for an interstitial mechanism of 8 to 11 ev, while for vacancy diffusion only 3 ev were obtained, thus strongly favoring the vacancy type of disorder. Moreover, the result obtained is in fair agreement with an observed energy of activation of 2.6 ev, as reported by Steigman, Nix, and Shockley (152) for the self diffusion in copper. There should be a contribution of this type of disorder to the electric resistance of metals which in some cases might be noticeable at high temperatures.

G. Dependence of Energy of Disorder on Temperature and Pressure. There is a certain dependence of disorder on pressure, accessible to experimental determination. This effect is of some importance in the discussion of observed ionic conductivity and rate of diffusion. In the case of Schottky disorder, the increase in volume, associated with the formation of 1 mol of vacancies, is equal to the molecular volume of the crystal under consideration.

Consequently, if V_c is the molecular volume of the crystal, a term $P V_c$ should be added to the energy of disorder, E_d, giving for the degree of disorder α an exponential term of the form

$$\alpha = \exp\left(-[E_d + P V_c]/ R T\right) \qquad [2.74]$$

for a lattice built up from one kind of particles only, or

$$\exp\left(-[E_d + P V_c]/2 R T\right) \qquad [2.75]$$

for a binary ionic crystal, such as NaCl. From [2.74] or [2.75] the pressure dependence of the degree of disorder, α, is seen at once. A term proportional to this expression will enter into the equations for diffusion and eletrolytic conduction. We have

$$\frac{1}{\alpha} \frac{d\alpha}{dp} = -\frac{V_c}{RT} \qquad [2.76]$$

corresponding to [2.74], and

$$\frac{1}{\alpha} \frac{d\alpha}{dp} = -\frac{V_c}{2RT} \qquad [2.77]$$

corresponding to [2.75], for binary ionic crystals. This pressure dependence is of observable magnitude, the degree of disorder decreasing with increasing pressure, cf. p. 152. The opposite is to be expected in the case of pure interstitial disorder where positive and negative ions are present in equal numbers on interlattice positions. Here disorder is connected with a volume decrease equal to the molecular volume. Hence, on account of this term alone, pure interstitial disorder would be favored by high pressure. Other influences, to be discussed below, would probably compensate for such an effect.

Frenkel disorder, to the degree of approximation aimed at, so far, is not connected with any change of volume and, therefore, no influence of pressure, dependent on such a volume change, is to be expected.

Schottky defects also contribute to the thermal expansion of a crystal (and, of course, there is a contribution of equal magnitude but of opposite sign in case of pure interstitial disorder, which will not be discussed here). In the case of a monatomic crystal or a molecular lattice, Mott and Gurney (13) derive for this effect

$$\frac{1}{V_c} \frac{dV_c}{dT} = \frac{a^3 N}{V_c} \frac{d\alpha}{dT} = \frac{Na^3}{V_c} \frac{\gamma BE_o}{RT^2} \exp\left(-E_0/RT\right) \qquad [2.78]$$

and in case of a binary ionic compound of the rock salt type we have

$$\frac{1}{V_c} \frac{dV_c}{dT} = \frac{Na^3}{V_c} \frac{\gamma BE_o}{2RT^2} \exp\left(-E_0/2RT\right) \qquad [2.79]$$

Here V_c is the molecular volume, N Avogadro's number, a the lattice distance (or more precisely: a^3 is the volume available for one

atom or molecule in the crystal), E_0 is the energy of disorder at $T = 0°$ K,
B and γ are magnitudes, connected with the temperature dependence
of E_d, which will be discussed below (see p. 117).

The pressure effects, discussed above, are not the only ones to
be expected. Since the energy of disorder depends on the lattice
distance, which is changed both by variations in temperature and in
pressure, a further pressure effect is to be expected, and also additional terms in the formula for the temperature dependence of the
degree of disorder.

There is a similar and even more marked influence of this type on
the energy barrier to be surmounted by a migrating particle in the
lattice, as first pointed out by Jost (101) and investigated both
theoretically and experimentally by Jost and Nehlep (104). A detailed treatment is due to Mott and Gurney (13). They consider a crystal consisting of N particles and containing n Schottky
holes, of energy $\varepsilon(v)$ per hole, this energy, $\varepsilon(v)$, being a function of
the volume. For the vibrational energy of the crystal, the Einstein
approximation is assumed, each particle in the undisturbed lattice
oscillating with a vibration frequency ν. For the x neighboring particles of a Schottky vacancy, a change in vibration frequency must
be expected. Mott and Gurney, as an approximation, assume that
for vibrations perpendicular to the line joining the neighboring particle
to the hole the frequency remains unchanged, equal to ν, while for
the vibrations parallel to this line one has $\nu' < \nu$. Then the free
energy of the crystal is

$$\Phi + n\,\varepsilon(v) + kT\,(3N - nx)\,\log\frac{h\nu}{kT} + nxkT\,\log\frac{h\nu'}{kT}$$
$$- kT\,\log\frac{N!}{n!(N-n)!}\,. \tag{2.80}$$

The equilibrium condition, $(\partial F/\partial n) = 0$, gives

$$\varepsilon(v) + xkT\,\log\frac{\nu'}{\nu} + kT\,\log\frac{n}{N-n} = 0 \tag{2.81}$$

and with $n \ll N$

$$\frac{n}{N} = \gamma\,\exp\,(-\varepsilon(v)/kT) \tag{2.82}$$

where

$$\gamma = (\nu/\nu')^x.$$

In the above equations v is the volume at the temperature under
consideration, and the energy $\varepsilon(v)$ is itself a function of temperature.
Assuming thermal expansion to be linear up to the temperature
considered, one may put

$$\varepsilon(v) = \varepsilon_0 + \alpha\,v_0\,T\,\frac{d\,\varepsilon(v)}{dv} \tag{2.83}$$

and, thus, one finally obtains

$$\frac{n}{N} = \gamma \, B \, \exp \, (-\varepsilon_0/kT) \, . \qquad [2.84]$$

In this formula ε_0 is the work necessary to form a vacant lattice point at $T = 0$, and

$$B = \exp \left(-\frac{\alpha \, v_0}{k} \, \frac{d \, \varepsilon(v)}{d \, v} \right) . \qquad [2.85]$$

Since $d\varepsilon(v)/dv < 0$, B is greater than 1, the same holds for γ. Instead of [2.85] we may write

$$B = \exp \left(-\frac{\alpha \, E_A(v)}{R} \, \frac{d \log E_A(v)}{d \log V_A} \right) \qquad [2.86]$$

where the magnitudes now refer to a gram atom instead of an atom. With the values for rock salt

$$\alpha = 1.2 \times 10^{-4}, \quad E_A(v) \approx 40 \ \text{kcal/g-atom}$$

and an estimated value

$$\frac{d \log E_A(v)}{d \log V_A} \approx 2$$

Mott and Gurney arrive at

$$B \approx \exp \, (4.8) \approx 100.$$

For $v/v' \approx 2$, and $x = 6$

$$\gamma \approx 64$$

is obtained. Thus

$$B\gamma \approx 10^3 \ \text{to} \ 10^4$$

both influences favoring the occurrence of the Schottky type of disorder. Since it is to be expected that large values of E are accompanied by large values of B, this leads to an understanding of empirically observed expressions for electrolytic conduction and diffusion (cf. Barrer (25)).

In the case of Frenkel disorder, just as in the case of Schottky disorder, a factor B occurs and is probably of equal order of magnitude. The influence of a change of the frequency of lattice vibrations in the neighborhood of a position of disorder, however, may differ from that in the Schottky case. If v and v' have the same meaning as above, and if v_i is the vibration frequency of an interstitial particle, v_i' that of its y neighbors, x being the number of neighbors of a vacancy, then we have

$$\frac{n}{\sqrt{N \, N'}} = \gamma \exp \, (-E/2kT) \qquad [2.87]$$

where N is the total number of atoms, N' the number of interstitial positions, and

$$\gamma^2 = \nu^{x+y+1}/\nu_i \nu_i'^y \nu'^x.$$

Since $\nu_i > \nu$, $\nu' < \nu$, γ may be greater or smaller than unity. Therefore, in case of Frenkel disorder (silver halides, etc., with exceptions of α-phases) values of γB might be expected which are smaller than in the case of Schottky disorder (as, for instance, with alkali halides).

V. Order-disorder*. Cooperative Phenomena

A. Experimental Results. Phenomena of disorder, treated so far on the basis of the Schottky-Wagner theory, included the case of an interchange of different types of particles. But in this case, as in all others treated, the assumption had to be introduced that the number of disordered particles is small compared with the total number of particles present. This made possible certain simplifications in the statistical treatment, and in addition it was not necessary to allow for a dependence of the energy of disorder on the degree of disorder.

There is, however, an important group of order-disorder phenomena for which these simplifications are no longer valid. Usually one considers order-disorder transformations in metallic alloys only, but one may expect analogous phenomena with other mixed crystals, too, and there is at least one example known, the transition from β-Ag$_2$HgI$_4$ to α-Ag$_2$HgI$_4$ (106, 107, 108, 109), which seems completely analogous to order-disorder transformations in metallic mixed crystals. In the case of alloys these phenomena are not connected directly with the mechanism of diffusion, because only normal lattice sites are involved, and therefore no centres of special mobility are created. In the case of the silver mercury complex salt, however, the order-disorder process also involves empty lattice sites, and this transition is directly connected with the mechanism of electrolytic conduction and of diffusion. In the metallic alloys an interchange of different particles must be due to a mechanism analogous to that of normal diffusion processes. Therefore, the kinetics of order-disorder transformations in alloys should be of special interest in connection with the general theory of diffusion processes in solids. The phenomena observed are, however, much more complicated than normal diffusion processes and far from being understood in all details.

It was first observed by Tammann (21, 159) that certain alloys showed limits of resistance towards chemical agents, like acids and

---

* For the subject of this section reference is made to the following monographs and comprehensive papers (5, 8, 14, 15, 16, 17, 26, 27).

ammonium sulfide, which coincided with concentrations corresponding to simple ratios of the component metals. He concluded from his observations that the lattice of the binary mixed crystal contains the

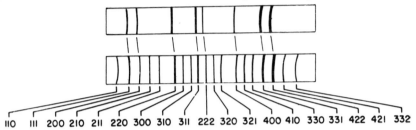

110 111 200 210 211 220 300 310 311 222 320 321 400 410 330 331 422 421 332

Fig. 2-18. Superstructure lines of Cu$_3$Au, lower diagram; upper: Debye-Scherrer lines of disordered Cu$_3$Au, schematically, after Sykes and Jones.

two types of atoms in a state of complete order. Tammann's argument seems inconclusive because a complete order is possible only for certain discrete concentration ratios, while the resistivity is observed over a continuous range of concentrations. Therefore an explanation of Tammann's experiments requires a more general definition of a state of order which still is valid when the composition does not permit a complete order of the lattice. The existence of order in certain alloys has later been confirmed by x-ray analysis (24, 90, 98, 140, 157). An ordered state of an alloy can give rise to so-called superstructure lines, observed in many cases, Fig. 2-18. Examples of superstructures, derived from x-ray observations, are seen in Figs. 2-19, 2-20. The possible limiting cases for a two-dimensional square lattice of a mixture $A : B = 1 : 1$ are show nin Fig. 2-10 and 2-11, p. 89/90. Fig. 2-11 refers to complete disorder, which will .be reached for sufficiently high temperatures, Fig. 2-10 shows complete order of the AB phase, which will be reached at sufficiently low temperatures, unless a separation into the two phases A and B sets in at low temperatures, Fig. 2-12, p. 90. Which one of the two cases actually occurrs depends on whether the energy of binding between A and B atoms is larger or smaller than the average of the binding energies of AA and BB. In the former case an ordered mixed

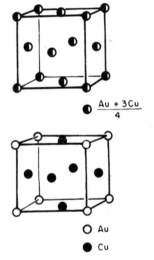

$\overset{\text{Au + 3Cu}}{\rule{1.5cm}{0.4pt}}$
$\quad 4$

○ Au

● Cu

Fig. 2-19. Structure of Cu$_3$Au, disordered.

Fig. 2-20. Structure of Cu$_3$Au, ordered (after Bijvoet, Kolkmeyer, Mac Gillavry).

crystal will be observed at low temperatures, in the latter a splitting into the two phases A and B. For the following we shall assume that we have to deal with the case of order-disorder transformation. Since for the transition from the ordered state to that of disorder energy must be supplied, we should either find a surplus of specific heat in such cases or a heat of transformation at a certain transformation point, or both. In the following Fig. 2-21 measured values of specific heats of β-brass are reproduced, in the temperature range of the transformation. An anomalous increase of specific heats is seen, dropping abruptly above a certain temperature, but not as far as to the Dulong-Petit value (114, 128, 157).

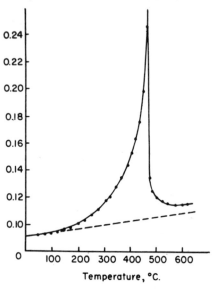

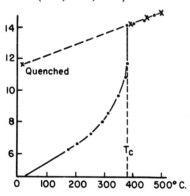

Fig. 2-21. Specific heat, cal/g centigrade, of β-brass as function of temperature (Moser).

Fig. 2-22. Electrical resistivity, Ohm · cm. 10^6 of Cu_3Au alloy. $\times$ at room temperature, quenched from temperature above transition point (Sykes and Evans).

The behavior of the electric resistance is very instructive (31, 97, 156). As is to be expected, with rising temperature and rising disorder the resistance increases rapidly and almost discontinuously at the transformation point. If afterwards the alloy is cooled very suddenly, the state of disorder of high temperatures is preserved and the resistance does not correspond to the equilibrium value, as originally observed, but corresponds to a resistance curve, extrapolated from high temperatures. The original values can be reproduced only after annealing, Fig. 2-22. Finally we reproduce curves for the resistivity at room temperature, as function of the composition, Fig. 2-23. Specimens, quenched from high temperature, and therefore in a state of disorder show a continuous curve of resistivity, while samples, which had been annealed at 200°C, have marked minima in resistivity at the compositions of 25 and 50 atom per cent Au, corresponding to the ordered phases Cu_3Au and $CuAu$.

B. The Bragg-Williams Theory. The methods of treating order-disorder transitions theoretically are quite different from the Schottky-Wagner theory of disorder in crystals with small degree of disorder. The first successful theory is due to Bragg and Williams (35, 36), (176). We shall briefly outline this theory since we make use of it in the case of Ag_2HgI_4. The fundamental concept of their theory is that of long-range order. Consider a binary alloy of composition AB where the atoms A and B may either be distributed at random or may be present in a state of more or less complete order. In case of complete order we shall have a sub-lattice with sites occupied by A atoms only, and another one occupied by B atoms, Fig. 2-24 a. But these two lattices, as shown in Fig. 2-24a, for the idealized case of a simple plane square lattice, are wholly equivalent, distinguished only by the fact that in a state of order the one contains an excess of A atoms while the other contains an equivalent excess of B atoms. But there is no inherent difference between the two lattices,

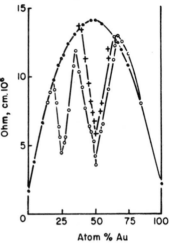

Fig. 2-23. Electrical resistance of Cu-Au alloys, as function of composition (Johannsson and Linde). Full circles: quenched from 650°C; open circles: annealed at 200°C; crosses: cooled in furnace.

```
A B A B A B      A B B A B A      A A B A A B
B A B A B A      B A A B A B      B A B A A B
A B A B A B      A B A B B A      A B B A B A
B A B A B A      B A B A A B      B B A B A B
A B A B A B      A B A A B A      A B A B B A
B A B A B A      B A B B A B      A B B A B A
        a               b               c
```

Fig. 2-24

and in a state of complete disorder there is no possibility of distinguishing between them. The most natural way would be to base the definition of order upon the average arrangement of neighboring atoms in the surroundings of individual atoms, as actually is done in Bethe's theory (29). But the theoretical treatment is much simplified if one considers long-range order only, choosing that sublattice as α-lattice which in case of complete order happens to be occupied by A atoms only, and conversely for the β lattice. Then the definition of order is based upon the occupation of these α-sites and β-sites respectively. Thus Fig. 2-24 (a) would mean that all α-sites are occupied by A atoms, correspondingly all β-sites by B atoms, and there is complete order. In Fig. 2-24 (c) there are equal numbers of A atoms on α- and on β-sites, and conversely for B atoms, thus a definition of order based upon fixed α- and β-lattices gives a state of complete disorder. From Fig. 2-24 (b) the inherent difficulty of this definition is seen. In this case the long-range order would be zero, equal number of α- and of β-sites being occupied by A and by B atoms*. Therefore we have to exclude in our present treatment structures like (b), where the choice of α- and β-sites would have to be done separately for each of the two parts.

If we want to define an order parameter, we must do it in such a way as to obtain, for instance, unity for complete order and zero for complete disorder. In the above example, AB, obviously an expression $\Sigma = 2(r_\alpha - 1/2)$ would represent a reasonable definition of order, r_α being the fraction of α-sites. occupied by (right) A-atoms. Since r_α varies from 1, complete order, to 1/2, complete disorder, Σ varies from 1 to 0. In order to generalize this definition, we introduce the following notation (cf. Nix and Shockley (15)).

$N =$ total number of atoms, equal to the total number of lattice sites

f_A and $f_B =$ fractions of A-atoms and of B-atoms, respectively (equal to the fractions of lattice sites which are α- and β-sites, respectively)

$r_\alpha =$ fraction of α-sites occupied by (right) A atoms, and conversely r_β for B atoms

w_α and $w_\beta =$ fractions of α- and β-sites, occupied by (wrong) B and A atoms, respectively, with

$w_\alpha = 1 - r_\alpha, \; w_\beta = 1 - r_\beta$.

There will be $w_\beta f_B N$ A-atoms on β-sites, and $w_\alpha f_A N$ B-atoms on α-sites, both numbers being equal

$$w_\alpha f_A = w_\beta f_B .$$ [2.88]

From the above definitions follow the further relations:

$$f_A + f_B = r_\alpha + w_\alpha = r_\beta + w_\beta = 1 .$$ [2.89]

* A mathematical problem, arising in this connection, has been solved by van der Waerden (166).

For complete order we have $r_a = r_\beta = 1$, while for complete disorder A and B atoms are distributed equally among α- and β-sites. Hence, for complete disorder the fraction of α-sites, occupied by A-atoms, r_a, must be equal to the fraction of β-sites, occupied by A-atoms, w_β, and equal to the fraction f_A of all atoms which are A-atoms

$$r_a = w_\beta = f_A, \quad w_\alpha = r_\beta = f_B \quad \text{for complete disorder.} \quad [2.90]$$

Our tentative definition of the degree of order, Σ, will have to be generalized

$$\Sigma = \frac{r_a - f_A}{1 - f_A}. \quad [2.91]$$

This expression, for $f_A = 1/2$, reduces to the previous value. The degree of order will depend upon temperature, on account of the energy of disorder, ε. As we have seen before, p. 119, energy must be supplied for an increase in disorder. Therefore ε will be defined as the energy increase produced by the exchange of an A-atom on an α-site with a B-atom on a β-site. Consequently, ε is the increase in energy per pair of disordered atoms. This energy must depend on the way in which the sites surrounding the original and final positions of A and B are occupied. Bragg and Williams do not take into account this influence of short-range order (which will cause fluctuations of ε) but, instead, use the simplified assumption that ε is determined by the degree of long-range order, $\varepsilon = \varepsilon(\Sigma)$.

We now wish to determine the probability of finding an A-atom on an α-site or on a β-site. The ratio of these two probabilities will be given by

$$w_\alpha f_A N / [r_\beta f_B N \exp(-\varepsilon/kT)]. \quad [2.92]$$

For, this ratio must be equal to the ratio of the $w_\alpha f_A N$ B-atoms on α-sites and $r_\beta f_B N$ B-atoms on β-sites, with which the A-atom under consideration may exchange its position, multiplied by a Boltzmann factor, containing the energy of disorder, ε, giving a lower probability for a β-site to be occupied by an A atom. In equilibrium [2.92] must hold for any A-atom under consideration, therefore, the equilibrium ratio of the number of A-atoms on α-sites, $r_a f_A N$, to that of A-atoms on β-sites, $w_\beta f_B N$, must be given by [2.92]

$$r_a f_A N / w_\beta f_B N = w_\alpha f_A N / [r_\beta f_B N \exp(-\varepsilon/kT)] \quad [2.93]$$

or

$$r_a r_\beta / w_\alpha w_\beta = \exp(\varepsilon/kT). \quad [2.94]$$

This may be transformed into

$$[1/f_B(1 - \Sigma) - 1] [1/f_A(1 - \Sigma) - 1] = \exp(\varepsilon/kT) \quad [2.95]$$

if we consider that

$$r_\alpha/w_\alpha = \frac{1-w_\alpha}{w_\alpha} = \frac{1}{w_\alpha} - 1 = \frac{1}{f_\beta(1-\Sigma)} - 1$$

and conversely for r_β/w_β.

Putting $\varepsilon/kT = X$, where $X = X(\Sigma)$ is a function of the long-range order Σ, as stated above, we have an equation for Σ as function of X. In our special case of an alloy AB, $f_A = f_B = 1/2$, we have

$$\Sigma = [\exp(\varepsilon/2kT) - 1]/[\exp(\varepsilon/2kT) + 1] = \tanh(X/4) \cdot \quad [2.96]$$

ε must depend on Σ in such a way that it has a definite value ε_0 for $\Sigma = 1$, while it must vanish for $\Sigma = 0$. Bragg and Williams introduce the simplest possible assumption

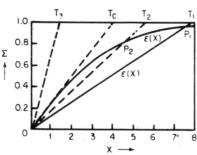

$$\varepsilon = \Sigma \varepsilon_0 . \quad [2.97]$$

This again is a rough approximation only, because even for $\Sigma = $ const., ε may vary with varying short-range order. A solution of [2.96] and [2.97] may be obtained graphically, Fig. 2-25. Equation [2.96] may be written

$$\Sigma = \Sigma(X)$$

Fig. 2-25. Treatment of AB case, after Bragg and Williams. $\Sigma(X)$, curve, and $\varepsilon(X)$.

and the resulting curve $\Sigma(X)$ for the alloy AB has been drawn in Fig. 2-25. [2.97] may be written

$$\Sigma = \varepsilon/\varepsilon_0 = (kT/\varepsilon_0)(\varepsilon/kT) = (kT/\varepsilon_0) X . \quad [2.98]$$

Equation [2.98], although an equation between Σ and X, will be denoted by $\varepsilon(X)$. In Fig. 2-25 several straight lines for $\varepsilon(X)$, corresponding to $T = $ const. have been drawn. For T below a certain critical value T_c, these straight lines intersect the curve $\Sigma(X)$ in a second point P, outside the origin, X, $\Sigma = 0$. For $T = T_1$, equilibrium is represented by P_1, etc. For $T \geq T_c$, the equilibrium value is $\Sigma = 0$, i. e., order ceases to exist above $T = T_c$. For $T = T_c$, the straight line is tangent to $\Sigma(X)$, consequently

$$kT_c/\varepsilon_0 = \frac{d}{dx}\tanh X \quad \text{for } X = 0 \quad [2.99]$$

and

$$kT_c/\varepsilon_0 = 1/4 \qquad T_c = \varepsilon_0/4k = 2E_0/R . \quad [2.100]$$

E_0 in [2.100] is an energy of transformation of the alloy referred to 1 g atom, and is related to the energy of disorder.

We find for the energy change of the alloy, connected with a change in order,

$$dE = -f_A f_B N \varepsilon_0 \Sigma d\Sigma \qquad [2.101]$$

because for a change $d\Sigma$, (on account of [2.91]), $N f_A dr_\alpha = f_\alpha f_B N d\Sigma$ A-atoms must be exchanged with B-atoms, each one causing an energy change $\varepsilon_0 \Sigma$. Putting $E = 0$ for the state of complete order, we obtain upon integration of [2.101]

$$E = \frac{f_A f_B N \varepsilon_0}{2}(1 - \Sigma^2) = E_0(1 - \Sigma^2) \qquad E_0 = f_A f_B N \varepsilon_0/2. \qquad [2.102]$$

For the alloys AB, $f_A = f_B = 1/2$, and AB_3, $f_A = 1/4$, $f_B = 3/4$, the corresponding values of E_0 are $N\varepsilon_0/8$ and $3N\varepsilon_0/32$, respectively.

For the alloy AB_3, the situation is more complicated. By an argument, analogous to that employed in the AB case, Bragg and Williams arrive at Fig. 2-26, where the straight lines again represent $\varepsilon(X)$, while the curve $\Sigma(X)$ now has a point of inflection (the graphical representation in Fig. 2-26 is exaggerated). Hence, within a certain range of temperature, there are three points of inter-

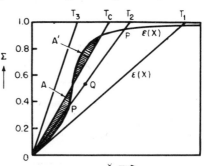

Fig. 2-26. AB_3 case, $\Sigma(X)$, curve, and $\varepsilon(X)$.

section for the straight lines $\varepsilon(X)$ and this curve; for instance for T_2 we have the points of intersection O, P', and P. It can be shown that, as in similar problems, the point P' represents an unstable state and that below the critical temperature T_c only the upper point P belongs to a stable state. Above T_c, only the state represented by the origin, i. e., the state of complete disorder, is stable. T_c is determined by the condition that the two shaded areas, Fig. 2-26, are equal. The proof will be given below. It follows for T_c

$$\Sigma = 0.467, \qquad T_c = 0.205\, \varepsilon_0/k = 2.18 E_0/R. \qquad [2.103]$$

Contrary to the situation, encountered in case of the alloy AB, where the degree of order decreased steadily, though rather sharply, just below T_c, reaching zero for $T = T_c$, we have a discontinuous change of order at $T = T_c$ in the case of the alloy AB_3. Σ drops from a value of 0.467, just below the critical temperature, to zero. While in the former case the transition was accompanied by an anomalous increase in specific heat only, we now have, in addition, a latent heat of transformation at $T = T_c$. We find from [2.102] for this heat of transformation, λ,

$$\lambda = E(0) - E(0.467) = E_0(0.467)^2 = 0.218\,E_0 = 0.100\,RT_c \quad [2.104]$$

In Fig. 2-27, 2-28 curves for the degree of order and for energy content and for the specific heat (without energy of lattice vibrations) are

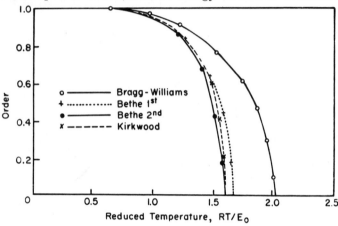

Fig. 2-27. Long range order Σ versus reduced temperature, AB case, in addition to value of Bragg-Williams theory, Bethe's 1st and 2nd approximation and Kirkwood's theory.

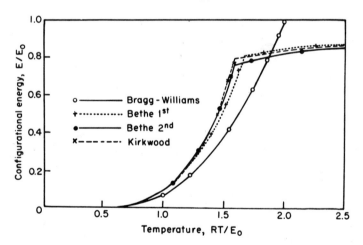

Fig. 2-28. Configurational energy versus reduced temperature for AB case (after Nix and Shockley).

reproduced, as functions of the reduced temperature (RT/E_0), for the alloys AB and AB_3. In addition to the values, calculated by the Bragg-Williams theory, the results of the refined theories of Bethe

(29), Peierls (139), and Kirkwood (111, 113) are inserted (cf., also Bethe, Kirkwood (30), Chang (42, 49)).

We now shall give the proof for the stability of the states chosen above. In this proof we shall follow the treatment given by Nix and Shockley (15). We first must calculate the entropy and free energy of the states under consideration.

The entropy S for the state of order Σ is given by Boltzmann's principle

$$S = k \log W(\Sigma) \qquad [2.105]$$

where $W(\Sigma)$ is the number of complexions, pertaining to the state with degree of order Σ. As in the calculation of the energy, we neglect eventual changes, due to a change in lattice vibrations. We have $r_\alpha f_A N$ A-atoms on α-sites and $r_\beta f_B N$ B-atoms on β-sites and the number of distinguishable permutations is W_α

$$W_\alpha = (f_A N)! / (r_\alpha f_A N)! \, (W_\beta f_A N)! \qquad [2.106]$$

with a corresponding expression W_β for β-sites:

$$W_\beta = (f_B N)! / (r_\beta f_B N)! \, (W_\alpha f_B N)! \, . \qquad [2.107]$$

Consequently,

$$W(\Sigma) = W_\alpha \, W_\beta \, . \qquad [2.108]$$

By applying Stirling's formula and by expressing r_α, r_β, W_α, W_β in terms of Σ, by means of the equations of p. 124 we find

$$\begin{aligned} S = k \log W(\Sigma) = -k\{ f_A[1 - f_B(1 - \Sigma)] \log [1 - f_B(1 - \Sigma)] \\ + f_A f_B (1 - \Sigma) \log [f_B(1 - \Sigma)] + f_B[1 - f_A(1 - \Sigma)] \qquad [2.109] \\ \log [1 - f_A(1 - \Sigma)] + f_B f_A(1 - \Sigma) \log [f_A(1 - \Sigma)] \} \, . \end{aligned}$$

[2.109] gives the limiting values

$$S(1) = 0 \qquad S(0) = -k[f_A \log f_A + f_B \log f_B] \qquad [2.110]$$

the known expressions either for a state of complete order or for a binary mixture of complete disorder. Consequently, we find for the entropy change of 1 gram atom of alloy, undergoing transition from order to disorder

$$AB \text{ case } \quad \Delta S = R \log 2 = 0.693 \, R = 1.37 \text{ cal./degree} \qquad [2.111]$$

$$\begin{aligned} AB_3 \text{ case } \quad \Delta S &= R(4 \log 4 - 3 \log 3)/4 = 0.562 \, R \\ &= 1.11 \text{ cal./degree} \, . \qquad [2.112] \end{aligned}$$

Finally we obtain for the free energy

$$F(\Sigma) = -kT \log Z$$

where Z is the partition function $Z = \Sigma \exp(-\varepsilon/kT)^*$. Since we have

---

* Σ meaning summation!

assumed equal energy for all states of the same long-range order Σ, [2.101], $E = N\varepsilon_0 f_A f_B (1 - \Sigma^2)/2$, we find, with equation [2.108] for the number of states with given degree of order, Σ,

$$F(\Sigma) = E(\Sigma) - kT \log W(\Sigma) . \qquad [2.113]$$

This expression might have been obtained immediately from equation [2.109], by means of the thermodynamic relation $F = E - TS$. The stable state for $T = $ const. is determined by the minimum of the Helmholtz free energy, with respect to Σ. Hence we obtain the condition

$$
\begin{aligned}
0 = \partial F(\Sigma)/\partial\Sigma &= \partial E(\Sigma)/\partial\Sigma - kT\partial \log W(\Sigma)/\partial\Sigma \\
&= -NkT f_A f_B \{\log[1/f_A(1-\Sigma)-1] \\
&\quad + \log[1/f_B(1-\Sigma)-1] - \varepsilon_0\Sigma/kT\} .
\end{aligned} \qquad [2.114]
$$

The factor outside the braces is irrelevant, because it is constant for constant temperature and constant composition. Omitting this factor we put

$$X_1(\Sigma) = \varepsilon_0\Sigma/kT \qquad [2.115]$$

and

$$X_2(\Sigma) = \log[1/f_A(1-\Sigma)-1] + \log[1/f_B(1-\Sigma)-1] . \qquad [2.116]$$

Thus the minimum condition becomes

$$X_1(\Sigma) = X_2(\Sigma) \qquad [2.117]$$

which may be solved graphically, Fig. 2-29, taken from Nix and Shockley.

Neglecting a factor of proportionality, we have

$$\partial F/\partial\Sigma \sim X_2 - X_1 . \qquad [2.118]$$

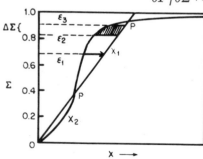

Fig. 2-29. Free-energy method, for AB_3 case, after Nix and Shockley.

Consequently, the horizontal distance between the two curves in Fig. 2-29 is a measure of $\partial F/\partial\Sigma$. For $\partial F/\partial\Sigma < 0$, as between P' and P, F will decrease with increasing Σ, until a stable state has been reached at P. The change of F, corresponding to a change $\Delta\Sigma$ in Σ is: $\Delta F = \int \partial F/\partial\Sigma \cdot d\Sigma$, proportional to the shaded area of Fig. 2-29. It is seen immediately that the free energy for point P' is larger than either for P or for $\Sigma = 0$. Equality of the free energies at P and at $\Sigma = 0$ is obtained only if the straight line for $T = T_c$ is chosen in such a way that the areas between the curve and the straight line above and below

P' are equal. This is the procedure, chosen on p. 125, without proof. Since it is readily seen that the functions X_1 and X_2, used here, are equivalent to the functions $\varepsilon(\Sigma)$ and $\Sigma(X)$, chosen above, p. 124, the method, employed previously, has now been justified statistically.

The Bragg-Williams theory is in good qualitative agreement with observations. The lack of quantitative agreement is due to neglecting the short-range order. If a crystal with ordered structure is heated up to, and above, its critical temperature, the long-range order breaks down; there remains, however, some short-range order even above the critical temperature, and consequently anomalies in specific heat persist above T_c. The theories of Bethe, Peierls, Kirkwood, *loc. cit.*, which start from the concept of local order show much closer agreement with observations. For these we must refer to the original papers and some comprehensive treatments (Nix and Shockley (15), Fowler and Guggenheim (5)).

These theories are also of importance for the theory of liquid mixtures (cf. for instance, Fowler and Rushbrooke (66), Guggenheim (74, 75, 76, 77, 78, 79), Kirkwood (112), Miller (12, 126) and Münster (130)).

REFERENCES

Monographs and review articles

1. van Arkel, A. E., and de Boer, J. H., Chemische Bindung als elektrostatische Erscheinung, Leipzig, 1931, p. 213.
2. Barrer, R. M., Diffusion in and through Solids, Cambridge, 1941.
2a. Bouman, J., Selected Topics in x-Ray Crystallography. B. Distortions in Crystals. North Holland Publishing Company, Amsterdam, 1950.
3. Bijvoet, J. M., Kolkmeijer, N. H., and MacGillavry, C. H., Röntgenanalyse von Kristallen. Berlin, 1940. x-Ray Analysis of Crystals. Amsterdam, 1949.
4. Dehlinger, U., Chemische Physik der Metalle und Legierungen. Leipzig, 1939.
5. Fowler, R. H., and Guggenheim, E. A., Statistical Thermodynamics. Cambridge, 1939.
6. Frenkel, I., Kinetic Theory of Liquids. Oxford, 1946.
7. Guggenheim, E. A., Modern Thermodynamics by the Methods of W. Gibbs. London, 1933.
8. Hume-Rothery, W., The Structure of Metals and Alloys. London, 1936.
8a. Jagodzinsk , H., *Fortschritte Mineral., Krist. Petr.* **28**, 95 (1949).
9. Landau, L., and Lifshitz, E., Statistical Physics. Oxford, 1938.
10. Laves, F., *Z. Elektrochem.* **45**, 2, (1939).
11. Manning, M. F., and Bell, M. E., *Rev. Mod. Phys.* **12**, 215 (1940).
12. Miller, A. R., The Theory of Solutions of High Polymers. Oxford, 1948.
13. Mott, N. F., and Gurney, R. W., Electronic Processes in Ionic crystals. Oxford, 1940. 2nd Edition. Oxford, 1948.
14. Mott, N. F., and Jones, H., The Theory of the Properties of Metals and Alloys. Oxford. 1936.

15. Nix, F. C., and Shockley, W., *Rev. Mod. Phys.* **10,** 1 (1938).
16. Schottky, W., *Z. Elektrochem.* **45,** 33 (1939).
17. Seitz, F., Modern Theory of Solids. New York, 1940.
18. Seitz, F., *Rev. Mod. Phys.* **18,** 384 (1946).
19. Seitz, F., Fundamental Aspects of Diffusion in Solids. Pittsburgh, 1948.
20. Strock, L. W., *Z. Krist.* **93,** 285 (1936).
21. Tammann, G., Lehrbuch der Metallkunde. Leipzig, 1932.
22. Wagner, C., and Schottky, W., *Z. physik. Chem.* **B 11,** 163 (1931).

General Bibliography

23. Anderson, C. S., *Proc. Roy. Soc. (London)* **A 185,** 69 (1946).
24. Bain, E. C., *Chem. & Met. Eng.* **28,** 65 (1923).
25. Barrer, R. M., *Trans. Faraday Soc.* **38,** 322 (1942).
26. Becker, R., *Metallwirtschaft* **16,** 573 (1937).
27. Becker, R., *Z. Metallkunde* **29,** 245 (1937).
28. Becker, R., *Ann. Physik* **32,** 128 (1938).
29. Bethe, H. A., *Proc. Roy. Soc. (London)* **A 150,** 552 (1935).
30. Bethe, H. A., and Kirkwood, J. G., *J. Chem. Phys.* **7,** 578 (1939).
30a. Betteridge, W., *J. Inst. Metals* **75,** 559 (1949). (Degree of order and lattice parameter of $Cu_3 Au$).
31. Borelius, G., *Z. Elektrochem.* **45,** 16 (1939).
32. Borelius, G., *J. Inst. Metals* **74,** 17 (1947).
32a. Borelius, G., *Physica* **15,** 135 (1949).
33. Born, M., *Z. Physik* **1,** 45 (1920).
34. Bradley, A. J., and Taylor, A., *Proc. Roy. Soc. (London)* **A 159,** 56 (1937).
35. Bragg, W. L., and Williams, E. J., *Proc. Roy. Soc. (London)* **A 145,** 699 (1934).
36. Bragg, W. L., and Williams, E. J., *Proc. Roy. Soc. (London)* **A 151,** 540 (1935).
36a. Brauer, G. and Tiesler, J., *Z. anorg. Chem.* **262,** 309, 319 (1950) ($Mg_2 P$ etc.).
37. Bruni, G., and Ferrari, A., *Z. physik. Chem.* **130,** 488 (1927); *Z. Krist.* **89,** 499 (1934).
38. Buerger, N. W., *Am. Mineral.* **25,** 205 (1940).
39. Buessem, W., Schusterius, C., and Ungewiss, A., *Ber. Deut. keram. Ges.* **18,** 433 (1937).
40. Bumm, H., *Z. Metallkunde* **31,** 318 (1939).
41. Buinov, N., and Komar, A., *J. Exp. Theoret. Phys. (U.S.S.R.)* **9,** 1135 (1939).
41a. Buinov, N., *J. Exper. Theoret. Phys. (U.S.S.R.)* **17,** 41 (1947).
42. Chang, T. S., *Proc. Roy. Soc. (London)* **A 161,** 546 (1937).
43. Chang, T. S., *Proc. Cambridge Phil. Soc.* **34,** 224 (1938).
44. Chang, T. S., *Proc. Cambridge Phil. Soc.* **35,** 265 (1939).
45. Chang, T. S., *Proc. Roy. Soc. (London)* **A 169,** 512 (1939).
46. Chang, T. S., *Proc. Cambridge Phil. Soc.* **35,** 70 (1939).
47. Chang, T. S., *Proc. Roy. Soc. (London)* **A 173,** 48 (1939).
48. Chang, T. S., *Proc. Cambridge Phil. Soc.* **35,** 274 (1939).
49. Chang, T. S., *J. Chem. Phys.* **9,** 169, 174 (1941).
50. Clusius, K., *Z. Elektrochem.* **44,** 23 (1938).
50a. Cowley, J. M., *Phys. Rev.* **77,** 669 (1950).
50b. Cowley, J. M., *J. applied Phys.* **21,** 24 (1950).
51. Cremer, E., *Z. physik. Chem.* **B 28,** 199 (1935).
53. Cremer, E., *Z. physik. Chem.* **B 39,** 445 (1938).
54. Cremer, E., *Z. physik. Chem.* **B 42,** 281 (1939).

55. Cremer, E., and Flügge, S., *Z. physik. Chem.* **B 41**, 453 (1938).
56. Croatto, U., *Gazz. chim. ital.* **73**, 257 (1943).
57. Croatto, U., *Gazz. chim. ital.* **74**, 20 (1944).
58. Croatto, U., and Bruno, M., *Gazz. chim. ital.* **76**, 246 (1946).
58a. Croatto, U., and Bruno, M., *Ricerca sci.* **18**, 578 (1949).
58b. Croatto, U., and Bruno, M., *Ricerca sci.* **18**, 579 (1949).
59. Dienes, G. J., J. *Chem. Phys.* **16**, 620 (1948).
60. Domb, C., *Proc. Roy. Soc. (London)* **A 196**, 36 (1949).
60a. Du Pré, F. K., Hutner, R. A., and Rittner, E. S., *J. Chem. Phys.* **18**, 379 (1950).
61. Ebert, F., and Cohn, E., *Z. anorg. u. allgem. Chem.* **213**, 321 (1933).
62. Edwards, O. S., and Lipson, H., *Proc. Roy. Soc. (London)* **A 180**, 268 (1942).
63. Fajans, K., *Verhandl. deut. physik. Ges.* **21**, 549, 709, 714 (1919).
64. Fokker, A. D., *Physica* **8**, 109 (1941).
65. Fowler, R. H., and Guggenheim, E. A., *Proc. Roy. Soc. (London)* **174**, 189 (1940).
66. Fowler, R. H., and Rushbrooke, G. S., *Trans. Faraday Soc.* **33**, 1272 (1937).
67. Frenkel, I., *Z. Physik* **35**, 652 (1926).
68. Fuchs, K., *Proc. Roy. Soc. (London)* **A 179**, 340 (1942).
69. Fuchs, K., *Proc. Roy. Soc. (London)* **A 181**, 411 (1944).
70. Germer, L. H., *Phys. Rev.* **61**, 614 (1942).
71. Germer, L. H., and Haworth, F. E. and Lander, J. J., *Phys. Rev.* **61**, 93 (1942).
71a. Gold, L., *Phys. Rev.* **75**, 1265 (1949).
71b. Goldman, J. E., and Smoluchowski, R., *Phys. Rev.* **75**, 140 (1949).
72. Gorsky, W. S., *Phys. Z. Sowjetunion* **8**, 443 (1935).
73. Gorsky, W. S., *Z. Physik* **50**, 64 (1928).
74. Guggenheim, E. A., *Proc. Roy. Soc. (London)* **A 135**, 181 (1932).
75. Guggenheim, E. A., *Proc. Roy. Soc. (London)* **A 148**, 304 (1935).
76. Guggenheim, E. A., *Proc. Roy. Soc. (London)* **A 169**, 134 (1938).
77. Guggenheim, E. A., *Nature* **153**, 255 (1944).
78. Guggenheim, E. A., *Proc. Roy. Soc. (London)* **A 183**, 203 (1944).
79. Guggenheim, E. A., *Proc. Roy. Soc. (London)* **A 183**, 213 (1944).
80. Guggenheim, E. A., *Trans. Faraday Soc.* **41**, 107 (1945).
81. Guggenheim, E. A., *Trans. Faraday Soc.* **44**, 1007 (1948).
82. Guinier, A., and Griffoul, R., *Acta Crystallogr.* **1**, 188 (1948).
82a. Guinier, A., and Griffoul, R., *Rev. Mét.* **45**, 387 (1948).
82b. Guinier, A., *Colloques Internationaux*, **X**, 39 (1948) (Lattices of imperfect periodicity).
83. Hägg, G., and Sucksdorff, I. *Z. physik. Chem.* **B 22**, 444 (1933).
84. Hägg, G., and Kindström, A., *Z. physik. Chem.* **B 22**, 453 (1933).
85. Hägg, G., and Söderholm, G., *Z. physik. Chem.* **B 29**, 88 (1935).
86. Hägg, G., *Z. physik. Chem.* **B 29**, 95 (1935).
86a. Hägg, G., *Colloques Internationaux*, **X**, 5 (1948).
87. Hartmann, H., *Z. Naturforsch.* **3a**, 617 (1948).
87a. Heiland, G., and Kelting, H., *Z. Physik* **126**, 689 (1949).
88. Hendricks, S. B., and Teller, E., *J. Chem. Phys.* **10**, 147 (1942).
89. Hendus, H., and Scheufele, E., *Z. Metallkunde* **32**, 275 (1940).
90. Holgersson, S., and Sedström, E., *Ann. Physik* **75** 143 (1924).
91. Huntington, H. B., and Seitz, F., *Phys. Rev.* **57**, 559 (1940).
92. Huntington, H. B., and Seitz, F., *Phys. Rev.* **61**, 315 (1942).
93. Huntington, H. B., *Phys. Rev.* **61**, 325 (1942).
93a. Hutner, R. A., Rittner, E. S. and du Pré, F. K., *J. Chem. Phys.* **17**, 204 (1949).

94. Jagitsch, R., *Ing. Vetenskaps Akad.* **2,** 114 (1942).
95. Jagodzinski, H., *Acta Crystallogr.* **2,** 201, 208, 298 (1949).
96. Jette, E. R., and Foote, F., *J. Chem. Phys.* **1,** 29 (1933).
97. Johansson, C. H., and Linde, J. O., *Ann. Physik* (4) **78,** 439 (1925).
98. Johansson, C. H., and Linde, J. O., *Ann. Physik* (5) **25,** 1 (1936).
99. Jones, F. W., and Sykes, C., *Proc. Roy. Soc. (London)* A **166,** 376 (1938).
100. Jost, W., *J. Chem. Phys.* **1,** 466 (1933).
101. Jost, W., *Z. physik. Chem.* A **169,** 129 (1934).
102. Jost, W., *Z. tech. Physik* **16,** 363 (1935).
103. Jost, W., *Trans. Faraday Soc.*, **34,** 860 (1938).
104. Jost, W., and Nehlep, G., *Z. physik. Chem.* B **32,** 1 (1936).
105. Jost, W., and Nehlep, G., *Z. physik. Chem.* B **34,** 348 (1936).
105a. Kelting, H., and Witt, H., *Z. Physik* **126,** 697 (1949).
106. Ketelaar, J. A. A., *Z. physik. Chem.* B **26,** 327 (1934).
107. Ketelaar, J. A. A., *Z. physik. Chem.* B **30,** 53 (1935).
108. Ketelaar, J. A. A., *Z. Krist.* **87,** 436 (1934).
109. Ketelaar, J. A. A., *Trans. Faraday Soc.* **34,** 874 (1938).
110. Ketelaar, J. A. A., and Willems, D. J. H., *Rec. trav. chim.* **56,** 29 (1937).
111. Kirkwood, J. G., *J. Chem. Phys.* **6,** 70 (1938).
112. Kirkwood, J. G., *J. Phys. Chem.* **43,** 97 (1939).
113. Kirkwood, J. G., *J. Chem. Phys.* **8,** 623 (1940).
113a. Klemm, W., *Z. Physik* **82,** 529 (1933).
114. Klinkhardt, H., *Ann. Physik* **84,** 167 (1927).
115. Koch, E., and Wagner, C., *Z. physik. Chem.* B **38,** 295 (1937).
115a. Komar, A. P., and Buinov, N., *J. Phys. U.S.S.R.* **11,** 5 (1947).
115b. Komar, A. P., *J. Exper. Theoret. Phys. U.S.S.R.* **17,** 753 (1947).
116. Landshoff, R., *Phys. Rev.* **55,** 631 (1939).
117. Latimer, W., Pitzer, K. S., and Slansky, C., *J. Chem. Phys.* **7,** 108 (1939).
118. Laves, F., and Jagodzinski, H., *Schweiz. mineralog. petrogr. Mitt.* **28,** 456 (1948).
119. Laves, F., and Nieuwenkamp, W., *Z. Krist.* **90,** 279 (1935).
119a. Lawson, A. W., *Phys. Rev.* **78,** 185 (1950).
120. Lennard-Jones, E., and Devonshire, A. F., *Proc. Roy. Soc. (London)* A **169,** 317 (1939).
121. Lennard-Jones, J. E., and Devonshire, A. F., *Proc. Roy. Soc. (London)* A **170,** 464 (1939).
122. Lipson, H., and Taylor, A., *Proc. Roy. Soc. (London)* A **173,** 232 (1939).
122a. Luttinger, J. M., and Tisza, L., *Phys. Rev.* **70,** 954 (1946); **72,** 257 (1947).
123. MacGillavry, C. H., and Strijk, B., *Physica* **11,** 369 (1946).
124. MacGillavry, C. H., and Strijk, B., *Physica* **12,** 129 (1946).
124a. Maurer, R. J., *Forschungen u. Fortschr.*, **26,** 3. Sonderh., 4 (1950) (Self diffusion and ionic conduction in Na Cl).
125. Miller, A. R., *Proc. Cambridge Phil. Soc.* **38,** 109 (1942).
126. Miller, A. R., *Proc. Cambridge Phil. Soc.* **39,** 54, 131 (1943).
127. Miller, A. R., *Proc. Cambridge Phil. Soc.* **42,** 303 (1946).
127a. Mitchell, J. W., *Phil. Mag.* (7) **40,** 249 (1949).
128. Moser, H., *Physik. Z.* **37,** 737 (1936).
129. Mott, N. F., and Littleton, M. J., *Trans. Faraday Soc.* **34,** 485 (1938).
130. Münster, A., *Z. Naturforschung* **3** a, 158 (1948).
131. Muto, Y., *J. Phys.-Math. Soc. Japan* **17,** 445 (1943).
132. Muto, Y., *J. Chem. Phys.* **16,** 519, 524 (1948).
133. Nagamiya, T., and Uemonsa, S., *J. Phys.-Math. Soc. Japan* **16,** 375 (1942).

133a. Niggli, P., *Helv. Chim. Acta* **30**, 1562 (1947).
134. Nix, F. C., B'eyer, H. G., and Dunning, J. R., *Phys. Rev.* **58**, 1031 (1940).
135. Nix, F. C., and MacNair, D., *Phys. Rev.* **60**, 320 (1941).
136. Nowacki, W., *Schweiz. Chem. Z. u. Tech.-Ind.* **25**, 57 (1942).
137. Orr, W. J. C., *Trans. Faraday Soc.* **40**, 306 (1944).
138. Onsager, L., *Phys. Rev.* **65**, 117 (1944).
139. Peierls, R., *Proc. Roy. Soc. (London)* **A 154**, 207 (1936).
140. Phragmén, G., *Stahl u. Eisen* **45**, 299 (1925).
140a. Pick, H. and Weber, H., *Z. Physik*, **128**, 409 (1950) (Change of density of KCl by addition of bivalent ions).
141. Rahlfs, P., *Z. physik. Chem.* **B 31**, 157 (1935).
142. van Reijen, L. L., *Physica* **11**, 114 (1944).
143. Rittner, E. S., Hutner, R. A., and du Pré, F. K., *J. Chem. Phys.* **17**, 198 (1949).
144. Roberts, J. K., and Miller, A. R., *Proc. Cambridge Phil. Soc.* **35**, 293 (1939).
145. Ruff, O., and Ebert, F., *Z. anorg. u. allgem. Chem.* **180**, 19 (1929).
146. Seitz, F., *Phys. Rev.* (2) **54**, 1111 (1938).
147. Seitz, F., *Phys. Rev.* (2) **56**, 1063 (1939).
147a. Seitz, F., *Acta Crystallogr.*, **3**, 355 (1950).
147b. Shull, C. G., and Siegel, S., *Phys. Rev.* **75**, 1008 (1949).
148. Siegel, S., *J. Chem. Phys.* **8**, 860 (1940).
148a. Siegel, S., *Phys. Rev.* **75**, 1823 (1949).
149. Sillén, L. G., and Aurivillius, B., *Z. Kryst.* **101**, 483 (1939).
150. Sillén, L. G., and Aurivillius, B., *Naturwissenschaften* **27**, 388 (1939).
151. Sillén, L. G., and Sillén, B., *Z. physik. Chem.* **B 49**, 27 (1941).
151a. Smirnov, A. A., *J. Exper. Theoret. Phys. U.S.S.R.* **17**, 730 (1947).
151b. Stasiw, O., and Teltow, J., *Gött. Nachr. Math.-Phys. Kl.* 1941, p. 93.
151c. Stasiw, O., and Teltow, J., *Gött. Nachr. Math.-Phys. Kl.* 1941, p. 100.
151d. Stasiw, O., and Teltow, J., *Gött. Nachr. Math.-Phys., Kl.*, 1941, p. 110.
151e. Stasiw, O., and Teltow, J., *Gött. Nachr. Math.-Phys. Kl.* 1944, p. 155.
151f. Stasiw, O., and Teltow, J., *Ann. Physik* (6) **1**, 261 (1947).
151g. Stasiw, O., and Teltow, J., *Z. anorg. u. all . Chem.* **257**, 103 (1948).
151h. Stasiw, O., and Teltow, J., *Z. anorg. u. allg. Chem.* **257**, 109 (1948).
151i. Stasiw, O., and Teltow, J., *Z. anorg. u. allg. Chemie* **259**, 143 (1949).
151k. Stasiw, O., *Ann. Physik* (6) **5**, 151 (1949).
151l. Stasiw, O., *Z. Physik* **127**, 522 (1950).
151m. Stasiw, O., *Sc. & Industr. phot.* (2) **20**, 334 (1949).
152. Steigman, J., Shockley, W., and Nix, F. C., *Phys. Rev.* **55**, 605 (1939); **56**, 13 (1939).
153. Stern, O., Estermann, I., and Leivo, W. J., *Phys. Rev.* **75**, 627 (1949).
154. Strock, L. W., *Z. physik. Chem.* **B 25**, 441 (1934).
155. Strock, L. W., *Z. physik. Chem.* **B 31**, 132 (1935).
156. Sykes, C., and Evans, H., *J. Inst. Metals* **58**, 255 (1936).
157. Sykes, C., and Jones, F. W., *Proc. Roy. Soc. (London)* **A 157**, 213 (1936).
158. Schottky, W., *Z. physik. Chem.* **B 29**, 335 (1935).
159. Tammann, G., *Z. anorg. u. allgem. Chem.* **107**, 1 (1919).
160. Taylor, A., and Weiss, J., *Nature* **141**, 1055 (1938).
160a. Teltow, J., *Ann. Physik* (6) **5**, 63 (1949).
160b. Teltow, J., *Ann. Physik* (6) **5**, 71 (1949).
160c. Teltow, J., *Z. physik. Chem.* **195**, 197 (1950).
160d. Teltow, J., *Z. physik. Chem.* **195**, 213 (1950).

161. Temperley, H. N. V., *Proc. Cambridge Phil. Soc.* **40**, 239 (1944).
162. Tubandt, C., and Lorenz, E., *Z. physik. Chem.* **87**, 513 (1914).
163. Verwey, E. J. W., *Z. Krist.* **91**, 65, 317 (1935).
164. Verwey, E. J. W., *J. Chem. Phys.* **3**, 592 (1935).
165. Verwey, E. J. W., *Physica* **2**, 1059 (1935).
166. van der Waerden, B. L., *Z. Physik* **118**, 473 (1941).
167. Wagner, C., *Naturwissenschaften* **31**, 265 (1943).
168. Wagner, C., and Beyer, J., *Z. physik. Chem.* **B 32**, 113 (1936).
169. Wagner, C., and Zimens, K. E., *Acta. Chem. Scand.* **1**, 539 (1947).
170. Wang, J. S., *Proc. Roy. Soc. (London)* **A 168**, 56, 68 (1938).
170a. Wang, J. S., *Phys. Rev.* **67**, 98 (1945).
171. Wannier, G. H., *Proc. Roy. Soc. (London)* **A 181**, 409 (1944).
172. Wannier, G. H., *Rev. Mod. Phys.* **17**, 50 (1945).
172a. Warren, B. E., *Phys. Rev.* **59**, 693 (1941) (Two dimensional disorder).
173. Webb, T. H., *J. Am. Chem. Soc.* **48**, 2589 (1926).
173a. Weil, L., *Report Conf. Strength of Solids*, July 1948.
174. Wilchinsky, Z. W., *Phys. Rev.* **63**, 223 (1943).
175. Wilchinsky, Z. W., *J. applied Phys.* **15**, 806 (1944).
176. Williams, E. J., *Proc. Roy. Soc. (London)* **A 152**, 231 (1935).
177. Wilson, T. C., *Phys. Rev.* (2) **56**, 598 (1939).
178. Wilson, A. J. C., *Proc. Roy. Soc. (London)* **A 180**, 277 (1942)
179. Wilson, A. J. C., *Proc. Roy. Soc. (London)* **A 181**, 360 (1943).
180. Yang, C. N., *J. Chem. Phys.* **13**, 66 (1945).
180a. Yiu-Yuan Li, *J. Chem. Phys.* **17**, 447 (1949).
180b. Yvon, *J. Cahiers phys.* **28**, 1 (1945).
180c. Zener, Cl., *Acta Crystallogr.* **3**, 346 (1950). (Disorder in metals).
181. Zernike, F., *Physica* **7**, 565 (1940).
182. Zintl, E., and Croatto, U., *Z. anorg. u. allgem. Chem.* **242**, 79 (1939).
183. Zintl, E., and Udgard, A., *Z. anorg. u. allgem. Chem.* **240**, 150 (1939).
184. Zachariasen, W. H., *Phys. Rev.* **71**, 715 (1947) (Two dimensional disorder).

CHAPTER III

THEORY OF DIFFUSION IN SOLIDS

I. Elementary Estimate of Rate of Diffusion

The most elementary picture of the diffusion process in gases leads to a formula

$$D \approx \frac{\lambda v}{3} \qquad [3.1]$$

where λ is the mean free path of the gas molecules, v the mean molecular velocity. Obviously this formula is not immediately applicable to diffusion processes in condensed phases, because for an average particle the concept of a free path is meaningless, only oscillations about permanent or temporary equilibrium positions being possible. But there may be a small fraction of favored particles in a crystal which are free to move and to which equation [3.1] might be applied. In case of a simple lattice,* containing vacancies, Fig. 2-13, cf. Chap. II, p. 91, particles in the vicinity of an unoccupied site may be free to move if they have sufficient energy in the appropriate degree of freedom to surmount an energy barrier U (per mol) separating their original equilibrium position from the site of the vacancy, Fig. 3-1. If n_v is the number of vacancies present per cubic centimeter, and if z is the number of nearest neighbors of a vacancy, then the number of particles per cubic centimeter free to move will be

$$n_f = n_v z \exp\left(-U/RT\right). \qquad [3.2]$$

For the number n_v of vacancies per cubic centimeter we have from [2.18]

$$n_v \approx n \exp\left(-E/RT\right) \qquad [3.3]$$

where E is the energy necessary for the formation of 1 mol of vacancies and n is the number of particles per cubic centimeter. Thus finally the number of particles in correct positions to move and with sufficient energy is

$$n_f = nz \exp\left(-[E + U]/RT\right). \qquad [3.4]$$

* In the case of a binary crystal of the type $A\,B$, E in the following equations, is to be replaced by $E/2$, cf. p. 155, Chap. II, 97.

In the case of a simple cubic lattice, z is equal to 6, but the probability that a particle next to a hole and with energy U has a velocity component toward the hole will be approximately $1/z$, so we may drop the factor z from equations [3.2] and [3.4]. By inserting the probability n_f/n, for a particle to be free to move, into equation [3.1] we obtain as an approximate expression for the coefficient of diffusion in a solid containing holes in equilibrium

$$D \approx \frac{dv}{3} \exp\left(-[E + U]/RT\right) = \frac{dv}{3} \exp\left(-Q/RT\right) \qquad [3.5]$$

where we have replaced λ by d, the distance between nearest neighbors in the lattice. Taking for v, the mean thermal velocity of the particles, a value of the order of magnitude of 10^4 cm. sec.$^{-1}$ we may calculate the order of magnitude of the diffusion coefficient. With $d = 3 \times 10^{-8}$ cm. and $v = 3 \times 10^4$ cm./sec. we obtain

$$D \approx 3 \times 10^{-4} \exp\left(-Q/RT\right) \text{ cm.}^2 \text{ sec.}^{-1} \qquad [3.6]$$

an expression which often gives values of the right order of magnitude. (For experimental values of D and for empirical constants in analogy to those of formula [3.6] see Chap. IV, p. 199ff). It might be emphasized that the argument leading to [3.6] is essentially correct, but that it is susceptible to considerable refinement. The numerical factor, dimensionally of a diffusion coefficient (cm.^{2} sec.$^{-1}$), multiplying the exponential in [3.6], therefore, cannot give more than the right order of magnitude, and a consideration of the temperature dependence of the energy terms entering into the exponentials may even change the order of magnitude of that factor, increasing it by up to 3—4 orders of magnitude, in accordance with a number of observations (Jost (61, 62,63), Jost and Nehlep (67), Mott and Gurney (15) Eyring *et al.* (7))*. [3.6], however, gives the right form for representation of observed diffusion coefficients, and often also the right order of magnitude. An equation of this type, for diffusion in solids, was first derived by Braune (30); later calculations, leading to similar expressions, have been published by a number of authors (van Liempt (74, 75, 76), Dushman and Langmuir (38, 39), Frenkel (6, 45), Braunbek (29), Cichocki (32), Barrer (1)). A derivation, similar to that given above, is due to Frenkel (45).

Instead of introducing the mean thermal velocity v into equation [3.6], one may use equally well the vibration frequency ν of a particle in the lattice. Assuming that the time necessary for a particle to move from one equilibrium position to the next one is of the order of magni-

---

* For a more refined treatment the free energy of disorder and of activation must be inserted instead of the energy as was, in fact, in the case of the Schottky-Frenkel theory, Chap. II, cf. also Rushbrooke (91).

tude of the time for one vibration (or half of it), we may replace v/d by the frequency ν, which is of the order of magnitude of 10^{12} per second. Hence equation [3.6] is almost identical with the following

$$D \approx \frac{d^2 \nu}{3} \exp\left(-Q / RT\right)*.$$ [3.7]

For another model, chosen for the evaluation of the diffusion coefficient, we should have obtained essentially the same formulae as above. If we had considered the migration of interstitial particles, Fig.2-16, instead of that of vacancies (by a migration of vacancies we always mean migration of particles surrounding the hole, which results in a migration of the vacancy) we should have arrived at the same formulae. Here we have only one particle which can move, in contrast to the above example. This particle, however, can move in the directions toward all the neighboring equilibrium positions in the interlattice space. Consequently, the number of particles, able to move, decreases by the same factor by which the number of possible movements of this particle increases. The net result, therefore, remains unchanged. In equations [3.3] etc., only the number of vacancies is to be replaced by that of interstitial particles, and consequently the two energy terms, entering into the exponential, now refer to the energy to be supplied for the production of 1 mol of interstitial particles, and to the energy barrier to be surmounted by a migrating interstitial particle on its way from one interstitial site to a neighboring one, respectively.

There arises another question which, however, does not lead to any difficulties. By a diffusion process, involving the migration of vacant points, we actually have a migration of normal lattice particles, giving at once the concentration changes characteristic for any diffusion process. If, on the other hand, interstitial particles are moving, which in their original and final positions do not belong to the normal lattice structure, the result of this process alone can still not be an equalization of concentrations in the lattice. Therefore an additional process is required to bring about this equalization of concentration. Obviously, this process is an interchange between particles on normal lattice sites and those on interstitial sites which does not enter our results explicitly.

---

* In the above formulae we might as well drop the factor 1/3. For instance in the case of a simple cubic lattice one would have for the probability of a particle with sufficient energy in the direction from its original position to that of an hole $\sim \exp\left(-E/RT\right)$ which is the fraction of particles having energy $\geqq E$ in one degree of freedom. In more complicated lattices where the directions of a possible movement are more than three and, consequently, cannot coincide, with the three rectangular coordinates, one needs a more refined treatment for the determination of this factor.

The condition to be fulfilled, if this process is not to be rate-determining, consists of the requirement that an interchange between normal lattice particles and particles on interstitial sites shall be a rapid process compared with the diffusion of particles on interlattice positions. An estimate, making use of reasonable numerical values, shows that normally this assumption will be true. There will be an additional energy barrier hindering the transition from normal lattice points into interstitial sites, cf. Chap. II. p. 96. Let us assume that this energy barrier is of the same order of magnitude as that to be surmounted either by interstitial particles moving into equivalent positions or by particles in the vicinity of holes moving into the hole as the nearest empty equivalent position. In special cases it has been possible to determine these energies experimentally (Koch and Wagner (73), cf. p. 153, 191 ff), e. g., for migration of silver ions in silver chloride and silver bromide. These energies are of the order of magnitude of 10 kcal. per mol. At the comparatively low temperature of 600° K an exponential term containing this energy of activation is of the order of $10^{-3.5}$. Now, if normal diffusion is proceeding over distances of the order of magnitude of 10^{-5} cm., which is a rather low value, homogenization over this distance, being inversely proportional to the square of the distance, will occur within a time about 10^{5} times longer than that required for homogenization over a distance of the order of some 10^{-8} cm., that between an interstitial particle and the nearest lattice site. Therefore even an additional exponential term of the order $10^{-3.5}$ would leave local homogenization a quick process compared with diffusion over observable distances. Consequently, our results, in general, are unaffected by the occurrence of this additional process, generally not mentioned explicitly.

Observable effects, however, might be found in homogenization over very short distance, e. g., 10^{-6} cm. or less. Here a drop in rate of diffusion might be observed if an interstitial mechanism is responsible, while for vacancy diffusion no such drop should occur, and also a discrepancy between observed rates of diffusion and of values calculated from electrolytic conductivity and transference numbers (in case of ionic crystals). Diffusion in very thin layers of metals has been investigated by the author (60), without any anomalies being discovered. This would suggest vacancy diffusion as being predominant in metals, in accordance with other estimates (Seitz (54, 55), Huntington (52, 53)).

If both vacancies and interstitial particles are present, the diffusion coefficient will be given by the sum of two expressions of the form [3.6], with individual values of the constants entering the equation.

As to the process of exchange between lattice particles and interstitial particles, we might add one more remark. Of course there is no difficulty for a lattice particle to enter into an interstitial site, these normally being unoccupied. The transition in the opposite direction, however, is possible only if a vacancy is present in the normal lattice. Since in almost all cases investigated so far interstitial disorder occurs in connection with vacancies, there arise no difficulties for this process.

Diffusion is also conceivable by a direct exchange of neighboring particles. Where estimates of energies involved have been possible such a process seems rather improbable, and no example is known, so far, where this mechanism has been proved to occur. In diffusion in ionic crystals it is possible, on the contrary, to prove that diffusion cannot be due to direct interchange of neighboring particles, cf. below, p. 143.

The most simple relations are to be expected for self diffusion, i.e., in the limiting case in which the difference between the two interdiffusing substances vanishes. It is practically possible to observe self diffusion by the use of radioactive isotopes. If the relative difference in masses is sufficiently low, as in most cases of practical importance, the difference between self diffusion and the diffusion of isotopes becomes negligible.

II. Diffusion of Charged Particles

1. The Nernst-Einstein Relation. Diffusion and Electrolytic Conduction

If the mobility of the diffusing particles is known independently, it is possible to calculate the diffusion coefficient from the mobility by means of the Nernst-Einstein relation (40, 85)

$$D = u R T / N = u k T \qquad [3.8]$$

where D is the coefficient of diffusion, u the mobility of the particles, i.e., velocity attained under the action of unit force*, k the Boltzmann constant and N Avogadro's number. This relation had been derived for solutions, but it holds for solids as well (Wagner (107)). We shall give here a proof due to Mott and Gurney (15). Suppose we have particles of charge e in an electric field $F = - \partial \varphi / \partial x$, then the density of particles at x is by Boltzmann's equation

$$n(x) = \text{const} \exp \left(- e \varphi / k T \right) . \qquad [3.9]$$

From the condition, that in a stationary state no current is flowing, we obtain

$$u n e^2 F - e D \frac{d n}{d x} = 0 \qquad [3.10]$$

* The velocity in unit electrical field being e. u.

where u is the mobility of the particles*. Integration of [3.10] gives

$$n = \text{const} \exp\left(-eu\varphi/D\right) \qquad [3.11]$$

and comparison of [3.9] with [3.11] shows that the following relation must hold

$$\frac{u}{D} = \frac{1}{kT} \qquad [3.12]$$

which is identical with [3.8]**.

On account of this relation it is possible to calculate self diffusion in ionic crystals from electrolytic conductivity and transference numbers. The electrolytic conductivity, σ, is given in terms of the mobility of the ions and the ionic charge $z_i e$ by

$$\sigma = \Sigma \sigma_i = \Sigma n_i z_i^2 e^2 u_i . \qquad [3.13]$$

[3.13] therefore permits a calculation of the mobility u_i, and therefore of the coefficient of self diffusion if the transference numbers t_i are known $(t_i = \sigma_i/\sigma)$.

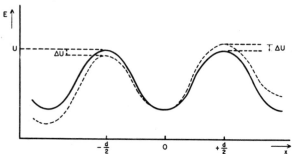

Fig. 3-1. Potential energy of migrating ion without and with electric field F (dashed curve); d distance between equivalent sites.

In the above model we can derive these relations without the explicit use of the Nernst-Einstein relation. If we consider the one-dimensional case, Fig. 3-1, we have a particle moving in the x-direction in a periodic field of force, the height of the potential barriers being given by the energy U per mol, introduced on p. 96, 135. If d is the distance between equivalent equilibrium positions and v is the mean thermal velocity of the particles, we have for the current of

---

* Here the first term gives the current caused by the field F, and the second term the current due to the concentration gradient dn/dx.

** The mobility $U = eu$ for unit electric field is valid only if the field is measured in absolute electrostatic units. If practical units, volts, are used this value must be multiplied by 300.

matter, flowing in the direction of positive x

$$J_+ = n' \exp\left(- U/RT\right) v \qquad [3.14]$$

where n' is the concentration of diffusing particles (taken as number of particles per cubic centimeter). For the current of particles in the opposite direction, one obtains accordingly

$$J_- = \left(n' + d\frac{\partial n'}{\partial x}\right) \exp\left(- U/RT\right) v \qquad [3.15]$$

and the resulting current in the direction of positive x is obtained as difference

$$J = - dv \exp\left(- U/RT\right)\frac{\partial n'}{\partial x}. \qquad [3.16]$$

Comparison with the general diffusion equation for the one dimensional case (cf. Chap. I, p. 2) gives

$$D = dv \exp\left(- U/RT\right). \qquad [3.17]$$

This is the expression for the diffusion coefficient of interstitial particles or of vacancies, i.e., of the particles surrounding a vacancy. By multiplying [3.17] by the fraction of vacancies or interstitial particles one finally obtains for the diffusion coefficient

$$D \approx dv \exp\left(-[E + U]/RT\right) \qquad [3.18]$$

in accordance with our former results. Again for binary ionic compounds E is to be replaced by $E/2$.

Now we can treat the same process in an electric field of force, $F = - d\varphi/dx$, and without concentration gradient. Due to the presence of the field, the original potential distribution is now distorted, Fig. 3-1, on account of an additional term in the potential energy $- ze\varphi$, if ze is the charge of the mobile particles. The expressions for the flow of matter in the direction of the field and opposite to it now are

$$J_+ = n' v \exp\left(-\left[U - Nze\frac{d\varphi}{dx}\frac{d}{2}\right]/RT\right) \qquad [3.19]$$

and

$$J_- = n' v \exp\left(-\left[U + Nze\frac{d\varphi}{dx}\frac{d}{2}\right]/RT\right) \qquad [3.20]$$

because the energy barriers to be surmounted by a particle moving from position 1 to 2 and from 2 to 1 in the opposite direction, now are

$$\frac{U}{N} - ze\frac{d\varphi}{dx}\frac{d}{2} \qquad [3.21]$$

and

$$\frac{U}{N} + ze\frac{d\varphi}{dx}\frac{d}{2} \qquad \text{per particle} \qquad [3.22]$$

respectively. Therefore one obtains for the resulting flow of matter

$$J = n' v \exp\left(-U / RT\right) \left\{ \exp\left(ze \frac{d\varphi}{dx} \frac{d}{2} / kT\right) - \exp\left(-ze \frac{d\varphi}{dx} \frac{d}{2} \Big/ kT\right) \right\} \quad [3.23]$$

which may be transformed into

$$J \approx n' v \exp\left(-U / RT\right) \left\{ 1 + \frac{zed}{2} \frac{d\varphi / dx}{kT} - 1 + \frac{zed\varphi / dx}{2kT} \right\}$$

$$\approx n' v \exp\left(-U / RT\right) \frac{zed}{kT} \cdot \frac{d\varphi}{dx} \quad [3.24]$$

if $\left(\frac{zed}{2}\right)\left(\frac{d\varphi}{dx}\right)$ is small compared with kT. This, actually, is the case under normal conditions, d being of the order of magnitude of 10^{-8} cm, $\left(\frac{zed}{2}\right)\left(\frac{d\varphi}{dx}\right)$, therefore, even for field strengths of 10^5 volt/cm. is only about 10^{-3} electron volt, while RT is of the order of magnitude of several hundredths of an electron volt. For very high field strengths, however, Ohm's law will no longer be valid, and an exponential increase of the current with increasing voltage is to be expected.

Multiplying [3.24] by the charge ze, we obtain the electric current

$$Jez = \frac{n' dv}{kT} z^2 e^2 \frac{d\varphi}{dx} \exp\left(-U/RT\right) \quad [3.25]$$

which is to be compared with Ohm's law

$$J_{el} = \sigma \cdot \frac{d\varphi}{dx} .$$

Consequently, we have for the electrolytic conductivity

$$\sigma = \frac{n' dv}{kT} z^2 e^2 \exp\left(-U/RT\right) \quad [3.26]$$

and for the mobility of the ions

$$u = dv/kT \exp\left(-U/RT\right). \quad [3.27]$$

Comparison with [3.18] shows that the Nernst-Einstein relation is fulfilled for our problem.

Consequently it is possible to calculate the rate of diffusion of ions in a solid from electrolytic conductivity and vice versa, at least for self diffusion. But we shall see below that for interdiffusion of different types of ions (for instance copper ions and silver ions, during the formation of a mixed crystal from AgCl und CuCl) a calculation is also possible, the calculation being quite analogous to Nernst's calculation for solutions of electrolytes.

The mobility u_i of one type of particle permits on the one hand the calculation of the coefficient of self diffusion of this type of particle, on the other hand that of the partial electrolytic conductivity, due to these particles

$$D_i = u_i k T \qquad\qquad [3.28]$$

and

$$\sigma_i = n_i z_i^2 e^2 u_i \qquad\qquad [3.29]$$

where $z_i e$ is the charge of a particle.

If σ is the total conductivity of the ionic crystal, t_i the transport number of the particles under consideration, the relation holds

$$\sigma_i = t_i \sigma . \qquad\qquad [3.30]$$

If several types of ions are mobile the total conductivity is given by a sum of expressions analogous to [3.26]. Also, if one type of ion can move by more than one mechanism, for instance by both the vacancy and the interstitial mechanism, then more than one term like [3.26] appear in the resulting formula, cf. the example p. 181. Since σ_i is proportional to u_i, the electrolytic conductivity will be given by the same exponential, or sum of exponentials, as the diffusion coefficient (for a refined treatment see below).

When we insert approximate numerical values into [3.29] after u_i has been substituted from [3.18], we obtain the relation between σ_i and D_i, correct as to the order of magnitude

$$\sigma \approx 3 \times 10^4 \, D . \qquad\qquad [3.31]$$

where σ is measured in Ohm^{-1}cm.$^{-1}$ and D is measured in cm.^{2} sec^{-1}.

2. Diffusion and Migration Mechanism

Where measurements of both electrolytic conduction (and transference numbers) and diffusion have been possible, there is sufficient agreement between the mobilities derived from either set of observations (for numerical values and a detailed discussion cf. Chap. IV p. 198ff). This fact permits certain conclusions to be made as to the nature of the conduction and diffusion mechanism in the ionic crystals under consideration. If interdiffusion in ionic compounds were due to a direct interchange of neighboring ions of equal charge (silver and copper ions in our example), this being the only mechanism of migration, then no electrolytic conduction in ionic solid crystals would be observable, for, a mutual interchange of two ions, each carrying the same electrical charge, can never result in a transport of electricity (Wagner (107)). Now, electrolytic conduction in solid crystals is not only known in many instances, but, as far as measurements are available, also leads to the same values of ionic mobilities as diffusion measurements, cf. Maurer and Mapother (78). This is definite proof that the mechanism of migration is the same in either case. Therefore, a mechanism, based upon a direct exchange of corresponding particles is ruled out for ionic crystals by direct experimental evidence. Consequently, it may be concluded with absolute certainty without further experiments that ionic conduction and the corresponding diffusion process in crystals are due to lattice defects. Disorder, vacancies or interstitial particles must be responsible for these transport phenomena.

However, it is not possible to conclude by an analogous argument that diffusion in metals, too, is always due to the presence of disorder, though such an assumption seems highly probable. In the case of interstitial mixed crystals, of course, it may be assumed that diffusion occurs on interstitial sites; (this probably is the case with mixed crystals of gold and lead, and with similar mixed crystals). There is a transport of matter caused by an electric current in metallic alloys (Jost (65, 84), Seith (92, 93), Schwarz (19), cf. Chap. VIII p. 324). This transport is of the order of magnitude which one can calculate from mobilities, derived from diffusion measurements, under the assumption of a not unreasonable electric charge for the metal atoms. If in substitutional mixed crystals of metals the number of lattice sites were conserved during diffusion, such a transport would rule out any mechanism of direct interchange of metal ions only in cases where the effective charges of both ions were equal. Since this need not be the case in metals, definite conclusions cannot be drawn from these observations. Experiments carried out by Smigelskas and Kirkendall (98) definitely show that a conservation of the number of lattice points is not necessary during metallic diffusion, cf. p. 159, 255. In spite of the impossibility of drawing conclusions regarding the diffusion mechanism in metals on analogous lines to those successful in the case of ionic crystals, the mechanism of diffusion in metals is probably the same as that in ionic crystals (cf. below, p. 165).

Till now we have simplified our considerations in that we have treated self diffusion, and its relation to electrolytic conductivity, of a pure substance. In cases of interdiffusion of two different substances, either two metals or non-polar solids, or two ionic crystals, for instance AgBr and CuBr, we may again have more than one elementary process, such as migration of vacancies and of interstitial particles. In addition, the elementary processes need not be immediately coupled, but only indirectly by the condition of electric neutrality, in the case of metals perhaps sometimes by an equivalent condition of approximate conservation of the number of lattice sites (see, however, Chap. V, p. 255). The latter condition would mean, for instance, that during diffusion of two pieces of gold and silver, brought into close contact, we should approach a final state where we have a homogeneous alloy, the two parts corresponding to the previously pure metals still consisting of the same number of lattice sites as before (which can be checked by bringing some small foreign bodies between the faces of the two diffusing substances, cf. p. 159).

This condition certainly cannot be fulfilled in all cases. If, for instance, gold is diffusing into lead, it is very probable that interstitial mixed crystals are being formed, the gold atoms or ions + electrons entering into the interstices of the lead lattice. Therefore, if we bring a piece of gold into contact with a sufficiently large piece of lead, all the gold may disappear, the number of lattice sites of lead being conserved, but new interstitial sites being occupied by the gold. Consequently, in the case of substitutional mixed crystals it may be possible that the number of lattice sites is conserved, but certainly not in the case of interstitial mixed crystals. Then in the former case, similar to ionic crystals, the same number of particles of one kind would diffuse in one direction as particles of the other kind diffuse in the opposite direction. In ionic crystals, such as AgBr-CuBr, this is necessary, because the anions are practically immobile and otherwise an uncompensated transport of electric charge would result.

These considerations permit further conclusions to be drawn regarding the mechanism of diffusion in ionic crystals.

3. Diffusion in Binary Mixtures

Interdiffusion in solid ionic crystals is governed by analogous formal laws to diffusion in electrolytic solutions. Suppose we have the normal case, diffusion of two different cations* in crystals with common anion, e.g., AgCl-NaCl, AgI-CuI, Ag_2S-Cu_2S etc. Here the two mobile cations play an analogous role to migrating anions and cations in a liquid electrolyte. The mobilities of both types of ions, generally, will not be identical. Hence a diffusion potential arises, coupling the motion of both species of particles. Whereas in diffusion of dissolved electrolytes anions and cations move in the same directions, thus maintaining electric neutrality, here the two types of cations must move in opposite direction in order to preserve electric neutrality. But as in the case of electrolyte solutions, the influence of the diffusion potential consists of an equalization of the speeds of the two types of ions. The equations for the flow of cations 1 and 2 of concentration n_1 and n_2 in the presence of both a concentration

---

* Due to the smaller size of the cations, disorder and mobility of cations is often favored in solid crystals. Accordingly many examples are known where the cations only are mobile. There are, however, cases where both types of ions are mobile or where even the mobility of the anions predominates.

gradient and a potential gradient $\partial \varphi / \partial x$, are

$$J_1 = -u_1 \left[kT \, \partial n_1 / \partial x - ezn_1 \partial \varphi / \partial x \right] \qquad [3.32]$$

$$J_2 = +u_2 \left[kT \, \partial n_1 / \partial x + ezn_2 \partial \varphi / \partial x \right]. \qquad [3.33]$$

In the equations, the diffusion coefficient D has been replaced by the mobilities, according to [3.28] $+ez$ is the charge of the cations, the same for both interdiffusing ions, and since $n_1 + n_2 = $ const. the concentration gradient of the second cation is equal to the negative value of that of the first one.

In [3.32], the second terms on the right give the current caused by the diffusion potential φ. The corresponding terms are of equal sign in [3.32] and [3.33]. Electric neutrality requires that $J_1 = -J_2$, i.e., that equal numbers of positive ions 1 move in one direction as ions 2 move in the opposite direction. Hence

$$0 = \frac{\partial n_1}{\partial x} [u_2 - u_1] \, kT + \frac{\partial \varphi}{\partial x} [u_1 n_1 + u_2 n_2] \, ez \qquad [3.34]$$

or

$$\frac{\partial \varphi}{\partial x} = \frac{\partial n_1}{\partial x} \frac{kT}{ze} \frac{u_1 - u_2}{n_1 u_1 + n_2 u_2} \qquad [3.35]$$

and

$$J_1 = -J_2 = -\frac{\partial n_1}{\partial x} \frac{kT \, u_1 u_2 \, (n_1 + n_2)}{u_1 n_1 + u_2 n_2}. \qquad [3.36]$$

This is identical with Nernst's formula for diffusion of electrolytes in solution. Thus the coefficient of interdiffusion, D_{12}, is given by

$$D_{12} = kT \frac{u_1 u_2}{n_1 u_1 + n_2 u_2} (n_1 + n_2) = kT \frac{u_1 u_2}{N_1 u_1 + N_2 u_2}, \qquad [3.37]$$

$$N_i = \frac{n_i}{n_1 + n_2} \qquad i = 1, 2$$

differing from the coefficient of self diffusion derived above only in the value of the mobility. An average mobility, as defined by

$$u_{12} = \frac{u_1 u_2}{N_1 u_1 + N_2 u_2} \qquad [3.38]$$

must be used. Of course in the limiting case, where the ions 1 and 2 become identical, the above formula must transform into our former expression for the coefficient of self diffusion. It is seen that by putting $u_1 = u_2$, $n_1 = n_2$ we obtain from [3.37] and [3.38]

$$u_{12} = u_1 = u_2 = u \qquad [3.37a]$$

and

$$D_{12} = ukT \qquad [3.38a]$$

in accordance with our former results. The above formulae for solid electrolytes were first derived by Wagner (107). We refer to the original paper for further details.

It often has been asked whether it is possible to derive the coefficient of self diffusion of one type of particles, say, cations 1 in a pure crystal, by measuring the rate of interdiffusion of particles 1 and 2 at various concentrations and extrapolating to zero concentration of particles 2. It is seen that in general the coefficient of self diffusion of particles 1 cannot be obtained by such a procedure, though there are methods of obtaining coefficients of self diffusion (cf. below). If in [3.37] we pass to the limit $n_2 \to 0$, we obtain

$$(D_{12})_0 = k\,T(u_2)_0 \qquad [3.39]$$

which is identical with the coefficient of self diffusion of the additional component 2 at infinite dilution, but not at all with the coefficient of self diffusion of the main component 1.

It is possible, however, to obtain the self diffusion constant of component 1 in the pure salt with cation 1, if we can find an independent way of calculating the ratio

$$\frac{N_1 u_1 + N_2 u_2}{u_2}. \qquad [3.40]$$

For, multiplication of [3.37] by this ratio leads to the required expression for the coefficient of self diffusion

$$D = k\,T u_1. \qquad [3.41]$$

Now, the transference number for cations 2 in the mixed crystal is

$$t_2 = \frac{N_2 u_2}{N_1 u_1 + N_2 u_2}. \qquad [3.42]$$

Consequently, by substituting this expression into [3.37], we obtain

$$D_1 = k\,T u_1 = D_{12}\frac{N_2}{t_2} \qquad [3.43]$$

which is the formula for the coefficient of self diffusion of particles 1 in a mixed crystal of concentration n_1. Therefore the self diffusion constant of cations 1 in the pure salt is

$$D_{10} = k\,T u_1 \frac{\sigma_0 N_1}{\sigma\ t_1} = D_{12} N_1 N_2 \frac{\sigma_0}{\sigma}\frac{1}{t_1 t_2}. \qquad [3.44]$$

Here σ is the conductivity at concentration N_2, σ_0 the conductivity at concentration $N_2 = 0$, t_1 and t_2 are the transference numbers of ions 1 and 2 at the concentrations N_1, N_2. [3.43] differs from [3.44] by a factor reducing the mobility u_1 of particles 1 at concentration N_1 to that corresponding to $N_1 = 1$, $N_2 = 0$.

Where measurements of electrolytic conductivity and of transference numbers are available, it is, therefore, possible, to calculate the coefficient of self diffusion from that of interdiffusion of two types of ions, Wagner (107). The first calculations of this type were carried out by Jost (59), and by Tubandt, Reinhold, and Jost (105). We shall see below that coefficients of self diffusion, calculated on this basis from diffusion measurements, are in sufficient agreement with coefficients of self diffusion, derived from conductivity measurements alone by means of the Nernst-Einstein formula.

It might be emphasized that the above relations are valid with the same restrictions as Nernst's formula for diffusion in dissolved electrolytes, i.e., as limiting law for infinite dilution of mobile ions.

The above result might seem of comparatively little value, because measurements of interdiffusion, of electrolytic conductivity and of transference numbers are necessary for a calculation of the self-diffusion coefficient, while from a fraction of these data the same coefficient may be calculated, by means of the Nernst-Einstein relation. For practical purposes, however, the above calculations may be of great value. It is a necessary premise for the applicability of equation [3.44] that the mechanism underlying diffusion is the same as that responsible for electrolytic conduction. Hence discrepancies encountered between coefficients of self diffusion, derived directly from measurements of conductivity, and those derived from measurements of diffusion constants in mixed crystals, might point to the presence of different types of mobility of particles not contributing to ionic conduction (cf. the mobility of ion pairs in alkali halides, Dienes (36), p. 164). Thus in the case of α-Ag_2S coefficients of self diffusion, calculated from measurements of interdiffusion of Ag_2S and Cu_2S, differed by a factor of almost 1000 from those derived directly from conductivity measurements and transference numbers (cf. p. 346). These results aided the discovery of the explanation for the mechanism of conduction in silver sulfide (cf. Chap. IV, p. 183). Here the reason for the discrepancies had consisted in anomalies encountered in the determination of transference numbers, which had given 100 per cent electrolytic conductivity while, actually, more than 99 per cent of the electric current in α-Ag_2S is transported by electrons.

In the case of Schottky type of disorder, viz., vacancies of either sign in equal numbers, the mobilities of the two cations in a mixed crystal should not be very different, for the vacancies of one sign present should be available for either cation in the vicinity of a hole. Differences in the mobility, therefore, can only be due to differences in the energy barrier to be surmounted by a neighboring ion, when jumping into a hole. Since these energies are not very large (cf. the values determined by Wagner and Koch (73) for AgBr and AgCl), their differences for different ions must still be smaller.

In the case of Frenkel type of disorder, however, where equal numbers of interstitial cations and holes in the cation lattice are present, the numbers of interstitial ions of either component may be quite different, while, of course, the vacancies present are again equally available for either cation. Hence mobilities due to the interstitial mechanism might turn out to differ by several orders of magnitude for the two types of cations. Since the mobilities u_1 and u_2 are given by individual exponentials, the accurate temperature dependence of D_{12}, as given by [3.37], may be quite complicated, though over a moderate range of temperature it might be approximated by a single exponential term.

Simple expressions are to be expected if one mobility is very large compared to the other. If, for instance, $u_1 \ll u_2$, it follows from [3.37] that unless $N_1 \ll N_2$

$$D_{12} \approx k T u_2 \frac{n_1 + n_2}{n_1} = k T \frac{u_2}{N_1} \qquad [3.45]$$

and

$$D_{12} \approx k T \frac{u_1}{N_2} \quad \text{for } u_2 \gg u_1 . \qquad [3.46]$$

[3.45] and [3.46] show that for very different mobilities of the ions the rate of diffusion is determined by that of the less mobile particles, and consequently, a single exponential term will suffice to represent the observations, unless even in this case the Frenkel mechanism gives rise to two different terms.

III. Refined Theory of Diffusion. Temperature Dependence of Energy of Activation and Effect of Pressure on Conductivity

As mentioned before, the constant factor A, multiplying the exponential in the formula for the diffusion coefficient [3.5], $D = A \exp (-Q/RT)$ is given by the most simple theory as being of the order of magnitude of

$$A \approx 10^{-3} \, \text{cm.}^2 \, \text{sec.}^{-1} .$$

Though in a number of cases observed values are of this order of magnitude, nevertheless considerable deviations are encountered. A formal explanation of observed values which may be higher than the above value by several orders of magnitude may be obtained by introducing the temperature dependence of the energy of activation (Jost (62), Jost and Nehlep (67))*. If in the equation for D, we put

$$Q = E_0 (1 - \beta T)$$

* Which means, essentially, reverting to the equations of the Wagner and Schottky theory (Chap. II) where free energies were replaced by energies of activation, and temperature dependence was ignored, in order to achieve simplification.

we obtain for D

$$D = A \ \exp \ (-E_0[1-\beta T]/RT) \approx A \ \exp \left(\frac{\beta E_0}{R}\right) \exp \left(-\frac{E_0}{RT}\right). \quad [3.47]$$

Therefore, the original constant factor now has been multiplied by a factor $\exp (\beta E_0/R)$, which is temperature independent and may be of the order of magnitude of several powers of 10.

This explanation was first tested by Jost and Nehlep (68). A first estimate of the order of magnitude of the effect to be expected may be obtained as follows. Considerable contributions to the energies appearing in the exponential of [3.47] will be due to the Born repulsive forces in the lattice, for particles moving from one equilibrium position to a neighboring one will approach on their way the neighboring particles much more closely than in their equilibrium positions. If the contribution of repulsive energy in Q is assumed to be approximately $Q/2 = E'$, we may represent the dependence of this energy on the lattice distance by an expression

$$E' \approx E_0' \left(\frac{r_0}{r}\right)^n \qquad [3.48]$$

where the exponent n is of the order of magnitude of 10.

If

$$\alpha = \frac{1}{r_0} \frac{dr}{dT}$$

is the coefficient of thermal expansion, and if the subscript refers to the absolute zero of temperature, we obtain from [3.48] approximately

$$E' \approx E_0' + \frac{\partial E'}{\partial T} T = E_0' + \frac{\partial E'}{\partial r} \frac{\partial r}{\partial T} T \approx E_0' - n E_0' \frac{1}{r} \frac{\partial r}{\partial T} T \approx E_0'(1 - n\alpha T). \qquad [3.49]$$

With $E_0' \approx 2.5 \times 10^4$ cal./mol., $n \approx 10$ and $\alpha \approx 4 \times 10^{-5}$, we have for the additional factor, appearing in [3.47]

$$A^* = \exp \left(\frac{\beta E_0}{R}\right) \approx \exp \left(\frac{n\alpha E_0'}{R}\right) \approx \exp (5) > 10^2. \qquad [3.50]$$

Thus, it is not difficult to obtain additional factors of the order of magnitude of a few powers of ten, accounting for the existing discrepancies. This relation also accounts for the frequently observed fact that high values of E' are associated with high values of A.

Furthermore, it is possible to test the correctness of this explanation without any specialized assumptions, as introduced above, regarding the dependence of the energy term on the lattice distance. Since electrolytic conduction is a process, completely analogous to that of diffusion, and since conductivity measurements can be carried out more easily and with higher precision than diffusion measurements, we shall choose electrolytic conduction for discussion. It is not difficult to measure changes in electrolytic conductivity of the order of magnitude of 10^{-4}, while the errors involved in diffusion measurements are, generally, at least higher by two powers of 10. The same reasoning which had led to a factor of the order of magnitude of 10^{-3}, as the constant in the formula for diffusion, leads to an expression for the electrolytic conductivity (cf. equation [3.31])

$$\sigma = \sigma_0 \exp\left(-Q/RT\right) \qquad [3.51]$$

where the constant factor is of the order of magnitude of $\sim 10^2$ ohms^{-1} cm.$^{-1}$. Observed values of this factor range up to 10^6. Here, too, an additional factor, of the order of magnitude of several powers of 10, must come into play.

The influence discussed above is essentially an effect of the lattice distance on either diffusion or electrolytic conduction. This influence must be the same whether a change in lattice distance has been produced by a change of temperature or by a change of pressure. What we may try to do is this: from observed values of the additional factor, entering the empirical expression for electrolytic conduction, we obtain the dependence of the energy of activation on the lattice distance. This result is sufficient for a prediction of the effect of pressure on the electrolytic conductivity, and it is comparatively easy to test this prediction experimentally.

If the energy of activation, Q, depends on the lattice distance r, we may put quite generally for the influence of temperature on Q

$$Q = Q_0 + \int_0^T \frac{\partial Q}{\partial r} \frac{\partial r}{\partial T} \, dT \approx Q_0 + \overline{\frac{\partial Q}{\partial r} \frac{\partial r}{\partial T}} T \qquad [3.52]$$

where the subscript 0 refers to absolute zero, and the bar indicates averaging. By inserting [3.52] into the exponential of the empirical formula for the conductivity, we obtain

$$\sigma = \sigma_0 \exp\left(-Q/RT\right) = \sigma_0 \exp\left(-Q_0/RT\right) \exp\left[-\left(\overline{\frac{\partial Q}{\partial r} \frac{\partial r}{\partial T}}\right)/RT\right]. \qquad [3.53]$$

Thus we have an additional, temperature indépendent factor A^*

$$A^* = \exp\left[-\overline{\frac{\partial Q}{\partial r} \frac{\partial r}{\partial T}}/R\right]. \qquad [3.54]$$

Assuming an average value for σ_0 of about 50, as given by the approximate theory, we obtain from experiments for A^*

$$A^* = \frac{(\sigma_0)_{obs}}{(\sigma_0)_{calc}} \approx 2 \times 10^{-2} (\sigma_0)_{obs}. \qquad [3.55]$$

Hence the right-hand term of equation [3.54] may be derived from simple conductivity measurements.

Now we shall calculate the influence of pressure on the electrolytic conductivity. We find

$$\frac{1}{\sigma}\frac{\partial\sigma}{\partial p} = \frac{1}{\sigma_0 \exp(-Q/RT)}\frac{\partial}{\partial p}[\sigma_0 \exp(-Q/RT]$$
$$= -\frac{1}{RT}\frac{\partial Q}{\partial r}\frac{\partial r}{\partial p}.\qquad\qquad[3.56]$$

Neglecting differences between $\partial Q/\partial r$ and $\overline{\partial Q/\partial r}$, we obtain from [3.54]

$$\partial Q/\partial r \approx -\log A^* \cdot R/(\partial r/\partial T).\qquad[3.57]$$

Substitution of this equation into [3.56] finally gives

$$\frac{1}{\sigma}\frac{\partial\sigma}{\partial p} \approx \frac{\log A^*}{T}\frac{\partial r}{\partial p}\bigg/\frac{\partial r}{\partial T}.\qquad[3.58]$$

Introducing the compressibility χ, and the coefficient of thermal expansion, α,

$$\chi = -\frac{1}{r_0}\frac{\partial r}{\partial p} \text{ and } \alpha = \frac{1}{r_0}\frac{\partial r}{\partial T}\qquad[3.59]$$

we obtain the equation

$$\frac{1}{\sigma}\frac{\partial\sigma}{\partial p} \approx -\frac{\log A^*}{T}\frac{\chi}{\alpha}\qquad[3.60]$$

which may be compared with experiments.

The validity of equation [3.60] was tested by Jost and Nehlep (68) with AgCl and AgBr. The values, entering into the above equations are:

	AgCl	AgBr
$(\sigma_0)_{obs}$....................	$5 \cdot 10^5$	$1.5 \cdot 10^6$ ohm^{-1} cm.$^{-1}$
$A^* = (\sigma_0)_{obs}/(\sigma_0)_{calc}$	10^4	$3 \cdot 10^4$
χ......................	$8 \cdot 10^{-7}$	$9 \cdot 10^{-7}$ cm.^{2}/kg.
α......................	$3.3 \cdot 10^{-5}$	$3.5 \cdot 10^{-5}$ centigrade^{-1}

Thus we obtain from [3.60]

AgCl at 300°C: $(1/\sigma)\,\partial\sigma/\partial p \approx -3.9 \times 10^{-4}$ cm.^{2}/kg.
AgBr at 300°C: $(1/\sigma)\,\partial\sigma/\partial p \approx -4.5 \times 10^{-4}$ cm.^{2}/kg.

This means that a pressure increase of 100 atmospheres should reduce the conductivity by about 4 to 5 per cent. The observed values are

AgCl at 300°C: $[(1/\sigma)\,\partial\sigma/\partial p]_{obs} = -2.5 \times 10^{-4}$ cm.^{2}/kg.
AgBr at 300°C: $[(1/\sigma)\,\partial\sigma/\partial p]_{obs} = -3.5 \times 10^{-4}$ cm.^{2}/kg.

The agreement between theory and experiment may be regarded as fair, considering that simplifications are contained in the estimate of $A*$. More complete data are seen below.

For experimental details we refer to the original paper. It may be mentioned that the effect of a pressure increase of 100 atmospheres is of the same order of magnitude as that of a temperature decrease by 1°C. Hence a high accuracy in the measurement of the temperature is required. The temperatures could be read by means of a platinum resistance thermometer to within 2×10^{-3} °C.

Attempts to measure the influence of pressure on the rate of diffusion have been reported (cf. van Ostrand and Dewey (86), Radavich and Smoluchowski (88), Seith and Etzold (93)). Since this influence is not higher than the error encountered with normal diffusion measurements, definite effects could be observed only with pressures higher by a factor 10 than those used for conductivity measurements.

In the meantime it has been possible to make use of measurements of the influence of pressure on conductivity to obtain further information on energies of disorder and on activation energies for diffusion.

In the case of silver chloride and silver bromide we have a detailed knowledge of the prevailing type of disorder (Frenkel disorder of the silver ions)*, equal numbers of vacancies in the lattice of the silver ions and of interstitial silver ions, and of the energies involved, from measurements and theoretical considerations by Koch and Wagner (73), cf. Chap. IV, p. 191ff. The degree of disorder is given by the expressions

$$\begin{array}{ll} \text{AgCl} & \alpha \approx 10^{1.56} \exp\left(-25{,}000/2\,R\,T\right) \\ \text{AgBr} & \alpha \approx 10^{1.46} \exp\left(-20{,}200/2\,R\,T\right) \end{array} \qquad [3.61]$$

the temperature-dependence of the mobility of the silver ions by

$$\begin{array}{ll} \text{AgCl} & \sim \exp\left(-6500/R\,T\right) \\ \text{AgBr} & \sim \exp\left(-8200/R\,T\right). \end{array} \qquad [3.62]$$

The energy entering into the exponentials of [3.61] is half the energy of disorder (cf. Chap. II p. 97), while the energies entering into the exponentials of [3.62] are the heights of the energy barriers involved in the transitions of neighboring ions into vacancies, and of interstitial ions into adjacent equilibrium positions assumed to be approximately equal. In the empirical conductivity formulas the sum of the energy terms of [3.61] and [3.62] is contained.

---

* See, however, Mitchell (81). Lawson (73b) points out that the thermal expansion of AgBr, as observed by Strelkow (101a), might be more readily explained by the assumption of Schottky disorder.

As discussed elsewhere (Chap. II, p. 94), the above results were derived from the measurement of the conductivity of anomalous mixed crystals of the silver halides with the corresponding lead and cadmium halides, respectively. Substitutional mixed crystals are formed, for every lead or cadmium ion taken up an additional vacancy in the lattice of the silver ions being created. Since the degree of disorder in the pure silver halides at the temperatures of these measurements is still rather small, the concentration of the additional vacancies is much higher than that of those present in thermal equilibrium in the pure substance. Consequently the concentration of vacancies in these anomalous mixed crystals does not vary appreciably with temperature, the temperature dependence of the conductivity measured is essentially that caused by the presence of an energy barrier to be surmounted by the ions in the vicinity of vacancies which jump into these vacancies.

Consequently, if the influence of pressure on the conductivity of these anomalous mixed crystals can be measured, the pressure dependence can only be caused by the dependence of the energy barrier on the lattice distance. Such measurements have lately been carried out by Jost, Mennenöh, and Müller (66) with the result to be expected. In these experiments the pressure effect on pure AgCl and AgBr was measured again and the following results were obtained

$$\text{AgCl} \quad 2.9 \text{ to } 3.8 \times 10^{-4} \quad \text{temperature range } 256 \text{ to } 314°C$$
$$\text{AgBr} \quad 3.6 \text{ to } 3.4 \times 10^{-1} \quad \text{,,} \quad \text{,,} \quad 249 \text{ to } 285°C$$

in sufficient agreement with Nehlep's measurements, the new value for AgCl being somewhat closer to the value theoretically predicted.

In accordance with expectation, the pressure effect observed with the anomalous mixed crystals is much smaller than that observed with the pure substances. The average values, thus obtained, are given in Table I.

TABLE I
AgBr + PbBr$_2$

	0	1.2	3.6	5.0	
516°K............	3.4	3.7	2.8	2.7	$-\dfrac{1}{\sigma}\dfrac{d\sigma}{dp} \cdot 10^4$ atmospheres^{-1}
563°K............	3.4	3.9	3.6	3.2	$-\dfrac{1}{\sigma}\dfrac{d\sigma}{dp} \cdot 10^4$ atmospheres^{-1}

AgCl + PbCl$_2$

	0	0.125	0.245	0.42	
530—580°K.......	3.0	1.7	1.4	1.3	$-\dfrac{1}{\sigma}\dfrac{\partial\sigma}{\partial p} \cdot 10^4$ atmospheres^{-1}

The top header row for AgBr table reads "mol per cent PbBr$_2$" and for AgCl table reads "mol per cent PbCl$_2$".

The average of $-\dfrac{1}{\sigma}\dfrac{\partial\sigma}{\partial p}$ is 1.4×10^{-4}, for silver chloride, containing lead chloride, as compared to a value of 2.9×10^{-4} for pure AgCl. The contribution of the energy barrier to the work function appearing in the exponential is about 0.34 of the total energy, while the pressure effect due to this energy barrier is 0.48 of the total pressure effect, observed with pure AgCl. If this difference is real, it would suggest a stronger dependence of the energy barrier on the lattice distance than the dependence of the energy of disorder on the lattice distance. This would not be unreasonable.

Mott and Gurney (15) give the following formula for the diffusion coefficient

$$D = \frac{n'}{n}\,Cv\,d^2\exp\left(-E_0/RT\right) \qquad [3.63]$$

where n'/n is the fraction of disordered particles, as derived Chap. II, p. 114ff, C is of the same order of magnitude as the factor B in the former equation, and given, in accordance with the preceding argument, by (v volume, α' coefficient of volume expansion)

$$C = \exp\left(-\frac{\alpha'\,v_0}{R}\frac{dE_0}{dv}\right). \qquad [3.64]$$

And for interstitial diffusion

$$D = (\gamma\,B\,C)\,v\,d^2\,\sqrt{\frac{N'}{N}}\,\exp\left(-\left[\frac{E}{2}+E_0\right]\bigg/RT\right) \qquad [3.65]$$

where $N' =$ number of interstitial sites, $N =$ number of ordinary lattice sites. The factors γ and B have been introduced on p. 116ff, and C is given by [3.64]. With

$$\gamma\,B\,C\,\sqrt{\frac{N'}{N}} \approx 10 \text{ to } 10^4 \qquad [3.66]$$

one obtains the formula

$$D = D_0\exp\left(-Q/RT\right)$$

where D_0 is of the order of magnitude of 0.1 to 100 cm^2. sec.$^{-1}$. For the pressure effect one has

$$\log\left(Bc\right) = -\frac{\alpha\,T}{\chi}\frac{\partial\log\sigma}{\partial p}. \qquad [3.67]$$

The authors conclude from Jost and Nehlep's (67) experiments that for silver halides the factor γ is smaller than 1 (cf. the deductions Chap. II, p. 114ff). From the above formula for the pressure effect they obtain

$$\text{AgCl: } BC \sim 350 \qquad [3.68]$$

$$\text{AgBr: } BC \sim 2500. \qquad [3.69]$$

The values σ_0 in the formula for the conductivity

$$\sigma = \sigma_0 \exp\left(-[E/2 + E_0]/RT\right) \qquad [3.70]$$

indicate that for

$$\text{AgCl: } \gamma BC \sim 150$$
$$\text{AgBr: } \gamma BC \sim 900$$

which would require

$$\text{AgCl: } \gamma \sim 1/2$$
$$\text{AgBr: } \gamma \sim 1/3 .$$

IV. Diffusion in Non-Ideal Mixtures

As mentioned above (p. 143) there is a fair agreement between self diffusion coefficients calculated from electrolytic conductivity and self diffusion coefficients derived from interdiffusion in mixed crystals, by means of the corrections discussed above (p. 147), but there remain certain differences.

A possible explanation for these differences, if they prove to be real, might be found in deviations from ideal behavior of the mixed crystals under consideration.

The most general form of the diffusion equation is

$$J = -\frac{cu}{N}\frac{\partial \mu}{\partial x} \qquad [3.71]$$

for the diffusion current, and from [3.71] one obtains for the rate of change of concentration

$$\frac{\partial c}{\partial t} = \frac{\partial}{\partial x}\left(\frac{cu}{N}\frac{\partial \mu}{\partial x}\right) \qquad [3.72]$$

where

c = molar concentration
u = mobility of the diffusing particle for unit force
μ = chemical potential
N = Avogadro's number.

Introducing the activity a and the activity coefficient γ into [3.71] and [3.72] we find

$$J = -cukT\frac{1}{a}\frac{\partial a}{\partial x} = -D_0\frac{\partial \log a}{\partial \log c}\frac{\partial c}{\partial x} = -D_0\left(1 + \frac{\partial \log \gamma}{\partial \log c}\right)\frac{\partial c}{\partial x} \qquad [3.73]$$

and

$$\frac{\partial c}{\partial t} = \frac{\partial}{\partial x}\left(D_0\frac{\partial \log a}{\partial \log c}\frac{\partial c}{\partial x}\right) = \frac{\partial}{\partial x}\left[D_0\left(1 + \frac{\partial \log \gamma}{\partial \log c}\right)\frac{\partial c}{\partial x}\right] \qquad [3.74]$$

putting $D_0 = ukT$, $d \log c = d \log N$, where N = mole fraction and assuming the total molecular concentrations of the two interdiffusing species to be constant.

If the coefficient of self diffusion is to be calculated from the coefficient of interdiffusion in a mixed crystal, we must start from the value D_0 of the above equations, which is corrected for non-ideal behavior of the mixture. Generally, for mixed crystals of ionic compounds measurements of activities will not be available.

To obtain an estimate of the order of magnitude of the effects to be observed due to deviations from the ideal laws of solutions, we may insert the value of the activity coefficient, calculated for regular solutions, (Hildebrand (9)), from observed heats of mixing. Putting for the Gibbs free energy of mixing

$$\Delta G = \Delta H + RT \{N_1 \log N_1 + N_2 \log N_2\} \qquad [3.75]$$

where N_1, N_2 are the mole fractions of components 1 and 2, we obtain for the chemical potential of one component of a binary mixture

$$\mu_i = \mu_i^0 + RT \log N_i + \Delta H_i \quad i = 1,2 \quad \Delta H_i = \frac{\partial}{\partial n_i} \Delta H \quad i = 1,2 \quad [3.76]$$

where ΔH_i must be derived from experimental values of the heat of mixing; and for the activity

$$a_i = N_i \exp (\Delta H_i / RT) \quad i = 1,2 \qquad [3.77]$$

and for the activity coefficient

$$\gamma_i = \exp (\Delta H_i / RT) . \qquad [3.78]$$

If we can approximate the heat of mixing by the symmetrical function of concentrations

$$\Delta H = A N_1 N_2 \qquad [3.79]$$

we obtain for the chemical potential, the activity and the activity coefficient, respectively,

$$\mu_i = \mu_i^0 + RT \log N_i + A (1 - N_i)^2 \qquad [3.80]$$

$$a_i = N_i \exp \{A (1 - N_i)^2 / RT\} \qquad [3.81]$$

and

$$\gamma_i = \exp \{A (1 - N_i)^2 / RT\} \quad i = 1,2 . \qquad [3.82]$$

With [3.81] or [3.82] we obtain for the diffusion coefficient

$$D = D_0 \left\{1 + \frac{2A}{RT} (N_i^2 - N_i)\right\} \qquad [3.83]$$

and for the ratio D_0/D

$$D_0/D = 1 \left/ \left\{1 + \frac{2A}{RT} (N_i^2 - N_i)\right\} \right. . \qquad [3.84]$$

Numerical values of this ratio, for a number of reasonable values of A, are reproduced in Table II.

TABLE II
Calculated values of D_0/D for $T = 1000°K.$

N_i	$A = 1000$	3000	5000 cal.
0.1 0.9	1.10	1.37	1.82
0.3 0.7	1.27	2.70	$(-20)^*$
0.5	1.33	4.00	$(-40)^*$

Examples of measured values of $\Delta H_{max} = A/4$ are

Au— Pt(solid):   ~1200 cal. (~1000° C)
Hg— Sn(liquid):   ~ 240 cal. (250° C)   Wagner   (22)

KCl—KI (solid):   600 cal.   Grimm and
KBr—KI (solid):   630 cal.   Herzfeld   (47)

In the case of interdiffusion in ionic crystals one may usually consider the crystal lattice as a stable frame of reference to which the

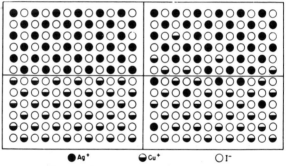

Fig. 3-2. Interdiffusion of AgI and CuI.

diffusion current is referred, Fig. 3-2. For in many cases the mobility of one type of ion (often that of the larger anion) is much smaller than that of the other ion. Therefore a migration of the less mobile ions is practically ruled out, and the conservation of electric neutrality then requires that diffusion proceeds on the average by an equivalent transport of, for instance, Ag^+-ions, in the example of Fig. 3-2, in the one direction and of Cu^+-ions in the opposite direction.

As mentioned before, the same may hold for substitutional metallic alloys, but it need not necessarily hold. If, for interdiffusion of metals, we have the concentration distribution, for $t = 0$, $c = c_0$ for $x < 0$,

---

* Negative values for the diffusion coefficients correspond to diffusion in an unstable region, leading to phase separation (cf. example quoted in Chap. V).

$c = 0$ for $x > 0$, then the distribution for $t > 0$, in case of pure diffusion, without superimposed convection, should be like that of Fig. 5-1, Chap. V. This concentration curve, in case D is depending on concentration, need not be exactly antisymmetrical with respect to $x = 0$ (the curve of the concentration gradient, $\partial c / \partial x$, consequently, need not be exactly symmetrical), Fig. 5-3, Chap. V, but the areas to the left and to the right of $x = 0$ must be equal, indicating that the diffusing substance which left the region $x < 0$, in the case of pure diffusion, has entered the region $x > 0$, and vice versa for the concentration of the second component. For the practical evaluation of diffusion experiments it is often necessary to determine the effective boundary from the above condition, after the end of an experiment. It does not always seem certain that the boundary, thus determined, coincides with the original interface of the diffusion system, as it should be the case (cf. for instance, distribution curves, as published for diffusion in metals by Grube and Jedele (48), Rhines and Mehl (89)).

Systematic experiments, regarding the behavior of the original interface during diffusion, have been carried out by Smigelskas and Kirkendall (98) (see also the discussion by Seitz (18)). They marked the original boundary between interdiffusing specimens of copper and brass by thin molybdenum wires which, at the temperatures employed, do not themselves diffuse appreciably into these metals. Using a rectangular, central bar of brass, plated with copper, Fig. 3-3, the authors were able to investigate the relative displacement of opposite faces due to diffusion. After a diffusion period of 56 days at 785°C. the distance between op-

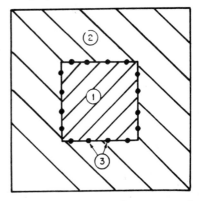

Fig. 3-3. Experimental arrangement in diffusion measurement by Smigelskas and Kirkendall: brass core 1, with copper plating 2; original interface marked by molybdenum wires 3.

posite faces had decreased by about 1 per. cent which is ten times as much as can be explained by a change in lattice constant due to diffusion. Furthermore, it could be shown that this displacement is proportional to the square root of the time, Fig. 3-4, and that more zinc had passed the original boundary in the outward direction than copper had passed in the opposite direction. Consequently, the number of lattice points cannot have been conserved during diffusion, and a direct interchange of neighboring particles, which seems improbable anyway, cannot be the prevailing mechanism of diffusion.

As Seitz (18) points out, there are two possible explanations for the observed effect.

1. Interstitial diffusion of zinc atoms from the core into the copper, shrinking of the core due to the loss of the zinc atoms and corresponding expansion of the copper, by formation of new lattice sites.

2. Migrations of vacancies from the outer surface of the copper through the copper into the brass core, resulting in a net flow of

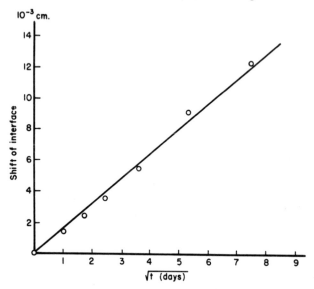

Fig. 3-4.
Displacement of opposite interfaces (Ordinate) after Smigelskas and Kirkendall.

atoms out of the core. It must be assumed that the vacancies present in the core in excess of thermal equilibrium have a tendency to coagulate and finally to disappear.

Mechanism (1) has been proposed by Smigelskas and Kirkendall (98) and by Darken (35), mechanism (2) by Seitz (18, 96).

V. Diffusion in Systems Consisting of More than One Phase

Diffusion in systems of more than one phase may become quite complicated as soon as we can no longer make use of Nernst's partition law in its simplest form (for this case solutions of the problem have been given in Chap. I, p. 68). Thus, for instance, Tubandt and Reinhold (104) examined the system

$$2AgI + Cu_2S = 2CuI + Ag_2S$$

where we have an iodide phase and a sulfide phase, miscibility being negligible. In addition the mobilities of iodine and sulfur ions are extremely small compared with those of the cations. Therefore, only an interchange of cations between both phases is observed. The equilibrium, according to the above reaction, is given by

$$2\mu_{AgI} + \mu_{Cu_2S} = \mu_{Ag_2S} + 2\mu_{CuI} \,. \qquad [3.85]$$

Since we have two mixed crystals, we may put approximately

$$\mu_{AgI} = \mu^0_{AgI} + RT \log c_{AgI}, \quad \text{etc.} \qquad [3.86]$$

provided that the mixtures are sufficiently close to ideal behavior. Substituting [3.86] into [3.85] we obtain

$$RT \log \frac{c^2_{AgI} \cdot c_{Cu_2S}}{c^2_{CuI} \cdot c_{Ag_2S}} + 2\mu^0_{AgI} + \mu^0_{Cu_2S} - 2\mu^0_{CuI} - \mu^0_{Ag_2S} = 0 \qquad [3.87]$$

or

$$\frac{c^2_{AgI} \cdot c_{Cu_2S}}{c^2_{CuI} \cdot c_{Ag_2S}} = K \qquad K = \exp\left(-\sum \nu_i \mu_i / RT\right). \qquad [3.88]$$

[3.88] is of the form of the ideal mass action law, though there enter magnitudes referring to two different phases. One may state this result in two different ways. If we consider the gas phase, we shall have an equilibrium as given by [3.88], all concentrations now being those in the single gas phase. If Henry's law holds, which is equivalent to the assumption of an ideal mixture, one arrives again at [3.88], with concentrations from two different phases. On the other hand, one may rewrite [3.88] to give

$$\frac{c^2_{AgI}}{c^2_{CuI}} \, \bigg| \, \frac{c_{Ag_2S}}{c_{Cu_2S}} = K \qquad [3.89]$$

which is the form of Nernst's partition law for solutions with different states of association of the solute.

Now we can formulate the corresponding diffusion problem, denoting by 1 and by 2 the Ag^+- and the Cu^+-ions, respectively, and by I and II the sulfide and the iodide phases, assumed to extend from $-a$ to 0 and from 0 to $+a$

$$(\partial c_1/\partial t)_I = D_I (\partial^2 c_1/\partial x^2)_I \,, \qquad [3.90]$$

and an analogous equation for phase II, with the boundary conditions

a. $D_I (\partial c_1/\partial x)_{I, x=0} = D_{II} (\partial c_1/\partial x)_{II, x=0}$, for $x = 0$

b. $(\partial c_1/\partial x)_{I, x=-a} = (\partial c_1/\partial x)_{II, x=+a} = 0$, for $x = \pm a$ [3.91]

c. $(c_1/[c_I - c_1])^2_I / (c_1/[c_{II} - c_1])_{II} = K$ for $x = 0$.

In [3.91] use has been made of [3.89], and the sums, $c_1 + c_2$, constant within either phase, have been put equal to c_I and c_{II}, respectively.

Due to the non-linear boundary condition [3.91 c] it will be very difficult to obtain a solution of [3.90].

Equilibrium data, obtained with this system by Tubandt and Reinhold (104) are seen in Table III.

TABLE III

Equilibrium in the system (Ag, Cu)I + (Ag, Cu)$_2$S at 200°C.
(after Tubandt and Reinhold (104))

| No. | Initial Composition (Mol Per Cent) | | | | Final Composition (Mol Per Cent) | | | | |
| | Iodide Pellet | | Sulfide Pellet | | Iodide Pellet | | Sulfide Pellet | | |
	AgI	CuI	Ag$_2$S	Cu$_2$S	AgI	CuI	Ag$_2$S	Cu$_2$S	K · 10^7
1		100	100		99.17	0.83	0.83	99.17	5.86
2		100	100		99.06	0.94	0.94	99.06	8.54
3		100	100		99.16	0.84	0.83	99.17	6.01
4	24.76	75.24	100		99.83	0.17	24.96	75.04	9.43
5	40.01	59.99	100		99.90	0.10	40.16	59.94	6.72
6	49.99	50.01	100		99.89	0.11	50.12	49.88	12.19
7	60.33	39.67	100		99.91	0.09	60.44	39.56	12.40
8	100		70.65	29.35	99.93	0.07	70.75	29.25	11.87
9	100		50.17	49.83	99.86	0.14	50.32	49.68	19.91
10	100		40.16	59.84	99.87	0.13	40.28	59.72	11.43
11	100		24.96	75.04	99.84	0.16	25.11	74.89	8.61
12	100		0.83	99.17	99.38	0.62	1.42	98.58	5.61
13	100			100	99.23	0.77	0.73	99.27	4.43

There are considerable fluctuations in the equilibrium constant at 200°C contained in the last column of Table III, the extremes varying by a factor 4. It is not possible to state with certainty the underlying cause. The fluctuations seem not to be systematic, cf. experiments 4, 9, and 11 with only slightly differing concentrations in the iodide phase, but with K values, differing by more than a factor 2. The method of analysis consisted of weighing the cylinders before and after an experiment (cf. Tubandt's method for the determination of transference numbers of solid ionic crystals, Chap. IV, p. 183). The fluctuations correspond to uncertainties in the weight of the iodide cylinders of not more than 0.0003 g. which, perhaps, might be within the limits of experimental errors. It is striking, however, that within each group of experiments deviations are much smaller. It would certainly be possible that the heat of mixing in either phase would not be negligible, causing a variation of K with concentration. But this would not explain the results of Table III. There might be deviations from the stoichiometric composition with respect to the ratio of cations and anions. This especially might be expected for the sulfide phase with high copper concentrations. Actually, the average deviations between the first group of experiments (1 to 5) and the third group (11 to 13) with

Cu_2S contents in the sulfide phase $\geqq$ 59.84 mol per cent are small compared with the deviations of these values from those of the second Group (6 to 10) with Cu_2S contents in the sulfide phase $<$ 59.84 mol per cent.

Assuming that the specific heats of both sulfides and both iodides are approximately equal, one calculates from the heat of reaction, 12.7 kcal., an equilibrium constant for 200°C.

$$(\log_{10} K)_{\text{calc}} \approx -5.9$$

compared with an average of the observed values

$$(\log_{10} K)_{\text{obs}} \approx -6.1 \ .$$

The difference between observed and calculated values is smaller than the fluctuations of the experiments.

VI. Energy Barriers

1. Calculation of Energy Barriers

It is possible to estimate energy barriers involved in migration of either "vacancies" or interstitial particles in ionic crystals (Jost (61, 62), Jost and Nehlep (67), Mott and Littleton (83), Seitz (18), Dienes (36)). A particle, moving from one equilibrium position to an adjacent one, Fig. 3-1, migrates on a potential surface with a saddle point between the original and final sites. It usually is not difficult to find the position of this saddle point (cf. the above example, migration of a positive ion into a vacant site of a plane square lattice). Corresponding conclusions are possible for interstitial particles. The height of the energy barrier is given by the height of the energy at the saddle point, measured from the equilibrium position of the particle. This energy is composed of the same contributions as the energy of disorder (cf. Chap. II, p. 106), i. e., energy due to the electrostatic interaction of the charges of the ions, repulsive energy (due to overlapping of the electron clouds of the ions), approximately represented by an inverse high power of the distance, or better by an exponential function of the distance (Born and Mayer (27), Seitz (17), Huggins (51)), energy of polarization, varying as the reciprocal of the distance, and finally energy of van der Waals forces. In general the height of the energy barrier is decreased considerably if the nearest neighbors which must be passed by the migrating ion are moving away from the path of the mobile ion. The latter contribution is essential, lowering the height of the energy barrier by several electron volts (Jost and Nehlep (67)). It is obvious that the energy barrier will be smaller for the smaller ions, therefore favouring unipolar conduction by the smaller ions (cf. the data on electrolytic conduction and transference numbers, Chap. IV, p. 185ff).

In Table IV we list values, obtained by Mott and Littleton (83) by a refined treatment of the problem, for the case of NaCl.

TABLE IV

Activation energies for vacancy diffusion of NaCl

	Positive Ion Absent	Negative Ion Absent
Energy barrier, U	0.51 ev	0.56 ev
$\frac{1}{2}$ · Energy of disorder, $E/2$	0.93 ev	0.93 ev
$Q = \frac{E}{2} + U$.....................	1.44 ev	1.49 ev

2. Calculation of Energy Barriers for Pairs of Vacancies

The activation energy for diffusion of coupled pairs of vacancies in alkali halide crystals has been investigated by Dienes (36) (cf. the preceding discussion by Seitz (18)). As mentioned in the chapter on

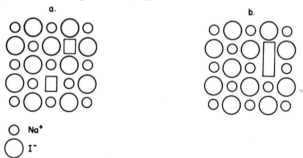

a. b.

○ Na⁺

◯ I⁻

Fig. 3-5. (a) Schottky disorder, vacancies in NaI lattice, schematically,
(b) Associated pair of vacancies.

disorder, there is a tendency for association of vacancies of opposite sign at low temperatures (cf. p. 110). Experiments on darkening of alkali halide crystals by x-rays and on accompanying density changes (Stern, Estermann and Leivo (101)) can best be explained by the assumption of a migration of coupled pairs of vacancies at low temperatures, normal diffusion due to single vacancies being too slow.

The migration of pairs of vacancies involves jumps of ions of either sign into the corresponding holes. Since the migration of the larger anions is the slower process, the jumping of the anions will be the rate determining step. Now it is seen that anions adjacent to the

positive hole of the pair of vacancies are less restricted in moving into
the negative hole than they would be if only the negative hole were
present, cf. Fig. 3-5. It is therefore to be expected that the energy
barrier involved in this process will be smaller than for diffusion of
single vacancies. The migration of the pair will proceed according to
the scheme of Fig. 3-6, state b corresponding to the saddle point of
the energy surface.

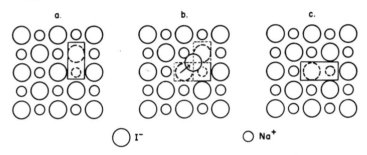

Fig. 3-6. Migration of associated pair of vacancies in alkali halide lattice.

Dienes has carried out a very thorough calculation of the energies
involved in this process. He arrives at an energy barrier of 0.375 ev
for this process, while from experiments it had been concluded that
the activation energy must be smaller than 0.5 ev in order to account
for the observed blackening and density change.

3. Migration in Metals

It requires a much more elaborate theoretical treatment to give
evidence for a certain type of migration mechanism in a metal, and
to calculate the energies involved, than in the case of ionic crystals.
Huntington and Seitz (54, 55) and Huntington (52, 53), however,
have been able to treat several cases of metallic diffusion, with the
result that a vacancy mechanism is most probable. This result, of
course, does not refer to interstitial mixed crystals of metals, as
probably occur in the solution of gold in lead, or to solid solutions
of non-metallic elements in metals (hydrogen, oxygen, nitrogen, carbon,
etc., in iron and other metals) which are of the interstitial type also,
cf. (25a), and where no additional energy is required to bring the
diffusing particles into interstitial sites. In such cases an interstitial
type of diffusion is favored.

In the case of metallic copper, the results obtained by Huntington
and Seitz seem quite conclusive, as seen from Table V taken from Seitz's
(18) report.

TABLE V

Energies of Interest for Self-Diffusion in Metallic Copper

Energy for direct interchange	11 ev
Energy to take atom from surface to interstitial position...	9.5 ev
Activation energy for interstitial atom.............	0.5 ev
Energy to take atom from normal site to surface thereby forming a vacancy	1.8 ev
Activation energy for motion of vacancy	1.0 ev

The energies obtained for the formation and migration of vacancies are much lower than for all other processes; moreover they agree well in order of magnitude with observed values. Here no doubt is possible as to the conclusiveness of this result.

Huntington also calculated the corresponding data for the alkali metals. The values obtained for vacancy and for interstitial mechanism do not differ as much as in the case of copper. Therefore the calculations, so far, do not permit a definite conclusion as to the prevalence of the vacancy mechanism.

Seitz (18) considers on the basis of the above calculations that for metals such as iron, nickel, copper, zinc, tin, and tungsten vacancy diffusion may safely be assumed. Some alkaline earth metals, e. g., beryllium and magnesium might be an exception, being somewhat more similar to the alkali metals. But even in these cases he considers a vacancy mechanism more probable, cf., howvever, Zener (117) and Seitz (96a).

VII. Empirical Relations for Ionic Crystals

Concerning the mechanism of migration in ionic crystals, we first mention a few rules derived from experimental observations:

1. In compounds of ions of different valency usually the mobility of the ion with the smaller charge is highest. Thus in Ag_2S, Cu_2S, Ag_2Se, etc., the mobility of the cations is by many orders of magnitude higher than that of the anions. In $PbCl_2$, $BaCl_2$, etc., only a mobility of the anions could be observed.

2. If analogous compounds are compared, for instance AgCl, AgBr, AgI, the mobility (here of the cations) is the higher the larger the anion (and the larger its polarizability).

In accordance with the second rule, the mobility of the lead ions in PbI_2 becomes considerable (its relative magnitude depending on temperature), in contrast to $PbCl_2$ and $PbBr_2$.

Mobility of the cations is predominant in the compounds:
silver halides, cuprous halides, alkali halides at sufficiently low tem-

peratures, silver and cuprous sulfides, selenides, tellurides (see, however, below).

Mobility of the anions is predominant in the compounds: $BaCl_2$, $BaBr_2$, BaF_2, $PbCl_2$, $PbBr_2$, and probably in a number of analogous compounds.

3. Mobility of both ions has been observed with the compounds: alkali halides at sufficiently high temperatures, PbI_2, (cf. Chap. IV, p. 190, however).

In addition to the electrolytic conductivity a marked or even predominant electronic conductivity is found in compounds such as: cuprous halides at not too high temperatures, sulfides, selenides, and tellurides of silver and monovalent copper. We shall not discuss the mechanism of electronic semiconductors (cf. the monographs and articles by Seitz (17), Mott and Gurney (15), Wilson (23), Meyer (14), Justi (11)). Some remarks, in connection with the mechanism of the formation of protective oxide, halide etc., films on metal surfaces will be found in Chap. IX, p. 386.

The above rules are in accordance with the preceding theoretical deductions. In the alkali halides we have Schottky disorder, i. e., vacancies of either sign. A difference in mobility of anions and cations is due only to the difference in the height of the energy barrier connected with the migration of vacancies. The migration of the smaller cations is usually favored by this barrier.

In the silver and cuprous halides we have (with the exception of the examples of the following section) interstitial disorder of the cations and therefore unipolar conduction due to the cations. The prevalence of this mechanism is largely due to the high polarizability of the cations with newly filled d-shells (and not of rare gas structure) which, together with the high polarizability of the large anions gives a large contribution of van der Waals energy to the lattice energy and corresponding terms in the energy of disorder (cf. Jost and Nehlep (67)).

AgBr has been the subject of many investigations on account of its application in photography (for references see especially Meidinger (80), Mees (79), Mott and Gurney (15), James and Kornfeld (57), Mitchell (81)). The prevalence of Frenkel disorder has been questioned by Mitchell, who suggests that Schottky disorder occurs instead. Stasiw and Teltow (99)* carried out very thorough measurements of ionic conductivity with certain additives. They interpret their results on the basis of Frenkel disorder with an additional, and not negligible amount of Schottky disorder.

* Stasiw and Teltow unpublished results, reported at Göttingen meeting July 28, 1949 (99a); cf. also the references quoted in Chap. II.

Zimens (116) investigated the exchange of silver and of bromine ions in photographic layers by means of radioactive isotopes. For silver ions he arrived at a rate of diffusion (at room temperature) of $D_{Ag} \sim 2 \times 10^{-12}$ cm.^{2} sec.$^{-1}$ while he observed no effect with bromine, which means $D < 10^{-15}$ cm.^{2} sec.$^{-1}$, in marked contrast to Kolthoff and O'Brien's results(73a), for which Zimens estimates $D \approx 2 \times 10^{-15}$ cm.^{2} sec.$^{-1}$. This difference could be due to the different state of the AgBr grains.

In the α-modifications of the iodides of silver and monovalent copper, and of the corresponding sulfides, selenides, and tellurides and in α-Ag$_2$HgI$_4$ we have crystal structures with disorder of the cation lattice favoring the mobility of the cations (cf. Chap. II., p. 97). In these cases exceptionally low activation energies for electrolytic conduction and diffusion have been found experimentally (of the order of magnitude of 1 kcal/mol).

VIII. Disorder and Ionic Conductance of Ag$_2$HgI$_4$

As discussed elsewhere (Chap. II, p. 88), Ketelaar (69, 70, 71, 72) has investigated the structure of Ag$_2$HgI$_4$, which in its β-modification, below 50.7°C., shows a normal tetragonal lattice with definite lattice sites for silver and mercury ions, and no vacant sites in the regular lattice structure. In the regular lattice, stable above 50.7°C., which is very similar to that of β-Ag$_2$HgI$_4$, three ions, one mercury and two silver ions, are distributed at random among four equivalent lattice sites, thus 25 per cent of these lattice sites are empty.

The transformation is not absolutely sharp (Ketelaar (72)) but starts at about 40°C., being completed at the transformation point of 50.7°C. The specific heat of the substance shows a dependence on the temperature which is quite analogous to that encountered in order-disorder transformations in alloys (cf. Chap. II, p. 120). The increase in specific heat above its normal value, starting at 40°C., is quite marked, reaching a value of about 147 cal./mol. which is about three times the Dulong-Petit value of the specific heat per mol. Ketelaar has stressed the parallel between this transformation and that encountered in the case of alloys, and he also has attempted to give a quantitative theoretical treatment. The transformation is more complicated than order-disorder transformations in binary alloys, because here three types of lattice sites are involved (referring to the lattice of β-Ag$_2$HgI$_4$), namely mercury sites, silver sites, and vacant sites. For simplification, Ketelaar neglects the difference of mercury sites and silver sites, and thus reduces the problem to that of 3 sites of one kind (cation sites) and one site of a different kind (vacancy sites). Therefore, he treats the problem of a phase of composition A_3B, which is equivalent to the case of the Cu_3Au alloy.

The activation energies for ionic conduction, determined experimentally, are 8,600 cal./mol. for the α-modification, the conductivity being represented by

$$\sigma = 4 \times 10^2 \exp\left(-8,600/RT\right). \qquad [3.92]$$

From the Bragg and Williams (28) theory and from the observed critical temperature, Ketelaar calculates a heat of transformation of 1.17 kcal./mol., which is to be compared with the experimental value of 1.43 kcal.

Ketelaar derived for the fraction p of ions on the normally unoccupied sites in the β-phase, $p \ll 1$

$$p \approx \sqrt{3} \exp\left(-E/2RT\right) \qquad [3.93]$$

where E should be the Bragg-Williams ordering energy. The empirical formula for conduction in the α-phase should contain only an energy barrier, $E' = 8,600$ cal. Thus the conductivity of either phase should be represented by the formula

$$\sigma = \text{const} \exp\left[-(E(\Sigma)/2 + E')/RT\right]. \qquad [3.94]$$

For the α-phase Σ, and consequently $E(\Sigma)$, also, is zero, while for the β-phase $E(\Sigma)$, the ordering energy, may be derived from conductivity measurements

$$E(\Sigma) = 2RT\left(\log \sigma_a - \log \sigma_\beta\right). \qquad [3.95]$$

The energy, thus calculated, increases with decreasing temperature up to a limiting value of 7,400 cal./mol. From the value of the specific heat, Ketelaar derives the degree of order, Σ, as function of temperature, obtaining $\Sigma = 0.90$ at the transformation point. The dependence of $E(\Sigma)$ on Σ, thus arrived at, is far from linear. Thus the results obtained may be summarized, that the Bragg-Williams theory leads to quite reasonable values, even in the case of this ionic compound; that the numerical agreement, however, is rather poor. This might partly be due to the fact that this theory is only a first approximation, but partly it might also be due to the approximations which are allowed with alloys but not with ionic compounds. Finally a considerable uncertainty of the results may have been introduced by neglecting the difference between silver and mercury ions.

IX. Kinetics of Order-Disorder Transformations

The phenomena connected with the kinetics of order-disorder transformations should be most interesting from the point of view of this book (cf. (37) and the report of Nix and Shockley (16)). But the results, obtained so far, seem not yet quite satisfactory. One may roughly characterize the rate of approach to equilibrium by a temperature, T_f, for freezing out, below which no change of order can be observed within reasonable time. In the cases where order-disorder transformations have been observed, this temperature certainly must be below the critical temperature for ordering. Therefore, ordering may be observed within the temperature range between T_f and T_c. If, however, T_f is higher than T_c, an ordering effect cannot be observed, even if a superlattice be stable thermodynamically.

Bragg and Williams (28) were the first to discuss the time of relaxation, involved in ordering processes. If we denote by δ the deviation of the fraction of rightly occupied sites from the equilibrium value, we can write the equation, given by Bragg and Williams for the rate of change of δ

$$\frac{d\delta}{dt} = -\delta \frac{C}{F_A N} \qquad [3.96]$$

where $F_A N$ is the number of A atoms in a binary mixture AB (for the notation, etc., cf. Chap. II, p. 122). The problem consists of an evaluation of C. If C were given, the decay of δ might be characterized by a time of relaxation

$$\tau = F_A N / C , \qquad [3.97]$$

thus

$$\delta = \delta_0 \exp(-t/\tau) . \qquad [3.98]$$

By considering a direct interchange of neighboring atoms (which is a rather improbable process, cf. p. 144, 165) Bragg and Williams arrive at a value of τ

$$\tau = A \exp(E/RT) . \qquad [3.99]$$

With reasonable assumptions they estimated A to be about 10^{-12} sec. For E/RT they assume a value of the order of magnitude of 24 which seems reasonable if the mechanism of direct interchange were replaced by a vacancy-diffusion mechanism. No direct connection of these values with independent observations has been possible.

Sykes and Evans (102), cf. Gorsky (46), determined times of relaxation for wires of a Cu_3Au alloy, by measuring its resistivity. The following values of A and E/R were derived from these measurements:

$$A = 10^{-8.5}, \quad E/R = 19100° \text{ K} .$$

The authors also determined τ for constant rates of cooling, and again derived values for A and E/R from the results thus obtained. These magnitudes are not at all in agreement with the other ones.

Siegel (97) investigated the kinetics of the order-disorder transformation of single crystals of Cu_3Au by measuring the elastic modulus. He did not find a simple exponential relation for his decay curves. Hence a time of relaxation, τ, had to be defined in a rather arbitrary way.

The relaxation time τ decreases rapidly with increasing amount of supercooling below the critical temperature, i. e., it varies in the opposite sense to that which Bragg and Williams', and Sykes and Evans' measurements indicate.

Siegel indicates that the results might be explained by the suggestions of Sykes and Evans. The process of ordering is one of formation and growth of nuclei of order. It shows characteristic features of such processes (cf. Volmer (21), Becker (26)), especially the appearance of a maximum in the curve $1/\tau$ vs. T. Siegel's measurements and those of Sykes and Evans, which refer to different temperature regions, suggest that a maximum of $1/\tau$ exists near 370°C, approximately 20°C below the critical temperature.

X. Diffusion and Absolute Reaction Rate Theory

Stearn and Eyring (100) and Barrer (25) have applied the theory of absolute reaction rate to the process of diffusion in crystals (for the theory of reaction rates cf. Pelzer and Wigner (87), Eyring (42, 43, 44), Evans and Polanyi (41), Glasstone, Laidler and Eyring (7); for the application to the diffusion process in solids see especially the excellent survey given by Seitz (18)).

The procedure of this theory is as follows. Consider a system which undergoes any kind of chemical change, which may be a chemical reaction in the usual sense, or a simple displacement of a particle, as in diffusion or viscous flow. We may describe this process as passage of a representative point over a potential barrier of height E along a reaction coordinate x. In the problems in which we are interested, x is simply the cartesian coordinate of a particle moving from one equilibrium position to an adjacent one, separated from the former by an energy surface of given shape and height, provided we neglect movements of surrounding particles.

In principle, it is always possible to calculate the energy surface connected with displacements of the migrating particle. The actual reaction path leads through the saddle point of this surface, giving the lowest energy of activation. In general chemical reactions, which will not be discussed here, the reaction coordinate x is a generalized coordinate referring to the motion of a point in phase space, representing the system under consideration. For an assembly of many systems we can calculate, by the methods of statistical mechanics, the number of systems passing the potential surface in unit time, thus obtaining the rate of reaction. This is done by first calculating the number of systems which are on top of the barrier in equilibrium, and second by calculating the speed by which these systems cross the barrier in the correct direction. It is meaningless to ask for the number of particles which are exactly on the height of the barrier, being located at a distinct value of x. We must calculate the number of particles within a certain range, δ, of the reaction coordinate, on top of the barrier. The barrier, for this purpose, must be idealized as being almost flat at its top.

If we denote the fraction of particles in the transition state, i. e., on the height of the barrier, by n^*/n, and by v the average velocity with which they cross the barrier in the correct direction then an argument, analogous to that of p. 135 leads to the expression for the diffusion coefficient

$$D = \frac{n^*}{n} d v \qquad [3.100]$$

where d is the distance between consecutive equilibrium positions.

Statistical mechanics (cf. (4), (5) (13), (20)) gives for the ratio of the numbers of systems in an activated state, and the number of systems in a normal ground state

$$\frac{n^*}{n} = \frac{f'}{f} \qquad [3.101]$$

where f' and f are the partition functions for the corresponding states. The partition function is defined by

$$f = \sum_i g_i \exp\left(-\varepsilon_i/kT\right) \qquad [3.102]$$

where ε_i is the energy of the system in its ith quantum state, and g_i is the number of degenerate states with energy ε_i. The summation is to be carried out over all accessible states of the system. Values of f for the cases of interest to us will be given below. The partition function f always contains a contribution of the translation in the direction of the reaction coordinate x. We shall consider this first. The partition function for a particle, moving in a uniform potential along one coordinate, and restricted to a length δ is

$$f_{tr} = (2\pi m k T)^{1/2} \delta/h \qquad [3.103]$$

where

$m =$ mass (in the general case to be replaced by a reduced mass μ)
$h =$ Planck's constant.

The mean velocity in the $+x$-direction of a particle in the activated state is

$$\overline{v} = \left(\frac{kT}{2\pi m} \right)^{1/2} \qquad [3.104]$$

and consequently the time τ, necessary to pass through the distance δ, is

$$\tau = \frac{\delta}{\overline{v}} = \delta \left(\frac{2\pi m}{kT} \right)^{1/2} . \qquad [3.105]$$

If n^* is the number of particles in the activated state, n^*/τ will be the number of particles crossing the energy barrier per unit time, i. e., the reaction velocity

$$w = n^* / \tau = n^* \left(\frac{kT}{2\pi m} \right)^{1/2} \frac{1}{\delta} . \qquad [3.106]$$

Now n^* always contains the partition function f as a factor, and consequently contains the translational partition function [3.103]. It is convenient to write instead of [3.101]

$$\frac{n^*}{n} = \frac{f^*}{f} \frac{(2\pi m kT)^{1/2} \delta}{h} \qquad [3.107]$$

where

$$f' = f^* (2\pi m kT)^{1/2} \; \delta/h . \qquad [3.108]$$

f^*, therefore, is the partition function of the activated state, without the contribution of the translational energy in the direction of the reaction coordinate. Finally, we obtain, upon substitution of [3.107] in [3.106]

$$w = n \frac{f^*}{f} \frac{kT}{h} . \qquad [3.109]$$

The factor kT/h has the dimensions of a frequency and is of the order of magnitude of 6×10^{12} per second.

It is convenient to write for the energies entering the exponentials in [3.102]

$$\varepsilon_i' = \varepsilon_0 + \varepsilon_i \qquad [3.110]$$

where ε_0 is the lowest energy for the activated state, referred to the lowest energy of the initial state as zero. Then we have instead of [3.109]

$$w = n \frac{f^*}{f} \frac{kT}{h} \exp\left(-\varepsilon_0 / kT \right) \qquad [3.111]$$

$$= n \frac{f^*}{f} \frac{kT}{h} \exp\left(-E_0 / RT \right).$$

By using the statistical relation between partition function and free energy, F,

$$F = -RT \log f \qquad [3.112]$$

(or the thermodynamic relation between free energy and equilibrium constant, considering that $f^*/f \exp(-\varepsilon_0/kT)$ gives the equilibrium constant between particles in their normal state and in the activated state), we may replace [3.111] by

$$w = n\frac{kT}{h}\exp(-\Delta F^*/RT).\qquad[3.113]$$

Here ΔF^* is the change in Gibbs free energy between normal state and transition state. With

$$\Delta F^* = \Delta H^* - T\Delta S^*\qquad[3.114]$$

we obtain

$$w = n\frac{kT}{h}\exp(\Delta S^*/R)\exp(-\Delta H^*/RT)\qquad[3.115]$$

Thus additional factors, multiplying the exponential, now appear in the form of an exponential, containing the entropy of activation ΔS^*. A high entropy of activation corresponds to a large factor multiplying the temperature dependent exponential.

The empirical energy of activation is given by

$$\Delta E = RT^2\frac{d\log w}{dT} = RT + \Delta H^*.\qquad[3.116]$$

The most important expressions for the partition functions entering f^* and f are

(a) f_{tr} for translation (per unit length)

$$f_{tr} = (2\pi mkT)^{1/2}/h\qquad[3.117]$$

(b) f_{rot} for rotation of a diatomic molecule at sufficiently high temperatures, neglecting weight factors

$$f_{rot} = 8\pi^2IkT/h^2, \quad \text{where } I = \text{moment of inertia}\qquad[3.118]$$

(c) f_{vib} for vibration of one degree of freedom

$$f_{vib} = \left[1 - \exp\left(-\frac{h\nu}{kT}\right)\right]^{-1}\qquad[3.119]$$

with the classical value as limiting case for $h\nu \ll kT$

$$f_{vib} = \frac{kT}{h\nu}.\qquad[3.120]$$

Equations [3.111], [3.113] and [3.115] give the number of particles crossing the energy barrier per second. This corresponds to the number of disordered particles times oscillation frequency in our treatment on p. 135. Consequently we obtain the diffusion coefficient of these particles by multiplying the frequency factor by the square of the distance d between equilibrium positions

$$D^* = d^2(f^*/f)(kT/h)\exp(-E_0/RT)\qquad E_0 = N\varepsilon_0\qquad[3.121]$$

$$D^* = d^2(kT/h)\exp(-\Delta F^*/RT)\qquad[3.122]$$

$$D^* = d^2(kT/h)\exp(\Delta S^*/R)\exp(-\Delta H^*/RT).\qquad[3.123]$$

This is the coefficient of diffusion for either vacancies or interstitial particles, because we considered as the process of activation only the passage over a barrier and did not include the disordering process. The disorder equilibria have been treated before (Chap. II, p. 92,95) and in order to obtain the diffusion coefficient of average particles equations [3.121], [3.122], or [3.123] must be multiplied by the ratio of numbers of centers of disorder, referred to the number of corresponding normal lattice sites, Chap. II, p. 117.

Barrer (24) has given a detailed discussion of diffusion coefficients thus derived. We give the formulas for diffusion in the cases of Schottky disorder, and Frenkel disorder, for zeolitic diffusion.

$$D = \frac{d^2 \nu}{6} \left(\frac{U}{RT}\right)^{\zeta-1} \frac{1}{(\zeta-1)!} \frac{N'-n_i}{N'} \exp\left(-U/RT\right) \qquad [3.124]$$

zeolitic diffusion

$$D = \frac{d^2 \nu}{6} \left(\frac{U}{RT}\right)^{\zeta-1} \frac{1}{(\zeta-1)!} \frac{n_v}{N-n_v} \exp\left(-[E+U]/RT\right) \qquad [3.125]$$

Schottky mechanism

$$D = \frac{d^2 \nu}{6} \left(\frac{U}{RT}\right)^{\zeta-1} \frac{n_i}{V(N'-n_i)(N-n_v)} \exp\left(-[E/2+U]/RT\right) \qquad [3.126]$$

Frenkel mechanism

where U energy barrier (energy distributed among ζ degrees of freedom), N total number of lattice sites, N' number of interstices, n_v number of vacant sites ($n_v = n_i$ for Frenkel disorder)

In Table VI, taken from Barrer (25), we give energies and entropies of activation for some examples of interstitial diffusion.

TABLE VI

Values of ΔS^* and ΔE^* at 500°K, with $d^2 = 10^{-15}$cm.^{2}, for some zeolitic diffusion systems

System	$D = D_0 \exp(-E/RT)$ cm.^{2} sec.$^{-1}$	ΔS^* at 500°K (cal./mol. deg.)	ΔE^* at 500°K (cal./mol.)
H_2—Pd	$1.5 \times 10^{-2} \exp(-6800/RT)$	— 1.27	5 810
H_2—Ni	$2.04 \times 10^{-3} \exp(-8700/RT)$	— 5.3	7 710
H_2—Fe	$1.65 \times 10^{-2} \exp(-9200/RT)$	— 1.08	8 210
C —Fe	$5.5 \times 10^{-2} \exp(-32\,200/RT)$	+ 1.33	31 210
N_2—Fe	$1.07 \times 10^{-1} \exp(-34\,000/RT)$	+ 3.66	33 010
NH_3—Analcite	$2.5 \times 10^{-3} \exp(-11\,480/RT)$	— 4.85	10 490

REFERENCES

Monographs and review articles

1. Barrer, R. M., *Proc. Phys. Soc. (London)* **52**, 58 (1940).
2. Barrer, R. M., Diffusion in and through Solids. Cambridge Univ. Press 1941.

3. Cohn, G., *Chem. Rev.* **42**, 527 (1948). Reactions in the solid state.
4. Fowler, R. H., Statistical Mechanics. Cambridge, 1936.
5. Fowler, R. H., and Guggenheim, E. A., Statistical Thermodynamics Cambridge, 1939.
6. Frenkel, I., Kinetic Theory of Liquids. Oxford, 1946.
7. Glasstone, S., Laidler, K. J., and Eyring, H., The Theory of Rate Processes, McGraw-Hill. New York, 1941.
8. Hedvall, J. A., Reaktionsfähigkeit fester Stoffe. Leipzig, 1938.
9. Hildebrand, J. H., Solubility of Non-Electrolytes. New York, 1936. 2nd ed. 1948.
10. Jost, W., Diffusion und chemische Reaktion in festen Stoffen. Steinkopff, Dresden und Leipzig, 1937.
11. Justi, E., Leitfähigkeit und Leitungsmechanismus fester Stoffe. Göttingen, 1948.
12. Manning, M. F., and Bell, M. E., *Rev. Mod. Phys.* **12**, 215 (1940).
13. Mayer, J. E., and Goeppert-Mayer, M., Statistical Mechanics. New York, 1940.
14. Meyer, W., *Z. Elektrochem.* **50**, 274 (1944).
15. Mott, N. F., and Gurney, R. W., Electronic Processes in Ionic Crystals. Oxford Univ. Press, 1940; 2nd Ed. Oxford, 1948.
16. Nix, F. C., and Shockley, W., *Rev. Mod. Phys.* **10**, 1, (1938).
17. Seitz, F., Modern Theory of Solids. McGraw-Hill, New York, 1940.
18. Seitz, F., Fundamental Aspects of Diffusion in Solids. Pittsburgh, 1948.
19. Schwarz, K. E., Elektrolytische Wanderung in flüssigen und festen Metallen. Leipzig, 1940.
20. Tolman, R. C., The Principles of Statistical Mechanics. Oxford, 1938.
21. Volmer, M., Kinetik der Phasenbildung. Steinkopff, Dresden und Leipzig, 1939.
22. Wagner, C. in G. Masing, Handbuch der Metallphysik, Vol. 1. Leipzig, 1940.
23. Wilson, A. H., The Theory of Metals. Cambridge, 1936.

General Bibliography

24. Barrer, R. M., *Trans. Faraday Soc.* **37**, 590 (1941).
25. Barrer, R. M., *Trans. Faraday Soc.* **38**, 78 (1942).
25a. Barrer, R. M. *Discussion Faraday Soc.* **1948**, p. 68.
26. Becker, R., *Ann. Physik* **32**, 128 (1938).
27. Born, M., and Mayer, J. E., *Z. Physik.* **75**, 1 (1932).
28. Bragg, W. L., and Williams, E. J., *Proc. Roy. Soc. (London)* **A 145**, 699 (1934).
29. Braunbek, W., *Z. Physik.* **44**, 684 (1927).
30. Braune, H., *Z. physik. Chem.* **110**, 147 (1924).
31. Breckenridge, R. G., *J. Chem. Phys.* **16**, 959 (1948).
31a. Breckenridge, R. G., *J. Chem. Phys.* **18**, 913 (1950). (Low frequency dispersion in ionic crystals containing foreign ions cf. 46a.)
32. Cichocki, J., *J. phys. radium* **7**, 420 (1936).
33. Cohen, E., and Bruins, H. R., *Z. physik. Chem.* **109**, 422 (1924).
34. Cremer, E., *Z. physik. Chem.* **B 39**, 445 (1938).
35. Darken, L. S., *Metals Technol.* **15**, Tech. Publ. 2311 (1948).
36. Dienes, G. J., *J. Chem. Phys.* **16**, 620 (1948).
37. Discussion on "Conduction of Electricity in Solids", *Proc. Phys. Soc. (London)* **49**, 77, 96 (1937).
37a. Du Pré, F. K., Hutner, R. A. and Rittner, E. S., *J. Chem. Phys.* **18**, 379 (1950).

38. Dushman, S., and Langmuir, I., *Phys. Rev.* **20**, 113 (1922).
39. Dushman, S., and Langmuir, I., *Phys. Rev.* **22**, 357 (1923).
40. Einstein, A., *Ann. Physik* (4) **17**, 549 (1905).
41. Evans, M. G., and Polanyi, M., *Trans. Faraday Soc.* **31**, 875 (1935).
42. Eyring, H., *Chem. Rev.* **17**, 65 (1935).
43. Eyring, H., *J. Chem. Phys.* **3**, 107 (1935).
44. Eyring, H., *J. Chem. Phys.* **4**, 283 (1936).
45. Frenkel, I., *Z. Physik* **35**, 652 (1926).
46. Gorsky, W. S., *Phys. Z. Sowjetunion* **8**, 443 (1935).
46a. Grimley, T. B., *J. Chem. Phys.* **17**, 496 (1949). (Low frequency dispersion in ionic crystals.)
47. Grimm, H. G., and Herzfeld, K. F., *Z. Physik* **15**, 77 (1923).
48. Grube, G., and Jedele, A., *Z. Elektrochem.* **38**, 799 (1932).
49. von Hevesy, G., *Z. Elektrochem.* **39**, 490 (1933).
50. von Hevesy, G., *Trans. Faraday Soc.* **34**, 841 (1938).
50a. Hillert, M., Johansson, G., and Zimen, K.-E., *J. Chem. Soc., London* **1949**, 392.
51. Huggins, M. L., *J. Chem. Phys.* **5**, 143 (1937).
52. Huntington, H., *Phys. Rev.* **58**, 209 (1940).
53. Huntington, H., *Phys. Rev.* **61**, 325 (1942).
54. Huntington, H., and Seitz, F., *Phys. Rev.* **57**, 559 (1940).
55. Huntington, H., and Seitz, F., *Phys. Rev.* **61**, 315 (1942).
56. Hutner, R. A., Rittner, E. S., and Du Pré, F. K., *J. Chem. Phys.* **17**, 204 (1949).
57. James, T. H., and Kornfeld, G., *J. Phys. Chem.* **46**, 1 (1942).
58. Johnson, R. P., *Phys. Rev.* **56**, 814 (1939).
59. Jost, W., Dissertation, Halle (1926).
60. Jost, W., *Z. physik. Chem.* **B 9**, 73 (1930).
61. Jost, W., *J. Chem. Phys.* **1**, 466 (1933).
62. Jost, W., *Z. physik. Chem.* **A 169**, 129 (1934).
63. Jost, W., *Physik. Z.* **36**, 757 (1935).
64. Jost, W., *Trans. Faraday Soc.* **34**, 860 (1938).
65. Jost, W., and Linke, R., *Z. physik. Chem.* **B 29**, 127 (1935).
66. Jost, W., Mennenöh, S., and Müller, F. H., *Z. Naturforschung* 4a, 227 (1949).
67. Jost, W., and Nehlep, G., *Z. physik. Chem.* **B 32**, 1 (1936).
68. Jost, W., and Nehlep, G., *Z. physik. Chem.* **B 34**, 348 (1936).
69. Ketelaar, J. A. A., *Z. Kryst.* **87**, 436 (1934).
70. Ketelaar, J. A. A., *Z. physik. Chem.* **B 26**, 327 (1934).
71. Ketelaar, J. A. A., *Z. physik. Chem.* **B 30**, 53 (1935).
72. Ketelaar, J. A. A., *Trans. Faraday Soc.* **34**, 874 (1938).
73. Koch, E., and Wagner, C., *Z. physik. Chem.* **B 38**, 295 (1938).
73a. Kolthoff, I. M., and O·Brien, A. S., *J. Am. Chem. Soc.* **61**, 3409, 3414 (1939). *J. Chem. Phys.* **7**, 401 (1939).
73b. Lawson, A. W., *Phys. Rev.* **78**, 185 (1950).
74. van Liempt, J. A. M., *Z. anorg. u. allgem. Chem.* **195**, 366 (1931).
75. van Liempt, J. A. M., *Rec. trav. chim.* **51**, 114 (1932).
76. van Liempt, J. A. M., *Rec. trav. chim.* **57**, 891 (1938).
77. van Liempt, J. A. M., *Z. Physik.* **96**, 534 (1935).
78. Maurer, R. J., and Mapother, D., *Phys. Rev.* **73**, 1260 (1948).
78a. Maurer, R. J., *Forschungen u. Fortschr.* **26**, 3, Sonderh. 4 (1950).
79. Mees, C. E. K., The Theory of the Photographic Process. MacMillan, New York, 1942.

80. Meidinger, W., Handb. d. wiss. u. angew. Photogr. Vol. V, Springer. Berlin, 1932.
81. Mitchell, J. W., *Phil. Mag.* (7) **40**, 249 (1949).
82. Mott, N. F., *Rept. Progr. Physics* **6**, 186 (1940).
83. Mott, N. F., and Littleton, M. J., *Trans. Faraday Soc.* **34**, 485 (1938).
84. Nehlep, G., Jost, W., and Linke, R., *Z. Elektrochem.* **42**, 150 (1936).
85. Nernst, W., *Z. physik. Chem.* **2**, 613 (1888).
86. van Ostrand, C. E., and Dewey, F. P., *U. S. Geol. Survey Prof. Paper* **95** G, 83 (1915).
87. Pelzer, H., and Wigner, E., *Z. physik. Chem.* **B 15**, 445 (1932).
88. Radavich, F., and Smoluchowski, R., *Phys. Rev.* **65**, 62 (1944).
89. Rhines, F. N., and Mehl, R. F., *Trans. Am. Inst. Mining Met. Engrs.* **128**, 185 (1938).
90. Rittner, E. S., Hutner, R. A., and Du Pré, F. K., *J. Chem. Phys.* **17**, 198 (1949).
91. Rushbrooke, G. S., *Trans. Faraday Soc.* **36**, 1055 (1940).
92. Seith, W., and Daur, Th., *Z. Elektrochem.* **44**, 829 (1934).
93. Seith, W., and Etzold, H., *Z. Elektrochem.* **40**, 829 (1934); **41**, 122 (1935).
94. Seitz, F., *Phys. Rev.* **54**, 1111 (1938).
95. Seitz, F., *Phys. Rev.* **56**, 1063 (1939).
96. Seitz, F., *Phys. Rev.* **74**, 1513 (1948).
96a. Seitz, F., *Acta Crystallogr.* **3**, 355 (1950),
97. Siegel, S., *J. Chem. Phys.* **8**, 860 (1940).
98. Smigelskas, A. D., and Kirkendall, E. O., *Metals Technol.* **13**, Tech. Publ. 2071 (1946).
98a. Smoluchowski, R., and Burgess, H., *Phys. Rev.* **76**, 309 (1949).
99. Stasiw, O., and Teltow, J., *Ann. Physik* (6) **1**, 261 (1947).
99a. Stasiw, O. and Teltow, J., *Forschungen u. Fortschr.* **26**, 3. Sonderh. 1 (1950).
100. Stearn, A. E., and Eyring, H., *J. Phys. Chem.* **44**, 955 (1940).
101. Stern, O., Estermann, I., and Leivo, W. J., *Phys. Rev.* **75**, 627 (1949).
101a. Strelkow, P. G., *Physik. Z. Sowjetunion* **12**, 77 (1937).
102. Sykes, C., and Evans, H., *J. Inst. Metals* **58**, 255 (1936).
103. Szigeti, B., *Trans. Faraday Soc.* **45**, 155 (1949).
104. Tubandt, C., and Reinhold, H., *Z. physik. Chem.* **140**, 291 (1929).
105. Tubandt, C., Reinhold, H., and Jost, W., *Z. physik. Chem.* **129**, 69 (1927).
106. Tubandt, C., Reinhold, H., and Jost, W., *Z. anorg. u. allgem. Chem.* **177**, 253 (1928).
107. Wagner, C., *Z. physik. Chem.* **B 11**, 139 (1930).
108. Wagner, C., *Z. physik. Chem.*, Bodenstein-Festb., p. 177 (1931).
109. Wagner, C., *Z. physik. Chem.* **B 22**, 181 (1933).
110. Wagner, C., *Z. physik. Chem.* **B 38**, 325 (1938).
111. Wagner, C., and Beyer, J., *Z. physik. Chem.* **B 32**, 113 (1936).
112. Wagner, C., and Schottky, W., *Z. physik. Chem.* **B 11**, 163 (1930).
112a. Wagner, E., and Hantelmann, P., *J. Phys. & Colloid Chem.* **54**, 426 (1950).
113. Wigner, E., *Z. physik. Chem.* **B 19**, 203 (1932).
114. Wyllie, G., *Proc. Phys. Soc. (London)* **59**, 694 (1947).
115. Zimens, K. E., *Ark. Kemi, Mineral Geol. Vet. Akad.* (Stockholm), Bd. 20 A No. 18 (1945); Bd. 21 A No. 16 (1945); Bd. 21 A No. 17 (1945); Bd. 23 A No. 16 (1946).
116. Zimens, K. E., *Z. Naturforschung* **4a**, 95 (1949).
117. Zener, Cl., *Acta Crystallogr.* **3**, 346 (1950).

CHAPTER IV

ELECTROLYTIC CONDUCTION AND DIFFUSION IN IONIC CRYSTALS

I. General remarks

There are two independent methods for the determination of the mean mobilities of constituent particles in ionic crystals: the first by means of measurement of the electrolytic conductivity and of transference numbers, the second by means of diffusion measurements. In metals, too, a transport of matter by an electric current has been observed, but it is not possible to draw quantative conclusions from these measurements with respect to the mobility of the migrating particles (cf. Chap. III p. 144). In ionic crystals a calculation of the rate of diffusion from conductivity and transference measurements is possible, and vice versa. It seems advisable, therefore, to give a short account of the methods and results of electrical measurements with ionic crystals.

Measurements of electrolytic conductivity are usually possible with much higher accuracy than diffusion measurements. Consequently certain effects of fundamental importance with respect to the mechanism of mobility, such as, for instance, the influence of pressure on the mobility, can be determined rather easily from conductivity measurement, while, so far, the corresponding effect with diffusion has not yet been determined with ionic crystals. On the other hand, the determination of transference numbers requires the passage of a certain minimum quantity of electric charge through the crystal under investigation. With specimens of rather low conductivity the necessary time may be so long that disturbing changes of the specimen can occur. Hence reliable transference measurements are available only for compounds with sufficiently high conductivity. In such cases the calculation of transference numbers, and perhaps of the conductivity, from diffusion measurements may become quite important. Considerable progress in this field is to be expected from the use of radioactive isotopes, both for the direct determination of transference numbers and for the indirect calculation of transference numbers and conductivities from measured rates of self diffusion.

The necessary theoretical relations have been derived earlier (Chap. III p. 139). The partial conductivity σ_i due to one type of ion with a single mechanism of migration is given by

$$\sigma_i = \sigma t_i = u_i e^2 n_i z_i^2 *. \qquad [4.1]$$

If more than one mechanism of migration is responsible for the conduction (for instance, migration of vacancies and of interstitial ions), equation [4.1] must be replaced by a sum of corresponding expressions, with individual values of u_i. u_i is the mobility of the migrating particles, i.e., the velocity acquired under the influence of unit force **. Consequently the total electrolytic conductivity σ is given by

$$\sigma = \Sigma \sigma_i \qquad [4.2]$$

and the transference number t_i of the ith constituent ion

$$t_i = \frac{\sigma_i}{\sigma}. \qquad [4.3]$$

In the examples of AgCl and AgBr, for instance, the conductivity due to the silver ions is given by a sum of two expressions like [4.1], for vacancies and for interstitial ions (Koch and Wagner (80)), the transference number of the silver ions, given by [4.3], is equal to 1 within the rather narrow limits of error, because the average mobility of the halogen ions is negligibly small.

If the electronic component of conductivity is not negligible, a term σ_{el} must be included in [4.2] and [4.3], and a transference number of electrons, t_{el}, must be considered, determined by

$$t_{el} = \frac{\sigma_{el}}{\sigma}. \qquad [4.4]$$

The mobility of one type of ion, due to a single mechanism, is given by (cf. Chap. III p. 137, 139)

$$u_i = \alpha_i \frac{d^2 \nu}{kT} = \frac{D_i}{kT} \qquad [4.5]$$

where α_i is the fraction of centres of disorder, either vacancies or interstitial particles (D_i self-diffusion coefficient of species i). In the special case of a binary mixture exhibiting Schottky or Frenkel disorder, we have

$$\alpha_i \approx \exp\left(-\frac{E_i}{2RT}\right)$$

cf. Chap. II, p. 94.

---

* Where σ = total conductivity, t_i = transference number, $z_i e$ = the charge of the ions, and n_i = number of ions per cc.

** Hence the mobility under a potential gradient of 1 Volt/cm. is equal to $u_i z_i e \cdot 300$.

Again several types of migration may occur, and the resulting mobility may be given by a sum of terms like [4.5].

The mobility of an ion for a single mechanism depends exponentially on temperature, and, consequently, the partial conductivity due to this ion and the mechanism under consideration is given by

$$\sigma_i = \sigma_{i_0} \exp\left(- Q_i/R T\right) \qquad [4.6]$$

Here the temperature independent factor σ_{i_0} is of the order of magnitude of 100 Ohm^{-1} cm.$^{-1}$, if no extra factors arise due to the effects discussed elsewhere (Chap. III p. 149ff). Actually, due to these effects σ_{i_0} may be of the order of $10^4 \sim 10^6$.

If the total conductivity is given by that of one type of ion only, as is often the case with solid electrolytes within a limited range of temperature, the conductivity may be expressed in the form

$$\sigma = \sigma_0 \exp\left(- Q/R T\right). \qquad [4.7]$$

This relation is often found empirically. If there is mobility of one type of ion only, but due to two different types of migration, as in the above quoted example of the silver halides, we have for the total conductivity an expression of the form

$$\sigma = \sigma_{10} \exp\left(-Q_1/R\ T\right) + \sigma_{20} \exp\left(-Q_2/RT\right),$$
$$Q_i = E/2 + U_i \qquad i = 1,2. \qquad [4.8]$$

where E is the energy of disorder, here of Frenkel disorder (cf. Chap. III p. 153), equal for vacancies and for interstitial ions. U_1 and U_2 are the energy barriers, to be surmounted by the migrating vacancies and interstitial ions, respectively. From theoretical considerations and from Koch and Wagner's (80) empirical determinations (which are not quite free of arbitrary assumptions) it may be concluded that U_1 and U_2 are smaller than E, and probably do not differ much. Then it is possible to represent the experimental values of the conductivity by the approximate equation

$$\sigma = \sigma_0 \exp\left(- Q/RT\right) \qquad [4.9]$$

where Q is an appropriate average of $E/2 + U_1$ and $E/2 + U_2$. It is possible, indeed, to approximate the empirical values of the conductivities of AgCl, AgBr and similar compounds, with Frenkel disorder, by a simple formula such as [4.9], for not too low temperatures.

There are certain deviations from equations such as [4.9], to be mentioned below. It is extremely difficult, however, to draw definite conclusions as to the nature of these deviations. They might sometimes be due to the appearance of several types of migration, but they might as well be due to small impurities. Since the fraction of disordered particles, is usually very small, even impurities below the limit of analytical sensitivity, may have a marked influence on the conductivity. Furthermore, the conductivity may be influenced by surfaces. In ionic compounds of not too high a conductivity marked differences in the conductivities of single crystal, of polycrystalline aggregates, and of compressed powders have been observed. Such effects can be due both to impurities, present at the grain boundaries, and to a higher mobility of ions on surfaces.

II. Faraday's law

The occurence of electrolytic conduction in solid compounds can be tested, as in the case of electrolytic solutions, by a determination of the products of decomposition at the electrodes. With compounds such as α-AgI (stable above 144.6°C), $BaCl_2$ and others it is easy to verify Faraday's law. If, for instance, one or several cylinders of AgI obtained by compressing precipitated AgI of sufficient purity (for the preparation of compounds of sufficient purity cf. for instance Tubandt (119)) are brought between suitable electrodes, for example a platinum cathode and a silver anode, Fig. 4-1, and are electrolyzed within the temperature range of stability of the α-phase, between the transformation point and the melting point, by a current of a few milliamperes, the following is observed. After an experiment, which may last for several hours, it is possible to separate the iodide cylinders from the anode and from each other at the former interfaces, though not from the silver deposited at the cathode. By weighing the anode, the separated cylinders and the cathode part of the system, one can determine the amount of silver dissolved at the anode, deposited at the cathode, and eventual changes in weight of the single cylinders. Thus Tubandt (125) found pure electrolytic conduction, within very narrow limits of error. In these experiments the silver is deposited close to the cathode, without penetrating into the adjacent iodide pellet. With many other solid electrolytes similar experiments fail, because the metal, deposited at the cathode, grows through the crystal, forming thin filaments and causing a metallic short circuit of the system.

Tubandt's method for testing Faraday's law consists in a combination of α-AgI, $BaCl_2$ or other so called protective electrolytes with the substance under investigation, to prevent metal threads from growing through the system. Thus for testing Faraday's law with AgBr, an arrangement as shown in Fig. 4-1 was employed. Usually, it is possible to find a combination which avoids the occurrence of low melting eutectics between the substances used. For instance for AgCl the combination AgCl—AgBr—AgI had to be used.

For sufficiently low temperatures, even ordinary aqueous solutions of electrolytes may be used as protective electrolytes (Tubandt and Reinhold (129)).

Ionic conduction has been found with the following groups of compounds: alkali halides, halides of the alkaline earth metals, silver halides, cuprous halides (which, at low temperatures and in presence of an excess of halogen, show in addition electronic conduction), silver and cuprous sulfides, selenides, tellurides, with additional electronic conduction, thallous halides, lead halides, and Ag_2HgI_4. A certain amount of electrolytic conductivity is almost certainly present in the case of all ionic compounds.

Special difficulties were encountered in the case of α-Ag_2S. Here, Tubandt and co-workers (134, 135, 136) found pure ionic conduction. Later experiments, however, showed that α-Ag_2S is a semi-conductor, with an electrolytic component of fairly high absolute magnitude but which is still small compared to the electronic conductivity (cf. Chap. IX, p. 343).

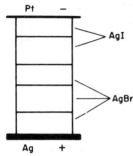

Fig. 4-1.
Tubandt's experimental set up for measuring transference numbers of AgBr, with AgI as protective eletrolyte.

III. Transference numbers

The experimental arrangement, as shown in figure 4-1 may be used also for the determination of transference numbers of solids. Since it is possible to obtain a sharp separation of the component cylinders employed, if the substances are of a high degree of purity, one can weigh the single cylinders after an experiment with an accuracy of almost 0.1 mg. Thus all data are available for the determination of transference numbers. We give one more example, from experiments carried out by Tubandt and co-workers (125, 136) Fig. 4-2.

In the experiment with AgCl, with AgI as protective electrolyte, the weight of all cylinders has remained unchanged during the experiment. At the silver anode an amount of silver has been dissolved equal to the amount of silver deposited in a silver coulometer. Since the weight of the silver

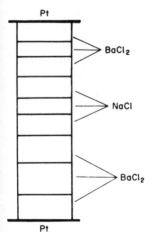

Fig. 4-2. NaCl, with $BaCl_2$ as protective electrolyte.

chloride cylinder next to the anode has remained unchanged, a quantity of silver ions equal to the amount of dissolved silver, must have migrated through the interface between this and the adjacent silver chloride cylinder. Thus 100 per cent conduction by silver ions

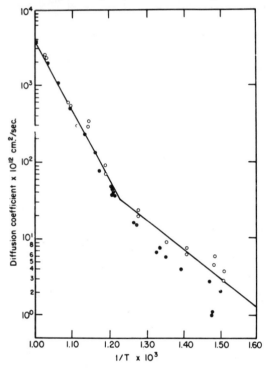

Fig. 4-3. Diffusion coefficient of sodium ions in NaCl, ○ directly measured by radioactive tracer method, ● calculated from conductivity, after Maurer and Mapother.

is occuring. The opposite is true with $BaCl_2$ where 100 per cent conduction by the anions has been observed. The final example, NaCl at 580° C, is intermediate between the two preceding ones, a mobility of either type of ion being observable. Measurements of self-diffusion coefficients of radioactive Na^+-ions in NaCl, by Maurer and Mapother (88), make it probable that transference numbers, derived by standard methods, are not reliable, cf. p. 205.

Maurer and Mapother (88, 85a) measured the rate of diffusion of radioactive Na^{24} in sodium chloride over a wide range of temperature, Fig. 4-3. The coefficient of self diffusion at high temperatures is in good agreement with that calculated from conductivity measurements.

The rate of self diffusion can be represented by an expression

$$D = D_0 \exp\left(-Q/RT\right)$$

with

$$D_0 = 3.13\ \text{cm}^2\ \text{sec}^{-1} \quad Q = 41.4\ \text{kcals for}\ T > 550°\text{C}$$

and

$$D_0 = 1.6 \times 10^{-5}\ \text{cm}^2\ \text{sec}^{-1}\ Q = 17.7\ \text{kcals, for}\ T < 550°\text{C}.$$

Instead of weighing different parts of the system one also may use the change in length for a determination of transference numbers.

Jost and Schweitzer (72) marked the interface between the cylinder, next to the anode and the adjacent one by a thin quartz fibre and measured microscopically the displacement of this fibre, relative to a platinum wire connected with the anode.

Transference numbers of solid electrolytes are contained in the following tables I, II, III, IV.

TABLE I
Temperature dependence of transference numbers
Ionic conductors

								Authors
NaF	$° K$	773	823	843	873	898		Tubandt and co-workers
	$t_{Na} = 1 - t_F$	1.00	1.00	0.97	0.92	0.86		(140)
PbI$_2$	$° K$	428	467	501	528	543	563	611	
	$t_{Pb} = 1 - t_I$	—	—	—	0.39	0.45	0.67	—	Tubandt (140)*
		0.004	0.03	0.12	0.33	0.45	0.60	0.82	Hevesy, Seith (57)**

* from transference measurements, ** from conductivity data of Pb^{++}.

TABLE II
Ionic + electronic conductors

CuCl	$° K$	291	313	451	491	505	527	573	Tubandt (140)
	$t_{el} = 1 - t_{Cu}$	1.0	0.98	0.95	0.71	0.50	0.10	0.02	
CuBr	$° K$	300	426	464	515	572	618		Tubandt (140)
	$t_{el} = 1 - t_{Cu}$	1.0	0.98	0.92	0.78	0.13	0.016		Geiler (46)

t_{el} = transference number of electron.

TABLE III
Transference numbers in NaCl (selected values)

$T °K$	t_{Cl}			
673	0.00			Tubandt (136), Phipps (94), Seelen (107)
773	0.016*		0.05**	*Tubandt (136), **Phipps (94)
823	0.06*		0.01**	*Tubandt (136), **Joffé (66)
853	0.1 average of 6 values for different samples			Tubandt (136)
873	0.06*	0.1*	0.36**	*Tubandt (136), **Phipps (94)
	0.08	0.04		Joffé (66)
	0.4 average of 4 values			Jost, Schweitzer (72)
893	0.12*		0.23**	*Tubandt (136), **Phipps (94)

TABLE IV

Concentration dependence of transference numbers

Component 1	2	Tempera-ture $°K$		mol per cent of second component 10	25	50	75	Authors
AgCl—NaCl		553	t_{Na} $= 1 - t_{Ag}$	—	0.015	0.032	0.055	Tubandt, Reinhold (128)
AgBr—CuBr		563	t_{Cu} $= 1 - t_{Ag}$	0.33	—	0.50	—	Reinhold, Schulz (99)
AgI—CuI		481	t_{Cu} $= 1 - t_{Ag}$	0.07	—	0.13	0.29	Tubandt (140)
Ag_2HgI_4		333	$t_{Ag} = 1 - t_{Hg}$ $= 0.94$	—	—	—	—	Ketelaar (77)
$PbCl_2$—$PbBr_2$		523	t_{Br} $= 1 - t_{Cl}$	—	0.21	0.49	0.89	Tubandt (140)

IV. Conductivity

Conductivity measurements with solid electrolytes can be carried out by the standard methods employed with liquid electrolytes,

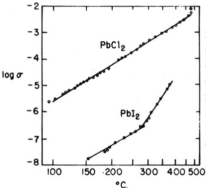

using alternating current. The specimen under investigation may be in the form of a compressed cylinder, of a single crystal, of a polycrystalline aggregate, molten and crystallized in a tube of known resistance capacity, etc. (cf. 18, 26, 48, 85, 93, 94, 95, 105, 108, 119, 120, 140). The results, thus obtained, can often be represented by a single exponential

Fig. 4-4. Conductivity of $PbCl_2$ and PbI_2 after Seith.

$$\sigma = \sigma_0 \exp\left(- Q/RT\right) \quad [4.10]$$

cf. figures 4-4 and 4-5 and the data contained in table VI.

For measurements covering a wider range of temperature, at least two exponential terms must be used

$$\sigma = \sigma_{10} \exp\left(- Q_1/RT\right) + \sigma_{20} \exp\left(- Q_2/RT\right)$$

cf. figures 4-4, 4-5, 4-6, 4-7, 4-8, 4-9 and tables V and VI.

As discussed before, a number of exponentials might be necessary for the representation of the different types of mobility involved in ionic conduction. Usually, however, the limited experimental accuracy does not permit the determination of the constants of more than two exponential terms.

TABLE V

Conductivity data of ionic crystals

$$\sigma = \sigma_0 \exp(-B/T), \quad B = Q/R$$

Alkali halides

Substance	Melting point °K	σ (Melting point) Ohm⁻¹·cm⁻¹	Temperature Interval °K	σ₀ Ohm⁻¹·cm⁻¹	B °K	Temperature Interval °K	σ₀ Ohm⁻¹·cm⁻¹	B °K	Authors
LiCl	879	$1.5 \cdot 10^{-3}$	303—623	1.15	6850	673—823	$2.5 \cdot 10^{5}$	16420	Ginnings, Phipps
LiBr	625		303—573	3.3	6450	623—773	$4.2 \cdot 10^{5}$	14100	(48)
LiI	723		303—423	0.14	4230	523—623	$1.8 \cdot 10^{5}$	10680	
NaF	1265	$1.7 \cdot 10^{-3}$				603—1253	$1.3 \cdot 10^{3}$	16520	Phipps, Lansing,
NaCl	1073	$1.3 \cdot 10^{-3}$	643—833	2.6—3.6	10200	833—1073	$4.3 \cdot 10^{4}$	20500	Cooke (93)
NaBr	1008	$1.3 \cdot 10^{-3}$	523—673	0.2	9270	873—1003	$1.5 \cdot 10^{6}$	19350	
NaI	934	$4.0 \cdot 10^{-3}$	443—623	0.06	6950	623—873	$8.1 \cdot 10^{3}$	14260	
KCl	1041	$2.0 \cdot 10^{-4}$	523—723	0.13—2.0	11500	773—998	$1—1.5 \cdot 10^{6}$	23500	Phipps, Partridge
KBr	1001	$2.0 \cdot 10^{-4}$	523—673	0.01—10	11300	773—998	$1—1.3 \cdot 10^{6}$	22900	(95)
KI	953	$1.5 \cdot 10^{-4}$	493—673	0.09—0.3	9900	723—948	$3.1—4.9 \cdot 10^{4}$	18750	

TABLE VI

Conductivity data of ionic crystals

Further halides

Substance	Melting point $°K$	Temperature Interval $°K$	σ (Melting point) Ohm$^{-1}\cdot$cm.$^{-1}$	σ_0 Ohm$^{-1}\cdot$cm.$^{-1}$	B $°K$	Authors
α-CuBr	761	743—761		$2.1\cdot10^3$	4870	Geiler (46)
β-CuBr		694—743		$1.2\cdot10^2$	2960	
γ-CuBr		513—653		$8.1\cdot10^{10}$	17500	
α-CuI	875	675—875		$2.5\cdot10^2$	2300	Tubandt, Reinhold, Jost (133)
AgCl	728	523—723	$6\cdot10^{-2}$	$1.5\cdot10^6$	11950	Tubandt, Lorenz
AgBr	695	523—692	$1\cdot10^{-1}$	$4.2\cdot10^6$	11030	(119—120)
α-AgI	828	417.6—823	2.5	5.5	600	
β-AgI		398—417.6		$3.9\cdot10^6$	9660	
α-Ag$_2$HgI$_4$		323—366.4		$4\cdot10^2$	4300	Ketelaar(76—77)
TlCl	700	below melting point	$5\cdot10^{-3}$	$2.5\cdot10^3$	9100	Lehfeldt (85)
TlBr	730		$5\cdot10^{-3}$	$1.7\cdot10^3$	9200	
PbCl$_2$	773		$5\cdot10^{-3}$	1.4	5410	Gyulai (51)
PbCl$_2$+ 0,005 KCl				6.1	4470	
PbI$_2$	676	423—648	$3\cdot10^{-5}$	$9.8\cdot10^{-4}$ 1.2$\cdot10^5$	4710* 15000**	Seith (108—109)

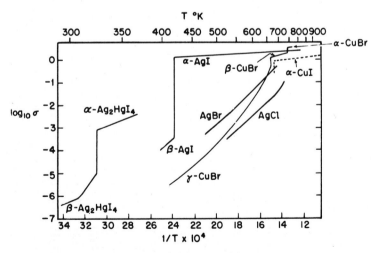

Fig. 4-5. Conductivity of some silver and cuprous halides, and of Ag$_2$HgI$_4$, with cation mobility.

* Partial conductivity of iodine ions.   ** Partial conductivity of lead ions.

Measured conductivities and constants of exponential formulae representing measured conductivities are reproduced in the above-quoted figures and tables.

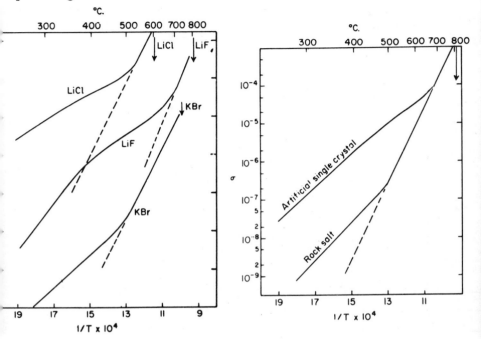

Fig. 4-6. Conductivity (log σ) of LiCl, LiF and KBr, as function of $1/T$, after Lehfeldt. Arrows indicate melting points.

Fig. 4-7. Conductivity (log σ) of two specimens of NaCl, after Lehfeldt. Arrow indicates melting point.

Curves of the type shown in Fig. 4-7 where log σ has been plotted versus $1/T$ are found quite often; perhaps they might be encountered generally if measurements were extended over a sufficiently wide range of temperatures. There are two almost straight branches, the one with the greater slope corresponding to the higher temperature, the transition from one to the other being either sharp or more or less smooth. A curve of this type is to be expected if the conductivity is given by a sum of two exponential terms

$$\sigma = \sigma_{10} \exp \left(- Q_1/RT\right) + \sigma_{20} \exp \left(- Q_2/RT\right) \qquad [4.12]$$

and if Q_2 is considerably larger than Q_1, for instance $Q_2 \approx 2 Q_1$, and if at the same time σ_{20} is considerably larger than σ_{10}, for instance by several powers of ten.

The explanation, first given by Smekal (114), may be correct in a number of cases. The term with the higher value of the constants and, therefore, the upper branch of the conductivity curve corresponds to the conduction due to the normal lattice, while the other term corresponds to the conduction of surface particles. Their number is much smaller than that of the lattice particles, and consequently σ_{10} is much smaller than σ_{20}, on the other hand the energy of activation,

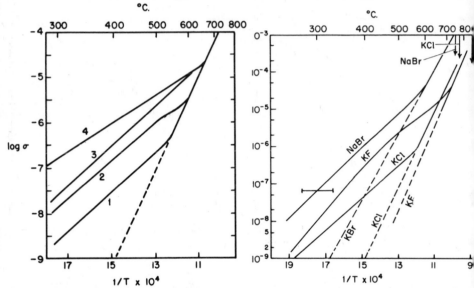

Fig. 4-8. Conductivity of KCl with additives, after Lehfeldt. 1. 0.2 Mol% Cu+ and Ag+. 2. natural KCl crystal. 3. 0.04 Mol% Pb++. 4. 0.07 Mol% Pb++.

Fig. 4-9. Conductivity of NaBr, KF and KCl, after Lehfeldt. Arrows indicate melting points.

Q_1, may be much smaller for the surface particles than the corresponding energy for the lattice particles, thus favouring surface conduction at low temperatures.

The above explanation is certainly not in all cases valid. In PbI$_2$, for instance, Fig. 4-4, the conductivity is represented by the formula

$$\sigma = 9.78 \cdot 10^{-4} e^{-\frac{9360}{RT}} + 1.15 \cdot 10^5 e^{-\frac{30\,000}{RT}} \qquad [4.13]$$

where the first term corresponds to the conductivity of the Pb-ions while the second one is the partial conductivity of the I-ions*.

There are still other possibilities for an explanation. When conduction is due to disorder of the lattice, as may be assumed with

* Mott and Gurney (9) have rejected this explanation, based on measurements of transference numbers by Tubandt (136) and on measurement of

certainty, then the establishment of the equilibrium of disorder involves a diffusion process, especially in the case of Schottky disorder, where vacancies must diffuse from the surface into the crystal. Though the diffusion of vacancies occurs much faster than the diffusion of the average lattice particles, given by the ratio of number of lattice particles/number of vacancies, the establishment of the disorder equilibrium requires some time, and it may well be that, below a certain temperature, equilibrium of disorder cannot be established during the time available for an experiment. Then the equilibrium of disorder will be frozen in at a certain temperature T_0, and below this temperature the temperature dependence of the conductivity will only be given by that of the mobility of the disordered particles. On the other hand, the constant factor σ_{10} will contain a factor equal to the degree of disorder at T_0, which is very small compared with unity. Thus the observations are readily explained by this assumption and thus one would have, for $T > T_0$

$$\sigma = \sigma_0 \exp\left(-\frac{E/2 + U}{RT}\right) \tag{4.14}$$

and for $T < T_0$

$$\sigma = \sigma_0 \exp\left(-\frac{E}{2RT_0}\right) \exp\left(\frac{-U}{RT}\right) \tag{4.15}$$

This view is supported by the experiments of Breckenridge (32), cf., however, Grimley (49).

Finally, impurities might be responsible for the observed shape of the curve $\log \sigma$ versus $1/T$. It is known that electrolytic conduction is highly sensitive toward small impurities, the more sensitive the lower the value of the conductivity. Hence it is possible that at sufficiently high temperatures the correct conductivity of the crystal is observed while with falling temperature the influence of impurities becomes more and more noticeable.

Probably all the influences discussed above play a role occasionally.

Examples of the influence of additives upon the conductivity of solid salts are found in the figures 4-8, 4-10, 4-11, 4-12, 4-13 and in table VII.

Koch and Wagner (80) have studied the influence of lead, and of cadmium, halides upon the conductivity of silver chloride and bromide. As discussed elsewhere, Chap. III p. 153, this was done in order to study the equilibrium of disorder within these compounds. The

diffusion and of electrolytic conductivity of PbI_2 by Hevesy and co-workers (57, 108). We agree with Mott and Gurney in so far as the term, representing the partial conductivity of iodine ions can scarcely refer to lattice ions.

equilibrium of disorder, corresponding, with very high probability, to the Frenkel type (cf. p. 153), with equal numbers of vacancies in the silver-ion lattice and of interstitial silver ions, is shifted toward the side of the vacancies by the addition of bivalent ions (cf. p. 94). The

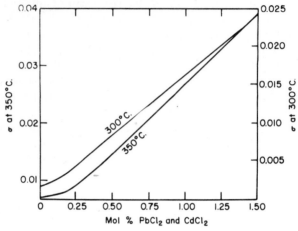

Fig. 4-10. Conductivity of AgCl with added PbCl₂ or CdCl₂, after Koch and Wagner.

lead or cadmium ions are taken up by the normal lattice of the cations, one new vacancy being created for every bivalent ion dissolved. The equilibrium thus obtained, to a first approximation, is given by the simple mass-action law. If the concentration of added bivalent ions is high compared with the original number of disordered particles, the degree of disorder will be solely determined by the concentration of the added substance. Consequently, in this case, practically only vacancies will be present, in a concentration independent of temperature. If the concentration of the added substance is such that for sufficiently high temperatures it is small compared with the concentration of the normally disordered particles, while for sufficiently low temperatures it is

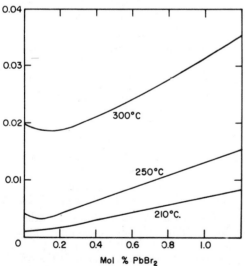

Fig. 4-11. Conductivity of AgBr + PbBr₂, for three temperatures, after Koch and Wagner.

high compared with the equilibrium value of the pure substance, then we shall again have the case of Fig. 4-8. At high temperatures the normal conductivity occurs, the temperature coefficient being determined by both the energy of disorder E and the energy barrier for migration U, while at low temperatures there is a fixed number of vacancies, and the temperature coefficient is due to the energy barrier only.

In figures 4-10 and 4-11 the conductivity of the silver halides is shown as function of the composition, i.e., the amount of added lead or cadmium halide. As is to be expected, for large additions, which are still within the range of miscibility, the conductivity increases linearly with the concentration of the additive. The behaviour of

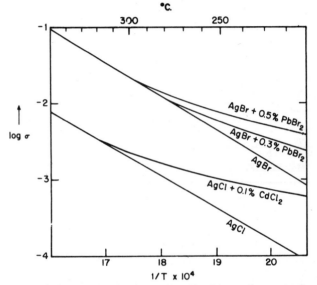

Fig. 4-12. Conductivity of AgCl and AgBr and of anomalous mixed crystals with CdCl$_2$ and with PbBr$_2$, respectively, as function of $1/T$, after Koch and Wagner.

silver bromide with small amounts of lead bromide is quite characteristic. Here a decrease in conductivity is first observed, the conductivity curve passing through a minimum. This is to be expected if the mobility of the interstitial ions is higher than that of the vacancies. Then small additions of bivalent ions will decrease the conductivity because the decrease in number of the particles with higher mobility has a stronger effect than the equivalent increase in number of particles with smaller mobility*.

* In Fig. 4-12, the conductivity of these mixed crystals is shown as a function of temperature, exhibiting the transition from a region of high temperature dependence to one of low temperature dependence.

Croatto and co-workers (35, 38) carried out investigations analogous to those of Koch and Wagner (80), with "anomalous" mixed crystals of $SrF_2 + LaF_3$ and of $CeO_2 + La_2O_3$. The conductivity curves in the system $SrF_2 + LaF_3$, as a function of the LaF_3 concentration, for several temperatures, are quite analogous to those obtained by Koch and Wagner, Fig. 4-13. Further details are seen from the following tables VII and VIII.

The results obtained by the same author with the system $CeO_2 + La_2O_3$ are not as unambiguous as those for the above system of fluorides. With increasing content of La_2O_3 the concentration of anion vacancies in the mixed crystals increases, and the conductivity increases too, for not too great concentrations of the added oxide. With the concentration of La_2O_3 further increasing, however, the conductivity passes through a maximum and then dereases. The authors explain this effect by a decrease of mobility of the anions with increasing concentration of lattice defects.

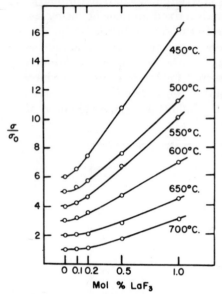

Fig. 4-13. Electrolytic conductivity in system $SrF_2 + LaF_3$, after Croatto. Scale of ordinate shifted by one unit for successive curves. Ordinate: relative conductivity, referred to pure SrF_2 as unit.

TABLE VII

Electric conductivity of anomalous mixed crystals $SrF_2 + LaF_3$ as function of temperature and composition (Croatto and Bruno (38))

$T^\circ K$	0	0.1	0.2	0.5	1	5	10	mol per cent LaF_3
1373	1.7	1.3	1.4	1.5	1.1	1.1	1.0	$\sigma \cdot 10^1$ Ohm$^{-1} \cdot$ cm.$^{-1}$
1173	5.5	1.9	2.7	3.5	2.5	2.0	1.8	$\sigma \cdot 10^2$ Ohm$^{-1} \cdot$ cm.$^{-1}$
973	1.3	1.2	1.4	2.2	4.0	3.3	3.2	$\sigma \cdot 10^3$ Ohm$^{-1} \cdot$ cm.$^{-1}$
773	2.5	2.8	4.5	9.0	18.0	14	22	$\sigma \cdot 10^5$ Ohm$^{-1} \cdot$ cm.$^{-1}$

R. G. Breckenridge (32) confirmed the results of Wagner and Koch's (80) measurements by the observation of a new low frequency dispersion in ionic crystals. Fig. 4-14 shows the dielectric properties of a NaCl crystal in the frequency region under consideration, dielectric constant and loss tangent. In Fig. 4-15 the loss tangent is reproduced as function of temperature for sodium fluoride. At a frequency of 10^3 cycles per sec. the maximum of the loss tangent is observed at $137°$ C. The loss tangent of silver chloride, Fig. 4-16,

TABLE VIII

Temperature dependence of product $K = x_{F_v} \cdot x_{F_i}{}^*$ and of the mobility $u_{F_i} \approx u_{F_v}$ (Croatto and Bruno (38))

$T°~K$	$K \cdot 10^7$	$u_{F_i} \cdot$ cm.^{2}/sec. $\cdot$ Volt	
973	6.9	1.3×10^{-4}	
923	4.9	7.9×10^{-5}	
873	2.4	3.5×10^{-5}	$\log K = -\ 14900/4.57\ T - 2.82$
823	1.2	1.6×10^{-5}	$\log u_{F_i} = -\ 23900/4.57\ T + 1.55$
773	1.2	6.2×10^{-6}	
723	0.5	$2\ \ \times 10^{-6}$	

shows two peaks. Breckenridge attributes the observed effects to a jumping of mobile ions. In the case of alkali halides, with Schottky defects, there are practically only cation holes with sufficient mobility

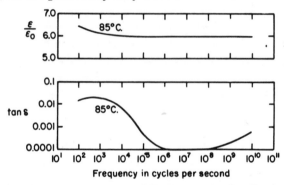

Fig. 4-14. Dielectric properties of NaCl crystal, after Breckenridge; $\varkappa/\varkappa_0$, dielectric constant referred to the value for $\nu = 0$, and loss tangent.

at low temperatures, giving rise to the one observed peak. In silver chloride, silver ion vacancies and interstitial silver ions are of comparable mobility, accounting for the two observed peaks.

The quantitative theory leads to a relation

$$2\pi\, \nu_m\, \tau_0 = \exp\left(-\,Q/R\,T\right) \qquad\qquad [4.14]$$

where ν_m is the frequency for which, at a given temperature T, the maximum of the dielectric loss has been found, τ_0 has been identified approximately with the time constant for the frequency of lattice vibrations, and Q is the energy barrier to be surmounted by a migrat-

* Lattice concentration $x_{F_i} = n_{F_i}/n_F$, n_F number of fluorine ions per c.c., n_{F_i} number of interstitial fluorine ions.

ing ion. Q values, thus calculated for the alkali halides and for silver chloride, are in reasonable, though not in complete, agreement with

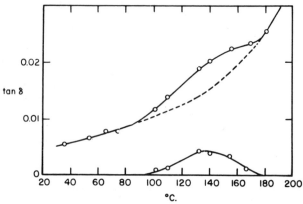

Fig. 4-15. Loss tangent of NaF crystal, as function of temperature, after Breckenridge.

values derived theoretically or from diffusion measurements in the region of temperature-independent disorder (Maurer and Mapother

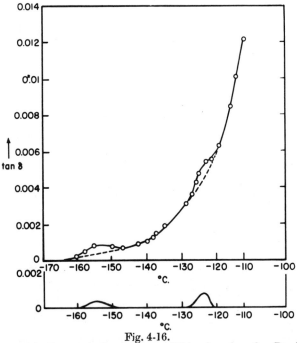

Fig. 4-16.
Loss tangent of AgCl crystal, showing two additional peaks, after Breckenridge.

(88)). Breckenridge further calculates the concentration of lattice defects from the maximum value of the loss tangent. The values, thus obtained, are rather high, indicating that the equilibrium disorder corresponding to a temperature near the melting point has been frozen in. This assumption is in accordance with the observation that annealing of the crystals used, at a temperature of 500°C, destroys the anomalous dielectric effects.

Kolthoff and co-workers (81) found an high thermal mobility of the constituent particles of freshly precipitated silver bromide. Fresh, air-dried silver bromide, when exposed to radioactive bromine gas (Br_2^*) gave an exchange according to the equation

$$2\,AgBr + Br_2^* = 2\,AgBr^* + Br_2. \qquad [4.15]$$

Within 100 minutes about 60 % of the bromide ions of the silver bromide had participated in the exchange, while only of the order of magnitude of 1 % would have participated in the exchange if the effect were restricted to the surface (as determined by the adsorption of dyes).

Kolthoff and Shapiro (81) measured the low temperature conductivity of silver bromide. Assuming a surface conductivity proportional to the measured surface, S, they propose an equation for the conductivity

$$\sigma = [A \exp(-E/2\,RT) + KS] \exp(-|U/RT) \qquad [4.16]$$

where E is the energy of Frenkel disorder, U the (average) energy barrier for Frenkel centres of disorder. The experimental values can be represented by an equation

$$\sigma = 3 \times 10^5 \exp(-18{,}000/RT) + A_s \exp(-8{,}300/RT) \qquad [4.17]$$

where the constant A_s varies proportionally with the surface. The energy barrier, 8300 cal. per mole, is in agreement with Koch and Wagner's (80) value. Transference experiments show that conduction is due to the motion of silver ions.

These observations do not explain the mobility of the bromide ions, as observed in the exchange experiments. One might consider the presence of associated Schottky holes, as discussed by Seitz (15) and Dienes (39) for alkali halides, which would not manifest themselves in conductance or transference experiments.

The influence of pressure on conductivity has been studied by Jost and Nehlep (74) and by Jost, Mennenöh and Müller (75). This effect has been discussed theoretically, Chap. III p. 149, 152. In their experiments it was possible to apply pressures up to 300 atmospheres at temperatures up to 400°C. In all experiments a decrease in conductivity with rising pressure was observed, of the order of magnitude of a few percent per 100 atmospheres pressure increase.

V. Diffusion in ionic crystals

1. Experimental methods and results

For the investigation of interdiffusion in ionic crystals the standard arrangements, as given in the mathematical treatment of Chap. I may be used. In general, the diffusion of one type of ion will be observed, for instance that of the cations in the examples of $AgI + CuI$, Ag_2S and Cu_2S, etc., and of the anions in $BaCl_2 + BaBr_2$. For such experiments two specimens differing with respect to the concentration of the diffusing species must be brought into close contact. One may take the pure components, such as, for instance, AgI and CuI etc., but since generally the diffusion coefficient may depend on concentration, it is advisable to take the concentration differences as small as possible, compatible with the accuracy of the analysis. Further it is preferable to choose an experimental arrangement which gives one-dimensional diffusion only, thus facilitating considerably the evaluation of the experiments. Especially if for concentration dependent diffusion coefficients Boltzmann's method of evaluation must be used, it is essential to have one-dimensional diffusion (cf. Chap. I p. 31). By choosing plates, cylinders etc. of differing concentrations, which are brought into contact in such a way that diffusion occurs only perpendicularly to the common interface, this condition may easily be fulfilled. Close contact may be established by simple pressing, by means of a screw or by weights, or by melting one layer upon the other. In this case care must be taken to avoid appreciable diffusion in the liquid phase before crystallization. In principle such a previous diffusion need not interfere with the proper experiment. For it is possible to determine the concentration distribution, due to this preceding diffusion experimentally, and further it is possible to integrate the one-dimensional diffusion equation for arbitrary initial conditions. But such a procedure would be very laborious and, therefore, should be avoided. One may take one or more layers of each of the two interdiffusing samples. Experiments have often been adapted to Kawalki's tables, for an easy and quick evaluation, by choosing one layer of the one component and three layers, of equal height, of the other one. When working with substances of sufficient purity it is often possible, as in Tubandt's (122, 123) transference experiments (cf. p. 183) to separate the samples after the end of an experiment at their original sharp interfaces. Then analysis may simply be obtained by weighing the single cylinders etc. Otherwise chemical or physical methods of analysis must be used. If either an easy separation at the original interface is impossible or if one wishes to have more layers for analysis than had been used in the preporation of the diffusion system, then thin layers may be taken off the system, by turning on a lathe, by grinding etc., occasionally by chemical dissolution. The height of the single layer may be determined by direct measurements of length, or by weighing.

TABLE IX
Coefficients of interdiffusion*

Cu in AgI	$T°K$	451	500	594	701	Tubandt, Rein-
$D_{Cu+} \cdot 10^5$ cm.²/sec.		1.33	1.74	2.47	3.42	hold, Jost (133)

$D_{Cu} = 16 \cdot 10^{-5} \cdot$ exp $(—1130/T)$ cm.²/sec.

Ag in CuI	$T°K$	685	722	753		Tubandt, Rein-
$D_{Ag+} \cdot 10^5$ cm.²/sec.		1.56	2.25	2.38		hold, Jost (133)

Ag in γ-CuI	$T°K$	527	621	645		Tubandt, Rein-
$D_{Ag+} \cdot 10^6$ cm.²/sec.		0.007	1.2	5.5		hold, Jost (133)

Li in AgI	$T°K$	473	523	578	653	Tubandt, Jost (133)
$D_{Li+} \cdot 10^6$ cm.²/sec.		4.5	11	15	23	

Cu in Ag₂S	$T°K$	443	503	603	693	Tubandt, Rein-
$D_{Cu+} \cdot 10^6$ cm.²/sec.		0.4	4.1	6.3	16.5	hold, Jost (133)

Cu in Ag₂S	$T°K$	493	601	708	991	Braune, Kahn
$D_{Cu+} \cdot 10^6$ cm.²/sec.		4.7	7.9	17	23	(30)**

$D_{Cu+} = 1.2 \cdot 10^{-4} \cdot$ exp $(— 1590/T)$ cm.²/sec.

Ag in Cu₂S	$T°K$	503	603	693		Tubandt, Rein-
$D_{Ag+} \cdot 10$ cm.²/sec.		1.85	4.6	9.4		hold, Jost (133)

Ag in Cu₂S	$T°K$	586	823	986	1192	Braune, Kahn
$D_{Ag+} \cdot 10^6$ cm.²/sec.		7.3	22.9	33	487	(30)**

$D_{Ag+} = 0.3 \cdot 10^{-5} \cdot$ exp $(— 2290/T)$ cm.²/sec.

Na in AgCl	$573°K$ $D_{Na+} = 2.1 \times 10^{-10}$ cm.²/sec.	Tubandt, Rein-hold, Jost (133)
Cu in AgCl	$511°K$ $D_{Cu+} = 2.4 \times 10^{-7}$ cm.²/sec.	Tubandt, Rein-hold, Jost (133)
Na in AgBr	$573°K$ $D_{Na+} = 2.3 \times 10^{-9}$ cm.²/sec.	Jost (67)
Li in AgBr	$573°K$ $D_{Li+} = 7.6 \times 10^{-8}$ cm.²/sec.	Tubandt, Rein-hold, Jost (133)
Ag in CuBr	$518°K$ $D_{Ag+} = 5.1 \times 10^{-5}$ cm.²/sec.	Tubandt, Rein-hold, Jost (133)

Se in Cu₂S	$T°K$	844	967	Braune, Kahn
$D_{Se} \times 10^9$ cm.²/sec.		1.1	4.9	(30)**

Cl in AgI	$453°K$ $D_{Cl} < 1.1 \times 10^{-10}$ cm.²/sec.	Jost (67)

* Experimental arrangement: interdiffusion of two mixed crystals or of pure component and one mixed crystal with concentration difference of the order of magnitude of 5 mol per cent.

** On account of algebraic error the original values are four times too high.

The height of a single layer employed in such experiments may vary between about 1 cm. and $\sim 10^{-3}$ cm., if the layer is taken off by grinding. By using the formula for the mean square displacement

$$\overline{\varDelta x^2} = 2\,Dt$$

one obtains a rough estimate of the sensitivity of the method. With a length of 1 cm. and a time of 1 hour diffusion coefficients as large as some 10^{-5} cm.²/sec. may be measured, the largest values observed with solids, for instance, in the case of AgI and CuI, Ag_2S and Cu_2S etc. With times of the order of magnitude of 100 days and layers of 10^{-3} cm. thickness, diffusion measurements are possible with diffusion coefficients as low as some 10^{-14} cm.²/sec., or somewhat below.

Experimental values of diffusion coefficients in ionic crystals are listed in Tables IX, X, XI.

As discussed, Chap. III, p. 147, it is possible to reduce observed coefficients of interdiffusion to the value of the coefficient of self-diffusion, if transference numbers and conductivities of the mixed crystal under consideration and of the pure substance are available, cf. Table XII.

TABLE X

Diffusion of copper in Cu_2Se of varying composition

$Cu_{1.89}Se/Cu_{1.78}Se$	$723°K$ $D_{Cu} = 5.6 \times 10^{-4}$ cm.²/sec.	Reinhold, Möhring (100)
	$298°K$ $D_{Cu} = 0.2 \times 10^{-5}$ cm.²/sec.	Reinhold, Möhring (100)

TABLE XI

Interdiffusion of silver in Cu_2Se of varying composition
(Reinhold, Seidel (101))

System	438	471	545	$°K$
$Cu_{1.77}\,Ag_{0.05}\,Se/Cu_{1.77}\,Se$	0.4	0.7	1.6	$\left.\vphantom{\begin{matrix}1\\1\\1\end{matrix}}\right\}$ $D \times 10^6$ cm.²/sec.
$Cu_{1.89}\,Ag_{0.05}\,Se/Cu_{1.89}\,Se$	1.6	2	3.6	
$Cu_{1.95}\,Ag_{0.05}\,Se/Cu_{1.95}\,Se$	1.1	1.3	4.4	

The above values are higher than those for self diffusion or interdiffusion, on account of the change in free energy.

2. Diffusion of color centers, of hydrogen and halogens in alkali halides

The alkali halides dissolve alkali vapors, producing so called color centres (*F*-centres), halogen vapors and hydrogen, as has been thoroughly investigated by Pohl and co-workers (11, 12), (cf. especially the comprehensive discussions by Mott and Gurney (9) and Seitz

TABLE XII

Self-diffusion coefficients calculated from interdiffusion, conductivity and
transference numbers (cf. p. 147)

Ag in AgCl	511 °K		D_{obs} cm.²/sec.	D_{calc} cm.²/sec.	Tubandt, Rein-
		NaCl	4.1×10^{-11}	10.4×10^{-10}	hold, Jost (132)
		CuCl	2.4×10^{-7}	24.3×10^{-10}	

Ag in AgI	$T°\ K$	mol per cent CuI	$D_{Cu^+ obs}$ cm.²/sec.	D_{calc} cm.²/sec.	Tubandt, Rein-
					hold, Jost (132)
	573	6	2.2×10^{-5}	2.7×10^{-5}	
	573	34.5	1.3×10^{-5}	2.0×10^{-5}	
	613	6	2.7×10^{-5}	3.2×10^{-5}	
	613	55	1.3×10^{-5}	2.9×10^{-5}	

Ag in AgBr	Mol per cent CuBr in mixed crystals	80	65	50	Reinhold, Schulz(99)
	D_{Cu} (obs, mixed crystal) cm.²/sec.	2.4×10^{-6}	3.7×10^{-6}	5.4×10^{-6}	
	D (calc, pure AgBr)	5.2×10^{-8}	4.4×10^{-8}	4.1×10^{-8}	

(15)). The experimental facts have been reviewed in Chap. VI, p. 281.
The solubility is certainly due to the presence of vacancies in the
alkali halide lattice. But despite the high mobility of the vacancies

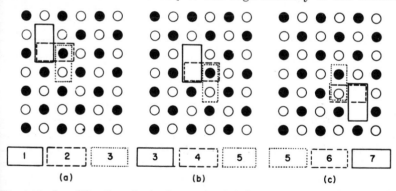

Fig. 4-17a, b, c. Migration of pair of vacancies. 1, 2, 3, 4, 5, 6, 7 consecutive sites of pair.

it is not possible to explain the high mobility observed with these
added substances without further assumptions, except in the case of
the color centres. For if either halogen or hydrogen molecules have
been taken up by vacancies, the high mobility of these vacancies has
been lost, the mobility depending on the possibility that ions from
the vicinity can jump into the vacant position which has now been
occupied by the dissolved particles. Therefore a high mobility of
foreign molecules dissolved in vacant lattice sites is possible only if

additional vacancies are associated with the original ones. Such an assumption is quite in line with Seitz's (15) deductions in the case of darkening of crystals by x-rays and with the calculations of Dienes (39). Therefore it seems most probable to assume that halogen and hydrogen molecules are dissolved by associated pairs of vacancies (or higher aggregates) which have preserved their mobility, as is evident from Fig. 4-17. Data obtained by Arzybyschew (22, 23, 24, 25) and others are summarized in Table XIII.

TABLE XIII

Mobilities u [$u = u_0 \exp{(-B/T)}$] and calculated diffusion coefficients [$D = u k T \approx D_0 \exp{(-B/T)}$] of some metals in sodium chloride

System	$10^{12} u_0$ cm./sec. dyne	D_0 cm.^{2}/sec.	$B \degree K$	Authors
Cu—NaCl	3.7	0.5	12600	Arzybyschew, Borissow (23, 24)
Ni—NaCl	1.7	0.2	12700	Parfianowitsch, Pogodaev (92, 96)
Au—NaCl	1.2	0.2	12300	Bogomolowa (28)
Cu—KCl	401	55	15200	Bogomolowa (28)
Au—KCl	83	11	15000	Arzybyschew, Bogomolowa (22, 28)

3. Diffusion of radioactive elements, with special reference to self diffusion

If instead of normal elements radioactive elements are used for diffusion measurements the highly sensitive methods of activity measurements are available, replacing normal analytical methods. Radioactive elements may be used for normal diffusion experiments, as is, for instance, the case with Hahn's (53) emanation method (cf. Chap. VII, p. 314). The special value of this method lies in the possibility of measuring coefficients of self diffusion, by employing radioactive isotopes of the constituent atoms of a compound under investigation, for instance radioactive lead isotopes with $PbCl_2$ or PbI_2. Thus Hevesy (54) was the first to determine coefficients of self diffusion. The application of radioactive elements offers further advantages than simply those of technique. It is possible to work under exactly the same conditions as one would without radioactive elements, as, for instance, in the investigation of the self diffusion of lead in lead sulfide by Anderson and Richards (21). These authors used compressed pellets of the sulfide, coated at one end with the radioactive sulfide. After the pellets had been kept for a sufficient time at the temperature of the experiment, the activity at the end which had been coated was measured, with the original pellet and after several thin layers, of the order of magnitude of 10^{-3} cm., had been removed by grinding. Thus the distribution of activity as a function of the depth of penetration was determined. The quantitative evaluation is easily achieved by means of the methods discussed in Chap. I. Diffusion coefficients of the order of magnitude of 10^{-11} cm.^{2} sec.$^{-1}$ were determined by this method. In Table XIV values of diffusion coefficients, thus obtained, are reproduced; they can be represented by an exponential

$$D = 1.3 \exp\left(-\, 42,000/R\,T\right) \text{cm.}^2 \text{ sec.}^{-1}.$$

The values are, however, not a true constant of the material, as was proved by further analysis of the experimental data and by special experiments First there is a variation of the diffusion coefficient with depth of penetration, which for ordinary diffusion would be quite normal, the diffusion coefficient being a function of the concentration of the diffusing substance. In the case of diffusion of isotopes an analogous effect is possible only if the composition of the substance varies due to some other reason. In the case of lead sulfide, this must be due to a variation of the sulfur content of the compound.

TABLE XIV
Self-diffusion of lead ion in PbS as function of time
(Anderson and Richards (21))

$T^\circ\,K$	733	833	938	1043
D_{Pb} cm^2/sec.	$4.3 \cdot 10^{-13}$	$2.2 \cdot 10^{-11}$	$1.3 \cdot 10^{-10}$	$1.4 \cdot 10^{-9}$
hours	265	97.5	71	67

TABLE XV
Self-diffusion of lead ion in PbS as function of depth of penetration
(Anderson and Richards (21))

	$843^\circ\,K$ Excess of sulfur						$833^\circ\,K$ Excess of lead					
	decreasing with increasing depth of penetration											
Depth of penetration $\times\,10^3$ cm	0.6	1.9	2.6	3.1	5.2	6.6	0.3	1.7	2.9	4.1	5.3	6.4
$D \cdot 10^{11}$ cm^2/sec.	33.0	6.1	4.0	3.4	4.0	3.3	0.04	0.3	0.5	0.9	1.3	1.2

Though detailed measurements with this substance are not known, it seems very probable that it contains a small excess of sulfur, and a corresponding number of vacancies in the cation lattice. Then an increase in partial pressure of sulfur should increase the degree of disorder, and consequently the rate of diffusion. The authors carried out two series of experiments, the one in presence of sulfur vapor, the other in vacuo. As was to be expected, the coefficient of self diffusion was higher in the sulfur rich sample, 2.3×10^{-11}, as compared with 7.9×10^{-12} cm^2/sec. for the sample heated in vacuo. The measurements refer to a temperature of $853 \pm 10°$ K.

The change of rate of diffusion with depth of penetration is seen from Table XV. In the first series, with sulfur vapor, the sulfur content and the rate of diffusion decrease with increasing depth of penetration, while in the second series, taken from one of the main experiments, the sulfur content and the rate of diffusion crease with increasing depth of penetration*.

If diffusion occurs only by means of vacancies created by an excess of sulfur this would explain the comparatively small constant factor multiplying the exponential in the above empirical formula. Then the energy of 42,000 cal. per mol would represent the energy barrier to be surmounted by migrating vacancies. This rather high value, however, might be possible in case of bivalent ions.

There is another great advantage, afforded by the properties of radioactive elements. Instead of using the conventional arrangement of diffusion experiments, where layers not much less than 10^{-3} cm. can be separated mechanically and analyzed, it is possible to have the finite range of the radiation, emitted by the element, determine the depth of the layer involved. Thus Hevesy and Obrutschewa (56) measured the α-ray activity of the lead isotope Ra D, with a range of $\sim 3 \times 10^{-3}$ cm., in lead. The sensitivity, thus obtained, is not higher than that in the above discussed measurements. But Hevesy and Seith (57) used the lead isotope Th B, and measured the activity due to the recoil atoms of the decomposition product Th C″, with a range of 3×10^{-6} cm. only. Thus the effective depth of penetration is smaller by three orders of magnitude, and consequently the sensitivity of the method has been increased by 6 powers of ten, permitting the determination of diffusion coefficients of the order of magnitude of $10^{-18} - 10^{-19}$ cm.^{2}/sec.

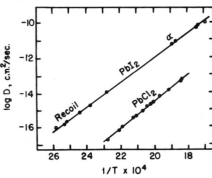

Fig. 4-18. Diffusion of lead ions in PbCl$_2$ and PbI$_2$, after Hevesy and Seith (recoil and α-ray methods).

* This method does not make use of the simplified techniques possible with radioactive tracers. As will be shown in Chap. V however, while less convenient, it is far more reliable.

Using the same isotope with lead chloride, where the range of the recoil atoms is 7.5×10^{-6} cm., Hevesy and Seith were able to measure the rate of self diffusion of the lead ions in lead chloride, and in an analogous way they measured the diffusion of the lead ions in lead iodide, using the recoil radiation at low temperatures and the α-radiation at high temperatures. The results obtained with lead chloride and iodide are reproduced in Fig. 4-18, and in Table XVI. The coefficients of self diffusion can be represented by the equations listed in Table XVI.

For PbI_2 the values are in reasonable agreement with those derived from the formula for the electrolytic conductivity (cf. Fig. 4-4)

$$\sigma_{PbI_2} = 9.8 \times 10^{-4} \exp\left(-9{,}360/RT\right) + 1.15 \times 10^5 \exp\left(-30{,}000/RT\right)$$

if the second term is attributed to the partial conductivity of the lead ions, and, accordingly, the first one to that of the iodide ions.

TABLE XVI
Self-diffusion coefficient of lead ions in PbI_2 and $PbCl_2$, ThB as tracer.
(Hevesy and Seith (57,109))

PbI_2

a) Recoil method	$T^\circ K$	387	395	397	410	420	438		
	$D \cdot 10^{16}$ cm.^{2}/sec.	0.7	1.1	1.7	4.9	14	74		

$$D = 4 \cdot \exp\left(-30\,000/RT\right) \text{ cm.}^2/\text{sec.}$$

b) α-ray method	$T^\circ K$	528	533	574	575	588			
	$D \cdot 10^{12}$ cm.^{2}/sec.	4.2	6.1	39.6	49.3	77			

$$D = 11 \cdot \exp\left(-30\,140/RT\right) \text{ cm.}^2/\text{sec.}$$

$PbCl_2$

Recoil method	$T^\circ K$	455	474	484	492	498	508	522	543
	$D \cdot 10^{16}$ cm.^{2}/sec.	0.7	3.1	5.4	14	21	40	60	366

$$D = 7.8 \exp\left(-35\,800/RT\right) \text{ cm.}^2/\text{sec.}$$

Maurer and Mapother (88) measured the rate of diffusion of radioactive Na^{24} in sodium chloride over a wide range of temperature, Fig. 4-3, p. 184. The coefficient of self diffusion is in good agreement with that calculated from conductivity measurements. There is a certain difficulty in reconciling this fact with the results of determinations of transference numbers in sodium chloride, giving a contribution of the anions to conduction which increases with increasing temperature. It might be possible that these measurements are affected by the reaction of chlorine with the anode material, usually gold or platinum, as indicated by the coloring of the sodium chloride cylinder, next to the anode in transference experiments. Maurer and Mapothers's experiments can be explained by the presence of an impurity containing bivalent cations, giving rise to a certain temperature independent concentration of cation holes, or to the freezing-in of Schottky disorder at low temperatures. In either case a lower branch of the $\log D$ versus $1/T$ curves with smaller temperature coefficient is obtained. The latter explanation is made probable by Breckenridge's (32) experiments (cf. p. 194ff.)*.

The rate of self diffusion can be represented by an expression

$$D = D_0 \exp\left(-Q/RT\right)$$

with

$$D_0 = 3.13 \text{ cm.}^2 \text{ sec.}^{-1} \qquad Q = 41.4 \text{ kcal above } 550°C$$

and

$$D_0 = 1.6 \times 10^{-5} \text{ cm.}^2 \text{ sec.}^{-1} \qquad Q = 17.7 \text{ kcal below } 550°C .$$

Wietig (149) investigated qualitatively the diffusion in mixed powders of barium compounds making use of the tracer technique.

Klemm (78, 79) made use of the difference in the mobility of ions in solid crystals to achieve a separation of copper and silver isotopes. The effects so obtained are very small, since the mobilities of different isotopes differ by no more than the reciprocal ratio of the square roots of the masses (cf. the measurements with hydrogen and deuterium, Chap. VI).

REFERENCES

Monographs and review articles

1. Flechsig, W., Hand- und Jahrb. chem. Physik, Vol. 6 II, 1933.
2. von Hevesy, G., Handb. Physik Vol. XIII, 263, 1928.
3. Joffé, A., Physics of Crystals. McGraw Hill, New York, 1928.
4. Jost, W., Diffusion und chem. Reaktion in festen Stoffen. Th. Stein-kopff, Dresden und Leipzig, 1937.
5. Jost, W., Müller-Pouillets Lehrb. d. Physik Vol. IV/4, (1934).
6. Justi, E., Leitfähigkeit und Leitungsmechanismus fester Stoffe. Vandenhoeck und Ruprecht, Göttingen 1948.
7. Manning, M. F., and Bell, M. E., Rev. Mod. Phys. 12, 215 (1940).
8. Meyer, W., Z. Elektrochem. 50, 274 (1944).
9. Mott, N. F., and Gurney, R. W., Electronic Processes in Ionic Crystals, Univ. Press Oxford, (1940); 2nd ed. (1948).
10. Mott, N. F., and Gurney, R. W., Proc. Roy. Soc. London A 164, 151 (1938).
11. Pohl, R. W., Proc. Phys. Soc. London 49, 3 (1937).
12. Pohl, R. W., Z. Physik. 39, 36 (1938).
13. Seith, W., Z. Elektrochem. 42, 635 (1936).
14. Seitz, F., Modern Theory of Solids, McGraw Hill, New York 1940.
15. Seitz, F., Rev. Mod. Phys. 18, 384 (1946).
16. Smekal, A., Handb. Physik Vol. XXIV/2, 1934.
17. Smekal, A., Physik in regelmäßigen Berichten 4, (1936) and 8, (1940).
18. Tubandt, C., Handb. exp. Physik Vol. XII/1, 1932.

* This explanation has been questioned, however, by Grimley (49).

General Bibliography

19. Amirkanov, K. H. I., *J. exp. theoret. Phys. USSR.* **14,** 187 (1944).
20. Anderson, J. S., and Morton, M. C., *Proc. Roy. Soc. London* **A 184,** 83 (1945).
21. Anderson, J. S., and Richards, J. R., *J. Chem. Soc. London* **1946,** 537.
22. Arzybyschew, S. A., *Compt. rend. Acad. Sci. USSR (N. S.)* **8,** 157 (1935).
23. Arzybyschew, S. A., and Borissow, N. B., *Phys. Z. Sowjetunion* **10,** 44 (1936).
24. Arzybyschew, S. A., and Borissow, N. B., *Phys. Z. Sowjetunion* **10,** 56 (1936).
25. Arzybyschew, S. A., *Phys. Z. Sowjetunion* **11,** 636 (1937).
26. Benrath, A., *Z. physik. Chem.* **77,** 257 (1916).
27. Beran, O., and Quittner, F., *Z. Physik* **64,** 760 (1930).
27a. Bevan, D. J. M., Shelton, J. P., and Anderson, J. S., *J. Chem. Soc.* **1948,** 1729.
27b. Blueh, O., and Jost, W., *Z. physik. Chem.* **B 1,** 270 (1928).
28. Bogomolowa, M. J., *Acta physicochim. USSR.* **5,** 161 (1936).
29. Braune, H., *Z. physik. Chem.* **110,** 147 (1924).
30. Braune, H., and Kahn, O., *Z. physik. Chem.* **112,** 270 (1924).
31. Braune, H., *Z. Elektrochem.* **31,** 570 (1925).
32. Breckenridge, R. G., *J. Chem. Phys.* **16,** 959 (1948).
32a. Breckenridge, R. G., *J. Chem. Phys.* **18,** 913 (1950) (Low frequency dispersion in ionic crystals containing foreign ions).
33. Brennecke, C. G., *J. appl. Phys.* **11,** 202 (1940)
34. Brown, F. C., *Phys. Rev.* **73,** 1257 (1948).
35. Croatto, U., and Mayer, A., *Gazz. Chim. Ital.* **73,** 199 (1943)
36. Croatto, U., *Chimica e industria (Milan)* **26,** 1 (1944).
37. Croatto, U., and Bruno, M., *Gazz. Chim. Ital.* **78,** 83 (1948)
38. Croatto, U., and Bruno, M., *Gazz. Chim. Ital.* **78,** 95 (1948).
38a. Danzin, A., *Compt. rend.* **X 228,** 487 (1949).
39. Dienes, G. J., *J. Chem. Phys.* **16,** 620 (1948).
40. Drisina, R., and Wenderowitsch, A., *Z. Physik* **98,** 108 (1936).
41. Duenwald, H., and Wagner, C., *Z. physik. Chem.* **B 22,** 212 (1933).
41a. Etzel, H. W., and Maurer, R. J., *J. Chem. Phys.* **18,** 1003 (1950) (Concentration and mobility of vacancies in NaCl).
42. Foex, M., *Compt. rend.* **215,** 534 (1942).
43. Foex, M., *Bull. Soc. Chim.* **11,** 6 (1944).
44. Foex, M., *Compt. rend.* **220,** 359 (1945).
45. Foex, M., *Compt. rend.* **223,** 1126 (1946).
46. Geiler, J., Diss. Halle 1928.
47. Geiler, R. F., *Metal Res. Nat. Bur. Stand.* **36,** 277 (1946).
48. Ginnings, D. C., and Phipps, T. E., *J. Am. Chem. Soc.* **52,** 1340 (1930).
49. Grimley, T. B., *J. Chem. Phys.* **17,** 496 (1949).
50. Groth, W., *Z. phys. chem. Unterr.* **53,** 179 (1940).
51. Gyulai, Z., *Z. Physik* **67,** 812 (1931).
52. Gyulai, Z., *Z. Physik* **113,** 28 (1934).
52a. Gyulai, Z., and Tomka, P., *Z. Physik* **125,** 505 (1949).
53. Hahn, O., *Z. physik. Chem.* **A 170,** 196 (1934).
54. von Hevesy, G., *Ann. Physik* **65,** 216 (1921).
55. von Hevesy, G., *Z. Physik* **10,** 80 (1922).
56. von Hevesy, G., and Obrutschewa, A., *Nature* **115,** 674 (1925).
57. von Hevesy, G., and Seith, W., *Z. Physik* **56,** 790 (1929).
58. von Hevesy, G., and Seith, W., *Z. anorg. u. allgem. Chem.* **180,** 150 (1929).

59. von Hevesy, G., *Trans. Faraday Soc.* **34**, 841 (1938).
60. Hochberg, B., and Walther, A., *Z. Physik* **64**, 392 (1930).
61. Jander, W., *Z. anorg. u. allgem. Chem.* **192**, 295 (1930).
62. Jander, W., *Z. anorg. u. allgem. Chem.* **199**, 306 (1931).
63. Jander, W., and Stamm, W., *Z. anorg. u. allgem. Chem.* **199**, 165 (1931).
64. Jander, W., and Stamm, W., *Z. anorg. u. allgem. Chem.* **207**, 289 (1932).
65. Joffé, A., *Ann. Physik* **72**, 461 (1923).
66. Joffé, A., *Z. Physik* **62**, 730 (1930).
67. Jost, W., Diss. Halle 1926.
68. Jost, W., *Z. physik. Chem.* **B 6**, 88 (1929).
69. Jost, W., *Z. physik. Chem.* **B 7**, 234 (1929).
70. Jost, W, and Schweitzer, H., *Z. physik. Chem.* **B 10**, 159 (1930).
71. Jost, W., *Z. physik. Chem.* **B 16**, 129 (1932).
72. Jost, W., and Schweitzer, H., *Z. physik Chem.* **B 20**, 118 (1933).
73. Jost, W., and Rueter, H., *Z. physik. Chem.* **B 21**, 48 (1933).
74. Jost, W., and Nehlep, G., *Z. physik. Chem.* **B 34**, 348 (1936).
75. Jost, W., Mennenoeh, S., and Mueller, F. H., *Z. Naturforschg.* **4a**, 227 (1949).
76. Ketelaar, J. A. A., *Z. Kristallogr.* (A) **87**, 436 (1934).
77. Ketelaar, J. A. A., *Z. physik. Chem.* **B 26**, 327 (1934).
78. Klemm, A., *Z. physik. Chem.* **193**, 29 (1943).
79. Klemm, A., *Naturwiss.* **32**, 69 (1944).
80. Koch, E., and Wagner, C., *Z. physik. Chem.* **B 38**, 295 (1937).
81. Kolthoff, I. M., and Shapiro, I., *J. Chem. Phys.* **15**, 41 (1947).
82. Kubaschewski, O., *Ber. naturforsch. Gesellsch.* Freiburg **35**, 109 (1937).
83. Kurzke, H., and Rottgardt, J., *Ann. Physik* (5) **39**, 619 (1941).
84. Langer, A., *J. Chem. Phys.* **10**, 321 (1942).
85. Lehfeldt, W., *Z. Physik* **85**, 717 (1933).
85a. Lindner, R. and Johansson, G., *Acta Chem. Scand.* **4**, 307 (1950) (Radioactive tracers for measuring self diffusion).
85b. Lindner, R., *Z. Elektrochem.* **54**, 430 (1950).
85c. Lindner, R., *J. Chem. Soc.* 1949, Suppl. Issue Nr. 2, 395.
85d. Mapother, D., Crooks, H. N., and Maurer, R. *J. Chem. Phys.* **18**,1231 (1950) (Self diffusion of Na in NaCl N ₁Br).
86. Maurer, R. J., *J. Chem. Phys.* **13**, 321 (1945).
87. Maurer, R. J., *J. appl. Phys.* **16**, 563 (1945).
88. Maurer, R. J., and Mapother, D., *Phys. Rev.* **73**, 1260 (1948).
88a.Mennenoeh, S., Dissertation, Marburg 1949. *Z. Elektrochem.* **54**, 433 (1950)
89. Mitchell, J. W., *Phil. Mag.* **7**, 249, 667 (1949).
90. Mollwo, E., *Nachr. Ges. Wiss. Göttingen, Math. Phys. Kl.* 89 (1943).
91. Nagel, K., and Wagner, C., *Z. physik. Chem.* **B 25**, 76 (1934).
92. Parfianowitsch, I. A., and Schipizyn, S. A., *Acta physicochim. USSR.* **6**, 263 (1937).
93. Phipps, T. E., Lansing, W. D., and Cooke, T. G., *J. Am. Chem. Soc.* **48**, 112 (1926).
94. Phipps, T. E., and Leslie, R. T., *J. Am. Chem. Soc.* **50**, 2412 (1928).
95. Phipps, T. E., and Partridge, E. G., *J. Am. Chem. Soc.* **51**, 1331 (1929).
96. Pogodaev, *Khim. Ref. Zhur.* **4**, Nr. 4, 12 (1941).
97. Polesitzkij, A. E., and Murin, A., *Compt. rend. Acad. Sci. USSR.* **45**, 238 (1944).
98. Quittner, F., *Z. Physik* **56**, 597 (1929).
99. Reinhold, H., and Schulz, R., *Z. physik. Chem.* **A 164**, 241 (1933).

100. Reinhold, H., and Moehring, H., Z. physik. Chem. **B 38,** 221 (1937).
101. Reinhold, H., and Seidel, H., Z. physik. Chem. **B 38,** 245 (1937).
102. Reinhold, H., and Braeuninger, H., Z. physik. Chem. **B 41,** 397 (1939).
103. Riehl, N., Chem. Z. **64,** 149 (1940).
103a. Ronge, G., and Wagner, C., J. Chem. Phys. **18,** 74 (1950) (Transport numbers in solid KCl with $SrCl_2$, K_2O and Na_2S).
104. Saegusa, H., and Matsumoto, T., Sci. Rep. Tôhoku Univ. **28,** 235 (1939).
105. Sandonini, C., Atti Accad. dei Linc. Rend. (5) **24,** 842 (1915).
106. Schwarz, R., and Halberstadt, J., Z. anorg. allgem. Chem. **199,** 33 (1931).
107. von Seelen, D., Z. Physik **29,** 125 (1924).
108. Seith, W., Z. Physik **56,** 802 (1929).
109. Seith, W., Z. Physik **57,** 869 (1929).
110. Seith, W., Ber. d. Naturforsch. Gesellsch. Freiburg **30,** 1 (1930).
111. Seith, W., Z. Elektrochem. **39,** 538 (1933).
112. Seitz, F., J. appl. Phys. **16,** 553 (1945).
112a. Shapiro, I. and Kolthoff, I. M., J. Phys. & Colloid Chem. **51,** 483 (1947) **52,** 1319 1948)
113. Sikorski, Y. A., Bull. acad. sci. Georgia USSR. **3,** Nr. 10, 1005 (1942).
114. Smekal, A., Z. techn. Phys. **8,** 561 (1927); Phys. Z. **26,** 707 (1925).
115. Smekal, A., Verh. dtsch. phys. Gesellsch. **21,** 26 (1940).
115a. Stasiw, O., and Teltow, J., Gött. Nachr. Math.-Phys. Kl. 1941 S. 93.
115b. Stasiw, O., and Teltow, J., Gött. Nachr. Math.-Phys. Kl. 1941 S. 100.
115c. Stasiw, O., and Teltow, J., Gött. Nachr. Math.-Phys. Kl. 1941, S. 110.
115d. Stasiw, O., and Teltow, J., Gött. Nachr. Math.-Phys. Kl. 1944, S.155.
116. Stasiw, O., and Teltow, J., Ann. Physik (6) **1,** 261 (1947).
116a. Stasiw, O., and Teltow, J., Z. anorg. allgem. Chem. **257,** 103 (1948).
116b. Stasiw, O., and Teltow, J., Z. anorg. allgem. Chem. **259,** 143 (1949).
116c. Stasiw, O., Ann. Physik. **5,** 151 (1949).
116d. Stasiw, O., Z. Physik **127,** 522 (1950).
117. Tammann, G., and Veszi, G., Z. anorg. allgem. Chem. **150,** 355 (1926).
117a. Teltow, J., Ann. Physik **5,** 63 (1949).
117b. Teltow, J., Ann. Physik **5,** 71 (1949).
117c. Teltow, J. Z. physik. Chem. **195,** 197 (1950).
117d. Teltow, J., Z. physik. Chem. **195,** 213 (1950).
118. Tschaly, W. P., Mem. Inst. Chem. Acad. Sci. Ukr. SSR. **5,** 231 (1938).
119. Tubandt, C., and Lorenz, E., Z. physik. Chem. **87,** 513 (1914).
120. Tubandt, C., and Lorenz, E., Z. physik. Chem. **87,** 543 (1914).
121. Tubandt, C., Mitt. Naturforsch. Gesellsch. Halle **4,** 1 (1917).
122. Tubandt, C., Z. Elektrochem. **26,** 338 (1920).
123. Tubandt, C., and Eggert, S., Z. anorg. allgem. Chem. **110,** 196 (1920).
124. Tubandt, C., Z. anorg. allgem. Chem. **110,** 234 (1920).
125. Tubandt, C., Z. anorg. allgem. Chem. **115,** 105 (1920).
126. Tubandt, C., Eggert, S., and Schibbe, G., Z. anorg. allgem. Chem. **117,** 1 (1921).
127. Tubandt, C., and Reinhold, H., Z. Elektrochem. **29,** 313 (1923).
128. Tubandt, C., and Reinhold, H., Z. Elektrochem. **31,** 84 (1925).
129. Tubandt, C., and Reinhold, H., Z. anorg. allgem. Chem. **160,** 222 (1927).
130. Tubandt, C., and Haedicke, M., Z. anorg. allgem. Chem. **160,** 297 (1927).
131. Tubandt, C., Rindtorff, E., and Jost, W., Z. anorg. allgem. Chem. **165,** 195 (1927).
132. Tubandt, C., Reinhold, H., and Jost, W., Z. physik. Chem. **129,** 69 (1927).

133. Tubandt, C., Reinhold, H., and Jost, W., Z. anorg. allgem. Chem. 177, 253 (1928).
134. Tubandt, C., and Reinhold, H., Z. Elektrochem. 37, 589 (1931).
135. Tubandt, C., and Reinhold, H., Z. physik. Chem. Bodenstein-Festband 1931, 874.
136. Tubandt, C., Reinhold, H., and Liebold, G., Z. anorg. allgem. Chem. 197, 225 (1931).
137. Tubandt, C., Reinhold, H., and Neumann, A., Z. Elektrochem. 39, 227 (1933).
138. Tubandt, C., Z. Elektrochem. 39, 500 (1933).
139. Tubandt, C., and Reinhold, H., Z. physik. Chem. B 24, 22 (1934).
140. Tubandt, C., and co-workers, in Landolt-Börnstein: Phys.-chem. Tabellen, Hw. II, p. 1062ff., 1923, Ergänzungsband I, p. 582ff. 1927, Ergänzungsband II, part 2, p. 1042ff. 1931, Ergänzungsband III, part 3, p. 2011ff. 1936, Berlin.
141. Wenderowitsch, A., Kolomoitzev, F., and Sinjakov, E., J. exp. theoret. Phys. USSR. 11, 448 (1941).
142. Wagner, C., Z. physik. Chem. B 11, 139 (1930).
143. Wagner, C., Z. physik. Chem. B 21, 42 (1933).
144. Wagner, C., Z. physik. Chem. B 22, 181 (1933).
145. Wagner, C., Z. physik. Chem. B 23, 469 (1933).
146. Wagner, C., and Nagel, K., Z. physik. Chem. B 25, 71 (1934).
147. Wagner, C., Z. physik. Chem. B 32, 447 (1936).
148. Wagner, C., and Gundermann, J., Z. physik. Chem. B 37, 155 (1937).
149. Wagner, C., and Zimens, K. E., Acta Chim. Scand. 1, 537 (1947).
149a. Wagner, C. and Hantelmann, P., J. Phys. & Colloid Chem. 54, 426 (1950) (AgCl—CdCl).
149b. Wagner, C., and Hantelmann, P., J. Chem. Phys. 18, 72 (1950) (Vacancies in solid KCl).
149c. Wagner, C., J. Chem. Phys. 18, 1227 (1950) (Diffusion of lead chloride).
150. Wietig, E., Z. physik. Chem. B 45, 374 (1940).
151. Wischnewskaja, K., Bull. Sci. Univ. Etat Kiev, Sér. Chim. (russ.) 3, 161 (1937).
152. Zimens, K. E., Ark. Kemi. Mineral. Geol. A 23, No. 16 (1946).

CHAPTER V

DIFFUSION IN METALS AND IN NON-POLAR CRYSTALS

I. General remarks. Experimental methods

It is more difficult to obtain results of fundamental importance with regard to the mechanism of disorder and of diffusion in the case of metals than it is with ionic crystals. On the other hand it is easier to carry out diffusion measurements with metals, on account of their mechanical and other physical properties, and in addition such measurements may be of practical importance. Therefore a large quantity of diffusion data, concerning metals, is available.

The rate of diffusion in molecular crystals seems to be rather low, and consequently measurements are available in exceptional cases only, as for example in solid hydrogen. Here the ortho-para hydrogen conversion provided a sensitive tool of investigation. As in the other fields of diffusion measurements, progress of research with non polar crystals is to be expected by the use of radioactive elements.

Metallic systems are just the systems in which the influence of concentration and of deviations from ideal behaviour of mixtures upon the rate of diffusion have been carefully investigated.

As with ionic conduction in solid crystals, the earliest experimental observations on diffusion in solid metals are due to Faraday. Later Spring (190, 191) made similar observations. Roberts-Austen (160) carried out the first quantitative measurements on diffusion in metals; further early investigations are due to Colson (53), Masing (131), Bruni and Meneghini (38), Rüst (163) and others. The modern research on diffusion in metals starts with the work of Groh and Hevesy (77) on self diffusion in solid lead. I. Runge (162) studied the diffusion of carbon in iron, and Fränkel and Houben (72) the diffusion of gold in silver. H. Weiss and co-workers (204, 205, 206, 207) investigated the diffusion of several metals.

For the investigation of diffusion in metals two (or more) specimens may be brought into close contact as in the case of ionic crystals, by pressing plane faces together, or by melting one component upon the other etc. Metals may be welded one upon the other. One may be electrodeposited upon the other or upon a suitable alloy, and sometimes it is sufficient merely to press a powder of one component against the other metal. Mixtures of powders may be taken if no high accuracy is required. Coating by means of cathodic sputtering may also be employed. If one component has a sufficiently high vapor pressure, as is the case for instance with zinc, cadmium, and mercury, a transition of this component on and into the other one may even be secured without direct contact, via the gas phase. The diffusion of zinc in brass, for instance, has been measured, by heating a piece of brass of appropriate geometrical shape in an evacuated tube part of which was kept at a lower temperature than the diffusion specimen, for condensation of the evaporating zinc.

As pointed out by Mehl (15) there are considerable discrepancies between the results obtained by different observers for the diffusion of zinc in brass, by the method of evaporation, and there is no agreement between these results and those observed by more conventional methods. It is difficult to give an explanation of this fact, though these observations might possibly be related to the effects observed by Smigelskas and Kirkendall (182). Actually the conditions at a surface where one component is evaporating or condensing are quite different from those at an interface between a pair of diffusing metals or alloys.

Many methods of analysis are available for metallic systems. First, of course, normal chemical methods may be used, after the diffusion system has been separated into two or more layers, for instance by turning on a lathe (with cylindrical specimens), by grinding, or by chemical dissolution. Other methods of analysis may be employed instead of the normal chemical analysis. For instance, spectroscopic analysis which in some cases is highly sensitive and permits an investigation of diffusion at very low concentrations of the diffusing substance. X-ray methods may prove very valuable if there is a sufficiently large change in lattice parameters with concentration. Measurement of electric conductivity can be used, being usually very sensitive towards a change in composition, and has especially been utilized in investigating the homogenization of multilayers of metals (obtained, for instance, by electrodepositing). Instead of the electric conductivity thermomagnetic observations have also been employed, for alloys with one ferromagnetic constituent. Micro-hardness tests, measurement of thermionic emission and of other physical properties proved of advantage in certain cases. Microscopic metallographic methods can be used, also. Fränkel and Houben (72) and others (126) made use of the limits of resistance, towards certain chemical agents, as found by Tammann for certain alloys (16, 195) at definite concentrations, in order to locate a definite value of concentration, either in a cross section for a certain depth of penetration, or in a surface, if diffusion is proceeding perpendicularly to this surface, for a certain time of diffusion (105).

As with ionic crystals, radioactive elements may be used either for normal diffusion measurements or for the measurement of self diffusion, enabling one to make use of the highly sensitive methods of radiation measurements for analysis, and also to work with a very low depth of penetration, given by the range of radiation (cf. p. 204), and to determine very small diffusion constants and to detect diffusion even at comparatively very low temperatures.

It is always advisable to determine the concentration of the diffusing substance in a number of layers, even though a single determination may be sufficient for the evaluation of an experiment, giving one mean value of the diffusion coefficient. If the coefficient of interdiffusion is independent of concentration, and if a symmetrical arrangement has been chosen, i.e., if two layers of equal height but of different, uniform concentration are combined, then the resulting concentration distribution after a certain time is qualitatively as shown in Fig. 5-1. The concentration distribution is antisymmetrical with respect to $x = 0$, the original plane separating the two specimens of different concentration. By antisymmetric we understand, that the concentration at a point with coordinate x may be expressed in terms of that at $-x$ by

$$c(x) = - c(-x) + c_0 \qquad [5.1]$$

if by c_0 we denote the concentration at the interface $x = 0$, which remains constant for $t > 0$, and equal to the arithmetic mean of the original concentrations for $x < 0$ and $x > 0$. The same holds for non symmetrical systems for the early stages of diffusion, as long as concentration changes have not yet reached one of the boundaries of the systems. For, as long as this is the case, the asymmetry caused by the presence of the boundaries, is irrelevant for distribution of concentration due to diffusion. In the case of an antisymmetric concentration distribution, the curve for the concentration gradient, $c'(x) = \dfrac{\partial c}{\partial x}$ in our one-dimensional example, is symmetrical with respect to $x = 0$, Fig. 5-2

$$c'(x) = c'(-x) . \qquad [5.2]$$

Where sufficiently thorough experiments are available, with determination of concentrations in a number of layers, it is usually found that the experimental curves of the concentration distribution do not correspond exactly to the type shown in figures 5-1 and 5-2 which indicates a concentration dependent coefficient of diffusion Fig. 5-3, 5-4. For an evaluation of such experiments it is essential to have one-dimensional diffusion only, i.e. either diffusion systems with a plane interface of contact, for instance plates, brought into contact,

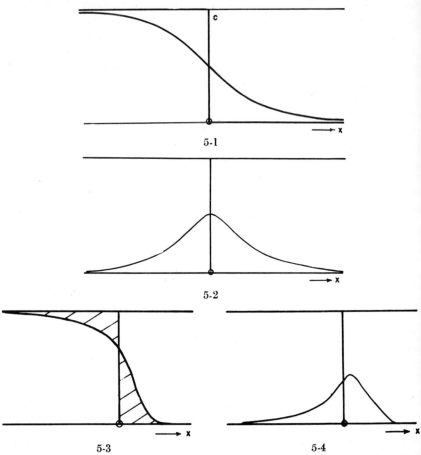

Fig. 5-1, 5-2, 5-3, 5-4. Concentration curves for constant (5-1) and concentration dependent (5-3) D, and corresponding curves for concentration gradient ($-\partial c/\partial x$), (5-2) and (5-4) respectively.

cylinders with plane end faces etc. with diffusion perpendicular to these planes, or in case of cylindrical or spherical diffusion systems, with diffusion across the cylindrical or spherical surfaces, a depth of penetration which is kept sufficiently small compared with the radius of curvature of these surfaces. If this condition is fulfilled, the diffusion system may be treated as a planar one, and Boltzmann's method of evaluation, valid only for this case, may be applied (cf. Chap. I, p. 31, and Matano (132), Rhines and Mehl (158)).

For an evaluation of such experiments it is necessary to have concentration determinations in more than two layers, and it is advisable to take the number of layers, separately analyzed, as high as possible.

Concentration dependent diffusion coefficients often have been evaluated from an experimental arrangement, adapted to the use of the Stefan-Kawalki tables, by simply reading the values of D resulting from the concentrations found in the different layers. It might be stressed that these tables have been calculated on the assumption of a concentration independent diffusion coefficient and, therefore, must not be taken for the evaluation of experiments with D depending on concentration. If systematic deviations in diffusion coefficients, taken from these tables, occur, this indicates that the method of evaluation is inadequate, and that it must be replaced by the Boltzmann method. The concentration dependent diffusion coefficients, taken from Kawalki's tables, therefore, are not true diffusion coefficients, but represent a special type of arbitrary averages, giving, however, the qualitative dependence of D on concentration correctly.

If one wishes to determine the dependence of diffusion coefficients on concentration it is usually advisable to use very small concentration differences (as small as are compatible with sufficient analytical accuracy), and to determine differential diffusion coefficients directly, instead of working with comparatively large concentration differences and evaluating the measurements by Boltzmann's method. If one is working with sufficiently small concentration differences, one has the further advantage that there are no restrictions with regard to the geometrical shape of the diffusion system.

II. Discussion of experimental results

A selection of experimental results obtained for the interdiffusion of metals is to be found in Tables I—XI, and Figs. 5-5 to 5-16; some details as to the method of investigation are listed on p. 268.

These results exhibit a number of characteristic features. When $\log D$ is plotted against $1/T$, straight lines are usually obtained, corresponding to the representation of the diffusion coefficient by a simple formula

$$D = D_0 \exp \left(- Q/RT\right) \qquad [5.3]$$

where, as in the case of electrolytic conduction and of diffusion in ionic crystals, the values of D_0 and of Q cover a rather wide range.

TABLE I

Diffusion in Aluminium (selected values)

Diffusing metal	Initial concentration in atom per cent	Temperature °C.	D (cm.²/sec.)	Method (cf p. 268)	Author
Ag	1.26	466	$1.9{-}2.25 \times 10^{-10}$	2	Beerwald (25)
	2.8 or 5.5	500	$2.0{-}1.1 \times 10^{-9}$	1	Mehl, Rhines, von den Steinen (137)
	1.26	573	3.5×10^{-9}	2	Beerwald (25)
Cu	Cu-Al eutectic	440	5.0×10^{-11}	3	Brick, Phillips (37)
	0.85	457	8.0×10^{-11}	2	Beerwald (25)
	3.05	500	$5.8{-}1.5 \times 10^{-10}$	1	Mehl, Rhines, von den Steinen (137)
	Cu-Al eutectic	540	1.4×10^{-9}	3	Brick, Phillips (37)
	0.17	565	$1.3{-}1.4 \times 10^{-9}$	2	Beerwald (25)
Mg	Al-Mg eutectic	365	0.86×10^{-11}	3	Brick, Phillips (37)
	5.5—11.0	395	$5.5{-}6.7 \times 10^{-11}$	2	Beerwald (25)
	14.9	420	$6.6{-}7.6 \times 10^{-11}$	1	Bungardt, Bollenrath (47)
	Al-Mg eutectic	440	3.3×10^{-10}	3	Brick, Phillips (37)

Table I, continued

	5.5—11.0	447	2.6×10^{-10}	2	Beerwald (25)
	1.32	450	1.9×10^{-9}	2	Freche (73)
	2.75	500	$1.1—2.1 \times 10^{-9}$	1	Mehl, Rhines, von den Steinen (137)
	5.5—11.0	577	4.4×10^{-9}	2	Beerwald (25)
Si	0.5	465	3.4×10^{-10}	2	Beerwald (25)
	2.44	500	$20.0—7.5 \times 10^{-10}$	1	Mehl, Rhines, von den Steinen (137)
	1.88	510	2.0×10^{-9}	2	Freche (73)
	0.5	600	9.3×10^{-9}	2	Beerwald (25)
Zn	0.84	415	2.5×10^{-10}	2	Beerwald (25)
		473	5.3×10^{-10}		
	9.4 or 21.6	500	$2.0—3.8 \times 10^{-9}$	1	Mehl, Rhines, von den Steinen (137)
	0.84	555	5.0×10^{-9}	2	Beerwald (25)

TABLE II
Diffusion in Copper

Diffusing metal	Initial concentration in atom per cent	Temperature °C.	D (cm.²/sec.)	Method (cf. p. 268)	Author
Cu (Cu ^{64}) self-diff.		650	3.2×10^{-12}	8a	Raynor, Thomassen, Rouse (156)
		750	6.5×10^{-12}	8a	Steigman, Shockley, Nix (193)
		830	4.0×10^{-11}	8b	Rollin (161)
		850	2.6×10^{-10}	8a	Raynor, Thomassen, Rouse (156)
		950	6.6×10^{-10}	8a	Steigman, Shockley, Nix (193)
		1030	2.8×10^{-9}	8b	Rollin (161)
Al	15—20.7	500	1.7×10^{-12}	5	Matano (134)
		850	2.2×10^{-9}		
Au	2.4—3.5	400	$4.3—7.2 \times 10^{-13}$	5	Matano (134)
		970	1.4×10^{-9}		
Mn	8—11.4	400	2.0×10^{-13}	5	Matano (134)
		850	1.3×10^{-10}		
Ni	7.5 — 11.8	550	7.1×10^{-13}	5	Matano (134)
		950	2.1×10^{-10}		
Pd	4.3—6.2	490	9.0×10^{-13}	5	Matano (134)
		950	$2.5—2.9 \times 10^{-10}$		
Pt	2.4—3.5	490	5.8×10^{-13}	5	Matano (134)
		960	$1.1—2.3 \times 10^{-10}$		
Sn	5.6	400	4.7×10^{-13}	5	Matano (134)
		650	6.9×10^{-11}		
		850	3.9×10^{-9}		

Table II, continued

Zn	α-brass	350	5.8×10^{-11}		Koehler (114)
	β-brass	350	1.3×10^{-9}		Koehler (114)
	α-brass	400	2.3×10^{-13}		Jenkins (98) *
	9.8	360	9.6×10^{-13}	5	Matano (134)
		880	5.5×10^{-11}		
	α-brass	600	8.6×10^{-11}	5	Kirkendall, Thomassen, Upthegrove (112)
		720	1.3×10^{-9}		
	0—9.25	641	5.1×10^{-14}	6	Dunn (64)
		775	9.1×10^{-13}	6	
		884	6.4×10^{-12}		
	0—28.6	641	5.1×10^{-14}	6	Dunn (64)
		775	4.2×10^{-12}		
		884	3.4×10^{-11}		
	0—33	800	1.2 —3.1×10^{-8}	6	Seith, Krauss (176)
	43—49 (β-phase)	800	1.2 —1.4×10^{-7}		
	28.0	700	2.67×10^{-10}	6	Hertzrücken and co-workers (89)
		780	0.93×10^{-9}		
	10.25	800	6.5 —7.3×10^{-10}		
	37.9 (β-phase)	800	0.86 —1.65×10^{-9}		
	28.0	820	4.6×10^{-9}		
	0—24	750	2.0×10^{-10} —6.1×10^{-9}	1	Rhines, Mehl (158)
		800	3.0×10^{-10} —7.0×10^{-9}		
		900	1.7×10^{-9} —2.85×10^{-8}		
	25.5	780	3.8×10^{-9}		Kirkendall (113)
	22.5	785	5.1×10^{-9}		Smigelskas, Kirkendall (182)

Further results of Rhines and Mehl, see Table XVI and Figs. 5-9, 5-11.

* Jenkins (99) gives slighly lower values.

TABLE III

Diffusion in Gold

Diffusing metal	Initial concentration in atom per cent	Temperature °C.	D (cm.²/sec.)	Method (cf. p. 268)	Author
Au[198] self-diff.		721	3.7×10^{-13}	8a	McKay (128)
		800	3.1×10^{-12}	8b	Sagrubskij (164, 165)
		893	7.2×10^{-12}	8a	McKay (128)
		900	2.5×10^{-11}	8b	Sagrubskij (164, 165)
		966	2.5×10^{-11}	8a	McKay (128)
		1020	1.5×10^{-10}	8b	Sagrubskij (164, 165)
Cu	pure Cu	301	1.5×10^{-13}	5	Jost (107)
	25.6	443	2.4×10^{-12}		
	pure Cu	616	2.2×10^{-10}		
	25.6	740	9.3×10^{-10}		
Fe	18.3	753	5.4×10^{-10}	5	Kubaschewski, Ebert (117)
		1003	7.5×10^{-9}		
Ni	15.0	800	7.7×10^{-10}	5	Kubaschewski, Ebert (117)
		1003	6.9×10^{-9}		
Pd	17.1	727	5.8×10^{-12}	5	Jost (107)
		970	3.2×10^{-10}		
Pt	20.1	740	4.7×10^{-12}	5	Jost (107)
		986	$1.7 - 2.8 \times 10^{-10}$		

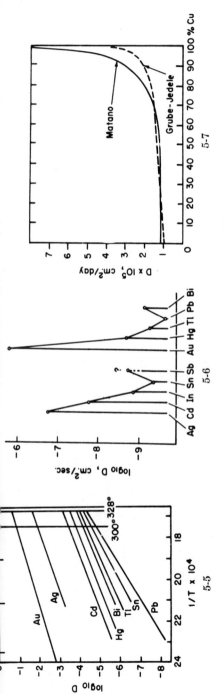

Fig. 5-5. Diffusion of several metals in lead, after Seith (log D: cm.²/day).

Fig. 5-6. Diffusion of several metals in lead, after Seith, log D versus atomic number of diffusing element, for 300°C.

Fig. 5-7. Diffusion in Cu-Ni system at 1025°C. Experiments by Grube and Jedele approximately evaluated by the authors (dashed line) and exactly evaluated by Matano, solid line (Boltzmann's method). (D: cm.²/day.)

Fig. 5-8. Diffusion coefficients in Au-Ni 1, Au-Pd 2, Au-Pt 3 at 900°C, measured and approximately evaluated by Jedele (a), exactly evaluated by Matano (b). (D: cm.²/day.)

TABLE IV

Diffusion of Carbon in Iron

	Concentration in weight per cent	Temperature °C.	D (cm.²/sec.)	Method (cf. p. 268)	Author
Gaseous carburizing agent	electrolyte-Fe	925	1.2×10^{-7}	9	I. Runge (162)
Gaseous carburizing agent	C = 0.07 P = 0.003 Mn = 0.27 Si, Si traces	925 1000	3.0×10^{-7} 1.93×10^{-6}	3	Tammann, Schoenert (196)
Gaseous carburizing agent	Armco-Fe C = 0.02 Si = 0.02 Mn = 0.05 S = 0.03 P = 0.012	800 900 950 1000 1050 1100	1.5×10^{-8} 7.5×10^{-8} 1.18×10^{-7} 2.0×10^{-7} 2.8×10^{-7} 4.5×10^{-7}	1	Bramley, Jinkings (31, 32) cf. also (33, 34)
Decarburization of white cast iron in CO—CO₂-mixture	C = 1.82—3.16 Si = 0.33—0.45 Mn = 0.36—0.52 P = 0.067—0.143	1.0 per cent C 950 1000 1050 1100	1.5 per cent C 1.3×10^{-7} 2.88×10^{-7} 5.27×10^{-7} 7.1×10^{-7} 1.0 per cent C 1.17×10^{-7} 2.83×10^{-7} 4.54×10^{-7} 8.3×10^{-7}	6	Baukloh and co-workers (23)
Welding of high carbon steel with Armco iron	high carbon steel C = 1.10 Si = 0.282 Mn = 0.230 P = 0.014 S = 0.006 Armco-Fe 0.030 0.005 0.027 0.012 0.028	925 1000 1100 1200 1250	1.08×10^{-7} 2.7×10^{-7} 7.23×10^{-7} $1.95—2.25 \times 10^{-6}$ 2.8×10^{-6}	1	Paschke, Hauttmann (150)

Table V
Diffusion of Metals in Iron

Diffusing metal	Initial concentration in atom per cent	Temperature °C.	D (cm.²/sec.)	Method (cf. p. 268)	Author
Al	pure	900	3.8×10^{-9}	3	Ageew, Vher (17)
		1050	2.0×10^{-8}		
Cr	pure	1150	6.8×10^{-10}	1	Bardenheuer,
		1300	$2.2-5.3 \times 10^{-8}$		Müller (21)
	Fe-Cr-powder	1200	$1.7-8.1 \times 10^{-9}$	5	Hicks (93)
Mn	~ 27	960	3.0×10^{-10}	1	Fry (74)
	3	1400	9.6×10^{-8}	1	Paschke, Hauttmann (150)
Mo	0—3.1	1200	$2.3-3.0 \times 10^{-9}$	1	Grube, Liebenwirth (79)
Ni	22	1200	9.3×10^{-11}	1	Fry (74)
Si	35	960	7.5×10^{-9}	1	Fry (74)
		1150	1.45×10^{-8}		
Sn	pure	950	9.7×10^{-10}	3	Bannister, Jones (20)
		1000	2.0×10^{-9}		
		1050	3.9×10^{-9}		
		1100	7.6×10^{-9}		
W	0—1.3	1280	3.7×10^{-10}	1	Grube, Schneider (80)
	0—1.2	1330	2.4×10^{-9}		
	0—3.4	1330	1.0×10^{-8}		

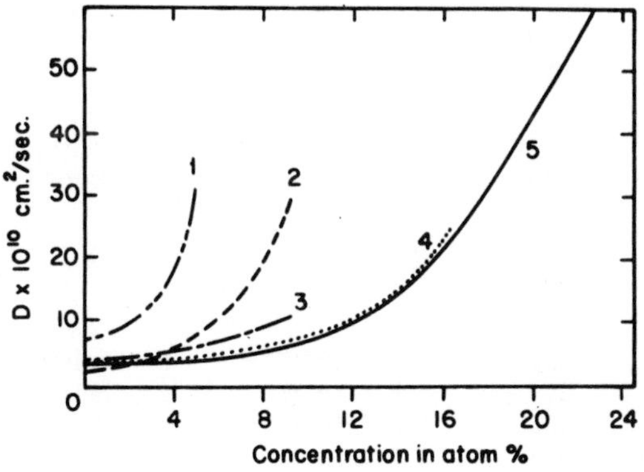

Fig. 5-9. Diffusion at 800°C in the systems 1. Cu — Sn, 2. Cu — Si, 3. Cu — Be, 4. Cu — Al, 5. Cu — Zn after Mehl and Rhines (evaluation by Boltzmann's method).

TABLE VI

Diffusion in Lead (selected values)

Diffusing metal	Initial concentration in atom per cent	Temperature °C.	D (cm.^{2}/sec.)	Method (cf. p. 268)	Author
Pb (Th B) self-diff.		106	1.7×10^{-16}	8a	v. Hevesy, Seith,
		238	8.4×10^{-12}		Keil (92)
		301	1.85×10^{-10}		
		324	5.5×10^{-10}		
Ag	0.12	220	1.5×10^{-8}	1	Seith, Laird (178)
		285	9.1×10^{-8}		
Au	0.03—0.09	100	2.3×10^{-9}	1	van Ostrand, De-
		150	5.0×10^{-8}		wey (148)
		200	8.6×10^{-8}	1	Roberts-Austen (159)
		240	4.4×10^{-7}	1	Seith, Etzold (171,172)
		300	1.5×10^{-6}		
Bi	2.0	220	4.8×10^{-11}	2	Seith, Laird (178)
		285	4.4×10^{-10}		
Cd	1,0	167	4.6×10^{-11}	2	Seith, Hofer (174)
		252	8.6×10^{-10}		Etzold
Mg	2	220	1.2×10^{-10}	2	Seith, Herrmann (173)
	0.26	250	$2.4—3.7 \times 10^{-10}$		
	4.3	250	$6.3—7.8 \times 10^{-10}$		
	1.26	270	9.4×10^{-10}		
	2	270	1.3×10^{-9}		
Ni	3.0	252	3.5×10^{-11}	2	Seith, Hofer (174)
		320	3.5×10^{-10}		Etzold
Sn	2.0	245	3.1×10^{-11}	2	Seith, Laird (178)
		285	1.6×10^{-10}		
Tl	2.0	220	2.8×10^{-11}	2	Seith, Laird (178)
	8.5—53.0	270	1.1×10^{-10}	2	Seith, Herrmann (173)
	2.0	285	3.1×10^{-10}	2	Seith, Laird (178)
	8.5—53.0	315	5.8×10^{-10}	2	Seith, Herrmann (173)

The variation of D_0 must probably be explained in analogy to other cases as being due to variation in entropy of activation (cf. Chap. III, p. 174), partly due to the change in lattice vibrations in the vicinity of centres of disorder and of migrating particles, and partly due to a temperature dependence of the energy of activation Q because of the change in lattice distance with temperature (cf. Chap. III, p. 151). Since this change of energy of activation is caused by the variation of the lattice distance with temperature, a variation of the lattice distance caused by a pressure increase should also exert an influence upon

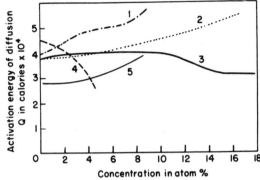

Fig. 5-10. Energies of activation Q, in empirical diffusion formula, as function of concentration, for the systems. 1. Cu — Si, 2. Cu — Al, 3. Cu — Zn, 4. Cu — Sn, 5. Cu — Be after Rhines and Mehl (158).

the rate of diffusion, as has been observed in case of electrolytic conductivity of ionic crystals (cf. Chap. IV, p. 197) and discussed theoretically (cf. Chap. III, p. 151). Since the accuracy of diffusion measurements is much smaller than that of measurements of electric conductivity, much higher pressure must

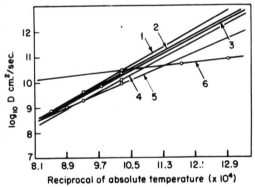

Fig. 5-11. Diffusion coefficients in copper (log D) extrapolated to zero concentration of solute, as functions of reciprocal absolute temperature, after Rhines and Mehl. 1. Cu — Si. 2. Cu — Al, 3. Cu — Zn, 4. Cu — Sn, 5. Cu — Be, 6. Cu — Cd.

be applied in order to obtain a distinct effect, but with pressures up to 7000 kg./cm.² it has been possible to observe a decrease in rate of diffusion of copper in aluminum at 500°C. of about 30 per cent (Radavich and Smoluchowski (155)).

Investigations over a very wide range of temperature or with a very high degree of accuracy would probably reveal systematic deviations from the simple straight line relationship and from equation [5.1] to be explained by the presence of impurities, by surface effects

TABLE VII

Diffusion in Silver (selected values)

Diffusing metal	Initial concentration in atom per cent	Temperature °C.	D (cm.²/sec.)		Method (cf. p. 268)	Author
Au	pure Au	218	$(2.6—6.6) \times 10^{-17}$		4	Jost (105)
		351	$(0.69—1.4) \times 10^{-14}$			
		456	4.9×10^{-13}			
		585	1×10^{-11}			
		601	1.1×10^{-11}			
Au	18.4	767	3.2×10^{-10}		1	Braune (36)
		847	6.4×10^{-10}			
		916	1.5×10^{-9}			
Cd	2	650	2.6×10^{-10}		2	Seith, Peretti (179)
		895	1.3×10^{-8}			
			5.2 per cent	10.4 per cent		
Cd	5.2	700	—	5.8×10^{-9}	6	Bugakov, Ssirotkin (46)
	10.4	800	1.3×10^{-9}	2.3×10^{-8}		
		900	6.2×10^{-9}	—	—	

Table VII, continued

			8.3 per cent	16.6 per cent	24.9 per cent		
Cu	2	650	2.9×10^{-10}			Seith, Peretti (179)	2
		760	3.6×10^{-10}				
		895	9.4×10^{-10}				
In	2	650	2.9×10^{-10}			Seith, Peretti (179)	2
		800	1.9×10^{-9}				
		895	1.3×10^{-8}				
Pd	20.2	444	1.3×10^{-12}			Jost (106)	5
		571	3.7×10^{-11}				
		642	1.2×10^{-10}				
		917	1.2×10^{-9}				
Sb	2	650	3.8×10^{-10}			Seith, Peretti (179)	2
		760	1.5×10^{-9}				
		895	4.3×10^{-9}				
Sn	2	650	6.2×10^{-10}			Seith, Peretti (179)	2
		895	7.3×10^{-9}				
Zn	8.3	650	—	—	3.5×10^{-9}	Bugakov, Ssirotkin (46)	6
	16.6	750	4.6×10^{-9}	6.9×10^{-9}	1.3×10^{-8}		
	24.9	850	1.2×10^{-8}	2.3×10^{-8}	—		

TABLE VIII

Diffusion in Tungsten

Diffusing metal	Temperature °C.	D (cm.²/sec.)		Method (cf. p. 268)	Author
C	1700	0.52—2.55×10^{-12} *		7	Zwikker (216), Dushman, Dennison,
Ce	1727	9.5×10^{-10}			Reynolds (65)
		1st ads. layer	2nd ads. layer		
Cs	27	1.2×10^{-11}	3.4×10^{-4}	7	Langmuir, Taylor (122,
	227	1.5×10^{-7}	2.2×10^{-3}		123)
	427	8.0×10^{-6}	3.2×10^{-3}		
	540	4.0×10^{-5}			
K	207	5.7×10^{-6}		7	Bosworth (30)
	317	1.0×10^{-4}			
	507	2.8×10^{-3}			
		single crystal	polycrystal		
Mo	1533	2.6×10^{-13}	1.3×10^{-12}	1	van Liempt (124)
	1770	1.12×10^{-12}	1.1×10^{-11}		
	2010	2.2×10^{-11}	1.06×10^{-10}		
	2260	7.8×10^{-11}	6.4×10^{-10}		
Na	20	8.0×10^{-6}		7	Bosworth (29)
	227	5.0×10^{-4}			
	417	2.7×10^{-3}			
	527	3.3×10^{-3}			
Th	1782	1.1×10^{-10}		7	Langmuir (119, 120,
	2027	1.12×10^{-9}			121)
	2127	3.57×10^{-9}			
	2227	6.8×10^{-9}			
U	1727	1.3×10^{-11}		7	Dushman, Dennison, Reynolds (65)
Y	1727	1.82×10^{-8}		7	Dushman, Dennison, Reynolds (65)
Zr	1727	3.24×10^{-9}		7	Dushman, Dennison, Reynolds (65)

* Wire of different preparation

TABLE IX

Diffusion in further metals (selected values)

Solvent metal	Diffusing metal	Initial concentration metal in atom per cent	Temperature °C.	D (cm.^{2}/sec.)	Method (cf. p.268)	Author
Cd	Hg	4	156	2.6×10^{-10}	6	Seith, Hofer, Etzold (174)
			202	2.5×10^{-9}		
	Pb	2	252	8.0×10^{-12}	2	Seith, Hofer, Etzold (174)
Pt	Cu	13.9	1041	$2.2 — 2.5 \times 10^{-11}$	5	Kubaschewski, Ebert (117)
			1213	1.4×10^{-10}		
			1401	1.7×10^{-9}		
	Ni	14.9	1043	5.2×10^{-11}		
			1241	4.8×10^{-10}		
			1401	1.5×10^{-9}		
Mo	Th		1615	3.6×10^{-10}	7	Nelting (145)
			2000	1.0×10^{-6}		

Table X

Anisotropy of Diffusion

	Temp. °C.	D (cm.^{2}/sec.)	Method *	Author
Bi single crystal (Th C) self-diffusion (melting point 271.0°C.) ‖ c	212	2.4×10^{-17}	8a	Seith (168)
	258	2.0×10^{-16}		
	269	2.15×10^{-16}		
⊥ c	209	2.0×10^{-17}	8a	Seith (168)
	255	1.65×10^{-11}		
	267	4.0×10^{-11}		
Zn single crystal (Zn [65]) self-diffusion (melting point 419.4°C.) ‖ c	355	3.0×10^{-9}	8b	Banks, Day (18, 19)
	374.4	5.0×10^{-9}		
	410.4	1.2×10^{-8}		

* cf. p. 268.

TABLE XI

Simultaneous diffusion of two metals

Solvent metal	Diffusing metals	Initial concentration in atom per cent	Tempera-ture °C.	D (cm.²/sec.)		Method (cf. p. 268)	Author
				Mg	Si		
Al	Mg + Si	1.34 per cent Mg 1.875 per cent Si } Mg₂Si + excess Mg	510	(5.8×10^{-9})	2.0×10^{-9}	2	Freche (73)
		1.34 per cent Mg 0.62 per cent Si } Mg₂Si	510	$3.52 - 3.99 \times 10^{-9}$	$1.88 - 1.85 \times 10^{-9}$		
		1.28 per zent Mg 1.30 per cent Si } Mg₂Si + excess Si	510	$1.02 - 1.09 \times 10^{-9}$	$1.07 - 1.53 \times 10^{-9}$		
				pure Al	Al + 2.7 weight per cent Zn		
Al	Mg + Zn 5.3—8.0		415	—	3.36×10^{-11}	1	Bungardt, Bollenrath (47)
			475	7.3×10^{-10}	3.7×10^{-10}		
			520	8.7×10^{-9}	2.2×10^{-9}		
			540	—	5.4×10^{-9}		

TABLE XI, continued

Solvent metal	Diffusing metal	Initial concentration in atom per cent	Temp. °C.	D (cm.²/sec.) alone	with Si	alone	with Ni	Method (cf. p. 268)	Author
Cu	Ni + Si	1 Si + 2 Ni	850	2.0×10^{-10}	7×10^{-11}	1.3×10^{-9}	1.0×10^{-10}	1	Mehl, Rhines (136)
		1.5 Si + 3 Ni	850	1.5×10^{-10}	7×10^{-11}	2.3×10^{-9}	1.0×10^{-10}		
		1 Si + 2 Ni	1000	1.0×10^{-9}	6×10^{-10}	7.1×10^{-9}	1.4×10^{-9}		
		2 Si + 4 Ni	1000	6.0×10^{-10}	6×10^{-10}	9.8×10^{-9}	8.0×10^{-10}		
		3 Si + 6 Ni	1000	5.0×10^{-10}	7×10^{-10}	1.5×10^{-8}	8.0×10^{-10}		
		(corresponding Ni₂Si)							
				pure Ni	Ni + 0.5 weight per cent Mn				
Ni	Cu + Mn	(extrapolated to 0 per cent Cu)	1000	1.2×10^{-10}	0.3×10^{-10}			1	Grube, Jedele (78)

(cf. Chap. IV, p. 190), by freezing out of equilibria of disorder, and, eventually, by the simultaneous action of more than one mechanism of migration.

Constants D_0 and Q of the empirical equation [5.1] are listed in Table XII. The values of Q lie within the range of less than 1 e.v. to 4 e.v., with higher values for metals with very high melting point

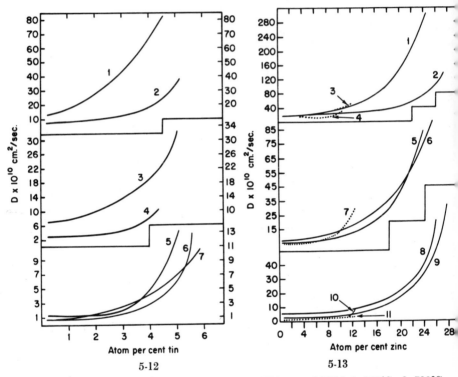

5-12

5-13

Fig. 5-12. Diffusion in Cu — Sn system, after Rhines and Mehl. 1. 802°C., 2. 798°C., 3. 753°C., 4. 751°C., 5. 700°C., 6. 700°C., 7. 700°C.

Fig. 5-13. Diffusion in Cu — Zn system, after Rhines and Mehl. 1. 900°C., 2. 897°C., 3. 900°C., 4. 897°C., 5. 840°C., 6. 840°C., 7. 841°C., 8. 750°C., 9. 750°C., 10. 751°C., 11. 751°C.

(~ 20 to ~ 90 kcals. per g. atom). The values of D_0 vary between 10^4 and 10^{-7} in the extreme cases, with the majority of values between about 10 and 10^{-5} cm.^{2} sec.$^{-1}$*.

There are certain regularities in the trend of the Q values, which, however, must be considered as approximate empirical rules, not as exact laws. Comparing the rate of diffusion of several elements,

* The value of 10^{46} reported for bismuth is to be regarded as doubtful.

dissolved and diffusing in the same basic metal, one usually finds self diffusion the slowest process, involving the highest energy of

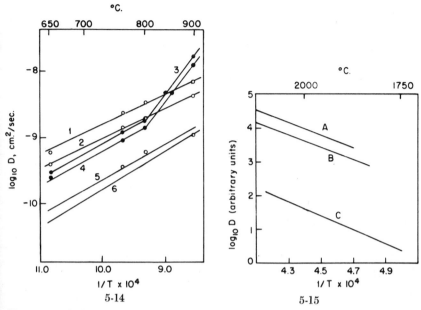

Fig. 5-14. Diffusion of several metals in silver, log D versus $1/T$, after Seith. 1. Sn, 2. Sb, 3. In, 4. Cd, 5. Cu, 6. Au.

Fig. 5-15. Diffusion of thorium in tungsten of different grain sizes after Fonda, Young and Walker. Crystal diameter: A 5.3 μ, B 7.3 μ, C 3000 μ.

activation, the rate of diffusion of other elements increasing with increasing distance in the periodic table of the diffusing metal from the base metal (Seith (169), Seith and Peretti (179, cf. 146), Fig. 5-6).

This influence might be explained by the fact that for self diffusion only the lattice disorder inherent in the pure metal is responsible, while by the formation of mixed crystals the tendency for disorder may be increased considerably, the more so, the less the dissolved particles fit into the lattice of the main component. This also explains the fact, that diffusion is often higher, the lower

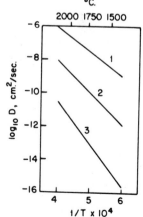

Fig. 5-16. Temperature dependence of diffusion of thorium in tungsten, after Langmuir. 1. surface, 2. grain boundary, 3. volume diffusion.

TABLE XII

Diffusion constants in metals $D = D_0 \exp\left(\dfrac{-Q}{RT}\right)$

Solvent metal	Diffusing metal	Concentration* (atom per cent)	Temperature interval °C.	D_0 (cm.²/sec.)	Q (kcal./g. atom)	Author
Ag	Ag	(self-diff.)	725—950	0.895	45.95	Johnson (102)
Ag	Au	pure Au	218—601	5.3×10^{-4}	29.8	Jost (105)
Ag	Au	18.4	767—895	1.1×10^{-4}	26.6	Braune (36)
Ag	Cd	2.0	650—895	4.9×10^{-5}	22.35	Seith, Peretti (179)
Ag	Cu	2.0	650—895	5.9×10^{-5}	24.8	Seith, Peretti (179)
Ag	In	2.0	650—895	7.3×10^{-5}	24.4	Seith, Peretti (179)
Ag	Pd	20.2	444—917	6.4×10^{-6}	20.2	Jost (106)
Ag	Sb	2.0	650—895	5.3×10^{-5}	21.7	Seith, Peretti (179)
Ag	Sn	2.0	650—895	7.8×10^{-5}	21.4	Seith, Peretti (179)
Al	Ag	1.26	466—573	1.1	32.6	Beerwald (25)
Al	Cu	eutectic	440—540	2.3	34.9	Brick, Phillips (37)
Al	Cu	0.85 or 0.17	457—565	8.4×10^{-2}	32.6	Beerwald (25)
Al	Mg	eutectic	365—440	1.5×10^{-2}	38.5	Brick, Phillips (37)
Al	Mg	5.5—11.0	395—577	1.2×10^{-1}	28.6	Beerwald (25)
Al	Mg	5.3— 8.0	420—520		38.0	Bungardt, Bollenrath (47)
Al	Si	0.50	465—600	9.0×10^{-1}	30.55	Beerwald (25)
Al	Zn	0.84	415—555	1.2×10^{1}	27.8	Beerwald (25)
Au	Au	(self-diff.)	800—1020	0.16	53.0	Sagrubskij (164, 165)
Au	Au	(self-diff.)	721—966	2×10^{-2}	51.0	McKay (128)
Au	Ag	9	850—1000	2.9×10^{-2}	38.0	Ebert, Trommsdorf (67)
Au	Cu	pure Cu	301—616	1.06×10^{-3}	27.4	Jost (107)
Au	Cu	25.6	443—740	5.8×10^{-4}	27.4	Jost (107)
Au	Fe	18.3	753—1003	1.16×10^{-4}	24.4	Kubaschewski, Ebert (117)
Au	Ni	15.0	800—1003	1.74×10^{-3}	31.2	Kubaschewski, Ebert (117)

* Initial concentration of alloy.

Table XII, continued

Au	Pd	17.1	727—970	1.13×10^{-3}	37.4	Jost (107)
Au	Pt	20.1	740—986	1.24×10^{-3}	39.0	Jost (107)
Bi	Bi	∥ c (self-diff.)	212—269	$\sim 10^{-3}$	31.0	Seith (168)
Bi	Bi	⊥ c (self-diff.)	209—269	$\sim 10^{47}$	140.0	Seith (168)
Cd	Hg	4	156—202	2.6	19.6	Seith, Hofer, Etzold (174)
Cu	Cu	(self-diff.)	830—1030	47	61.4	Rollin (161)
Cu	Cu	(self-diff.)	750—950	11	57.2	Steigman, Shockley, Nix (193)
Cu	Ag	3	720—860	2.9×10^{-2}	37.2	Kubaschewski (116)
Cu	Al	15—21	500—850	7.1×10^{-2}	39.2	Matano (134)
Cu	Au	2.4—3.5	400—970	6.8×10^{-6}	22.5	Matano (134)
Cu	Cd	3	720—860	3.04×10^{-4}	23.7	Kubaschewski (116)
Cu	Mn	8 —11.4	400—850	7.2×10^{-6}	23.2	Matano (134)
Cu	Ni	7.5—11.8	550—950	6.5×10^{-5}	29.8	Matano (134)
Cu	Pd	4.3—6.2	490—950	1.6×10^{-6}	21.9	Matano (134)
Cu	Pt	2.4—3.5	490—960	1.0×10^{-6}	21.9	Matano (134)
Cu	Sn	3.9—5.6	400—850	4.1×10^{-3}	31.2	Matano (134)
Cu	Zn	6.8—9.7	360—880	3×10^{-6}	19.7	Matano (134)
Cu	Zn	3	720—860	3.7×10^{-6}	22.0	Kubaschewski (116)*
Cu	Zn	0 —9.25	641—884	5.8×10^{-4}	42.0	Dunn (64)
Cu	Zn	0 —28.6	641—884	3.2×10^{-3}	42.0	Dunn (64)
Cu	Zn	27.5—35.4	700—950		24.5	Bugakov, Neskutchaev (44)
Cu	Zn	α-brass	727—955		18.5	Petrenko, Rubinstein (152)
Cu	Zn	β-brass	600—720		39.0	Kirkendall, Thomassen, Upthegrove (112)
Cu	Zn	29	400—600		46.0	Jenkins (99)
Fe	α-Fe	(self-diff.)	715—887	3.4×10^{4}	77.2	Birchenall, Mehl (27)
Fe	γ-Fe	(self-diff.)	935—1112	1.04×10^{-3}	48.0	Birchenall, Mehl (27)
Fe	C	carburization	800—1100	1.67×10^{-2}	28.7	Bramley, Jinkings (31, 32)
Fe	C	1.1 weightper cent	900—1250	4.86×10^{-1}	36.6	Paschke, Hauttmann (150)

* Mean values of measurements of Matano, Kubaschewski and Rhines-Mehl. Data of the latter authors see Table XVI

Table XII, continued

Solvent metal	Diffusing metal	Concentration (atom per cent)	Temperature interval °C.	D_0 (cm.²/sec.)	Q (kcal./g. atom)	Author
Fe	C	0.1 — 1 weight per cent	750—1250	0.12 ± 0.07	32.0 ± 1.0	Wells, Mehl (208)
Pb	Pb	(self-diff.)	106—324	6.6	27.9	v. Hevesy, Seith, Keil (92)
Pb	Ag	< 0.12	220—285	7.4×10^{-2}	15.2	Seith, Laird (178)
Pb	Au	pure Au or 0.03—0.09	100—300	0.35	14.0	Roberts-Austen (159), van Ostrand, Dewey (148), Seith, Etzold (171, 172)
Pb	Bi	2.0	220—285	1.83×10^{-2}	18.4	Seith, Laird (178)
Pb	Cd	1.0	167—252	1.83×10^{-3}	15.4	Seith, Hofer, Etzold (174)
Pb	β-Sn	2.0	245—285	4.0	26.2	Seith, Laird (178)
Pb	Tl	2.0	220—285	2.5×10^{-2}	19.4	Seith, Laird (178)
Pb	Tl	various concentrations of Tl	270—315	1.03	24.6	Seith, Herrmann (173)
Pt	Cu	13.9	1041—1401	4.8×10^{-2}	55.7	Kubaschewski, Ebert (117)
Pt	Ni	14.9	1043—1401	7.8×10^{-4}	43.1	Kubaschewski, Ebert (117)
W	Fe	0.04 p.c.Fe	1927—2527	11.5	140	van Liempt (127)
W	C		1702—1727	0.31	59.0	Pirani, Sandor (153)
W	Ce		1727	1.15	83	Dushman, Dennison, Reynolds (65)
W	Cs	1st layer of adsorption	27—427	0.2	14.0	Langmuir, Taylor (122, 123)
W.		2nd layer of adsorption	27—427	0.0164	2.3	Langmuir, Taylor (122, 123)
W	K		207—507		15.2	Bosworth (30)
W	Mo	single crystal	1533—2260	6.3×10^{-4}	80.5	van Liempt (124)
W	Mo	polycrystal	1533—2260	5×10^{-3}	80.5	van Liempt (124)
W	Na		20—527	0.1	5.56	Bosworth (29)

Table XII, continued

			Temp. °K.			Author
W	Th	grain boundary diff.	1780—2227	1.13	94.0	Langmuir (experimental) (119)
W	Th	grain boundary diff.	1780—2227	0.47	90.0	Langmuir (calculated) (120) (121)
W	Th	volume diff.	2127	1.0	120	Langmuir (121)
W	Th	surface diff.	1380	0.47	66.4	Langmuir (121)
W	U		1727	1.14	100	Dushman, Dennison, Reynolds (65)
W	Y		1727	0.11	62	Dushman, Dennison, Reynolds (65)
W	Zr		1727	1.1	78	Dushman, Dennison, Reynolds (65)
Zn		$\parallel c$ self-diff.	355—410	4.6×10^{-2}	20.4	Banks, Day (18, 19)
Zn		$\perp c$ self-diff.	340—410	92	31.0	Miller, Banks (139, 140)

TABLE XIII. Diffusion in lead

Diffusing metal	Ag	Cd	In	Sn	Sb	Au	Hg	Tl	Pb	Bi
Solid solubility	0.17	11	>40	30	3	0.09	33	60	100	35
Atomic radius in Å	1.44	1.52	1.57	1.58	1.61	1.44	1.55	1.71	1.75	1.82
Melting point °K.	1234	594	430	505	903	1336	234	576	601	544
Activation energy Q kcal./g. atom	15.2	15.4	—	26.2	—	14.0	(19.0)	19.4—24.6	27.9	18.4

TABLE XIV. Relation between activation energy Q and melting temperature T_m. (Solvent metal gold)

Diffusing metal	Miscibility	D_0 (cm.²/sec.)	Q (kcal./g. atom)	T_m °K.	Q/T_m	Author
Au (self-diffusion)	complete	0.16	53	1336	39.7	Sagrubskij (164, 165)'
Cu	complete	5.8—10.6 $\times 10^{-4}$	27.4	1356	20.2	Jost (107)
Fe	partial (two transition points)					
Ni	complete	1.2×10^{-4}	24.4	1803	13.5	Kubaschewski, Ebert (117)
Pd	complete	1.7×10^{-3}	31.2	1728	18.0	Kubaschewski, Ebert (117)
Pt	complete	1.11×10^{-3}	37.4	1826	20.5	Jost (107)
	complete	1.24×10^{-3}	39.0	2047	19.0	Jost (107)

the mutual solubility of the components, cf. Table XIII. For mixed crystals in systems with incomplete miscibility the energy content is higher than for the constituents, thus the energy of disorder might be lowered, in accordance with the preceding observations. Abnormally high rates of diffusion are found for gold and silver in lead. This fact, together with the very low solubility makes it probable that the gold and silver atoms are dissolved on interstitial sites (175, 200). The process of migration, therefore, would not require a disorder of the lead lattice, but only that an energy barrier would have to be surmounted by the migrating interstitial atoms.

For self diffusion and for interdiffusion of pairs of metals with high or complete miscibility and equal order of magnitude of D_0, the energy of activation is found to be higher the higher the melting point of the main component; in some cases a fairly close proportionality of Q to the absolute melting temperature has been observed, cf. Jost (6) and Tables XIV, XV.

III. The influence of concentration on the rate of diffusion

Where experiments with sufficiently wide variation of the concentration have been carried out, for instance with gold-nickel, copper-nickel etc. (Grube (78) and Jedele (97)) concentration distributions have been found with more or less pronounced deviations from a curve which is antisymmetrical with respect to the original boundary between the diffusion layers, cf. Figs. 5-3, 5-4, 5-17. This fact is borne out most clearly by the representation of the concentration gradient $\frac{\partial c}{\partial x}$, which, in the case of constant D, should be symmetrical with respect to the original interface (Figs. 5-2 and 5-4).

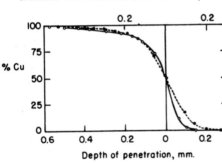

Fig. 5-17. Concentration distribution in system Cu-Ni, 120 hours at 1025°C., after Grube and Jedele. Solid line: Ni containing Mn, dashed line: pure Ni.

Grube and Jedele have evaluated these experiments by means of Kawalki's (108) tables (cf. the remarks p. 215). Later Matano (132, 133) using Boltzmann's method, computed the exact values of the diffusion coefficients. The results, thus obtained, are reproduced in Table II and Figs. 5-7, 5-8. It is seen that the trend of the diffusion coefficients obtained by Grube and Jedele is similar to that of the correct values; the variation of the exact values with concentration, however, is much more pronounced than that of the approximate values.

TABLE XV

Relation between activation energy of self-diffusion Q, melting point T_m, and heat of sublimation L. $D = D_0 \exp(-Q/RT)$

Metal	D_0 (cm.²/sec.)	Q (kcal./g. atom)	T_m °K.	Q/T_m	L (kcal.)	Q/L	Method 8	Author
Ag	0.895	45.9	1234	37	68.0	0.68	b	Johnson (102)
Au	0.16	53.0	1336	40	92	0.58	b	Sagrubskij (164, 165)
	0.02	51.0	1336	38	92	0.55	a	McKay (128)
Cu	47	61.4	1356	45	81.2	0.76	b	Rollin (161)
	11	57.2	1356	42	81.2	0.70	a	Steigman, Shockley, Nix (193)
α-Fe	3.4×10^4	77.2	1803	43	96	0.80	a	Birchenall, Mehl (27)
γ-Fe	1.04×10^{-3}	48.0	1803	26.7			a	Birchenall, Mehl (27)
Pb	6.7	27.9	600	46.5	47.5	0.60	a	Seith, Keil (175)
β-W		140.0	3673	38	203	0.69		van Liempt* (127)
Non regular metals								
Bi ∥ c	1.2×10^{-3}	31.0	554	57	47.8	0.65	a	Seith (168)
⊥ c	6.9×10^{46}	140,0	554	257	47.8	2.92	a	Seith (168)
Zn ∥ c	4.6×10^{-2}	20.4	693	29.5	27.4		b	Banks, Day (18, 19)
⊥ c	92	31.0	693	44.7	27.4		b	Miller, Banks (139, 140)

* Not self-diffusion but diffusion of Fe extrapolated to zero concentration.

Rhines and Mehl (158) carried through a very thorough investigation of diffusion coefficients in the alpha solid solutions of copper, employing the systems Cu-Zn, Cu-Al, Cu-Be, Cu-Pd, Cu-Si and Cu-Sn. Rods of these alloys were prepared and annealed to remove local inhomogeneities. After these rods had been turned on a lathe to 0.65 in. diameter within an accuracy of 0.0003 in. they were plated with copper. For details of the very careful procedure we must refer to the original paper. Then these samples were heated to temperatures between 500 and 900°C. for a period of 1 to about 90 days, the time being so chosen in every case that diffusion did not reach the outer surface of the copper plating and the system could be treated as of infinite length for evaluation. The concentration distribution was determined chemically, samples were taken by turning in a precision lathe successive layers of thickness of about 0.003 in. About 40 layers were turned from each specimen. Since diffusion coefficients proved to depend strongly on concentration, evaluation of the experiments by means of Boltzmann's method was necessary (cf. Chap. I, p. 31). Approximate evaluation by means of the error function and exact evaluation by Boltzmann's method show, as in the above cited cases (Figs. 5-7, 5-8) that the approximate solution is unsatisfactory. A survey of diffusion coefficients thus obtained is seen in Figs. 5-9 to 5-13 taken from Rhines and Mehl, cf. Table XVI.

Experimental concentration curves such as Fig. 5-17 usually show clearly that the original interface and the interface, defined by the condition that as much of the diffusing component has migrated from the one side as has entered the other, do not coincide. This fact must probably be understood in connection with the experiments of Smigelskas and Kirkendall (182) and their theoretical interpretation, Darken (60), Seitz (13, 180).

The diffusion of thallium in hexagonally crystallized selenium has been investigated by Gudden and Lehovec (81). At 216°C. the (concentration dependent) diffusion coefficient is of the order of magnitude of 5×10^{-8} cm.²/sec. at a thallium concentration of 3×10^{-3}. There is a marked influence of an electric field of a few volts per cm. upon the rate of migration of the thallium, indicating that positive thallium ions are moving.

IV. Concentration dependence of D and deviations from ideal behaviour of mixtures

In Chap. III, p. 156 we have given the general equation for diffusion in the x-direction

$$J = -\frac{uc}{N}\frac{\partial \mu}{\partial x} \qquad [5.4]$$

which may be written, replacing u by $\dfrac{D_0}{kT}$

$$J = -\frac{D_0}{RT} c \frac{\partial \mu}{\partial x} = -\frac{c D_0}{RT} \frac{\partial \mu}{\partial c} \frac{\partial c}{\partial x}. \qquad [5.5]$$

In [5.5] D_0 may still depend on concentration, due to a variation of the average mobility with concentration, i.e., due to a variation of disorder and of the energy barrier for migration, but the influence of non-ideality of the mixture is no longer contained in the diffusion coefficient, being corrected for by the thermodynamic factor

$$\frac{c}{RT} \frac{\partial \mu}{\partial c} = \frac{d \log a}{d \log c} = 1 + \frac{d \log \gamma}{d \log c} \qquad [5.6]$$

where a = activity, and γ = activity coefficient, of the diffusing species*.

In order to apply this correction, one must know the activity of the diffusing component in the mixture.

Before dealing with the experiments, we add one more remark. Emphasizing the fact that we are considering diffusion in a binary mixture, we may write for [5.5]

$$J_1 = -J_2 = -(D_{12})_0 \frac{\partial c_1}{\partial x} \frac{c_1}{RT} \frac{\partial \mu_1}{\partial c_1}. \qquad [5.7]$$

where D_{12} is the coefficient of interdiffusion of the components 1 and 2, and where the subscripts 1 and 2 refer to the components 1 and 2. Now the chemical potentials in a mixture are interrelated by the Gibbs-Duhem equation

$$\Sigma N_i d\mu_i = 0 \qquad [5.8]$$

which may be written in the alternative forms, for a binary mixture

$$N_1 \frac{\partial \mu_1}{\partial N_1} = -N_2 \frac{\partial \mu_2}{\partial N_2}, \quad \frac{\partial \log a_1}{\partial \log N_1} = \frac{\partial \log a_2}{\partial \log N_2}. \qquad [5.9]$$

If, further, we measure the concentrations in moles per unit volume, we have for the concentration gradients of either component

$$\frac{\partial c_1}{\partial x} = -\frac{\partial c_2}{\partial x} \qquad [5.10]$$

and, consequently, we may write for the diffusion flow

$$J_1 = -J_2 = -(D_{12})_0 \frac{\partial \log a_1}{\partial \log N_1} \frac{\partial c_1}{\partial x} = +(D_{12})_0 \frac{\partial \log a_2}{\partial \log N_2} \frac{\partial c_2}{\partial x}, \qquad [5.11]$$

the equation showing, as it should, complete symmetry with respect to the two components.

---

* While originally the concentration unit may be chosen quite arbitrarily, it is convenient, in discussing non-ideal systems, to use molar concentrations. Then with obvious assumptions these may be replaced by mole fractions.

TABLE XVI

Concentration dependence of D_0 and Q

a. Diffusion of various metals in copper at 800°C. Rhines and Mehl, (158), Method 1

| Diffusing metal | Concentration in atom per cent | | | | | | | | | |
| | 0 | | 4 | | 8 | | 12 | | 16 | |
	D_0 cm.²/sec.	Q kcal.	D_0 cm.²/sec.	Q kcal.	D_0 cm.²/sec.	Q kcal.	D_0 cm.²/sec.	Q kcal.	D_0 cm.²/sec.	Q kcal.
Al	0.0175 (0.8 per cent extrapolated)	37.7	0.0454	39.5	0.375	43	6.75	48	252	54
Be	2.3×10^{-4}	28	7.1×10^{-4}	30	3.3×10^{-2}	37				
Cd	2.0×10^{-9}	8	*							
Si	0.037	40.0	0.405	48.2	18.7	53.8				
Sn	1.13	45	0.0032	30.5						
Zn	0.0166	37.7	0.0525	40	0.0776	40	0.0046	31	0.0068	31

* For 0.5 atom per cent $D_0 = 2 \times 10^{-8}$, $Q = 10$ kcal.

Table XVI, continued

b. Diffusion of manganese or nickel in γ-iron, Wells and Mehl (209, 210), Method 1

Diffusing metal	Concentration in weight per cent		Temperature °C.	D_0 (cm.²/sec.)	Q (kcal./g. atom)
Mn	4 per cent Mn	0.02 per cent C	1080—1450	0.57 ± 0.11	66.2 ± 0.5
	14 „ „ Mn	0.02 „ „ C		0.54 ± 0.09	65.4 ± 0.5
	4 „ „ Mn	1.25 „ „ C	1000—1250	0.51 ± 0.18	61.2 ± 1.0
	14 „ „ Mn	1.25 „ „ C		0.54 ± 0.18	61.0 ± 1.0
Ni	4 „ „ Ni	0.03 „ „ C	1100—1450	0.44 ± 0.11	67.7 ± 0.75
	14 „ „ Ni	0.03 „ „ C		0.51 ± 0.12	67.3 ± 0.75
	4 „ „ Ni	0.06 „ „ C	1050—1300	0.46 ± 0.15	65.6 ± 1.0
	14 „ „ Ni	0.06 „ „ C		0.42 ± 0.13	64.5 ± 1.0

c. Diffusion of carbon in γ-iron, Wells and Mehl (208), Method 1

	Concentration in weight per cent		Temperature °C	D_0(cm.²/sec.)	Q(kcal./g. atom)
Welding of high carbon steel with low carbon steel	Si = 0.003—0.37	0.1 per cent C	750—1250	0.072	31.0
	P = 0.003—0.0039				
	S = 0.001—0.036				
	Cu = 0 —0.13				
	O = 0 —0.19	1.0 per cent C	750—1250	0.185	33.0
	Mn = 0.003—16				
	Ni = 0 —20.3				

For practical application the following should be noted. The thermodynamic term in the diffusion equation contains only $\frac{\partial \log a}{\partial \log N}$ or $\frac{\partial \log \gamma}{\partial \log N}$, therefore the result is independent of an arbitrary factor in c, in a, or in γ, and the activities may be referred to an arbitrary standard state. In the experimental determinations of activities in mixtures of metals, Mehl and co-workers (26) made use of measurements of vapor pressures of the more volatile component (zinc in brass). Since on the assumption of ideal behavior of the vapor, the activity is proportional to the vapor pressure, the activity in equations [5.6] etc. may be replaced by the vapor pressure, without further corrections.

Birchenall and Mehl (26), following an analysis due to W. A. Johnson (102) started from the assumption that diffusion should be proportional to the activity gradient, $\frac{\partial a}{\partial x}$, instead of the concentration gradient, as in the ideal case. They arrive at an expression for the diffusion coefficient

$$D = D_0 \left(\gamma + c \frac{\partial \gamma}{\partial c} \right) \qquad [5.12]$$

where D_0 is a diffusion coefficient, independent of deviations from ideal behaviour of the mixture, c is the concentration of the diffusing substance and γ the activity coefficient of the diffusing component. For interdiffusion in a binary system [5.12] does not yet give the necessary symmetry with respect to the two components. Therefore, the authors introduce, empirically, the symmetric expression

$$D = D_{12} \left(\gamma_1 + c_1 \frac{\partial \gamma_1}{\partial c_1} \right) \left(\gamma_2 + c_2 \frac{\partial \gamma_2}{\partial c_2} \right) \qquad [5.13]$$

where D_{12} corresponds to the above D_0, and the other notations are obvious. Eqs. [5.12] and [5.13] must be considered as tentative empirical relations. They are not identical with the relations derived elsewhere for non-ideal mixtures (Chap. III, p. 156). In the systems copper-zinc (alpha brass) (158), and iron-carbon (diffusion of C in austenite) (208) coefficients D_{12}, calculated according to Eqs. [5.13] and [5.12] respectively, show a remarkable independence of concentration, as seen from Table XVII. This table gives selected values from Birchenall's and Mehl's results. The activity data in the copper zinc system were obtained from vapor pressure measurements by Hargreaves (82) together with data given by Maier (129) and by Schneider and Schmid (167). For the carbon-iron system activity data were based upon results of Smith (183), also depending on vapor equilibria.

The concentration dependence of the values of D_0 (in the carbon iron system) and of D_{12} (for the copper zinc system), thus obtained, is considerably reduced compared with that of the original D values. The D_0 values in the system iron-carbon (calculated from eq. [5.12]) are almost independent of concentration, cf. Barrer (22).

TABLE XVIIa

Selected values of D_0, calculated according to eqs. [5.12] and [5.14]
for diffusion of carbon in austenite at 1000°C, after Birchenall and Mehl

Wt. Pct. C	γ	$\dfrac{\partial \gamma}{\partial c}$	D obs.$\times 10^7$ (208)	(D_0) calc.$\times 10^7$ Krücke	(D_0) calc.$\times 10^7$ B. a. M.
0,1	9.99	0.15	2.55	2,55	0.255
0,5	10.42	2.71	3.00	2,65	0.255
1,0	12.18	4.29	4.43	3,26	0.269

TABLE XVIIb

Values of $(D_{12})_0$, calculated according to $D = (D_{12})_0 \left(1 + \dfrac{c}{\gamma}\dfrac{\partial \gamma}{\partial c}\right)$ Zn for inter-

diffusion in α-brass, at 750°C after Birchenall and Mehl

At. Pct. Zn	γ_{Zn}	$\left(\dfrac{\partial \gamma}{\partial c}\right)_{Zn}$	D obs.$\times 10^{10}$ (158)	$(D_{12})_0$ calc.$\times 10^{10}$ Krücke	(D_{12}) calc.$\times 10^{10}$ B. a. M.
2	0.056	0.0007	2.5	2.4	37.3
10	0.070	0.0032	5.5	3.8	35.0
20	0.115	0.0059	19.5	9.6	47.8
26	0.158	0.0086	61.0	25.3	84.0

We have recalculated* the results of Birchenall and Mehl, using their activity data, but applying the quasi-thermodynamic relation (cf. Chap. III, p. 156)

$$D = (D_{12})_0 \left[1 + \frac{\partial \log \gamma}{\partial \log N}\right] \qquad [5.14]$$

first given by Hartley (84), and Onsager and Fuoss (147), which, on account of the Gibbs-Duhem relation, is automatically symmetrical with respect to both constituents of a binary mixture. The results, thus obtained, are seen in Table XVII. There still remains a certain concentration dependence of D_0 in the system iron-carbon which must be due to a dependence of the mobility on concentration, as observed in other systems also.

V. Diffusion in systems consisting of more than one phase, and related phenomena

Diffusion in systems consisting of two phases has been treated theoretically by the author (6) and by C. Wagner (201) (cf. Chap. I,

* The author is indebted to E. Krücke for carrying out these calculations.

p. 68). In the treatment given by the author constancy of the diffusion coefficient within a single phase has been assumed, and the additional assumption has been made that the quantities of the phases do not change essentially during diffusion. Consequently, the interface between these phases is not shifted relative to the system. C. Wagner has treated theoretically a number of cases where the restrictions concerning the displacement of the plane of discontinuity have been dropped (cf. Chap. I, p. 69).

In the cases treated by the author there is a discontinuity in equilibrium composition at the interface of the two phases, in addition to a discontinuity in the diffusion coefficient. Typical curves have been reproduced in Chap. I, p. 26. Such conditions should prevail, for instance, in the case of diffusion of carbon from a metal I into another metal II, if miscibility of the metals is negligible, Fig. 5-18. It is very possible that in such cases diffusion is directed from the phase with the lower concentration toward that of higher concentration, as seen in Fig. 5-18 b. This will always occur when the concentration in one phase is lower than that in the other, but the ratio of the concentrations is higher than that given by Nernst's partition coefficient for equilibrium.

Thus diffusion occurs "uphill", from the phase with lower concentration toward that with higher concentration. Equilibrium is not determined by a uniform distribution of concentration, but by a uniform distribution of chemical potential (or of absolute activities).

Similar conditions may prevail even in systems which, from a thermodynamic point of view, do not consist of two distinct phases*. Suppose we have two alloyed steels, differing in composition, but both belonging to the same type of mixed crystals, as was the case in diffusion experiments, carried out by Darken (61)**. We consider the rate of diffusion of carbon from one steel into the other, the rate of diffusion of the other alloy components being negligible compared with that of the carbon. Then, with respect to the diffusion of carbon, this system is equivalent to a two phase system. The diffusion coefficient will be different for the two alloys, and the equilibrium distribution will be given by a partition coefficient, generally differing from unity.

Fig. 5-18a, taken from Darken, shows schematically the change of composition with time, in a ternary system, this change occurring during the primary stage practically without change of the concen-

---

* In the strictest sense "phase" means a region of uniform concentration. Throughout this book we shall use the wider concept of "phase" as is used in metallography.
** Cf. also Seith and Bartschat (170) and Smoluchowski (184).

tration of the third component, while after sufficient time has elapsed, of course, a state of equal concentration distribution will be obtained, as given by point C.

Concentration distributions, similar to those discussed above, may also be obtained in homogeneous systems with rather sudden change of the diffusion coefficient within a narrow range of concentration. This change may be due either to a change in mobility or to a change in thermodynamic properties of the mixture, $\frac{\partial \log \gamma}{\partial \log N}$. In Fig. 5-19 we show the stationary concentration distribution in a system with sudden

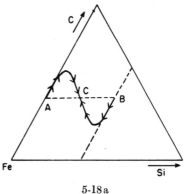

5-18 a

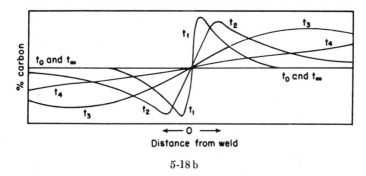

5-18 b

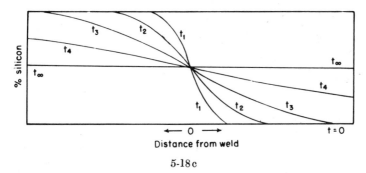

5-18 c

Fig. 5-18. Diffusion in ternary system Fe-C-Si, after Darken. (a) Schematic diagram in triangular coordinates, indicating concentration changes from original compositions A and B towards final composition C. (b) Showing local variation of carbon concentration as function of distance from weld, for different times t, (c) Same as (b), for silicon concentration.

change of the diffusion coefficient. Here it has been assumed that definite, constant, concentrations of the diffusing substance are maintained at either end of the system, the stationary concentration distribution being determined by the condition (cf. Chap. I, p. 8ff.)

$$D \frac{\partial c}{\partial x} = \text{constant} . \qquad [5.15]$$

Concentration curves, similar to those of Fig. 5-19, have been observed in many cases, Grube and coworkers (79, 80), Hicks (93).

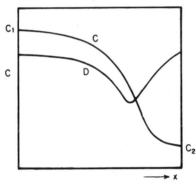

Fig. 5-19. Distribution of concentration c and of diffusion coefficient D during steady state diffusion in x-direction.

Diffusion may be accompanied by recrystallization (125, 2). If we have to deal with non-regular crystals, the diffusion coefficients may differ considerably for different crystallographic directions, even by several orders of magnitude (cf. p. 229, 259). If recrystallization occurs during diffusion and if the direction of the concentration gradient causes a certain orientation of the newly formed crystals, as has been shown by Mehl (212) and co-workers, considerable changes in rate of diffusion may thus arise.

Orientation in diffusion layers was investigated by Woo, Barrett and Mehl (212). Mehl had suggested that an orientation observed between parent and new crystal when one solid phase is generated from another, is the same, irrespective of the type of phase change involved. This assumption was tested and proved valid in the copper-zinc system. The authors think it highly probable that the process of nucleation, identical in all cases, is responsible for these observations.

In systems consisting of more than two components, generally there will be a mutual dependence of the diffusion coefficients. In the previous example of carbon, diffusing in alloyed steels of different composition, we have a change of composition with time as shown in Fig. 5-18a, taken from Darken (61). This refers to the change of composition with time of two points on opposite sides of the weld. The change of composition of the whole system is shown qualitatively in Figs. 5-18b, 5-18c, also taken from Darken. It refers to diffusion in a system of two steel rods, with equal carbon content, but of different silicon content. Since the mobility of the carbon is much higher than that of the silicon, the initially uniform carbon distribution becomes unequal after some time, approaching uniform distribution again for t→∞, after the silicon distribution has also been equalized. The silicon distribution approaches equilibrium, as shown in Figs. 5-18a and 5-18c.

Diffusion of carbon in alloyed steels has been investigated by Seith and Bartschat (170), by measurements similar to Darken's. Diffusion coefficients were determined by means of the author's method (cf. Chap. I, p. 68), valid, however, for constant D only. Hence the same objections may be raised against these results as against those of Grube and Jedele (p. 238). It is possible to evaluate even these experiments by means of Boltzmann's method (Jost (107a)).

The mutual interaction of several diffusing substances may give rise to apparently anomalous concentration distributions, as shown in Fig. 5-20 for the diffusion of phosphorus, and carbon, in iron (Bramley (35)).

Darken worked with rods of steel of varying composition. Rods $2^1/_2$ in. long and $^3/_8$, $^1/_2$ or $^5/_8$ in. diameter, ground flat at one end, were welded together in an helium atmosphere. The composition of the steels used is seen from Table XVIII, the data of the diffusion experiments are contained in Table XIX. The zone of fusion (during welding) extended about 0.002 in., consequently penetration due to diffusion should be large compared with this value, if disturbances due to diffusion during welding are to be negligible. Actually the depth of penetration was of

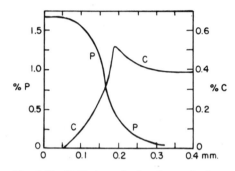

Fig. 5-20. Diffusion of phosphorus in iron (80 hours at 1000°C.) with 0.4% carbon content, after Bramley, taken from Seith (11).

TABLE XVIII

Composition of Steels used by Darken

Designation	per cent C	per cent Mn	per cent Si	per cent P	per cent S	per cent Cr	per cent Mo
a	0.49	0.25	3.80	0.011	0.006	0.31	
b	0.04	0.28	4.78	0.006	0.011		
c	0.45	0.88	0.05	0.020	0.008		
d	0.58	0.45	0.14	0.035	0.008		
e	1.19	0.28	0.20				0.02
f	1.34	0.20	0.07				6.07

the order of magnitude of 1 in., as seen from Figs. 5-21, 5-22, giving the resulting concentration distributions in Darken's experiments.

If diffusion within either species is the rate determining process, the transition from one side of the weld to the other being very fast, then the carbon concentrations obtained at either side of the weld should be such as to give equal values of the chemical potentials at either side. This consequence has been tested by Darken, who used

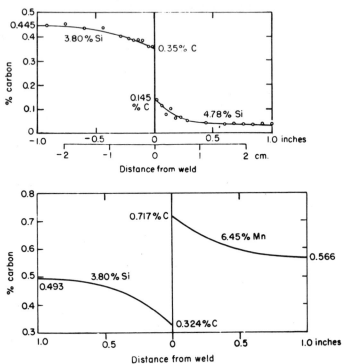

Fig. 5-21, 5-22. Distributions of carbon during diffusion in two-phase system consisting of alloyed steels after Darken. Temperature 1050°C, diffusion times 14 and 10 days respectively.

TABLE XIX

Data on Welds (Darken)

Weld-Number	Steels Welded	Diameter (In.)	Time of Diffusion, Seconds	Temperature during Diffusion
1	a—b	3/8	1.210×10^6	
2	a—c	1/2	1.109	1050°C.
3	a—d	1/2	0.821	
4	e—f	5/8	1.210	

the activity measurements of R. P. Smith (183). The results are quite satisfactory, as seen from Table XX.

The evaluation of diffusion coefficients, for which we refer to the original paper, gave the values for D, listed in Table XXI.

TABLE XX

Comparison of Activity of Carbon on the Sides of the Welds after Darken

| Weld-Nr. | Left Side (Fig. 5-21, 5-22) | | | | Right Side | | | |
	per cent C	per cent Si	per cent Mn	Activity of Carbon	per cent C	per cent Si	per cent Mn	Activity of Carbon
2	0.315	3.80	0.25	0.30	0.586	0.05	0.88	0.29
3	0.324	3.80	0.25	0.31	0.717	0.14	6.45	0.29

TABLE XXI

Diffusivity of Carbon in Austenite at 1050°C. after Darken

| Steel | Weld | Mean per cent C | Diffusivity, cm.²/sec. | | | |
			Method 1*	Method 2*	Average	From (208)
a	1	0.4	3.9×10^{-7}	3.4×10^{-7}		
	2	0.4	4.0	4.0	3.9×10^{-7}	
	3	0.4	4.1	4.2		
c	2	0.5	5.9	5.5	5.7	5.3×10^{-7}
d	3	0.6	5.7	5.2	5.4	(6)
e	4	1.1	6.9	6.5	6.7	7.4

Measurements with two-phase systems were also carried out by Smoluchowski (184), with the system Fe - C - Co. From the author's solution he derived the relation, valid for the interface of the two phases at $x = 0$

$$\frac{D_{II}}{D_I} = \left(\frac{C_{I0} - C_I}{C_{II}}\right)^2$$

where C_I, C_{II} are the concentrations of diffusing species (carbon) in phases I and II, and C_{I0} is the concentration in phase I for $t = 0$. Diffusion coefficients, derived by Smoluchowski are reproduced in Table XXII.

The simultaneous diffusion of nickel and of silicon in copper has been studied by Mehl and Rhines (136). Results are given in Fig. 5-23 and Table XI. The rate of diffusion of silicon is markedly decreased

---

* For details of method cf. original paper (68).

TABLE XXII

Diffusion coefficients of carbon in Fe-Co alloys of varying Co content, with
2.2 atom per cent C, Smoluchowski (184)

	$D \times 10^7$ cm.^{2} sec.$^{-1}$		
	0	1.98	3.91 per cent Co
1273°K.	3.7	4.3	4.7
1463°K.	18.8	21.9	26.7

by the presence of nickel, while the rate of diffusion of nickel is little,
if at all, affected by the presence of silicon.

"Anomalous" concentration curves for diffusion in binary systems,
as shown schematically in Fig. 5-19, p. 248 for the stationary case,
have been observed repeatedly in non-stationary diffusion. We give
two examples in Figs. 5-24, 5-25. In these cases one cannot, however,
as for a stationary state
of diffusion, immedi-
ately read relative dif-
fusion coefficients from
the slope of the curve
for the concentration

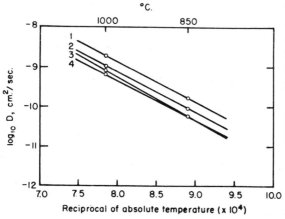

Fig. 5-23. Simultaneous diffusion of nickel and silicon
in copper.

a.) 0.5 atom% Si ⎤ 1 Si
    1   atom% Ni ⎦ 3 Ni

b.) 1.5 atom% Si ⎤ 2 Si
    3   atom% Ni ⎦ 4 Ni

After Mehl and Rhines (136).

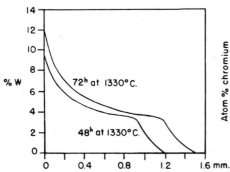

Fig. 5-24. "Anomalous" concentration
distribution during diffusion of W in
iron, after Grube.

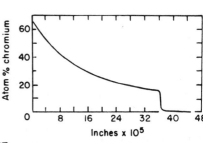

Fig. 5-25. "Anomalous" concentration
distribution for diffusion of chromium
in iron, at 1200°C., after Hicks.

distribution. The qualitative consequences, however, are similar to those in the former case. Let us consider, Fig. 5-25, an almost discontinuous concentration distribution. Fick's second law states

$$\frac{\partial c}{\partial t} = D \frac{\partial^2 c}{\partial x^2} \qquad [5.16]$$

or

$$\frac{\partial c}{\partial t} = \frac{\partial}{\partial x}\left(D\frac{\partial c}{\partial x}\right) \qquad [5.17]$$

depending on whether D may be considered as constant or not. Thus the rate of local change of concentration with time is given by the right side of the preceding equations. Immediately to the left of the discontinuity $\frac{\partial^2 c}{\partial x^2}$ has a very high negative value, while immediately to the right $\frac{\partial^2 c}{\partial x^2}$ has very high positive values. Thus an equalization of the concentration discontinuity should occur quickly if D were constant. Therefore, D must vary with concentration, in such a way that $\frac{\partial}{\partial x}\left(D\frac{\partial c}{\partial x}\right)$ remains comparatively small over the region of discontinuity. For otherwise an almost discontinuous curve could not exist. This means that $D\frac{\partial c}{\partial x}$, though not exactly constant as in the stationary case, varies but little with position, and the quantitative conclusions of p. 248 remain, qualitatively, approximately valid. There remains the question of why this sudden change in rate of diffusion with concentration does occur. Seith (11) points out that the discontinuity observed by Grube (79, 80) for diffusion of tungsten in iron at 4 per cent W could not be a mere concentration effect because no discontinuity could be observed with electrolytic iron. It seems that a concentration effect has not been ruled out definitely by this observation, but it seems highly probable that the presence of carbon may play a role in connection with this effect.

VI. Evaluation of steady-state measurements

It has been discussed several times (cf. p. 248) that by measuring the concentration distribution during stationary diffusion one can obtain at once relative diffusion coefficients, on account of the relation

$$D\frac{\partial c}{\partial x} = \text{const.} \qquad [5.18]$$

D being inversely proportional to the concentration gradient $\frac{\partial c}{\partial x}$. If, instead of the concentration distribution during the steady state, only the concentrations at the two surfaces of a plane parallel plate and the average concentration in the interior have been determined, an evaluation of the concentration dependent D is not possible without further assumptions. F. E. Harris (83) has attempted an evaluation of such experiments, introducing the special assumption that D varies linearly with concentration. It can be shown that the above measurements are sufficient for the evaluation of the single constant, characterizing the variation of D with concentration. For small concentration differences, as applied in Harris' experiments, the assumption of linearity certainly appears justified.

One may consider Harris' method as a special case of a more general method, where a power series has been assumed for the variation of the diffusion coefficient with concentration

$$D = D_0 + D_1 c + D_2 c^2 + \ldots \ . \qquad [5.19]$$

With a relation for the diffusion coefficient of the form [5.19] one may carry out experiments such as those of Harris between several consecutive concentrations $c_1, c_2, c_3 \ldots$, where $c_1 < c_2 < c_3 < \ldots$, and where the consecutive concentration differences are sufficiently small to allow of a linear interpolation for the diffusion coefficient. From these experiments one would obtain a series of linear equations for the diffusion coefficient. Supposing that experiments with $n + 1$ concentrations have been carried out, the results may be approximated by an expression of n-th order, identical with the power series of [5.19], broken off with the $(n + 1)^{th}$ term.

Harris carried out his experiments in the following way. A test plate of iron is welded to the end of a tube, the inner side of which is passed by a decarburizing gas while the outside is in contact with a carburizing gas, the whole system being heated in a furnace until a stationary state has been reached. Instead of measuring the concentrations at either side of the test plate itself, Harris heated two additional iron plates in the same furnace, one in contact with the carburizing and the other in contact with the decarburizing gas. Analysis of these latter iron plates gives the surface concentrations in the diffusion specimen, provided that equilibrium at the surface had been established. Analysis of the test plate gives the average carbon concentration during steady diffusion. The values obtained in an experiment at 1700°F. were: surface concentrations 0.05 and 1.38 per cent of carbon, respectively, while the average concentration in the diffusion plate was 0.84 per cent, which is higher than the arithmetic mean of the surface concentrations. From this fact alone one may conclude at once, qualitatively, that the concentration curve was above the straight line, valid for constant diffusion coefficient, Fig. 5-26, and, therefore, the differential coefficient at the low concentration side must be higher than that at the high concentration side. Consequently, the diffusion coefficient, being inversely proportional to the differential coefficient, must be higher at the high concentration side, thus increasing with increasing carbon content. Actually, the equation found by Harris for the concentration dependence of D is

$$D = D_0 \left[1 + 2.15 \,(\text{per cent C})\right] \quad [5.20]$$

while Wells and Mehl (208) had found a smaller dependence, corresponding to

$$D = D_0 \left[1 + 0.9 \,(\text{per cent C})\right] \quad [5.21]$$

For details and for experiments with non-stationary diffusion we refer to the original paper.

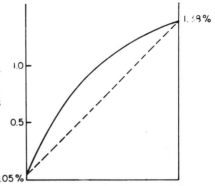

Fig. 5-26. Harris' method for evaluation of concentration dependent diffusion coefficients.

VII. The Experiments of Smigelskas and Kirkendall

The experiments of Smigelskas and Kirkendall (182), discussed in Chap. III, p. 159, are of fundamental importance for the understanding of the interdiffusion of metals. By marking the original boundary between a brass core and a copper plating by molybdenum wires, not participating in diffusion, they were able to prove that even with substitutional mixed crystals the diffusion process need not consist in a mere exchange of atoms of both constituents. Measurement of the distance between the wires at opposite sides of the core revealed that the dimensions of the core decreased linearly with the square root of time, indicating a decrease of the number of lattice points with time. This might be due either to an independent movement of copper and of zinc atoms, as assumed by the authors and by Darken (60), or by a diffusion of 'vacancies' from the outside into the brass core where they finally coagulate and the material shrinks, by a plastic flow, as Seitz (13, 180) assumes in his theory of the process. Actually it has been found that far more zinc has diffused out of the core into the copper than copper has diffused in the opposite direction. Seitz suggests experiments to distinguish between the possible explanations. If the brass core and the copper plating are interchanged, the core should grow during diffusion if the first explanation were correct, while no effect should be observed if the Seitz mechanism is the correct one. For a further discussion cf. Bardeen (20a), Seitz (180a), Zener (215a).

VIII. Self diffusion

In general, the rate of diffusion of a dissolved substance will differ from the rate of self-diffusion of the main component. Even by using very small concentrations of the dissolved metal and by extrapolating to the concentration zero, one does not obtain the coefficient of self diffusion, as seen in the cases of copper (158, 193) and lead (173) already quoted. This fact is easily understood, cf. Manning (130). For, the mobility of a foreign component will not be identical with that of the main component. Let us assume a vacancy mechanism for diffusion in a substitutional mixed crystal of two metals. Then the same vacancies are available for the motion of either component. The energy barrier, however, to be surmounted by a migrating particle, jumping into a vacancy, will depend on the nature of this particle. In addition the vibration frequencies will be different for different particles. Therefore, even in this case the mobilities of the two components will differ. (To a small degree even the mobilities of isotopes will differ, though this difference will be negligible in most cases. In principle, however, a separation of isotopes is possible by means of the small remaining effects.) If, on the other hand, the dissolved component of an interstitial mixed crystal is diffusing, for instance, carbon in iron, this mobility is completely independent of that of the main component, even for vanishing concentration of the solute.

The situation is somewhat different in experiments, as carried out by Johnson (103), with a gold silver alloy of approximate composition $Au : Ag = 1 : 1$. Johnson determined the self diffusion of silver and of gold in this alloy, and in addition the rate of interdiffusion of gold and silver in alloys of composition near to that given above. The results may be represented as follows

$$D_{Au} = 0.12 \times \exp\left(-44,100/RT\right) \text{ cm.}^2 \text{ sec.}^{-1} \qquad [5.22]$$

$$D_{Ag} = 0.30 \times \exp\left(-44,700/RT\right) \quad ,, \qquad ,, \qquad [5.23]$$

$$D_{Ag,Au} = 0.14 \times \exp\left(-41,700/RT\right) \quad ,, \qquad ,, \qquad [5.24]$$

where D_{Au}, and D_{Ag} are coefficients of self-diffusion for Au and Ag, respectively, and $D_{Ag, Au}$ is the coefficient of interdiffusion of Ag and Au. The latter value is higher than either of the former ones. This is best seen when the results are represented by means of an average value of 44,100 for the energy of activation (cf. F. Seitz (180))

$$D_{Au} = 0.12 \exp\left(-44,100/RT\right) \text{ cm.}^2 \text{ sec}^{-1} \qquad [5.22a]$$

$$D_{Ag} = 0.30 \exp\left(-44,100/RT\right) \quad ,, \qquad ,, \qquad [5.23a]$$

$$D_{Ag, Au} = 0.41 \exp\left(-44,100/RT\right) \quad ,, \qquad ,, \qquad [5.24a]$$

In this case one might expect the value for interdiffusion to be intermediate between the values for self diffusion of either component. The value for interdiffusion, however, is approximately twice the arithmetic mean of the values for self diffusion. Deviations may partly be due to deviations from ideal behaviour of the mixed crystals under consideration, and may partly be explained on the basis of a generalized theory of diffusion, as developed by Darken (60) and by Seitz (180).

It is obvious that for the diffusion of isotopes, as long as differences due to the differences in mass of the isotopes are negligible (which, for instance, does not hold in the case of hydrogen and deuterium), the laws of ideal mixtures and, thus, Fick's law should hold with concentration independent diffusion coefficients. For interdiffusion of gold and silver, however, the deviations from ideality of the mixed crystals become important.

In the special case under consideration, viz. mole fractions of silver and of gold approximately equal to 0.5, the result of Darken's theory is identical with that obtained on the assumption that the mobility responsible for $D_{Ag,Au}$ is the arithmetic mean of that entering the values of D_{Ag} and D_{Au}, if correction is made for the non-ideal behaviour of the mixture. Thus one should have

$$D_{Ag,Au} = \frac{D_{Ag} + D_{Au}}{2} \left[1 + \frac{d \log \gamma_{Au}}{d \log N_{Au}} \right] \qquad [5.25]$$

$$= \frac{D_{Ag} + D_{Au}}{2} \left[1 + \frac{d \log \gamma_{Ag}}{d \log N_{Ag}} \right]$$

(cf. Chap. III, p. 156). Darken (60) computed $d \log \gamma / d \log N$ from the measurements of Wagner and Engelhard (202) and Wachter (199) who used the electromotive force method. The results, thus obtained, are seen in table XXIII. The remaining deviations between observed and calculated values of $D_{Ag,Au}$ may well be within the limits of experimental error.

The highest sensitivity in measurements of self diffusion is obtained if a thin layer of the radioactive isotope is deposited on the surface of the metal and the decrease in surface activity is measured. If a radiation of a sufficiently short range is being observed, as, for instance that of recoil atoms (v. Hevesy (91)) then it is possible to determine by this method diffusion coefficients of very small order of magnitude.

The accuracy, thus obtained (lead (76, 90, 91), copper (193), gold (128)) seems, however, to be much smaller than that obtained by means of the more conventional methods of analysis. In the following we report in some detail measurements of self diffusion, carried out by Johnson (102), who was able to achieve a very high degree of accuracy. Measurements with copper (161), gold (164) and zinc (19, 140) have been carried out by the same technique. Radio-

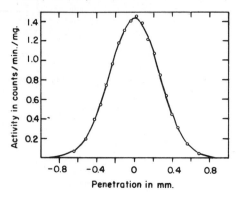

Fig. 5-27. Concentration penetration curve for diffusion of radioactive silver in ordinary silver after 4.78 days at 876.0°C., after Johnson.

active silver. (Ag^{105}, half-life 45 days, and Ag^{106}, half-life 8.2 days) was prepared by proton bombardment of palladium in a cyclotron, and chemically separated from the palladium. From a cyanide solution of the radioactive silver (containing additional non-radioactive silver) a layer of radioactive silver about 4×10^{-4} cm. thick was deposited on one surface of a silver disk, by standard electroplating technique. The silver disk was

of $^7/_8$ in. diameter and $^1/_4$ in. thickness. A second similar disk was welded to the active surface of the first disk. Thus the initial conditions for diffusion approached very closely those for diffusion from an infinitely thin layer into a rod of infinite length, cf. Chap. I, p. 17. The concentration distribution, to be expected after diffusion has proceeded for t seconds, is (Chap. I, p. 17)

$$c = \frac{s}{2\sqrt{\pi D t}} \times \exp\left(-x^2/4 D t\right) \quad [5.26]$$

where c is the concentration, x the perpendicular distance from the

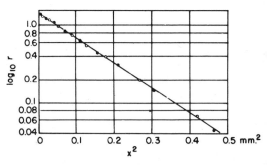

Fig. 5-28. Self diffusion of silver. Log_{10} radioactivity, r, versus square of distance from radioactive layer, after Johnson. ○ values from left side. ● values from right side.

radioactive layer, D the diffusion coefficient and s the amount of radioactive silver, originally present per cm.^{2} of the radioactive layer. After diffusion had taken place successive layers of thickness from 0.002 to 0.005 in. parallel to the active layer were turned off in a lathe. These layers were dissolved in nitric acid and their radioactivity was measured by a Geiger-Müller counter tube. A concentration penetration curve, thus obtained by Johnson is seen in Fig. 5-27. It follows from equation [5.26] that

$$\log_{10} c = -0.4343\, x^2/4\, Dt + \log k \qquad [5.27]$$

with

$$\log_{10} k = \log_{10} \left(s/2 \sqrt{\pi D t} \right). \qquad [5.28]$$

k is a constant within any one experiment because it refers to $t =$ const. In accordance with eq. [5.27] log radioactivity (proportional to c) has been plotted versus x^2, Fig. 5-28. Diffusion coefficients were determined from the slope of the straight line thus obtained, according to equa-

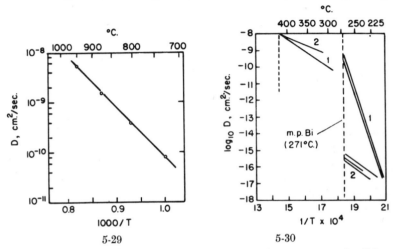

Fig. 5-29. Variation of self-diffusion coefficient of silver with temperature after Johnson.
Fig. 5-30. Anisotropy of self diffusion in bismuth (right) and zinc (left). $1 \perp c$ axis of hexagonal crystal, $2 \parallel c$ axis of hexagonal crystal, after Seith and Miller and Banks.

tion [5.27]. A correction was made for the thermal expansion of the silver, amounting to 2.6 per cent at 725°C. and 3.5 per cent at 950°C. Measured values of D are seen in Fig. 5-29. They can be represented by the equation

$$D = 0.89 \exp\left(-45{,}950/RT\right) \qquad [5.29]$$

TABLE XXIII

Comparison of Observed and Calculated Diffusivity for the Silver-Gold System, Darken (60)

	800°C.	900°C.	1000°C.
D observed.	4.5×10^{-10}	24×10^{-10}	9.7×10^{-9}
D calculated from eq. [5.25] . . .	3.8×10^{-10}	21×10^{-10}	9.3×10^{-9}

The accuracy of an experiment is estimated to be within 3 to 4 per cent which is a very high accuracy for diffusion measurements with a solid.

Data on self diffusion, given by Johnson, are reproduced in Table XXIII.

Values of self diffusion in anisotropic crystals of bismuth and zinc are seen in Fig. 5-30.

IX. Diffusion processes, preceding phase splitting

V. Daniel (57) studied diffusion in a two phase alloy. It was possible to observe a diffusion process in the homogeneous phase, preceding phase splitting, connected with a decrease in free energy, but with an increase of concentration difference. R. Becker (24)* had given a theory of such processes, involving negative diffusion coefficients in the region of demixing.

The alloy, Cu_4FeNi_3, studied by Daniel (58, 59) shows some striking features. Above the critical temperature of mixing, 800°C., the alloy is face centred cubic, while at lower temperatures it splits into two face centred phases. The proportion of nickel to iron remains almost unchanged in either phase, 3 : 1, while their copper content is different. If a homogeneous specimen of Cu_4FeNi_3 is annealed for some time below the critical temperature, a characteristic intermediate structure appears. This may be described approximately as follows. A single coherent lattice remains, but periodic variations of copper concentration with distance are observed, given by a sine curve. X-ray photographs allow of a determination of the wave length Qa of this periodicity as well as of the maximum variation in copper concentration, p, a being the lattice distance. Prolonged heating leads to an increase in Q and finally to a normal phase splitting.

It has been possible to investigate the increase with time of the change in concentration difference, the wave length being kept constant. Becker's equation for such processes is**

$$\frac{\partial c}{\partial t} = \operatorname{div}\left\{D_0\left[1 - N\left(1 - N\right)\frac{K}{RT}\right]\operatorname{grad} c\right\} \qquad [5.30]$$

where K is given by

$$K = 2\,z\,N\left\{\varepsilon_{ab} - \frac{1}{2}\left(\varepsilon_{aa} + \varepsilon_{bb}\right)\right\} \qquad [5.31]$$

z being the coordination number, N Avogadro's number, ε_{ab} etc. the energies of interaction per bond. The case of phase splitting corre-

---

* Cf. also Dehlinger (4, 62, 63) and Ilkevich (101).
** Cf. Chap. III, p. 156 ff.

sponds to $K>0$, while for $K<0$ there is a tendency for the formation of a superlattice. Eq. [5.30] means that the diffusion coefficient has been put equal to the expression

$$D(c) = D_0 \left[1 - N(1-N) \frac{K}{RT} \right] \qquad [5.32]$$

which, for $K>0$, may be positive or negative.

The author attempts a solution in the form

$$C(x,t) = c(x,t) - \frac{1}{2} = \sum_{n=1}^{\infty} p_n(t) \cos \frac{2n\pi x}{Qa} . \qquad [5.33]$$

With $p_n(t) = \exp\left(-\frac{n^2\pi^2 Dt}{Q^2 a^2} \right)$, this is the solution for $D = $ const. (cf. Chap. I, p. 35). Retaining the first term only, one obtains

$$\frac{dp_1}{dt} = D_1 \frac{t\pi^2}{Q^2 a^2} p_1 \left(\frac{1}{4} p_1^2 - q^2 \right) \qquad [5.34]$$

where

$$q^2 = \frac{1}{4} - RT/K .$$

Using a simplified equation, derived from the experiments, the author found the following values, Table XXIV.

TABLE XXIV (after Daniel)

Temperature (°C.)	Q unit cells	D (cm.²/sec.)	D average cm.²/sec.
		Rising amplitudes	
450	70	6.6×10^{-19}	
	118	0.9×10^{-19}	3.7×10^{-19}
550	50	4.8×10^{-17}	
	68	1.8×10^{-17}	3.0×10^{-17}
	110	3.4×10^{-17}	
650	122	3.8×10^{-15}	
	119	1.3×10^{-15}	2.5×10^{-15}
740	122	6.0×10^{-15}	6.0×10^{-15}

Temperature (°C.)	Q unit cells	D (cm.²/sec.)
		Falling amplitudes
750	1300	2.2×10^{-13}
820	1300	3.3×10^{-13}
850	5400	1.4×10^{-12}

Since the wave length is very small, of the order of magnitude of 10^{-6} cm., very small diffusion coefficients can be measured. The measured values of D can be represented by

$$D = 47 \exp \left(-[66.000 \pm 4.000]/RT\right) \text{cm.}^2 \text{sec.}^{-1}. \qquad [5.35]$$

Measurements of the grain growth show that this process definitely slows down with increasing temperature, by a factor between 10 and 100 for a temperature increase from 550° to 750°C. Since the mobility of the diffusing particles increases with increasing temperature, this should be due to the thermodynamic factor.

Though these results are of the greatest interest, an analysis on the basis of a more refined theory seems highly desirable.

X. Diffusion in molecular crystals

There are but few experiments available referring to diffusion in non-metallic homopolar crystals. Cremer and Polanyi (55) measured the rate of transformation of para-hydrogen in the solid state. This is a bimolecular process, involving the interaction of neighboring molecules. When the reaction has proceeded so far that most of the para-hydrogen molecules left are isolated, a drop in rate of conversion is observed, diffusion now playing a role in the further reaction. From these observations it is possible to draw conclusions with respect to self diffusion in solid hydrogen. Results, thus obtained (56), are listed in Table XXV. It is highly probable that a vacancy mechanism is

TABLE XXV

Self diffusion in solid hydrogen, E. Cremer (56)

$$D = D_0 \exp \left(-Q/RT\right)$$

Temperature °K.	D (cm.^{2}/sec.)	Q cal./g.atom
11.3	$\leq 1.7 \times 10^{-22}$	
11.8	$(3.5 \pm 3.5) \times 10^{-22}$	790 ± 130
13.2	$(1.2 \pm 0.25) \times 10^{-20}$	
13.6	$\geq 2 \times 10^{-20}$	

responsible for the diffusion observed. This has been discussed in connection with the process of disorder in homopolar crystals, (cf. Chap. II, p. 110).

It should be possible to obtain further information on the diffusion in homopolar crystals by the use of radioactive tracers.

REFERENCES

Monographs and review articles

1. Barrer, R. M., Diffusion in and through solids. Cambridge 1941.
2. Burgers, W. G., Handbuch der Metallphysik, Vol. III, 2 p. 136, 444. Leipzig 1941.
3. Chevenard, P., and Waché, X., Etude expérimentale de la diffusion métallique par la méthode thermomagnétique appliquée à des agrégats multilames, Mémoire Revue de Métallurgie. Paris 1945.
4. Dehlinger, U., Chemische Physik der Metalle und Legierungen. Leipzig 1939.
5. Hauk, J., *Metallforschung* **2**, 49 (1947).
6. Jost, W., Diffusion und chemische Reaktion in festen Stoffen. Th. Steinkopff, Leipzig und Dresden 1937.
7. Jost, W., Article, "Diffusion in Metals", Metals Reference Book, London, 1949.
8. Mehl, R. F., *Trans. Am. Inst. Mining Met. Engrs.* **122**, 11 (1936).
9. Mehl, R. F., *J. appl. Physics* **8**, 174 (1937).
10. Nabarro, F. R. N., *J. Inst. Metals* **73**, 237 (1947).
11. Seith, W., Diffusion in Metallen (Platzwechselreaktionen). Springer-Verlag, Berlin 1939.
12. Seitz, F., The Physics of Metals. New York 1943.
13. Seitz, F., Fundamental Aspects of Diffusion in Solids.
13a. Smithells, C. J., Metals Reference Book. Butterworths Ltd., London 1949.
14. Symposium, Amer. Soc. Metals "Age-Hardening of Metals". Cleveland/Ohio 1940.
15. Symposium, *Trans. Amer. Inst. Mining Met. Engrs.* **156**, 325 (1944).
16. Tammann, G., Lehrbuch der Metallkunde. Leipzig 1932.

General Bibliography

17. Ageew, N. W., and Vher, O. I., *J. Inst. Met. (London)* **44**, 83 (1930).
17a. Auerbach, B. L., *Trans. Am. Soc. Steel Treating* **41 A**, 262 (1949).
18. Banks, F. R., and Day, H., *Phys. Rev.* **57**, 1067 (1940).
19. Banks, F. R., *Phys. Rev.* **59**, 376 (1941).
20. Bannister, C. O., and Jones, W. D., *J. Iron Steel Inst.* **124**, 71 (1931).
20a. Bardeen, J., *Phys. Rev.* **76**, 1403 (1949).
21. Bardenheuer, P., and Müller, R., *Mitt. Kaiser-Wilh.-Inst. Eisenforschung* **14**, 295 (1932).
22. Barrer, R. M., *Discussion Faraday Soc.* **1948**, 68.
23. Baukloh, W., F. Schulte, and H. Friedrichs, *Arch. Eisenhüttenw.* **16**, 341 (1943).
24. Becker, R., *Z. Metallk.* **29**, 245 (1937).
25. Beerwald, A., *Z. Elektrochem.* **45**, 789 (1939).
26. Birchenall, C. E., and Mehl, R. F., *Metals Technology Techn. Publ.* Nr. 2168, 1947.
27. Birchenall, C. E., and Mehl, R. F., *J. applied Phys.* **19**, 217 (1948).
28. Bitter, F., *Phys. Rev.* **37**, 1527 (1931).
28a. Blanter, M. E., *Zavodskaja Lab.* **14**, 296 (1948).
29. Bosworth, R. C. L., *Proc. Roy. Soc. (London)* **A 150**, 58 (1935).
30. Bosworth, R. C. L., *Proc. Roy. Soc. (London)* **A 154**, 112 (1936).

31. Bramley, A. and Jinkings, A. J., *Iron Steel Inst. Carnegie Scolarship Mem.* **15,** 127 (1926).
32. Bramley, A., *Iron Steel Inst. Carnegie Scholarship Mem.* **15,** 155 (1926).
33. Bramley, A., and Lawton, *Iron Steel Inst. Carnegie Scolarship Mem.* **16,** 35 (1927).
34. Bramley, A., and Lord, H. D., *Iron Steel Inst. Carnegie Scolarship Mem.* **18,** 1 (1929).
35. Bramley, A, Haywood, F. W., Coopers, A. T., and Watts, J. T., *Trans. Faraday Soc.* **31,** 707 (1935).
36. Braune, H., *Z. phys. Chem.* **110,** 147 (1924).
37. Brick, R. M., and Phillips, A., *Metals Technol.* **4,** *Techn. Publ.* Nr. 781 (1937).
38. Bruni, G., and Meneghini, E., *Rend. Acad. Lincei, (Roma)* **202,** 927 (1911).
39. Bruni, G., and Meneghini, E., *Int. Zeitschr. Metallogr.* **2,** 26 (1912).
40. Bruni, G., and Meneghini, E., *Int. Zeitschr. Metallogr.* **4,** 224 (1914).
41. Bückle, H., *Z. Metallk.* **34,** 130 (1942).
42. Bückle, H., *Z. Elektrochem.* **49,** 238 (1943).
43. Bückle, H., *Metallforschung* **1,** 47, 175 (1946).
43a. Bückle, H., and Keil, A., *Mikroskopie* **4,** 266 (1949).
43b. Bückle, H., *Recherche Aéronautique,* Nr. 12, p. 45 (1949).
43c. Bückle, H., and Descamps, J., *Compt. rend.* **230,** 752 (1950).
43d. Bückle, H., and Jacquet, P. A., *Compt. rend.* **230,** 2198 (1950).
44. Bugakov, W., and Neskutchaev, W., *J. techn. Phys. USSR* **4,** 1342 (1934).
45. Bugakov, W., and Rybalko, F., *Journ. techn. Phys. USSR* **5,** 1729 (1936).
46. Bugakov, W., and Ssirotkin, B., *J. techn. Phys. USSR* **7,** 1577 (1937).
47. Bungardt, W., and Bollenrath, F., *Z. Metallk.* **30,** 377 (1938).
48. Burkhardt, A., and Sachs, G., *Metallwirtsch.* **14,** 1 (1935).
49. Chevenard, P., and Waché, X., *Compt. Rend.* **218,** 619 (1944).
50. Chevenard, P., and Waché, X., *Rev. métallurg.* **41,** 353, 389 (1944).
51. Coleman, H. S. and Yeagley, H. L., *Trans. Am. Soc. Met.* **31,** 105 (1943).
52. Coleman, H. S., and Yeagley, H. L., *Phys. Rev.* **65,** 56 (1944).
53. Colson, A., *Compt. Rend.* **93,** 1075 (1881).
54. Cornelius, H., and Bollenrath, F., *Arch. Eisenhüttenw.* **15,** 145 (1941).
54a. Cottrell, A. M., and Churchman, A. T., *J. Iron Steel Inst. (London)* **162,** 271 (1949).
55. Cremer, E., and Polanyi, M., *Z. physik. Chem.* **B 21,** 459 (1933).
56. Cremer, E., *Z. physik. Chem.* **B 39,** 445 (1938).
57. Daniel, V., *Proc. Roy. Soc. (London)* **A 192,** 575 (1948).
58. Daniel, V., and Lipson, H., *Proc. Roy. Soc. (London)* **A 181,** 368 (1943).
59. Daniel, V., and Lipson, H., *Proc. Roy. Soc. (London)* **A 182,** 378 (1944).
60. Darken, L. S., *Am. Inst. Mining Met. Engrs. Inst. Met. Div. Metals Technol.* 15 *Techn. Publ.* 2311 (1948).
61. Darken, L. S., *Am. Inst. Mining Met. Engrs. Inst. Met. Div. Metals Technol. Techn. Publ.* 2443 (1948).
62. Dehlinger, U., *Z. Physik* **102,** 633 (1936).
63. Dehlinger, U., *Metallk.* **29,** 401 (1937).
64. Dunn, J. St., *J. Chem. Soc. (London)* **1926,** 2973.
65. Dushman, S., Dennison, D., and Reynolds, N. B., *Phys. Rev.* **29,** 903 (1927).
66. Duwez, P., and Jordan, C. B., *Trans. Am. Soc. Metals Preprint* **1948** Nr. 37.
67. Ebert, H., and Trommsdorf, G., *Z. Elektrochem.* **54,** 294 (1950).
68. Eucken, A., and Schuerenberg, H., *Ann. Physik* **33,** 1 (1938).
69. Fisher, J. G., Hollomon, J. H., and Turnbull, D., *Am. Inst. Mining Met. Engrs. Inst. Met. Div. Metals Techn. Publ.* 2344 (1948).

70. Fischbeck, K., *Z. Elektrochem.* **40**, 386 (1934).
71. Fonda, G. R., Young, A. H., and Walker, A., *Physics* **4**, 1 (1933).
72. Fraenkel, W., and Houben, H., *Z. anorg. allgem. Chem.* **116**, 1 (1921).
73. Freche, H. R., *Trans. Am. Inst. Mining Met. Engrs.* **122**, 324 (1936).
74. Fry, A., *Stahl und Eisen* **43**, 1039 (1923).
75. Gorsky, W., *Phys. Z. Sowjetunion* **8**, 457 (1935).
76. Groh, J., and v. Hevesy, G., *Ann. Physik* **63**, 85 (1920).
77. Groh, J., and v. Hevesy, G., *Ann. Physik* **65**, 216 (1920).
78. Grube, G., and Jedele, A., *Z. Elektrochem.* **38**, 799 (1932).
79. Grube, G., and Liebenwirth, F., *Z. anorg. allgem. Chem.* **188**, 274 (1930),
80. Grube, G., and Schneider, K., *Z. anorg. allgem. Chem.* **168**, 17 (1927).
80a. Gruberg, L. D., *Can. Metal. Met. Inds.* **12**, 20, 34 (1949).
81. Gudden, B., and Lehovec, K., *Z. Naturforschg.* **1**, 508 (1946).
81a. Guy, A. G., *J. Metals* **1**, Nr. 9 Trans. 607 (1949).
81b. Guy, A. G., *Iron Age* **163**, Nr. 4, 74 (1949).
82. Hargreaves, R., *J. Inst. Metals* **64**, 115 (1939).
83. Harris, F. E., *Metals Technology* **14**, Techn. Publ. Nr. 2216 (1947).
84. Hartley, G. S., *Phil. Mag.* (7) **12**, 473 (1931).
85. Harwood, J. J., *Nucleonics* **2**, 57 (1948).
86. Hashiguchi, R., *J. Central Aeronaut. Research. Inst.* **1**, 189 (1943).
87. Hashiguchi, R., *J. Central. Aeronaut. Research Inst.* **2**, 95 (1943).
88. Hawkes, M. F., and Mehl, R. F., *MetalsTechnology* **14**, Techn. Publ. Nr. 2211 (1947).
89. Hertzruecken, S. D., and co-workers, *J. techn. Phys. USSR* **10**, 786 (1940).
90. v. Hevesy, G., and Obrutschewa, A., *Nature London* **115**, 674 (1925).
91. v. Hevesy, G., and Seith, W., *Z. Physik* **56**, 790 (1929).
92. v. Hevesy, G., Seith, W., and Keil, A., *Z. Physik* **79**, 197 (1932).
93. Hicks, L. C., *Trans. Am. Inst. Mining Met. Engrs.* **113**, 163 (1934).
94. Houdremont, E., and Schrader, A., *Arch. Eisenhüttenw.* **8**, 445 (1935).
95. Huntington, H. B., *Phys. Rev.* **63**, 383 (1943).
96. Jagodzinski, H., and Laves, F., *Z. Metallk.* **40**, 296 (1949).
97. Jedele, A., *Z. Elektrochem.* **39**, 691 (1933).
98. Jenkins, I., cf. Intern. Crit. Tables V, 77 (1926).
99. Jenkins, I., *J. Inst. Met.* **73**, 641 (1947).
100. Jensen, D. P., *Iron Age* **161**, 66 (1948).
101. Ilkevich, G. P., *Journ. exp. theoret. Phys. USSR* **10**, 659 (1940).
102. Johnson, W. A., *Trans. Am. Inst. Mining Met. Engrs.* **143**, 107 (1941).
103. Johnson, W. A., *Trans. Am. Inst. Mining Met. Engrs.* **147**, 331 (1942).
104. Johnson, W. A., *Trans. Am. Inst. Mining Met. Engrs.* **166**, 114 (1946).
105. Jost, W., *Z. phys. Chem.* B **9**, 73 (1930).
106. Jost, W., *Z. phys. Chem.* B **21**, 158 (1933).
107. Jost, W., *Z. phys. Chem.* B **16**, 123 (1932).
107a. Jost, W., *Z. Physik* **127**, 163 (1950).
108. Kawalki, W., *Wied. Ann.* **52**, 166 (1894).
109. Kê, T'ing-Sui, *Phys. Rev.* **71**, 533 (1947).
110. Kê, T'ing-Sui, *Phys. Rev.* **73**, 267 (1948).
111. Kê, T'ing-Sui, *Phys. Rev.* **19**, 285 (1948); **20**, 274 (1949).
112. Kirkendall, E., Thomassen, L., and Upthegrove, C., *Trans Am. Inst. Mining Met. Engrs.* **133**, 186 (1939).
113. Kirkendall, E., *Trans. Am. Inst. Mining Engrs.* **147**, 104 (1942).
114. Koehler, W., *Zentralbl. Hütten- und Walzwerke* **31**, 650 (1928).
115. Konobeevsky, S. T., *Jour. exp. theoret. Phys. USSR* **13**, 185, 200, 418 (1943).

116. Kubaschewski, O., *Trans. Faraday Soc.* **46,** 713 (1950).
117. Kubaschewski, O., and Ebert, H., *Z. Elektrochem.* **50,** 138 (1944).
118. Kuczynski, G. C., *J. appl. Phys.* **19,** 308 (1948).
118a. Kuczynski, G. C., *J. Metals* **1,** Nr. 2 Trans. 169 (1949).
118b. Laissus, J., Groupement franc. dévelop. recherches aéronaut. *Note techn.* **29,** II 24 (1945).
118c. Laissus, J., Groupement franc. dévelop. recherches aéronaut. *Note techn.* **29,** 61 (1945).
119. Langmuir, I., *Phys. Rev.* **20,** 113 (1922).
120. Langmuir, I., *Phys. Rev.* **22,** 357 (1923).
121. Langmuir, I., *J. Frankl. Inst.* **217,** 534 (1934).
122. Langmuir, I., and Taylor, J. B., *Phys. Rev.* **40,** 463 (1932).
123. Langmuir, I., and Taylor, J. B., *Phys. Rev.* **44,** 423 (1933).
124. Van Liempt, J. A. M., *Rec. trav. chim.* **51,** 114 (1932).
125. Van Liempt, J. A. M., *Z. Physik* **96,** 534 (1935).
126. Van Liempt, J. A. M., *Rec. trav. chim.* **60,** 634 (1941).
127. Van Liempt, J. A. M., *Rec. trav. chim.* **64,** 239 (1945).
128. McKay, H. A. C., *Trans. Faraday Soc.* **34;** 845 (1938).
129. Maier, C. G., *US Bureau of Mines Bull.* 324 (1930).
130. Manning, M. F., *Phys. Rev.* **55,** 682 (1939).
131. Masing, G., *Z. anorg. allgem. Chem.* **62,** 265 (1909).
132. Matano, C., *Japan. J. Phys.* **8,** 109 (1933).
133. Matano, C., *Proc. Phys. Math. Soc. Japan* **15,** 405 (1933).
134. Matano, C., *Japan. J. Phys.* **9,** 41 (1934).
135. Matuda, S., *Sci. Pap. Inst. Phys. Chem. Res. Tokyo* **40,** 207 (1943).
136. Mehl, R. F., and Rhines, F. N., *Metals Technol.* **6,** *Techn. Publ.* 1072 (1939).
137. Mehl, R. F., Rhines, F. N., and von den Steinen, K. A., *Metals and Alloys* **13,** 41 (1941).
138. Miller, P. H., *J. applied Phys.* **12,** 303 (1941).
139. Miller, P. H., and Banks, F. R., *Phys. Rev.* **59,** 943 (1941).
140. Miller, P. H., and Banks, F. R., *Phys. Rev.* **61,** 648 (1942).
140a. Miyake, S., and Kubo, M., *J. Phys. Soc. Japan* **2,** 20 (1949).
141. du Mond, J., and Youtz, J. P., *J. applied Phys.* **11,** 357 (1940).
142. Mooradian, V. G., and Norton, J. T., *Trans. Am. Inst. Mining Met. Engrs.* **117,** 89 (1935).
143. Mott, N. F., *Proc. Phys. Soc. (London)* **60,** 391 (1948).
144. Nabarro, F. R. N., *J. Inst. Metals* **73,** 237 (1947).
145. Nelting, H., *Z. Physik* **115,** 469 (1940).
146. Norbury, B. G., *Trans. Faraday Soc.* **16,** 570 (1921).
147. Onsager, L., and Fuoss, R. M., *J. Phys. Chem.* **36,** 2689 (1932).
148. van Ostrand, C. E., and Dewey, F. P., *US Geol. Survey Prof. Paper* **1915,** 95.
149. Paič, M., *Compt. Rend.* **220,** 559 (1945).
150. Paschke, M., and Hauttmann, A., *Arch. Eisenhüttenw.* **9,** 305 (1935).
151. Pauling, L., *J. Am. Chem. Soc.* **69,** 544 (1947).
152. Petrenko, B. G., and Rubinstein, B. E., *J. phys. Chem. USSR* **13,** 508 (1939).
153. Pirani, M. and Sandor, J., *J. Inst. Met.* **73,** 385 (1947).
154. Polder, D., *Philips Res. Report* **1,** 1 (1945).
155. Radavich, F., and Smoluchowski, R., *Phys. Rev.* **65,** 62, 248 (1944).
156. Raynor, C. L., Thomassen, L. and Rouse, L., *J. Trans. Am. Soc. Met.* **30,** 313 (1942).
157. Rhines, F. N., *Powder Met. Bull.* **3,** 28 (1948).

158. Rhines, F. N., and Mehl, R. F., *Trans. Am. Inst. Mining Met. Engrs.* **128**, 185 (1938).
159. Roberts-Austen, W. C., *Phil. Trans. Roy. Soc. (London)* **A 187**, 404 (1896).
160. Roberts-Austen, W. C., *Proc. Roy. Soc. (London)* **59**, 288 (1896).
161. Rollin, B. V., *Phys. Rev.* **55**, 231 (1939).
162. Runge, I., *Z. anorg. allgem. Chem.* **115**, 293 (1921).
163. Rüst, E., *Naturwiss.* **4**, 265 (1909).
164. Sagrubskij, A. M., *Bull. Acad. Sci. URSS Sér. phys.* **1937**, 903.
165. Sagrubskij, A. M., *Phys. Z. Sowjetunion* **12**, 118 (1937).
166. Sagrubskij, A., and Bugakow, W., *J. techn. Phys. USSR* **9**, 1767, 1771 (1939).
166a. Scheil, E., *Angew. Chem.* **62**, 145 (1950).
167. Schneider, A., and Schmid, H., *Z. Elektrochem.* **48**, 627 (1942).
168. Seith, W., *Z. Elektrochem.* **39**, 538 (1933).
169. Seith, W., *Z. Elektrochem.* **41**, 872 (1935).
170. Seith, W., and Bartschat, F., *Z. Metallkunde* **34**, 125 (1942).
171. Seith, W., and Etzold, H., *Z. Elektrochem.* **40**, 829 (1934).
172. Seith, W., and Etzold, H., *Z. Elektrochem.* **41**, 122 (1935).
173. Seith, W., and Herrmann, J., *Z. Elektrochem.* **46**, 213 (1940).
174. Seith, W., Hofer, E. and Etzold, H., *Z. Elektrochem.* **40**, 322 (1934).
175. Seith, W., and Keil, A., *Z. phys. Chem.* **B 22**, 350 (1933).
176. Seith, W., and Krauss, W., *Z. Elektrochem.* **44**, 98 (1938).
177. Seith, W., and Kubaschewski, O., *Z. Elektrochem.* **41**, 551 (1935).
178. Seith, W., and Laird, J. G., *Z. Metallkunde* **24**, 193 (1932).
179. Seith, W., and Peretti, E., *Z. Elektrochem.* **42**, 570 (1936).
179a. Seith, W., and Schmelken, H., *Z. Elektrochem.* **54**, 222 (1950).
180. Seitz, F., *Phys. Rev.* **74**, 1513 (1948).
180a. Seitz, F., *Acta Crystallogr.* **3**, 355 (1950).
181. Shaler, A. J., and Wulff, J., *Phys. Rev.* **73**, 926 (1948).
182. Smigelskas, A. D., and Kirkendall, E. O., *Metals Technol.* **13**, *Techn. Publ.* 2071 (1946).
183. Smith, R. P., *J. Am. Chem. Soc.* **68**, 1163 (1946).
184. Smoluchowski, R., *Phys. Rev.* **62**, 539 (1942).
185. Smoluchowski, R., *Phys. Rev.* **63**, 438 (1943).
186. Snoek, J. L., *Physica* **6**, 591 (1939).
187. Snoek, J. L., *Physica* **8**, 711 (1941).
188. Snoek, J. L., *Physica* **8**, 734 (1941).
189. Snoek, J. L., *Physica* **9**, 862 (1942).
190. Spring, W., *Bull. Acad. Belg.* **49**, 323 (1880).
191. Spring, W., *Ber. dtsch. Chem. Ges.* **15**, 1 (1882).
191a. Stanley, J. K., *J. Metals* **1**, Nr. 10 Trans. 752 (1949).
192. Steigman, J., Shockley, W., and Nix, F. C., *Phys. Rev.* **55**, 605 (1939).
193. Steigman, J., Shockley, W., and Nix, F. C., *Phys. Rev.* **56**, 13 (1939).
194. Sully, A. H., *J. Scient. Instr.* **22**, 244 (1945).
195. Tammann, G., *Z. anorg. allgem. Chem.* **107**, 1 (1919).
196. Tammann, G., and Schoenert, K., *Z. anorg. allgem. Chem.* **122**, 27 (1922).
197. Tanaka, S., and Matano, C., *Mem. Coll. Sci. Kyoto Imp. Univ.* **14**, 59 (1931).
198. Veroe, J. A., *Mitt. berg- u. hüttenmänn. Abt. Univ. Sopron (Hungary)* **12**, 141 (1940).
199. Wachter, A., *J. Am. Chem. Soc.* **54**, 4609 (1932).
200. Wagner, C., *Z. phys. Chem.* **B 38**, 325 (1938).
201. Wagner, C., unpublished.
202. Wagner, C., and Engelhard, G., *Z. phys. Chem.* **A 159**, 241 (1932).

203. Weinbaum, S., *J. applied Phys.* **19**, 897 (1948).
204. Weiss, H., and co-workers, *Compt. Rend. Paris* **171**, 168 (1920).
205. Weiss, H., and co-workers, *Compt. Rend. Paris* **173**, 146 (1921).
206. Weiss, H., and co-workers, *Compt. Rend. Paris* **174**, 292, 1426 (1922).
207. Weiss, H., and co-workers, *Compt. Rend. Paris* **175**, 1402 (1922).
208. Wells, C., and Mehl, R. F., *Metals Technology* **7**, *Techn. Publ.* 1180 (1940).
209. Wells, C., and Mehl, R. F., *Metals Technology* **8**, *Techn. Publ.* 1282 (1941).
210. Wells, C., and Mehl, R. F., *Metals Technology* **8**, *Techn. Publ.* 1281 (1941).
211. Wertenstein, M. L., and Dobrowolska, H., *J. Phys. Radium* **4**, 324 (1923).
212. Woo, S., Barrett, C. S. and Mehl, R. F. *Metals Technology, Techn. Publ.* 1694 (1944).
213. Wyllie, G., *Proc. Phys. Soc. (London)* **59**, 694 (1947).
214. Zener, C., *Trans. Am. Inst. Mining Met. Engrs.* **152**, 122 (1943).
215. Zener, C., *Phys. Rev.* **71**, 34 (1947).
215a. Zener, C., *Acta Crystallogr.* **3**, 346 (1950) *(Ring diffusion in metals, cf.* 180a).
216. Zwikker, C., *Physica* **7**, 189 (1927).

METHODS USED FOR THE EXPERIMENTAL DETERMINATION OF DIFFUSION COEFFICIENT IN METALS, REFERRED TO IN TABLES I—XI, XV, XVI

1.and 2.Separation of diffusion system into two or more layers and subsequent analysis, either chemical 1, or spectroscopic 2.

3. Metallographic method, examination of cross section.

4. Modified metallographic methods. 4a. method of Brick and Phillips (37), examination of quenched and annealed sample after diffusion experiment. 4b. method making use of limits of resistance towards certain chemical agents, Tammann (195), Fraenkel (72), Jost (105), van Liempt (126).

5. X-ray-methods, Jost (107), Burckhardt-Sachs (48), Sully (194), Paič (149), Du Mond-Youtz (141), Mooradian-Norton (142).

6. Evaporation method applicable only if one component has a rather high vapor pressure e.g. zinc, cadmium, mercury, cf. Dunn (64), Bugakow (44, 166), Hertzrücken and co-workers (89), Seith and Krauss (176). There are certain objections against this method, see p. 212.

7. Thermionic emission has in some cases been used for the determination of surface concentration.

8. Use of radiation of radioactive elements. 8a. Measurement of surface activity of diffusion system. 8b. measurement of activity of several layers of diffusion system. 8c. modified method, suggested by Kuczynski (118), using more than one intensity measurement in sample without separation.

9. Use of micro-hardness measurements for concentration determination, Bückle (41).

10. Conductivity method, especially applied with multiple layers (177, 197).

11. Thermomagnetic method, using displacement of Curie temperature with concentration. Has been applied with alloys containing Cr, Mn, Fe, Co, Ni, Chevenard and Waché (3, 49, 50).

12. Observation of homogenization of heterogeneous alloys, Verö (198).

CHAPTER VI

SOLUBILITY IN SOLIDS

The problem of solubility in crystals (cf. Fowler and Guggenheim (3)), has attracted, so far, comparably little theoretical interest. A fairly satisfactory theoretical treatment is available only for the solution of gases in metals. Since there cannot be any diffusion of gases in metals or other solids without a preceding solution, we shall deal briefly with the theory of solubility.

I. Solubility of Gases in Metals

1. Hydrogen in Metals

First we shall consider the case of low solubility which allows of an easy theoretical approach. The results are not confined to solutions of gases in metals but also apply to other impurities present in small concentrations. Fowler and Smithells (18) have treated this case, assuming that a free volume V_H, referring especially to the case of dissolved hydrogen, is available to the dissolved particles, hydrogen atoms or other atoms, whether they are present as atoms or as ions (protons) plus free electrons. $V_H < V$, if V is the volume of the metal. For the dissolved particles, a uniform potential energy ε_H is assumed, referred to the energy of the free atoms as zero. It is possible to calculate the chemical potential for the particles both dissolved in the metal and in the gas phase. By equating these expressions, one obtains for the concentration in the free volume of the metal, n_H / V_H

$$\frac{n_H}{V_H} = \left(\frac{m_H^3}{16 \pi I^2 h^2 kT} \right)^{1/4} p^{1/2} \exp\left[-\left(\varepsilon_H + \frac{1}{2} \varepsilon_d \right) / kT \right] \qquad [6.1]$$

where m_H is the mass of the H-atoms, I the moment of inertia of the molecules H_2, ε_d the energy of dissociation of the H_2-molecule in its lowest state. If the solubility is measured in cubic-centimetres of gas at N.T.P., dissolved per 100 g. of metal, if $s*$ is equal to unit solubility, i. e., 1 cc. at N.T.P., and $p*$ is unit gas pressure, 1 atm., ρ the density of the metal, then, inserting numerical values, we obtain

$$\frac{s}{s*} \approx 1.6 \times 10^4 \left(\frac{V_H}{V} \right) \left(\frac{p}{p*} \right)^{1/2} \frac{1}{\rho T^{1/4}} \exp\left[-\left(\varepsilon_H + \frac{1}{2} \varepsilon_d \right) / kT \right]. \qquad [6.2]$$

[6.2] is in sufficient agreement with experimental values, but an absolute calculation of the solubility is impossible since the energy ε_H is not known. To represent measured solubilities, values for V_H/V between 1 (copper) and $\sim 1/10$ (for the metals of the iron group) must be chosen, which seem reasonable. $\varepsilon_H + \frac{1}{2}\varepsilon_d$ is positive in all cases referred to, and thus the solubility is rather small.

In cases of high solubility a different method of approach is necessary. Fowler and Smithells (18) consider non-localized absorbed atoms. For absorption αN sites are available, where N is the number of metal atoms, and α should be a small integer*. Here, except for small concentrations, the concentration of absorbed atoms will not rise proportionally with the gas pressure (or with the square root of the pressure, as in the case of hydrogen) because the number of sites, available for further absorption, decreases with increasing absorption.

The essential difference between this and the preceding case is not the assumption of non-localized or localized absorption. These are only the most convenient ways of treating either case. In the case of weak absorption, too, absorption certainly is localized, as seen from the fact that an heat of activation is to be supplied for diffusion. But in the former case we could neglect the decrease of available space due to absorption, while now it is essential to take account of it. This might also be done by using the model of the preceding section. Then, if we have αN sites, corresponding to a free volume V_H, a volume $V_H/\alpha N$ would have to be attributed to every absorbed particle.

The final result thus obtained for the solubility s, (measured quite arbitrarily, because a dimensionless fraction only enters into the final equation) is in analogy with the previous one

$$\frac{s}{s^* - s} \approx 5 \times 10^{-4}\left(\frac{p}{p^*}\right)^{1/2}\exp\left[-\left(\varepsilon_H + \frac{1}{2}\varepsilon_d\right)/kT\right]. \qquad [6.3]$$

Here numerical values have been inserted; p^* is again unit pressure, 1 atm., s^* is the saturation value of s, corresponding to $n_H = \alpha N$, ε_H and ε_d have the same meaning as before. [6.3] is of the form of the Langmuir isotherm for adsorbed gases (with p replaced by $p^{1/2}$ on account of the dissociation equilibrium). This may readily be seen when [6.3] is solved for s, giving

$$s \approx \frac{s^* \beta p^{1/2}}{1 + \beta p^{1/2}}$$

if the right-hand side of eq. [6.3] is abbreviated by writing $\beta p^{1/2}$. A quantitative test of [6.3] is again not possible, for lack of experimental data, but there is qualitative agreement with observed solubilities of

* In the case of hydrogen-palladium, treated below, α proves to be < 1.

hydrogen in zirconium and thorium (41). Here the solubility decreases with increasing T, consequently $\varepsilon_H + \frac{1}{2}\varepsilon_d$ must be negative, which means the positive $\varepsilon_d/2$ must have been compensated by a negative ε_H of sufficiently large absolute magnitude.

2. The absorption of hydrogen by palladium

In the preceding section we have accounted for an interaction of absorbed particles in so far as we considered their proper volume, by assuming that a site taken by one particle was no longer available to other particles. This is the analogue of the volume correction in van der Waals' equation of state, though the methods employed are not comparable. For the van der Waals equation is an approximation for moderately compressed gases, while we were interested in values of the absorption up to saturation. New phenomena may be expected if we introduce an interaction between absorbed particles beyond the consideration of their proper volume. This will be done by the assumption of a mutual potential energy of absorbed particles (28, 29). A refined treatment of this type leads, in case of adsorbed particles, to the phenomenon of two-dimensional condensation, which has been treated theoretically, though so far it has not been definitely established experimentally. The corresponding phenomenon in the case of absorption is the splitting into two separate phases, as has actually been observed in the case of hydrogen, dissolved in palladium. The simplest possible way of taking into account an interaction of dissolved particles is by ascribing a certain potential energy to a pair of neighboring particles, neglecting the interaction of particles further apart. A potential energy of interaction may be defined in such a way that the energy per pair is $2\varepsilon_{HH}/z$, if z is the number of nearest neighbors. The statistical evaluation of this assumption (28, 29), leads to an expression

$$\frac{\theta}{1-\theta} = \left(\frac{p}{kT}\right)^{1/2} q(T) \left\{\frac{(4\pi m k T)^{3/2}}{h^3} \frac{8\pi^2 I kT}{2h^2}\right\}^{-1/2} \times$$
$$\exp\left[-(\varepsilon_H + \frac{1}{2}\varepsilon_d + 2\theta\varepsilon_{HH}) / kT\right]. \qquad [6.4]$$

Here θ is the fraction of available sites, occupied by H-atoms. ε_H, ε_{HH} and ε_d have been defined above, and $q(T)$ is the partition function for the vibrational energy of the absorbed atoms in the lattice. A simple expression for the absorption isotherm is obtained by calculating the ratio

$$p(\theta)/p(^1/_2) = \left(\frac{\theta}{1-\theta}\right)^2 \exp[2(2\theta-1)\varepsilon_{HH}/kT]. \qquad [6.5]$$

It is seen that the isotherms are antisymmetrical with respect to $\theta = {}^{1}/_{2}$. There exists a critical temperature, T_c, where $\theta = {}^{1}/_{2}$ and $\partial p / \partial \theta = 0$. From [6.5] it follows that for this temperature

$$- \varepsilon_{\mathrm{HH}} / k\, T_c = 2 \qquad [6.6]$$

For $T < T_c$ a certain region is unstable, situated symmetrically with respect to $\theta = {}^{1}/_{2}$.

The limits of stability, θ' and θ'' are given by the intersection of the horizontal through the point $\theta = {}^{1}/_{2}$ with the curve [6.6], Fig. 6-1. θ' and θ'', there-

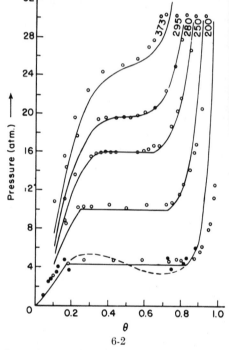

Fig. 6-1. Solubility of hydrogen in palladium, theoretical curve, eq. [6.6], after Lacher.
Fig. 6-2. Solubility of hydrogen in palladium, after Lacher.
(First isotherm at 313, not 373°C!)

fore, are the compositions of two phases, coexisting at given temperature and pressure. Saturation of palladium with hydrogen is obtained for 0.6 atoms hydrogen per palladium atom*. Therefore, θ is to be chosen in such a way as to give $\theta = 1$ for 0.6 atoms of H per atom of Pd. From [6.5] and [6.6] we then have

$$p\,(\theta) / p \left(\frac{1}{2} \right) = [\theta / (1 - \theta)]^2 \exp\left[- 4\,(2\,\theta - 1)\, T_c / T \right]$$
$$\text{for } \theta < \theta' \text{ and } \theta > \theta'' , \qquad [6.7]$$

* This, certainly, is an oversimplification. There will be more interstitial sites available for hydrogen atoms or protons, but further sorption will be connected with a sharp increase in energy.

while for $\theta' < \theta < \theta''$

$$p(\theta)/p\,(^1/_2) = 1 \qquad [6.8]$$

giving the horizontal line between θ' and θ'', [6.7] and [6.8] determining θ' and θ'' for every temperature below T_c. By inserting numerical values into [6.4], one obtains for $\theta = \,^1/_2$

$$p\,(^1/_2)/p^* \approx 1.2 \times 10^6 \; \{(T/500)^{7/2}/[q(T)]^2\} \, \exp\left[2\,(\varepsilon_H + \varepsilon_{HH} + \frac{1}{2}\,\varepsilon_d)/k\,T\right] \qquad [6.9]$$

where again $p^* = 1$ atm. The exponent and $q(T)$ must be determined from experiments. Alternatively one may use Gillespie's (19, 20) empirical equation

$$p\,(^1/_2)/p^* \approx 4 \times 10^{14} \exp\,(-\,1878/T)\,. \qquad [6.10]$$

A comparison of theory and experiment is given in Fig. 6-2, taken from Lacher (29), cf. also Wagner (46).

Addition of silver or boron in small concentrations increases considerably the solubility of hydrogen in palladium at low pressures, the opposite being observed both at high concentrations of the addition and at high hydrogen pressures (40, 42, 43). Wagner (47) attempted a theoretical explanation of these observations.

II. Solution in Zeolites

Barrer (8, 9, 12, 13) carried out detailed experimental and theoretical investigations of the solution of gases in zeolites, cf. McBain (4) and Smithells (6). Following Fowler and Guggenheim's treatment he arrives at expressions for the Gibbs free energy of the gas and of the gas molecules, dissolved by the zeolite, and by equating both expressions, he obtains the equilibrium condition (10)

$$\frac{\theta}{1-\theta} = \frac{p}{p_0} \qquad [6.11]$$

where θ gives the ratio of number of occupied interstices and the total number of interstitial sites, p is the gas pressure and p_0 is defined by

$$p_0 = \frac{kT\,(2\pi\,m\,kT)^{3/2}}{h^3}\,\frac{q\,(T)}{q_a\,(T)} \qquad [6.12]$$

where m is the mass of the gas molecules, $q(T)$ is the partition function of the gas molecules for all degrees of freedom except the translational ones, and $q_a(T)$ is correspondingly the partition function of the dissolved molecules for all degrees of freedom.

Barrer has evaluated the ratio $q(T)/q_a(T)$ for a number of cases. Among the assumptions, necessary for an evaluation, are the following

1. The lattice is unchanged by the process of dissolution,
2. the energy of dissolution is independent of θ.

The partition function $q_a(T)$ may be written $q_0(T) \exp(-\varepsilon/kT)$, where ε is the energy necessary to remove an absorbed molecule from the zeolite. $q_0(T)$ is the partition function for the internal motions of the absorbed molecules and for their motions relative to the lattice. In so far as the internal motions are unaltered by the process of absorption, $q_0(T)$ may contain $q(T)$ or part of it.

Barrer (10) has calculated values of p_0 for a number of typical models, for which reference must be made to the original paper. The assumptions underlying these models, are: 1. the molecules are completely free in the zeolite, i.e., there exist free translation and free rotation, 2., 3., 4. Successively one, two and three translational degrees of freedom are lost and replaced by new vibrational degrees of freedom, 5., 6., 7. One, two and three degrees of rotation are lost, being replaced by vibrational degrees of freedom, thus finally arriving at 6 new vibrational degrees of freedom, not counting the inner vibrations of the molecule.

Marked differences of entropy of dissolved molecules are obtained for the different models. Increase of entropy of the solid solution corresponds to increased solubility, this being highest for model 1, with completely free mobility of the dissolved molecules. Decreases by 38.47 entropy units are obtained for each translational degree of freedom which is converted to a vibrational degree, for a special choice of the constants, assumed in numerical calculation. The influence of the loss of a rotational degree of freedom on entropy is less marked, the entropy decrease being 3.22 entropy units.

The model, most suitable for the representation of the observed values is that of a three dimensional oscillator. Of course it is sufficient to assume a small fraction of mobile molecules, i.e., molecules with at least one translational degree of freedom, to account for the observed speed of sorption and desorption.

Special conditions are encountered with long chain molecules which can occupy not a single interstitial position of the zeolite, but a series of interstices, i.e., a channel instead of a hole. The long chain molecule not only must loose its translational degrees of freedom, but its rotational degrees of freedom as well (except, perhaps, for rotation about its axis). Also many configurations possible in the gas space, become impossible in the absorbed state, thus further decreasing the entropy and the probability for being dissolved. These influences are quite considerable for long chain molecules. For details reference must be made to Barrer's papers. Barrer (9a) also gives some data, referring to the above case of dissolution of hydrogen in metals. With the values for the dissociation equilibrium of hydrogen

$$p_{\mathrm{H}}^2 / p_{\mathrm{H_2}} = K_p \approx \exp[2.303 \times 5.567 - 101{,}000/RT]$$

and

$$\frac{\theta}{(1-\theta)\, p_{\mathrm{H}}} = K\left(= \frac{\theta}{(1-\theta)\sqrt{K_p}} \text{ , for } p_{\mathrm{H_2}} = 1\,\text{atm}\right)$$

he writes the equation for the solubility s, at $p_{\mathrm{H_2}} = 1$ atm., when s^* is the solubility at saturation of the metal

$$\log \frac{s}{s^* - s} - \frac{1}{2}\log K_p = \log K . \qquad [6.13]$$

Thus the free energy ΔF_0 is

$$\Delta F_0 = -RT\log K = -RT\log\frac{s}{s^*-s} + \frac{1}{2}RT\log K_p$$

$$= -RT\log\frac{s}{s^*-s} - 50{,}500 + 2.303 \times 5.567 \times T . \qquad [6.14]$$

III. Solubility in elastomers

Barrer (11) further worked out a theory for the solubility of gases in elastomers, based on the statistical thermodynamics of monomer-polymer mixtures, cf. also (2, 14, 15, 22). The lattice model for mixtures has been used; each lattice site may be occupied by one monomer molecule or by one segment of a polymer molecule. This problem has been treated repeatedly (16, 17, 23, 24, 25, 26, 30, 32, 34, 37, 38). Without going into details, we shall give the results obtained for the solubility isotherms. Barrer first treats the case of negligible resultant energy of interaction, ε, i.e.,

$$\varepsilon = \frac{z}{2}\left(2\,\varepsilon_{\alpha\beta} - \varepsilon_{\alpha\alpha} - \varepsilon_{\beta\beta}\right) \qquad [6.15]$$

where $\varepsilon_{\alpha\alpha}$ is the energy between two sorbed molecules, $\varepsilon_{\beta\beta}$ that between two rubber segments, $\varepsilon_{\alpha\beta}$ that between a sorbed molecule and a rubber segment. Here the following expression is obtained

$$V_0 \left/ \left[\left\{1 - (1 - 1/n)\frac{2}{z}V_r\right\}^{z/2} n_1\right]\right. = K = \left(\frac{kT}{2\pi m}\right)^{3/2} \times \frac{1}{v^3}\exp(\chi/RT) \quad [6.16]$$

where K is the solubility constant. And with ΔE, defined by

$$\partial\log K/\partial T = \Delta E/RT^2$$

finally

$$V_0 \left/ \left[\left\{1 - (1 - 1/n)\frac{2}{z}V_r\right\}^{z/2} n_1\right]\right. =$$

$$= \left(\frac{kT}{2\pi m}\right)^{3/2} \times \frac{1}{v^3}\ \exp\left(\left[-\Delta E + \frac{3}{2}RT\right]\middle/ RT\right). \qquad [6.17]$$

18*

The magnitudes entering into [6.16] and [6.17] are

V_0 = volume fraction of sorbed molecules,

V_r = volume fraction of elastomer,

n = number of segments per polymer molecule,

z = coordination number of lattice site,

n_1 = number of gas molecules per cm.^{3},

m = mass of gas molecules,

v = a mean vibration frequency for the gas molecules in the mixture,

χ = the energy, required to remove a mole of gas molecules from the mixture to the gas phase, provided that ε is zero. If ε differs from zero, $-\chi$ is the heat of condensation of a mole of gas to give a hypothetical condensed phase, corresponding to the assumed lattice structure of the mixture.

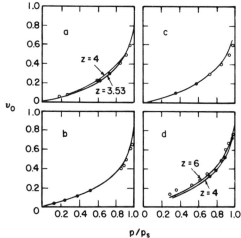

Fig. 6-3. Absorption isotherms, after Barrer. — The isotherm eq. [6.20] applied to several vapor-rubber equilibria.

(a) Benzene-rubber:

Experimental data at 100°C. and at 25°C.

The full curves are calculated isotherms using $z = 4.0$ and 3.53.

(b) n-Heptane-rubber:

Experimental data at 40°C.

The full   curve   is   calculated   using $z = 3.5$.

(c)   Toluene-rubber:

Experimental data at 30°C.

The full   curve   is   calculated   using $z = 3.5$.

(d) Chloroform-rubber:

Experimental data at 35°C. (upper series) and at 25°C. (lower series)

The full curves are calculated using $z = 4$ and $z = 6$.

For small 'solubilities $V_0 \ll 1$ and $V_r \approx 1$, [6.17] reduces to

$$V_0/n_1 = \left(\frac{kT}{2\pi m}\right)^{3/2} \frac{1}{\nu^3} \exp\left[\left(-\Delta E + \frac{3}{2}RT\right)\Big/RT\right] \times \left[1 - \frac{2}{z}\right]^{z/2} \quad [6.18]$$

i.e., in the limiting case Henry's law is obtained.

In [6.17] n_1 may be replaced by the gas pressure, $p = n_1 kT$, which gives

$$V_0\Big/\left[\left\{1-(1-1/n)\frac{2}{z}V_r\right\}^{z/2} p\right] =$$

$$= \frac{1}{kT}\left(\frac{kT}{2\pi m}\right)^{3/2}\frac{1}{\nu^3}\exp\left(\left[-\Delta H + \frac{1}{2}RT\right]\Big/RT\right). \quad [6.19]$$

If a vapor is absorbed, $K = \dfrac{1}{p_s}$, where p_s is the vapor pressure. In this case [6.19] may be written

$$V_0\Big/\left[1-\frac{2}{z}V_r\right]^{z/2} = p/p_s \quad [6.20]$$

where again it has been assumed that $n \gg 1$.

Isotherms, according to eq. [6.20] are shown in Fig. 6-3, taken from Barrer. Table I shows that with reasonable values of ν agreement between observation and calculation, eq. [6.18], may be obtained.

TABLE I

Test of the Isotherm for Permanent Gases in Elastomers after Barrer (11)

Gas	Elastomer	Volume Fraction V_0 of Gas dissolved at 300°K. and 1 atm.	Value of ν (sec.$^{-1}$) to give Agreement between Observed and Calculated V_0	Experimental Sorption Heat (cal./mol)
H_2	Vulcanised "Neoprene". Butadiene-acrylonitrile interpolymer	6.25×10^{-5}	3.3×10^{12}	— 970
		3.11×10^{-5}	3.2×10^{12}	— 500
N_2	Vulcanised "Neoprene". Butadiene-acrylonitrile interpolymer	7.9×10^{-5}	1.0×10^{12}	— 1400
		8.2×10^{-5}	1.1×10^{12}	— 1700
	Butadiene-styrene interpolymer	1.32×10^{-4}	0.77×10^{12}	— 1000
	Butadiene-methyl methacrylate interpolymer	1.29×10^{-4}	0.98×10^{12}	— 2000
A	Vulcanised "Neoprene"	2.08×10^{-4}	0.72×10^{12}	— 1630
	Butadiene-styrene interpolymer	2.75×10^{-4}	0.63×10^{12}	— 1100
	Butadiene-methyl-methacrylate interpolymer	1.66×10^{-4}	0.69×10^{12}	— 1450

IV. Solubility in anomalous mixed crystals*

We shall try to get an estimate for the solubility in so-called anomalous mixed crystals, for instance of $AgCl + PbCl_2$. From the investigations of Wagner and collaborators (27) it is known that $PbCl_2$ is taken up by solid AgCl to a concentration of 0.6 mol per cent. Ag^+ ions in the lattice are substituted by Pb^{++}-ions, a corresponding number of vacancies arising at the same time in the lattice of the Ag^+ ions, cf. Fig. 2-15. Thus we may say that, by dissolution of $PbCl_2$ in AgCl, the number of lattice positions of either type is increased by twice the number of $PbCl_2$ molecules dissolved, all the lattice sites of the one sublattice being occupied by chloride ions, while of the newly created sites in the lattice of the cations only every other site is occupied by a doubly charged lead ion. An equivalent number of vacancies is left, thus one Pb^{++} ion replaces two Ag^+ ions, to satisfy electric neutrality.

In the saturated solid solution of $PbCl_2$ in AgCl the chemical potential of $PbCl_2$ must be equal to that of the pure solid $PbCl_2$.** In order to obtain the theoretical expression for the solubility of $PbCl_2$ in AgCl, we must, therefore, calculate the chemical potential of $PbCl_2$ dissolved in AgCl. If we can derive an expression for the Gibbs free energy of the mixed crystal

$$G = H - TS \qquad [6.21]$$

we obtain μ_{PbCl_2} by differentiating [6.21] with respect to the number of moles of $PbCl_2$, n,

$$\mu_{PbCl_2} = \partial G / \partial n . \qquad [6.22]$$

H might either be determined experimentally or calculated from lattice data. S must be calculated statistically. If, as a first approximation, we assume that the energy of lattice vibrations for the mixed crystal is equal to the sum of that of the components, we need only calculate the combinatory term of the entropy.

Let there be N AgCl molecules and n $PbCl_2$ molecules, then we have

$N + 2n$ chlorine lattice sites, occupied by chlorine ions,
$N + 2n$ silver lattice sites, of which,
N are occupied by silver ions,
n are occupied by lead ions, and
n are left vacant.

---

* Cf. Wagner (48, 49).
** Provided the solubility of AgCl in $PbCl_2$ is neglected. This idealization is assumed in what follows.

In the above it is assumed that the concentration of the dissolved component, though small, is large compared with the degree of disorder in the pure silver chloride, which, therefore, can be neglected.

Thus, the number of distinguishable complexions, W, is

$$W = \frac{(N+2n)!}{N!\,n!\,n!} \cdot \qquad [6.23]$$

This is the number of arrangements of N silver ions, n lead ions and n vacancies on $N + 2n$ lattice sites. Only one arrangement of the chloride ions is possible. In order to obtain the entropy from Boltzmann's principle, $S = k \log W$, we proceed in the conventional manner by applying Stirling's formula to [6.23]

$$\log W \approx (N + 2n)\,[\log(N + 2n) - 1] - N\,[\log N - 1] - 2n\,[\log n - 1]$$

$$= N \log \frac{N + 2n}{N} + 2n \log \frac{N + 2n}{n} \cdot \qquad [6.24]$$

We, finally, obtain for the Gibbs free energy of the mixed crystal

$$G = H - RT \left\{ N \log \frac{N + 2n}{N} + 2n \log \frac{N + 2n}{n} \right\} \qquad [6.25]$$

neglecting the effect of lattice vibrations and neglecting the term pV which will be of importance only if the influence of external pressure on the solubility is to be discussed. Dissolution is connected with a volume increase, hence with increasing pressure the solubility will be diminished. An estimate however shows that for pressures up to a few hundred atmospheres the pressure influence is negligible.

From [6.25] we have by differentiating with respect to n

$$\mu_{PbCl_2} = N \partial G / \partial n = N \partial H / \partial n - 2\,RT\,\log \frac{N + 2n}{n} \qquad [6.26]$$

where $N =$ Avogadro's number.

μ_{PbCl_2} of the pure lead chloride may be put equal to H_0, neglecting the contribution of lattice vibrations to the free energy, because in the final result this term must cancel under the assumptions introduced above. Equating both expressions for μ, we obtain

$$H_0 = N \partial H / \partial n - 2\,RT \log \frac{N + 2n}{n} \qquad [6.27]$$

or

$$\log \frac{N + 2n}{n} = \frac{\Delta H}{2\,RT}, \; \Delta H = N \partial H / \partial n - H_0 \qquad [6.28]$$

and finally

$$x = \frac{n}{N + 2n} \approx \exp(-\Delta H / 2\,RT) \qquad [6.29]$$

if by x we denote the fraction of sites in the cation lattice, occupied by lead ions. For the present we shall not aim at an absolute calculation of x (involving an absolute calculation of ΔH), but we shall restrict ourselves to a comparison of the solubilities of $CdCl_2$ and $PbCl_2$ in AgCl, the former being about 16 times larger than the latter [6.29] gives for the ratio x_{Cd}/x_{Pb}

$$x_{Cd}/x_{Pb} = \exp\left[(\Delta H_{Pb} - \Delta H_{Cd})/2RT\right] \qquad [6.30]$$

to the present approximation.

To a first aproximation one might expect the ratio of the solubilities in solid silver chloride, to be similar to that encountered with the solubility in water.

If we had assumed formation of interstitial mixed crystals, a similar but not identical result for the solubility would have been obtained

Again consider N molecules of AgCl and n molecules of $PbCl_2$ Consequently we have N Ag^+ and N Cl^- lattice positions, both occupied by the corresponding ions (we may neglect the equilibrium concentration of vacancies and interstitial Ag^+ ions), and αN interstitial positions, (α being a small integer), of which n are occupied by Pb^{++} ions and $2n$ by Cl^- ions. Needless to say that on account of the size of the chloride ions this type of solution would be negligible in the example under discussion, but in other cases it might be of importance.

The number of complexions is now given by

$$W = (\alpha N)!/[n!(2n)!(\alpha N - 3n)!] . \qquad [6.31]$$

By use of Stirling's formula one obtains

$$\log W \approx \alpha N \log \frac{\alpha N}{\alpha N - 3n} - n \log \frac{n}{\alpha N - 3n} - 2n \log \frac{2n}{\alpha N - 3n} \qquad [6.32]$$

and finally

$$\mu_i = H_i + 3RT \log \frac{n}{\alpha N - 3n} + \mu_{osc}, (H_i = N \partial H/\partial n_i). \qquad [6.33]$$

With the same approximations as above, and $H_i - H_0 = \Delta H$, we obtain for the solubility

$$\frac{n}{\alpha N - 3n} = \exp(-\Delta H/3kT). \qquad [6.34]$$

Thus, for the same value of ΔH, the interstitial type of solution would be favored compared with the preceding type, viz. substitution plus formation of vacancies. But actually ΔH, in this case, will be so much higher for the interstitial type, that in spite of the factor 3/2 in the exponent the substitution-plus-vacancy type will be strongly favored. But it is seen from eq. [6.34] that for sufficiently small particles interstitial solution might well prevail (cf. the group of zeolites).

It seems worth while to add the corresponding equation for the simple substitution type of mixed crystal, for instance $KCl + NaCl$ or $PbCl_2 + CdCl_2$.*

a. Alkali halide type. N molecules of KCl and n molecules of NaCl. Since the anions are identical the total number of complexions is

$$W = (N + n)! / (N! \, n!) \qquad [6.35]$$

and

$$\log W \approx (N + n) \log (N + n) - N \log N - n \log n \,. \qquad [6.36]$$

Consequently

$$G = H - TS = H - RT \log W \qquad [6.37]$$

and

$$\mu = N \, \partial G / \partial n = H_i + RT \log \frac{n}{N + n} \,. \qquad [6.38]$$

The number of dissolved molecules n, then, is given by

$$n / (N + n) = \exp (- \Delta H / RT) \qquad [6.39]$$

where ΔH is defined as above and the same simplifications have been made.

b. N molecules of $PbCl_2$ and n molecules of $CdCl_2$. $N + n$ cation sites and $2 (N + n)$ anion sites, the latter again occupied by indistinguishable particles. The number of complexions is the same as above, and with the same simplifications we obtain as before

$$n / (N + n) = \exp (- \Delta H / RT) \qquad [6.40]$$

V. Solubility of alkali metals in alkali metal halides

Alkali halides dissolve alkali metal from the vapor phase, forming so called 'color centres', F-centres, as investigated by Pohl and coworkers (35, 36). The concentration in the crystal is found to be proportional to the gas pressure, decreasing with increasing temperature, which indicates an exothermic process of solution. A theoretical treatment of the solubility of these color centres has been given by Mott (5), assuming that an alkali atom is dissolved by forming a positive ion and a vacancy in the lattice of the negative ions, the electron being trapped by a vacancy. Thus the color centre may be described either as an alkali atom, adjacent to a lattice site where a negative ion is missing, or as an electron shared between the six neighbours of a vacant negative lattice point corresponding to a positive charge. The combinatory term in the entropy of a crystal consisting of N ion pairs,

* Where we shall always assume sufficiently small solubilities, i.e.. if necessary, sufficiently low temperatures.

n_F color centres and n_F excess positive ions is

$$R \log \frac{(N + n_F)!}{n_F ! N!}$$

thus the chemical potential

$$\mu = N \varepsilon_F + R T \log \frac{n_F}{N + n_F}$$

if ε_F is the work required to add an atom to the crystal to form a color centre. Equating this to the corresponding expression for a monatomic vapor, one obtains*

$$\varepsilon_F + kT \frac{n_F}{N + n_F} - kT \log \left(\frac{2\pi\, m\, kT}{h^2} \right)^{3/2} + kT \log \frac{1}{n_v} = 0$$

and

$$\frac{n_F}{N + n_F} = n_v \left(\frac{2\pi\, m\, kT}{h^2} \right)^{3/2} \exp \left(- \varepsilon_F / kT \right).$$

From the temperature dependence of the solubility Pohl and collaborators derived for ε_F

KCl   KBr

-0.10 -0.25 electron volts.

Theoretical calculations of this energy have been carried out by Gurney and Mott. (21)

VI. Anomalous solubilities of gases in metals

Attempts have been made to explain certain anomalies encountered with dissolution of gases in metals. Thus, for instance, the solubility of oxygen in silver first decreases and then increases with increasing temperature, exhibiting a minimum at 400°C. To explain this it has been assumed (39, 44, 45) that an unstable oxide of silver, Ag_2O, is dissolved at low temperatures, while at temperatures above 400°C. the oxide is no longer stable and a true, endothermic solution is formed. This explanation, however, leads to certain difficulties. A dilute solid solution of Ag_2O in metallic silver could hardly be imagined to occur in another way than by a substitution of lattice sites by the constituent atoms or ions of the oxide, and perhaps by occupation of interstitial sites. Therefore, there is no essential difference between a true solution of oxygen in silver and solution of silver oxide in silver. The assumption, that oxygen atoms can occupy two different lattice sites in the silver lattice, one with positive the other with negative ΔH, would lead to a formal explanation of the observations. The only possibility for such a process seems to be that the oxygen atoms either may occupy silver sites (exothermically) or interstitial sites (endothermically).

* n_v = number of atoms per cc. of vapor.

REFERENCES

Monographs and review articles

1. Barrer, R. M., Diffusion in and through solids. Cambridge University Press, Cambridge, 1941.
2. Brunauer, S., The adsorption of gases and vapors. Oxford University Press, Oxford 1944.
3. Fowler, R. H., and Guggenheim, E. A., Statistical Thermodynamics. Cambridge 1939.
4. McBain, J. W., Sorption of Gases and Vapours by Solids. Routledge 1932.
5. Mott, N. F., and Gurney, R. W., Electronic Processes in Ionic Crystals. Clarendon Press, Oxford 1940. 2nd ed. 1948.
6. Smithells, C. J., Gases and Metals. London 1937.
6a. Smithells, C. J., Metals Reference Book. London 1949.
7. Smith, D. P., Hydrogen in Metals, University of Chicago Press 1948.

General Bibliography

8. Barrer, R. M., *Proc. Roy. Soc. (London)* **A 167**, 392 (1938).
9. Barrer, R. M., *Proc. Roy. Soc.* (London) **A 167**, 406 (1938).
9a. Barrer, R. M., *Trans. Faraday Soc.* **36**, 1235 (1940).
10. Barrer, R. M., *Trans. Faraday Soc.* **40**, 374 (1944).
11. Barrer, R. M., *Trans. Faraday Soc.* **43**, 3 (1947).
12. Barrer, R. M., and Ibbitson, D. A., *Trans. Faraday Soc.* **40**, 195 (1944).
13. Barrer, R. M. and Ibbitson, D. A., *Trans. Faraday Soc.* **40**, 206 (1944).
13a. Barrer, R. M., *Discussion Faraday Soc.* **1948**, 68.
14. Brunauer, S., Emmett, P. H. and Teller, C., *J. Am. Chem. Soc.* **60**, 309 (1938).
15. Brunauer, S., Deming, L. S., Deming, W. E., and Teller, C., *J. Am. Chem. Soc.* **62**, 1723 (1940).
15a. Darken, L. S. and Smith, R. P., *Corrosion* **5**, 1 (1949).
16. Flory, J., *J. Chem. Phys.* **9**, 660 (1941).
17. Flory, J., *J. Chem. Phys.* **10**, 51 (1942).
18. Fowler, R. H., and Smithells, C. J., *Proc. Roy. Soc. (London)* **A 160**, 37 (1937).
19. Gillespie, L. J., and Galstaun, L. S., *J. Am. Chem. Soc.* **58**, 2565 (1936).
20. Gillespie, L. J., and Hall, F. P., *J. Am. Chem. Soc.* **48**, 1207 (1926).
21. Gurney, R. W., and Mott, N. F., *Trans. Faraday Soc.* **34**, 506 (1938).
21a. Heiland, G., and Kelting, H., *Z. Physik* **126**, 689 (1949).
22. Hill, T. L., *J. Chem. Phys.* **14**, 263 (1946).
22a. Himmler, W., *Z. physik. Chem.* **195**, 244 (1950).
22b. Himmler, W., *Z. physik. Chem.* **195**, 253, (1950).
23. Huggins, M. L., *J. Chem. Phys.* **9**, 440 (1941).
24. Huggins, M. L., *Ann. N. Y. Acad. Sci.* **43**, 1 (1942).
25. Huggins, M. L., *J. Phys. Chem.* **46**, 1 (1942).
26. Huggins, M. L., *J. Amer. Chem. Soc.* **64**, 1712 (1942).
26a. Kelting, H., and Witt, H., *Z. Physik* **126**, 697 (1949).
27. Koch, E., and Wagner, C., *Z. physik. Chem.* **B 38**, 295 (1938).
28. Lacher, J. R., *Proc. Cambr. Phil. Soc.* **33**, 518 (1937).
29. Lacher, J. R., *Proc. Roy. Soc. (London)* **A 161**, 525 (1937).
30. Meyer, K. H., *Helv. Chim. Acta* **23**, 1063 (1940).
31. Miller, A. R., *Proc. Cambr. Phil. Soc.* **38**, 109 (1942).

32. Miller, A. R., The Theory of solutions of high Polymers. Oxford 1948.
33. Münster, A., *Kolloid-Z.* **110,** 58 (1948); **111,** 190 (1948).
34. Orr, W. J. C., *Trans. Faraday Soc.* **40,** 320 (1944).
35. Pohl, R. W., *Proc. Phys. Soc.* **49,** 3 (1937).
36. Pohl, R. W., *Physik. Z.* **39,** 36 (1938).
36a. Portevin, A., *Metal Progress* **50,** 1206 (1946).
37. Scott, R. L., *J. Chem. Phys.* **13,** 178 (1945).
38. Scott, R. L., and Magat, M., *J. Chem. Phys.* **13,** 172 (1945).
39. Sieverts, A. and Hagenacker, J., *Z. physik. Chem.* **68,** 115 (1910).
40. Sieverts, A., Jurisch, E., and Metz, A., *Z. anorg. u. allgem. Chem.* **92,** 329 (1915).
41. Sieverts, A., and Roell, E., *Z. anorg. allgem. Chem.* **153,** 289 (1926).
42. Sieverts, A., and Bruening, K., *Z. physik. Chem.* A **168,** 411 (1934).
43. Sieverts, A., and Hagen, H., *Z. physik. Chem.* A **174,** 247 (1935).
44. Simmons, J. H., *J. Phys. Chem.* **36,** 652 (1933).
45. Steacie, E.W.R., and Johnson, F., *Proc. Roy. Soc. (London)* A **112,** 542 (1926).
46. Wagner, C., *Z. physik. Chem.* **193,** 386 (1944).
47. Wagner, C., *Z. physik. Chem.* **193,** 407 (1944).
48. Wagner, C., and Hantelmann, P., *J. Phys. & Colloid Chem.* **54,** 426 (1949).
49. Wagner, C., *J. Chem. Phys.* **18,** 62 (1950).

CHAPTER VII

PERMEATION. DIFFUSION OF GASES IN SOLIDS

I. General remarks. Definitions.

It has long been known that gases can permeate through many solids and through colloidal membranes. If the solid material is porous, contains cracks etc., this permeation may essentially be a flow through capillaries. We shall exclude this case from our considerations, and deal with true diffusion processes only. In most cases it is possible to distinguish between the two types of process. True diffusion is usually a highly specific process, depending both on the solubility and on the mobility of the gas molecules or atoms in the solid. Thus the solubility of hydrogen in palladium, in the form of atomic hydrogen, is very high at elevated temperatures, and the rate of diffusion is high also, while there is hardly a perceptible permeation of other gases through palladium. Gas flow through capillaries does not show very pronounced differences for different gases, unless the gas molecules are of dimensions comparable with those of the capillaries. Also, true diffusion generally shows a comparatively strong dependence on temperature, while the variation with temperature of gas flow through capillaries is rather small, being due to the variation of viscosity with temperature and to the change in gas density, which varies in the opposite direction from that of the viscosity.

The experimental methods for measuring diffusion of gases through solids are simple in principle. For absolute measurements a plate of known dimensions is taken, in contact on either side with the diffusing gas, kept at different pressures. Instead of a plate, thin sheets of other geometrical shape may be employed, if the thickness can be kept uniform and the surface may be exactly determined; for instance, with a tube, closed at one end. In many observations the pressure at the low pressure side is chosen so small that it may be considered as zero, compared with that at the high pressure side. The rate of flow may be taken from pressure readings at either end of a capillary or an orifice*, during the steady state of streaming. This capillary, for instance, may be kept at the low pressure side, the pressure at

* Depending on whether a membrane of low or high permeability is used.

the end, connected to the pump being almost zero, the pressure at the other end lying within the range of measurement of a McLeod gauge. This pressure can usually still be treated as zero, compared with that at the other face of the plate, (usually lying between a few cm. of mercury and atmospheric pressure).

Instead of measuring the pressure drop during stationary flow, one may also connect the low pressure side with a known volume, measuring the pressure rise during a definite time interval. Of course, this pressure rise must be kept small compared with the pressure on the high pressure side.

If relative measurements, only, are required, the diffusion membrane may have any shape: with glass or quartz, for instance, that of a cylinder or a bulb, the thickness in such cases never being quite uniform.

For condensable substances observation times may be greatly reduced by a method, described by F. H. Müller (108, 109, 110). He observed the pressure rise in a very small volume v into which the vapor had been condensed at the low pressure side, Fig. 7-1. For absorbable gases Vieweg and Gast (154), developed an electric torsion balance which allows of an automatic recording of the amount of

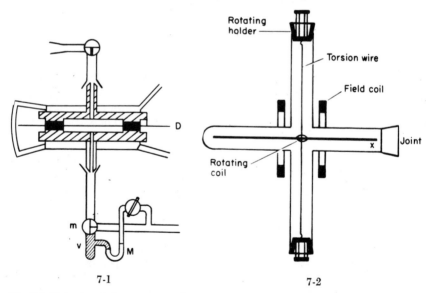

7-1   7-2

Fig. 7-1. Experimental arrangement for measurement of permeation, after F. H. Müller. General lay-out, membrane at D. Manometer for reading pressure change at M. Small measuring volume v.

Fig. 7-2. Automatic torsion balance for the measurement of permeation of absorbable gases, after Vieweg and Gast.

permeating vapor. Sensitivity is very high (several γ), Fig. 7-2. A survey of methods and results up to 1937. has been given by Manegold (5, 6).

There are further possibilities for measuring diffusion of gases in solids, some of which will be discussed in connection with special measurements.

The flux for diffusion of a gas through unit area of a membrane in the stationary state is given by

$$J = -D\partial c/\partial x \qquad [7.1]$$

where c is the concentration of the gas within the membrane. If D is independent of concentration, and if the concentration in the membrane is given by Henry's law, $c = \sigma p$, p being the gas pressure, then for the concentration gradient, assumed constant throughout the whole membrane, we may write in the stationary state

$$\partial c/\partial x = \Delta c/\delta = \sigma \Delta p/\delta \qquad [7.2]$$

where δ is the thickness of the membrane. By inserting [7.2] into [7.1] one obtains

$$J = -D\sigma\Delta p/\delta \qquad [7.3]$$

The permeability constant, P, may be defined, as equal to [7.3] for certain standard conditions. It is usual (1) to measure the diffusion current in cm.[3] of gas at N.T.P., passing per sec. through unit area of the membrane for $\delta = 1$ mm. and $\Delta p = 1$ cm. of mercury. [7.3] then may be written in the alternative form

$$J = P\Delta p/\delta \qquad [7.4]$$

where J, p, and δ must be measured in the above specified units. In

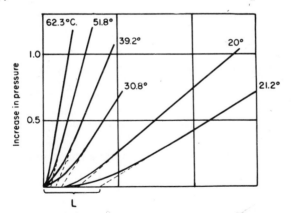

Fig. 7-3. Permeation, rate of pressure rise on low pressure side. Time lag L indicated by intersection of extrapolated straight line with abscissa, after Barrer. Absorption of argon by butadiene methacrylate interpolymer (nitrogen at 21.2°).

many cases, c or σ are not known, and therefore direct measurements can give P only.

It takes a certain time until the steady state of flow is established, after a pressure difference has been applied to a gas-free membrane. The pressure rise at the low pressure side, as a function of time, is shown in Fig. 7-3, taken from measurements of Barrer (20). Now Barrer has pointed out that it is possible to make use of this for an evaluation of D and σ simply from permeation measurements. For large values of t, the permeation is constant, the pressure rise being proportional with time, hence a linear relation between time and amount of gas is obtained, Fig. 7-3, cf. Chap. I, p. 42. The intersection of the corresponding straight line with the t-axis gives the time lag L.

The problem under discussion has been solved by Daynes (47) for a special case. We have treated this diffusion problem in Chap. I, p. 42. The formulae obtained for the time lag are

$$L = \frac{h^2}{6D} - \frac{c_0 h^2}{2Dc_1} \tag{7.5}$$

$$L = \frac{h^2}{D(c_1 - c_{00})} \left[\frac{c_1}{6} + \frac{c_{00}}{3} - \frac{c_0}{2} \right] \tag{7.6}$$

$$L = \frac{h^2}{6D}. \tag{7.7}$$

For the symbols used etc. cf. Chap. I, p. 42, 44.

Hence D can be determined directly, and with D known, σ may also be obtained from eq. [7.3]. Barrer states that in the case of rubber-like polymers with $h = 10^{-1}$ cm., $D = 10^{-1}$ cm.^{2}sec.$^{-1}$, L is of the order of magnitude of 1,200 to 1,800 seconds, and therefore easily accessible to measurement.

II. Measured permeabilities. Experiments of Barrer.

Permeability constants, as determined by Barrer (20) for various organic polymers, are contained in the following Tables I, II, III.

Solubilities, derived from these measurements, are listed in the following Tables IV and V.

Temperature coefficients of permeability constants, Q, defined by

$$P = P_0 \exp(-Q/RT)$$

are contained in Table VI.

Diffusion coefficients are listed in Table VII.

As with diffusion in liquids, activation energies for the diffusion in organic membranes were found to be comparatively low and to

TABLE I

Nature of membranes used (taken from Barrer (20))

Name	Main chemical constituent	Formulae of simple or polymerised molecules
Rubber (vulcanized) . . .	Polyisoprene, cross-linked by sulfur	$CH_2{=}C{-}CH{=}CH_2$ $\mid$ CH_3
Rubber (unvulcanized) . .	Polyisoprene	
"Neoprene" (vulcanized commercial)	Polychloroprene, crosslinked by sulfur	$CH_2{=}C{-}CH \;=\; CH_2$ $\mid$
"Neoprene" (unvulcanized commercial) . .	Polychloroprene	Cl
Polychloroprene "Vulcaplas"	Polysulfide	$-R{-}S{-}S{-}R{-}S{-}S{-}R$
Butadiene-Methyl Methacrylate interpolymer. .	—	$CH_2{=}C{-}COOCH_3,$ $\mid$ CH_3 $CH_2{=}CH{-}CH{-}CH_2$
Butadiene-Acrylonitrile . .	—	$CH_2{=}CH{-}CN,$ $CH_2{=}CH{-}CH{=}CH_2$
Butadiene-Styrene interpolymer	—	$C_6H_5{-}CH{=}CH_2,$ $CH_2{=}CH{-}CH{=}CH_2$

TABLE II

Permeability Constants, taken from Barrer (20), selected values

System	Temp. °C.	$P \times 10^6$
Helium (c.c./sec./cm.²/mm. thick/cm. Hg).		
He-"Neoprene" (vulcanized and with fillers)	0	0.0022
	30.4	0.0078
	57.0	0.035
He-"Neoprene" (raw, unvulcanized) . . .	21.6	0.0039
	37.6	0.0116 (material softening)
He-rubber (2 per cent. S, 5 min.- vulcanized)	19.2	0.0051
	57.0	0.0179
He-"Vulcaplas"	50.0	0.000174
	59.0	0.000342

Table II (Continued)

Permeability Constants, taken from Barrer (20), selected values

System	Temp. °C	$P \times 10^6$
Hydrogen (c. c./sec./cm.^{2}/mm. thick/cm. Hg pressure)		
H$_2$-"Neoprene" (vulcanized commercial		
polychloroprene)	17.5	0.0085
	26.9	0.0128
	63.7	0.0534
H$_2$-German rubber (Butadiene-Acry-		
lonitrile polymer)	0	0.0032
	20.0	0.0085
H$_2$-Butadiene-methyl methacrylate polymer	20.0	0.023
H$_2$-Polystyrene-Butadiene polymer. . . .	19.9	0.0084
H$_2$-Chloroprene polymer; pure.	31.8	0.0049
	60.8	0.0175
Nitrogen (c. c./cm.^{2}/mm. thick/sec./cm. Hg pressure)		
N$_2$-"Neoprene"	27.1	0.00137
	65.4	0.0106
N$_2$-German rubber (butadiene acrylonitrile		
polymer	20.0	0.00061
	59.5	0.0048
N$_2$-butadiene methyl methacrylate polymer	21.2	0.0028
	61.9	0.0132
N$_2$-polystyrene-butadiene polymer	20.0	0.0029
	64.2	0.0161
Argon (c. c./cm.^{2}/mm. thick/sec. cm. Hg pressure)		
A-"Neoprene" (commercial vulzanised poly-		
chloroprene)	36.1	0.0068
	52.2	0.0144
A-butadiene-methyl methacrylate polymer	20.0	0.0059
	62.3	0.0395
A-Polystyrene-butadiene polymer	19.5	0.0109
	64.6	0.074

TABLE III

Relative permeabilities of various membranes (taken from Barrer (20))

Membrane Gas	H$_2$	He	A	N$_2$	O$_2$	CO	CO$_2$	NH$_3$
Rubber (vulcanized)								
25°C.	1.00	0.62	—	0.16	0.44	—	2.88	8.00
Rubber (unvulcanized)	1.00	0.30	0.19	0.11	0.35	0.16	2.50	—
"room temperature"								
"Neoprene", vulcanized	1.00	0.61	0.29	0.10				
"Chloroprene"	1.00	0.22	—	—				
Butadiene acry-								
lonitrile	1.00	—	—	0.08				
Butadiene methyl-								
methacrylate . . .	1.00	—	0.26	0.11				
Butadiene polystyrene	1.00	—	0.95	0.27				

TABLE IV

σ, P and D for vulcanized rubber, after Barrer (20), at 25°C.

Gas	Solubility σ (c.c./c.c. Rubber per Atmospheric Pressure)	Permeability Constant P (c.c./cm.^{2}/mm. thick/cm. Hg press./sec.)	Diffusion Constant D (cm.^{2} sec.$^{-1}$)
H_2	0.040	0.045×10^{-6}	0.85×10^{-5}
O_2	0.070	0.020×10^{-6}	0.21×10^{-5}
N_2	0.035	0.0071×10^{-6}	0.15×10^{-5}
CO_2	0.90	0.132×10^{-6}	0.11×10^{-5}

TABLE V

Solubilities of Gases in organic Polymers, selected values, after Barrer (20)

Polymer	Gas	Temp. °C	Solubility σ (c. c./c. c. polymer per Atmos.)	$\log_{10} \sigma = A - \dfrac{\Delta H}{2.303\,RT}$
"Neoprene" (vulcanized) .	H_2	0.0 17.0	0.065 0.051	$\log_{10} \sigma = -1{,}97 + \dfrac{970}{4.60T}$
"Neoprene" (vulcanized) .	A	36.1	0.155	$\log \sigma = -1{,}86 + \dfrac{1630}{4.60T}$
"Neoprene" (vulcanized) .	N_2	27.1	0.054	$\log \sigma = -2.28 + \dfrac{1400}{4.60T}$
"Chloroprene" polymer .	H_2	31.8	0.115	$\log \sigma = -2.09 + \dfrac{1600}{4.60T}$
Butadiene acrylonitrile polymer	N_2	17.0	0.063	$\log \sigma = -2.44 + \dfrac{1700}{4.60T}$
Butadiene acrylonitrile .	H_2	0 20	0.040 0.037	$\log \sigma = -1.80 + \dfrac{500}{4.60T}$
Butadiene methyl methacrylate polymer Sample I		39.5	0.084	$\log \sigma = -2.45 + \dfrac{2000}{4.60T}$
Butadiene methyl methacrylate polymer	A	20.0	0.134	$\log \sigma = -1.95 + \dfrac{1450}{4.60T}$
Butadiene polystyrene polymer Sample I . . .	N_2	20.0	0.094	$\log \sigma = -1.87 + \dfrac{1000}{4.60T}$
Butadiene polystyrene polymer Sample II . .	A	19.5	0.218	$\log \sigma = -1.63 + \dfrac{1100}{4.60T}$

Table VI

Heats of activation, Q, of permeability constants (in cal./mol) taken from Barrer (20)

Membrane	Q (cal./mol)	He	H_2	N_2	A	O_2	CO	CO_2	H_2O
Rubber (vulcanized)		6300	6000	—	—	—	—	7600	2800
Rubber (unvulcanized) ...		6400	6500						
		7800	9500	—	—	8200	9500	9600	—
"Neoprene" (vulcanized) ..		8000	8300	10500	10700				
Butadiene acrylonitrile ...		—	8200	9800	—				
Butadiene methyl methacrylate		—	—	9500	8850				
Butadiene polystyrene ...		—	—	7900	7900				
Chloroprene		—	8300	—	—				

Table VII

Diffusion Constants $D = D_0 \exp(-Q/RT)$ (cm.^{2} sec.$^{-1}$), after Barrer (20)

	Temp. °C.	D cm.^{2}sec.$^{-1} \times 10^5$	D_0 cm.^{2}sec.$^{-1}$	Q kcal./mol
H_2-"Neoprene" (vulcanized) ..	0.0	0.037	9.0	9.25
	17.0	0.103		
A-"Neoprene" (vulcanized) ..	36.1	0.033	54.6	11.70
N_2-"Neoprene" (vulcanized) ..	27.1	0.019	79	11.90
H_2-"Chloroprene" polymer ..	31.8	0.33	39.4	9.90
H_2-Butadiene acrylonitrile interpolymer	0	0.061	54.4	8.70
	20.0	0.177		
N_2-Butadiene acrylonitrile interpolymer	17	0.0066	28.1	11.50
N_2-Butadiene methyl methacrylate interpolymer Sample I	39.5	0.041	38	11.50
A-Butadiene methyl-methacrylate interpolymer. Sample II	20	0.034	15.1	10.30
A-Butadiene polystyrene interpolymer. Sample I	19.5	0.038	1.84	9.00
N_2-Butadiene polystyrene interpolymer. Sample II.....	20.0	0.0237	0.93	8.90

vary within a rather narrow range only, between about 6,000 and 12,000 cal./mol. There are some values for diffusion in inorganic solids which are of this order of magnitude, while, on the other hand, for the diffusion of nitrogen and argon in glasses much higher heats of activation are found (Table VIII).

TABLE VIII

Activation Energies for Diffusion in Elastic and Rigid Membranes after Barrer (21)

	Q (Neoprene) kcal./mol Barrer (20)	$Q*$ (SiO_2 Glass) kcal./mol Barrer (17)	Q (Heulandite) kcal./mol Tiselius (147)	$Q*$ (Cellulose Compound) kcal./mol de Boer and Fast (31)
He	8.00	5.6	—	—
H_2	9.25	10.0	—	7.6 to 5.6
N_2	11.90	26.0	—	—
A	11.70	32.0	—	—
H_2O	6.90 (in rubber)**	—	5.4 ($\perp$ 201 face) ($\perp$ 001 face)	—

Assuming a simple model, consisting of a plane square net of methane molecules, Barrer shows that the activation energy for diffusion may be lowered considerably by the displacement of molecules surrounding a migrating particle, Table IX. Thus by elastic displace-

TABLE IX

The Interaction Energy E in Passing through an Elastic Two-Dimensional Crystal of Methane calculated by Barrer (21)

Gas	E (kcal./mol) for a Rigid Lattice	E (kcal./mol) for an Elastic Lattice
He	0.14	0.14
H_2	9.70	0.60
A	26.50	1.65
CH_4	44.20	2.35

ments the energy of activation is much reduced, which, at the same time, accounts for the rather narrow range of variation of activation energies. The observed activation energies are larger than those calculated for a two-dimensional lattice. The difference is due to the three-dimensional structure and cross-linking of chains.

* In these cases the effect of the heat of solution upon the temperature coefficient has been neglected, since the heat of the solution process is very small.
** Value obtained from data of Boggs and Blake (32).

In these high polymers, diffusion and viscous flow are still related processes, both being connected with the formation of holes in the structure, cf. Müller (110). But since diffusion is possible even where, due to cross-linking, no permanent place change of the constituent molecules or sections thereof is possible, there is no direct numerical relation between both processes. But the heat of activation, in both processes, due to the formation of holes, is still approximately the same. The temperature coefficient of the viscosity (60) of rubber corresponds to a heat of activation of about 10,000 cal., while heats of activation for diffusion range between 8,100 and 11,900 cal.

From a comparison of observed values with the theoretical equations it is seen that a considerable entropy of activation must be assumed. Barrer used the formulae (cf. Chap. III, p. 174).

$$D = \frac{\nu}{6} \frac{E}{RT} d^2 \exp\left(-E/RT\right) \quad \text{cf. Bradley (35), Wheeler (158)} \qquad [7.8]$$

and

$$D = \frac{kT}{h} \frac{f^*}{f_n} d^2 \exp\left(-E/RT\right) \qquad \text{cf. Glasstone (2), Eyring (61)} \qquad [7.9]$$

where d is the distance, traversed in an elementary displacement, corresponding to the lattice distance in the case of crystals. ν is a frequency, comparable to the frequency of a particle in a crystal, for which Barrer used an average value of $\nu = 2.5 \times 10^{12}$. In Eyring's formula, f_n is the partition function in the normal state, f^* that of the transition state, where the coordinate in which diffusion occurs, is excluded. In f_n and f^* the contributions of the surroundings of the migrating particle should be included. Numerical values, thus obtained, are seen in Table X. It is obvious that, without taking into account high entropies of activation, quite unreasonably high values for d would be obtained. For liquid systems, much lower d-values are calculated, Table XI. To account for the discrepancies one either may use Wheeler's formula (158)

$$\frac{1}{6} \frac{\nu}{(f-1)!} \left(\frac{E}{RT}\right)^{f-1} d^2 \exp\left(-E/RT\right) \qquad [7.10]$$

which is analogous to the formula used in chemical kinetics where a number of degrees of freedom f is involved in activation or, alternatively, assume a sufficiently high entropy of activation. It is seen from the table, that a considerable number of degrees of freedom ($f > 10$), or correspondingly high entropies of activation (~ 14 to 18 e. u.), must be considered. The formula, given by the transition state theory, transcribed in thermodynamic language, is

$$D = \frac{kT}{h} d^2 \exp\left(\frac{-\Delta H^*}{RT}\right) \exp\left(\frac{\Delta S^*}{R}\right) = D_0 \exp\left(-E/RT\right) \qquad [7.11]$$

with

$$D_0 = \exp\left(\Delta S^*/R\right)\frac{kT}{h}d^2\frac{1}{2.72}.$$ [7.12]

The factor $\dfrac{1}{e} = \dfrac{1}{2.72} = \exp\left(-\dfrac{RT}{RT}\right)$ enters into the equation as shown in Chap. III, p. 174. The entropies of activation are calculated for a value $d = 5 \times 10^{-8}$ cm. Certainly, the surroundings of the migrating particle must contribute to the large entropy of activation, cf. Barrer (25).

TABLE X

Diffusion in Gas-Polymer-Systems.

Mean Free Paths calculated using various Formulae for the Diffusion Constant, after Barrer (21)

Diffusion System	D_0 cm.^{2}sec.$^{-1}$	Q cal./mol.	d^*_{calc}	d^{**}_{calc}	$\sqrt{\frac{f^*}{f}}\,d^{***}_{calc}$
H$_2$-Butadiene Acrylonitrile Polymer	56	8700	1160Å	480Å	182Å
N$_2$-Butadiene acrylonitrile polymer	28	11500	820	316	130
H$_2$-"Neoprene"	9.4	9250	476	204	74
A -"Neoprene"	55	11700	1150	410	185
N$_2$-"Neoprene"	78	11900	1370	490	215
N$_2$-Butadiene Methyl methacrylate polymer	37	11500	946	350	150

TABLE XI

Diffusion in Liquid-Liquid-Systems

Mean Free Paths calculated using various Formulae for the Diffusion Constants, after Barrer (21)

Diffusion System	D_0 cm.^{2}sec.$^{-1}$	Q cal./mol.	d^*_{calc}	d^{**}_{calc}	$\sqrt{\frac{f^*}{f}}\,d^{***}_{calc}$
H$_2$O in H$_2$O	0.197	5300	69 Å	36 Å	11,0Å
C$_6$H$_5$OH in CH$_3$OH .	3.4 $\times 10^{-3}$	3150	9.1	6.9	1.4
C$_6$H$_5$OH in C$_6$H$_6$ . .	3.16 $\times 10^{-3}$	3080	8.7	6.9	1.4
sym.-C$_2$H$_2$Br$_4$ in sym.-C$_2$H$_2$Cl$_4$ . .	1.68 $\times 10^{-3}$	3365	6.4	5.0	1.0
Br$_2$ in CS$_2$	0.43 $\times 10^{-3}$	1536	3.2	3.4	0.4

  * d calculated from eq. $D_0 = \nu\, d^2/6$
 ** d calculated from eq. $D_0 = (\nu/6 \times 2.72) \times d^2 \times Q/RT$.
*** $\sqrt{\frac{f^*}{f}}\,d$ calculated from eq. $D_0 = (2.72\, kT/h) \times d^2 \times f^*/f$.

A number of diffusion constants for different media are listed in the preceding tables. Distribution curves for D_0 for rubber, liquids and solids are represented graphically in Fig. 7-4.

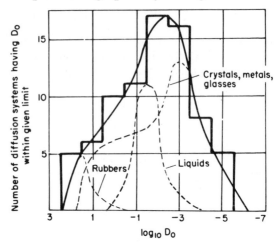

Fig. 7-4. Abundance of experimental values D_0 in empirical equation for diffusion coefficient $D = D_0 \exp (-Q/RT)$, after Barrer.

Kuhn, Suhr and Ryffel (95) investigated the diffusion of foreign molecules in swollen and in elastically solid rubber. The substances used were

1. Phenol,   Molecular weight   M =   94
2. Carotine,   M =   536
3. p, p'-azo-phenol-distearate,   M =   746
4. dye of formula $C_{70}H_{94}O_6N_4$ M = 1086
5.   ,,   ,,   ,, $C_{70}H_{94}O_5N_6$ M = 1098
6.   ,,   ,,   ,, $C_{82}H_{102}O_6N_4$ M = 1238
7.   ,,   ,,   ,, $C_{82}H_{102}O_5N_6$ M = 1250.

The diffusion was measured in weakly vulcanized rubber, swollen in benzene at 20°C. to about 5 times its original volume. With carotine a diffusion coefficient at 20°C. of 2×10^{-6} cm.^{2} sec. $^{-1}$ was observed, a remarkably high value. Substance 3. with a molecular weight of 746 gave a diffusion coefficient of only $\sim 2 \times 10^{-7}$ cm.^{2} sec^{-1}, substances 4. and 5. gave about 10^{-8} while with 6. and 7. about 5×10^{-9} cm.^{2} sec.$^{-1}$ was obtained.

Diffusion in solvent free rubber was much smaller, the respective values being: Phenol 10^{-8} cm.^{2} sec.$^{-1}$ at 20°C.; for molecules 4. and 7. below 10^{-12} cm.^{2} sec.$^{-1}$.

Some hydrogen and water permeabilities are contained in the following Tables XII and XIII and Figs. 7-6 and 7-7.

Diffusion coefficients of water vapor in membranes as function of concentration were measured by Rouse (123), Fig. 7-5. The influence of plasticizers was studied by Deeg (48) and by Doty (51). Contrary to the effect of plasticizers, the rate of permeation often is reduced by the pressure of nonpermeable fillers (Deeg (49)).

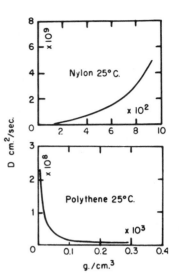

Fig. 7-5. Diffusion constants of water in nylon and in polythene, at 25°C., as function of concentration of absorbed water, after Rouse.

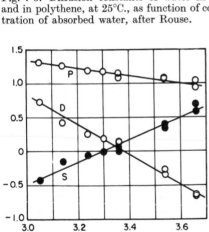

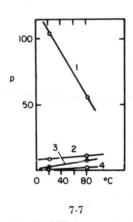

Fig. 7-6. Temperature dependence of permeation constant P, diffusion constant D and solubility S, for permeation of water vapor through polyvinylchloride, after Doty, Aiken, Mark.

Fig. 7-7. Temperature dependence of permeability coefficients of water in several substances 1. cellulose triacetate, 2. benzyl cellulose, 3. polystyrene, 4. polyvinylchloride, after F. H. Müller.

III. Anomalies in Permeation

Anomalies have been reported with diffusion of vapors through organic membranes (1, 39, 103, 143). Thus, for instance, polystyrene shows a permeability constant, apparently increasing with increasing

TABLE XII

Permeabilites for Hydrogen and Water, taken from Barrer (1)

Membrane	$P \times 10^6$ at 25°C. for Hydrogen	$P \times 10^6$ for Water
Cellophane	0.00008	0.12—0.24 at 38°C.
Cellulose acetate . .	0.018	54 at 25°C.
Polyethylene sulfide	0.001	0.076 at 21°C.
Polychloroprene . .	0.011	0.91 at 21°C.
Rubbers	0.019 (smoked sheet rubber)	0.52 at 25°C. (hard rubber)
	0.019 (ether soluble rubber)	2.5 at 25°C. (soft vulcanized rubber)

TABLE XIII

Permeation constants* of water vapor for various substances, after F. H. Müller

Material	Müller (8)	Taylor, Herrmann, Kemp (143)	Badum, Leilich (16)
1 Cellophane	170	—	70
2 Cellulose triacetate	35	55	29
3 Polymethylacrylester	10	—	—
4 Copolymerisate polyvinyl chloride + polyacrylic acid derivative	3.5	—	7
5 Polystyrene	1.4	1.4	0.7
6 Soft rubber (vulcanized)	0.7	2.5—3.0	2.0—3.0
7 Guttapercha.	0.35	0.5	0.4
8 Polyvinyl chloride	0.35	0.07	—
9 Polyethylene sulfide	—	0.07	—
10 Polyisobutylene	0.07	—	—
11 Ozokerite	0.035	—	—
12 Paraffine	0.028	0.021	—
13 Polyisobutylene + carbon black .	0.015	—	—
14 Krönig-Wax	0.014	—	—

* cubic centimetres (at N.T.P.) per second, per cm.^{2} for $\Delta p = 1$ cm. Hg and 1 mm. thickness $\times 10^6$.

thickness of the membrane, towards water vapor near its saturation pressure, the rate of permeation increasing with increasing vapor pressure. This is also the case with rubber. On the other hand the concentration distribution of the water in the membrane has been measured, by using a series of thin laminae of rubber. Strong deviations from a linear distribution have been found, the actual concentrations being much smaller than those corresponding to a linear drop of concentrations. In these cases strong deviations from Henry's law have also been observed, and in the case of the series of rubber membranes, the actual, non-linear concentration curve is not much different from a concentration curve, calculated from the assumption of linear distribution of vapor pressure of water within the membrane, by using the observed solubility data for varying pressure.

These observations, if correct, show that at least part of the observed deviations is due to deviations from the ideal laws of solution. Deviations from the simple Fick law (cf. Chap. I, p. 3).

$$\partial c/\partial t = D\partial^2 c/\partial x^2 \qquad [7.13]$$

may be due to one of the following causes.

a. The mobility is a function of concentration,

b. There are marked deviations from the ideal laws of solution.

In either case, eq. [7.13] is to be replaced by (cf. Chap. I, p. 3)

$$\partial c/\partial t = \partial/\partial x \, (D\partial c/\partial x) \qquad [7.14]$$

giving for the steady state

$$D\partial c/\partial x = \text{const.} \qquad [7.15]$$

Typical concentration curves, calculated by Barrer, are reproduced in Chap. I, p. 15, 16. Relative values of D may be read from the slope of the concentration curve during the steady state, D being inversely proportional to $\partial c/\partial x$. If deviations from the laws of ideal solutions are alone responsible for the observed anomalies, we may write

$$\partial c/\partial t = \frac{u}{N} \frac{\partial}{\partial x} \left(c \frac{\partial \mu}{\partial x} \right). \qquad [7.16]$$

Thus for the steady state

$$c \frac{\partial \mu}{\partial x} = \text{const.} \qquad [7.16\,a]$$

and if both influences a. and b. come into play, we must rewrite [7.16]

$$\partial c/\partial t = \frac{1}{N} \frac{\partial}{\partial x} \left(u c \frac{\partial \mu}{\partial x} \right) \qquad [7.17]$$

u being the mobility of the diffusing particles (cf. p. 156). With $d\mu = RT \, d \log a = RT \, d \log \gamma c$ where $a =$ the activity, and $\gamma =$ the activity coefficient, we obtain from [7.16a]

$$c \frac{d \log a}{d x} = \left[1 + \frac{d \log \gamma}{d \log c} \right] \frac{d c}{d x} = \text{const.} \qquad [7.18]$$

The expression in brackets may be taken from experimental c-p relations, being equal to $d \log p/d \log c$. It accounts for part of the observed anomaly, but not for all of it. Consequently, eq. [7.17] must be applied, which, since $\partial c/\partial t = $ const. may also be written

$$D_0\left[1 + \frac{d \log \gamma}{d \log c}\right]\frac{dc}{dx} = \text{const.} \qquad [7.19]$$

from which D_0, which still depends on concentration, can be determined.

IV. Diffusion of gases through glasses and ionic crystals

Rayleigh (117, 118) found the permeability of a number of ionic crystals, (among them quartz, fluorite, rock salt), towards helium to be below the limit of sensitivity of the method employed, P being less than 10^{-9}. We give a few numerical values of permeation constants for glasses in Table XIV

TABLE XIV

$H_2\text{-}SiO_2$ (17)

Temp. °C	300	500	700	900		
$P \times 10^9$	0.48	1.72	4.25	6.72		

$He\text{-}SiO_2$ (17).

Temp. °C.	300	500	700	900		
$P \times 10^9$	0.099	0.70	2.52	6.4		

$N_2\text{-}SiO_2$ (17).

Temp. °C.			700	900		
$P \times 10^9$			0.15	0.95		

$He\text{-}Pyrex$ (151, 152).

Temp. °C.	0	100	200	300	400	500
$P \times 10^9$	0.0037	0.026	0.12	0.38	0.7	1.6

Where solubilities are known, permeation constants may be converted to diffusion coefficients, cf. eq. [7.4]. Barrer (1) gives the following expressions for diffusion coefficients, if expressed as functions of T by

$$D = D_0 \exp\left(-Q/RT\right)$$

He-SiO$_2$ (20°C.)	$D =$	(7.9 to 3.5) $\times 10^{-6} \exp\left(- 5{,}600/RT\right)$ cm.^{2} sec.$^{-1}$
He-SiO$_2$ (500°C.)	$D =$	(5.2 to 0.64) $\times 10^{-6} \exp\left(- 5{,}600/RT\right)$,, ,,
H$_2$-SiO$_2$ (500°C.)	$D =$	(8.3 to 14.5) $\times 10^{-6} \exp\left(- 10{,}100/RT\right)$,, ,,
H$_2$-SiO$_2$ (200°C.)	$D =$	(13.7 to 35) $\times 10^{-6} \exp\left(- 10{,}100/RT\right)$,, ,,
He-Pyrex (20°C.)	$D =$	$1.3 \times 10^{-6} \exp\left(- 8{,}700/RT\right)$,, ,,
He-Pyrex (500°C.)	$D =$	$5.5 \times 10^{-6} \exp\left(- 8{,}700/RT\right)$,, ,,

V. Diffusion in Zeolites*

Zeolites are silicate compounds, with a marked system of interstices, containing water molecules. Many zeolites may be dehydrated,

* cf. Barrer (1).

without a collapse of their lattice structure, and are then capable of taking up other compounds, especially gases und vapors. The diffusion process in zeolites, therefore, is of the interstitial type, not involving any mobility of the constituent particles of the crystals. Tiselius (146, 147, 148) carried out a thorough investigation of diffusion in zeolites, using the double refraction of light as a measure of the water content. The rate of diffusion in zeolites is rather high. Tiselius found, at room temperature, for water within the planes of the laminated structure of Heulandite, diffusion coefficients of some 10^{-7} cm.^{2} sec.$^{-1}$, while normal to these planes diffusion was quite slow, $D \approx 10^{-11}$ cm.^{2} sec.$^{-1}$. Within the planes, there is still a marked anisotropy, the ratio of D_{201}, normal to the 201 face, to D_{001}, normal to the 001 face, being about 12 to 20. The main axes of diffusion within the plane are almost parallel and normal to the 001 face, the ratio of the main diffusion coefficients is ~ 14.

The temperature dependence of D is seen from the following Table XV.

TABLE XV

°C.	$D_{201} \times 10^7$ cm.^{2} sec.$^{-1}$	$D_{001} \times 10^7$ cm.^{2} sec.$^{-1}$
20	2.7	0.23
33.8	4.1	0.45
46.1	4.8	0.66
60.0·	7.6	1.45
75.0	11.1	2.8

There is a marked dependence of D on the water content in the crystal. By means of the Boltzmann method, the following values were obtained.

Water content, per cent	10	12	14	16	18	19
$D \times 10^7$, cm.^{2} sec.$^{-1}$	(0.04)	0.7	2.0	3.6	4.0	3.3

The dependence on water concentration, exhibiting a maximum of D, is explained by the fact that the first molecules of water are absorbed with the greatest heat of sorption, and are, therefore, least mobile, while near saturation, the rate of solution must drop again, because the presence of vacant sites is necessary for migration.

Diffusion of ammonia in Analcite (147) is somewhat slower in speed than that of water in Heulandite, giving a D of 1.2×10^{-8} cm.^{2} sec.$^{-1}$ at 302°C.

The kinetics of the formation of zeolite solid solution has been further investigated by Barrer and Ibbitson (27). In preceding papers (19, 26) these authors had reported sorption measurements with zeolites of different types of lattice, with the following results.

a. Zeolites with pronounced three-dimensional network structure (chabazite, analcite) occluded polar and non polar gases.

b. Those of laminar network structures (heulandite), and,

c. those of fibrous network structures (natrolite, scolecite), occluded only polar molecules, but suffered considerable lattice changes during outgassing. Zeolites of type a. also dissolve long-chain hydrocarbons.

From a kinetic point of view, the authors divided the solute molecules into three groups

a. molecules dissolved extremely rapidly,

b. molecules dissolved slowly at room temperature,

c. molecules excluded from the zeolite lattice.

Small molecules fall into group a., e. g. O_2, H_2, N_2, He, A, CH_4, C_2H_6. They are absorbed so rapidly that the limiting factor might be the dissipation of the heat of absorption. Molecules with side chains, like iso-paraffins, and aromatic hydrocarbons belong to group c.

Those of group b, for example n-hydrocarbons, were most suitable for kinetic investigations.

During the initial stages of sorption, results could be approximated by a "parabolic" diffusion law

$$\frac{S_t - S_0}{S_\infty - S_0} = k \sqrt{t} \quad \text{or} \quad \frac{S_\infty - S_t}{S_\infty - S_0} = 1 - k \sqrt{t} \qquad [7.20]$$

valid within a range $1 > \dfrac{S_\infty - S_t}{S_\infty - S_0} > 0.8$, S being the amount of substance solved, the subscripts referring to t equal to 0, t, and ∞. The 'constant' k, determined from [7.20], decreased with increasing sorption. For the interstitial type of diffusion, as in the case of zeolites, diffusion constants should be proportional to the fraction of unoccupied sites, i.e., to $(1 - \theta)$, where θ is the fraction of occupied sites. For the probability of a particle finding an unoccupied neighboring site, into which it may jump, is proportional to this fraction.

The rate of sorption is found to increase with pressure according to a function quite analogous to that representing equilibrium solubility as function of pressure, Fig. 7-8. This might be expected, because the rate of diffusion into the solid phase should be proportional to the concentration established at the surface. It follows that at pressures where saturation is reached, the rate of sorption should become independent of pressure. The equation for diffusion into or out of a body of finite dimensions, for instance a plate (cf. Chap. I, p. 97) is

$$S_t = \delta c_0 \left\{ 1 - \frac{8}{\pi^2} \sum_{n=0}^{n=\infty} \frac{1}{(2n+1)^2} \exp\left[-\frac{(2n+1)^2 \pi^2 D t}{\delta^2} \right] \right\} \qquad [7.21]$$

where δ is the thickness of the plate, c_0 the equilibrium concentration at the surfaces $x = 0$ and $x = \delta$. S is the amount of substance sorbed per unit area of the plate. (The results for a cylinder or a sphere would be similar, cf. Chap. I, p. 37, 45. The amount of gas, sorbed for a constant time, therefore, is proportional to c_0, and c_0 is connected with the gas pressure by the equation

$$\frac{c}{(c_S - c)p} = K \qquad [7.22]$$

where c_S is the saturation concentration, and K the solubility constant. Consequently, the rate of sorption, if defined by S_τ/τ, for a constant value of τ, is proportional to the equilibrium concentration given by [7.22] as function of pressure. This, finally, gives

$$S_\tau/\tau \sim \frac{p}{1 + \alpha p} \qquad [7.23]$$

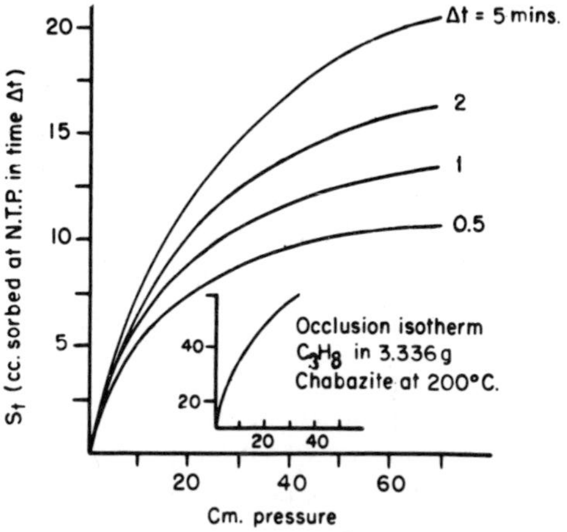

Fig. 7-8. Rate of absorption of propane by chabazite at 200°C., as function of pressure, after Barrer and Ibbitson. For comparison experimental absorption isotherm.

in accordance with observations.

The preceding argument needs some refinement. For, proportionality of the rate of diffusion with concentration is only to be expected in the case of ideal solutions. If, however, Henry's law does not hold, we certainly are no longer dealing with an ideal solution. The experiments are readily explicable by an antagonism of deviations from ideality of mobility and thermodynamic properties (28).

The heat of activation for sorption of hydrocarbons was determined either from the relation

$$\partial \log k / \partial (1/T) = - E/4.6\ R \qquad [7.24]$$

where k is the constant of the parabolic law, or from

$$\partial \log (1/\tau) / \partial (1/T) = - E/2.3\ R \qquad [7.25]$$

where τ is the time, necessary for the sorption of a given volume of gas. In the right-hand term of [7.24] the nominator contains an additional factor 2, because k of equation [7.20] is proportional to $\sqrt{D}$. Values of E, determined by both methods, are listed in Table XVI, taken from Barrer and Ibbitson (27).

TABLE XVI

Apparent Energies of Activation for Sorption by Analcite and Chabazite, from Barrer and Ibbitson (27)

Gas	Mineral	$Q*$ cal./mol	Temp. Range °C.	$Q**$	Temp. Range °C.	S_t***
HCl	Synthetic in-active Analcite	13,800	44.5—175.2	15,100	90.4—175.2	0.80
C_3H_8	Active Analcite	6,800	18 —135	7,300	18 —135	0.33
C_3H_8	Chabazite	4,500	22.7—224.7	6,700	39 —147.2	0.41
$n\text{-}C_4H_{10}$	Chabazite	8,900	22.7—155.5	8,600	22.7—155.5	0.41
$n\text{-}C_5H_{12}$	Chabazite	7,100	223.5—294.5	6,800	223.5—294.5	3.25
$n\text{-}C_7H_{16}$	Chabazite	11,100 11,400	182 —300 55.7—286.7	9,600	182.5—300	1.40

As Barrer and Ibbitson point out, the rate of sorption depends upon the cross section of the solute molecules. For methane and ethane, and for propane and iso-butane, respectively, the diameters corresponding to the cross section are 4.0, 4.89 and 5.58 Ångstroms. One may conclude, since iso-paraffins are not sorbed, that the narrowest cross section in the interstitial channels of both chabazite and analcite must lie between 4.89 and 5.58×10^{-8} cm.

VI. Diffusion of gases through metals

As with other membranes, the permeability of metals to gases is proportional to the solubility of these gases in the metal. A comprehensive treatment of gas solubilities in metals has been given by Smithells (9). The technique of permeation measurements is closely related to that described for organic membranes. Some experimental details will be found below. A survey of permeability constants, taken from Barrer (1), is given in Table XVII. Here the permeability is expressed as function of temperature by $P = P_0 \exp(-Q/RT)$, containing, of course, both the dependence on temperature of solubility and of the diffusion coefficient.

* Calculated from eq. [7.24].
**   ,,   ,, eq. [7.25].
*** cm.³ of gas at N.T.P. per gram of mineral.

TABLE XVII

Permeability data for gas-metal systems taken from Barrer (1),
$$P = P_0 \exp\left(-Q/RT\right)$$

System	P_o c. c. at N.T.P. per sec., cm.^{2} and mm. thickn. at atmosph. pressure	Q (cal./g. atom)	Author
H$_2$-Ni		14600, 13100 below Curie point	Post and Ham (115, 116)
		13100, 12040 above Curie point	Post and Ham (115, 116)
	1.3×10^{-2}	15420	Lombard (100)
	0.85×10^{-2}	13860	Deming and Hendricks (50)
	1.4×10^{-2}	13800	Borelius and Lindblom (33)
	1.05×10^{-2}	13400	Ham (70)
	1.44×10^{-2}	13260	Smithells and Ransley (135)
		13400	Post and Ham (116)
H$_2$-Pt-Ni		13400	Ham (70)
H$_2$-Pt	1.41×10^{-2}	19600	Richardson, Nicol, and Pornell (121)
	1.18×10^{-2}	18000	Ham (70)
	2.6×10^{-1}	19800	Jouan (86)
H$_2$-Ni-Pt		18000	Ham (70)
H$_2$-Mo	0.93×10^{-2}	20200	Smithells and Ransley (135)
H$_2$-Pd		5000	Melville and Rideal (105)
		17800	Melville and Rideal (105)
	2.3×10^{-1}	4620	Lombard, Eichner and Albert (102)
	3.0×10^{-2}	10500	Barrer (23)
H$_2$-Ni-Pd		14300	Melville and Rideal (105)
H$_2$-Cu	2.3×10^{-3}	16600	Smithells and Ransley (135)
	1.5×10^{-3}	18700	Braaten and Clark (34)
H$_2$-Cu-Pd		13700	Melville and Rideal (105)
		11400	Melville and Rideal (105)
H$_2$-Fe	1.63×10^{-3}	9600	Smithells and Ransley (135)
	1.60×10^{-3}	9400	Borelius and Lindblom (33)
	2.4×10^{-3}	11000	Ryder (125)
		8700 below 900°C.	Post and Ham (116)
		18860 above 900°C.	Post and Ham (116)
H$_2$-Al	3.3 —4.2	30800	Smithells and Ransley (136)
O$_2$-Ag	3.75×10^{-2}	22500	Spencer (138)
	2.06×10^{-2}	22600	Johnson and Larose (85)
N$_2$-Mo	8.3×10^{-2}	45000	Smithells and Ransley (135)
N$_2$-Fe	$4.5. \times 10^{-2}$	23800	Ryder (125)

The dependence of the rate of permeation on the pressure is often found to be proportional to $\sqrt{p}$, i.e., for pressures p_1 and p_2 ($p_1 > p_2$) applied to the faces of a membrane, the rate of permeation is

$$P = k\,(\sqrt{p_1} - \sqrt{p_2}) \qquad [7.26]$$

or, if p_2 is negligibly small

$$P = k\sqrt{p_1}. \qquad [7.27]$$

In accordance with this law, a linear relation is often found between rate of permeation P and the square root of the pressure p, the pressure at the low pressure face being kept at almost zero. This law, found for diatomic gases like H_2, O_2, N_2, indicates that not molecules, but rather free atoms, are diffusing through the metal, their equilibrium concentration being proportional to $\sqrt{p}$.

There are however exceptions to this relation. Thus for instance Smithells and Ransley (135) observed a linear relation between $\sqrt{p}$ and rate of permeation for sufficiently high pressures only, while for the lowest pressures employed, this relation breaks down. The range of validity of the linear relation extends to pressures which are lower, the higher the temperature of the experiments.

Ham (70, 71, 72, 73, 74) and co-workers observed that deviations from the square-root law occured with impure metals only, and attempted an explanation on this basis, attributing the deviations to a volume effect, see below. For at least part of the observation, the explanation, first put forward by Barrer (1), seems quite convincing. Permeation is a process consisting of at least three different stages. First transition from diatomic molecules in the gas phase to atoms, dissolved in the metal. Second diffusion of the dissolved atoms within the metal. And finally transition of these atoms at the low pressure side, into the gas phase, forming diatomic molecules again. The two phase boundary reactions may be of a composite nature themselves. The simple square root law can be expected to hold only if these reactions at phase boundaries are very fast compared with the diffusion through the membrane. Deviations will be the more marked the lower temperature. Since, further, it has been observed that the rate of permeation is highly dependent on previous surface treatment, it is seen that surface processes certainly do play a role in the observed permeation processes, cf. Table XVIII, after Smithells and Ransley (135).

As one might presume, this influence is more pronounced at low temperatures than at higher ones. There are large differences, too, between the rates of permeation, found by different observers for the same metal. These may be due at least partly to a different state of the surfaces. However, there is no doubt that the state of the metal

TABLE XVIII

Effect of surface treatment upon permeability (135)

Metal	Treatment	Temp.°K.	Pressure, mm. Hg	Permeation rate c.c. at N.T.P. per sec. per cm.^{2}, and mm. thickness
Ni	Polished	1023	0.042	1.39×10^{-6}
Ni	Oxidized and reduced . .	1023	0.042	2.70×10^{-6}
Ni	Polished	1023	0.091	2.91×10^{-6}
Ni	Oxidized and reduced . .	1023	0.091	4.23×10^{-6}
Fe	Polished	673	0.77	0.47×10^{-7}
Fe	Etched	673	0.77	$4.4 \ \times 10^{-7}$
Fe	Polished	863	0.073	1.28×10^{-7}
Fe	Oxidized and reduced at 600°C.	863	0.073	0.76×10^{-7}
Fe	Oxidized and reduced at 800° C.	863	0.073	1.54×10^{-7}

also influences the rate of diffusion. It is extremely difficult to eliminate such influences, because by the process of solution the lattice distances of the metals are increased, causing more or less severe strain. In diffusion measurements, carried out in the author's laboratory, with a palladium sphere of 30 mm diameter, this sphere was completely torn when a hydrogen pressure of a few hundred mm. Hg was applied to it. It afterwards exhibited large crevices, penetrating through almost the whole of the sphere.

Barrer (22) showed that great discontinuities in chemical potential may arise at the phase boundary during diffusion of gases through metals. Thus, for instance, for the H_2-Ni system, investigated by Smithells and Ransley (137) at pressures up to 112 atmospheres*, one has to assume that the concentration just inside the first surface was not near its saturation value. Barrer (23) was able to show from measurements of both the permeation constant and the coefficient of diffusion that in the system H_2-Pd the concentration gradient within the membrane was much smaller than calculated with equi-

---

* They found the square root law valid up to this pressure. Similar results, though for pressures up to 26 and 28 atmospheres only, were obtained by Lombard and Eichner (101) for H_2-Pd, and by Borelius and Lindblom (33) for H_2-Fe. A limiting velocity was observed with O_2-Ni, ascribed to the formation of an oxide layer (137). For hydrogen in quartz glass Wüstner (159) had found a linear dependance of the rate of permeation on pressure, up to 800 atmospheres.

librium concentrations. Table XIX, taken from Barrer's monograph, summarizes diffusion coefficients, and permeation constants for palladium of low (Barrer) and high permeability (Lombard and Eichner (101)) and concentration differences, derived from both sets of observations.

As in pure diffusion, cf. (78, 103, 107), there are differences in the rate of permeation of hydrogen and of deuterium through metals (62, 63, 105). There is agreement in the results of different observers that

TABLE XIX

Rate of Diffusion and Permeation in Palladium, and concentration differences, derived therefrom. (Barrer)

T°C.	D cm.^{2}/sec. $\times 10^5$	P^{**} (Barrer) $\times 10^5$	$c_1 - c_2$ (Barrer)	P (extrap. Lombard) $\times 10^3$	$c_1 - c_2$ (Lombard)	$c_1 - c_2$ (equilibrium)
350	6.8	0.65	0.73	0.84	11.8	12.0
334	5.4	0.52	0.73	0.78	12.6	12.5
310	3.7	0.366	0.75	0.70	16.5	13.6
272	2.0	0.193	0.74	—	—	—

** P c. c. at N.T.P. per second, cm.^{2}, mm. thickness and 1 cm. Hg pressure diff. c_1, c_2 concentrations, c. c. at N.T.P. per c. c. of metal.

the rate of permeation of hydrogen through palladium is higher than that of deuterium, the ratio P_H/P_D ranging from about 1.2 to 2.5, depending on temperature and observer. Since the rate of permeation depends on both solubility and diffusion coefficient, an unambiguous interpretation of the results is hardly possible. Also it is very difficult to distinguish between the influence of diffusion and reaction at the phase boundary (155) although attempts have been made to determine both influences separately. For the temperature dependence of the ratio P_H/P_D apparent heats of activation from about 400 to 1000 cal. have been found.

Ham (70—74) and co-workers obtained a high precision in permeation measurements with metals. They used the two methods described earlier (p. 285/6) as the trapping method and the steady state method. In the first method the pressure increase in a known volume at the low pressure side is measured by means of a McLeod gauge, while in the steady state method the pressure drop at the low pressure side, caused by a small aperture between diffusor and pump, is measured. The latter method gives only relative values, but the authors reached a high precision in these relative measurements.

Employing this method, they carried out measurements with oxygen free copper. The metal was welded to the inside of a nickel tube under an atmosphere of hydrogen, and then a closed end tube was formed by boring in a lathe. The thickness of the walls was about 0.067″. Spectroscopic analysis of the finished diffusor showed no evidence of oxygen, nickel or iron.

The authors could represent their permeation data by a relation

$$P = A\, p^y\, T^{1/2} \exp\left(-\,b/T\right)$$

where $y = 0.50 \pm 0.01$. They suggest that the exponent of T is accurate to within 0.2, i.e., 0.5 ± 0.2. b is equal to $3{,}780 \times 2.3 = 8{,}700°K$, or 17,400 cal./g atom in the formula $\exp\left(-Q/RT\right)$. The measurements ranged from 450 to 1050°C. The assumption that oxygen was responsible for anomalies in the permeation isotherms, otherwise observed, was shown to be correct by special experiments, where oxygen had been admitted to the copper.

These observations, however, do not rule out the explanation, given by Barrer, that the surface is responsible for the observed deviations. The fact that exclusion of mercury vapor, particularly at the entrance side, was necessary, might also point in the same direction.

For the determination of diffusion coefficients of gases in metals there are essentially two methods available, that of Daynes (47) and Barrer (1, 20, 22, 23), and the determination of the rate of sorption or desorption of gases by metals.

The former method permits of a calculation of the diffusion coefficient from the time lag involved in the establishment of a steady state of flow through a membrane, cf. Chap. I, provided reactions at phase boundaries can be considered as infinitely fast. Permeability data may be evaluated where solubilities have been measured, as in the case of hydrogen-palladium, p. 308, 311.

The formulae applying to the diffusion out of a slab, cylinder or sphere have been brought into a convenient approximate form by van Liempt (99). We give his formula for a plate. The solution of the diffusion equation for a semi-infinite solid is, when the surface concentration is kept constant at c_0, cf. Chap. I, Fig. 7-9.

$$\frac{c}{c_0} = 1 - erf\left(\frac{x}{2\sqrt{Dt}}\right). \tag{7.28}$$

The area enclosed by the curve $c_0/\sqrt{\pi}$, Fig. 7-9, is equal to that of the triangle with corners at the origin, at $c/c_0 = 1$ and at $x/2\sqrt{Dt} = a/2\sqrt{Dt} = 2/\sqrt{\pi} = 1.13$. a is called apparent penetration depth or apparent out-gassing depth, depending on the process under consideration. For a plate of thickness d and breadth b, the amount of gas evolved per cm. length is

$$s = 2 \times \frac{1}{2}\, c_0\, a\, b \tag{7.29}$$

since the plate has two sides, provided a is sufficiently small compared with $d/2$. The total quantity, originally absorbed, is

$$s_0 = c_0\, db \qquad\qquad\qquad [7.30]$$

thus

$$s/s_0 = a/d = 4\sqrt{Dt/\pi}/d \qquad\qquad [7.31]$$

from which D is easily calculated.

For the diffusion coefficient of hydrogen in nickel, Euringer (59) found by outgassing nickel wires (cf. Barrer (1))

$$D = 2.04\times 10^{-3}\exp\left(-18{,}700/RT\right).$$

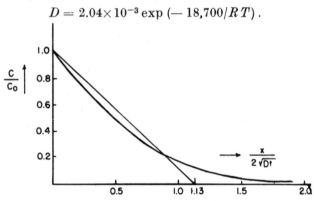

Fig. 7-9. Evaluation of diffusion constants from absorption (or desorption) measurements, after van Liempt. (Straight line passing through $x/2\sqrt{Dt} = 2/\sqrt{\pi}$).

Edwards' (58) measurements on the rate of permeation of nascent hydrogen through iron have been evaluated by Barrer (1), using the time lag method. The values obtained are

°C.	10	20	40	50	75	100
D cm.^{2} sec^{-1}	1.66×10^{-9}	2.59×10^{-9}	6.68×10^{-9}	1.14×10^{-8}	2.87×10^{-8}	1.24×10^{-7}

In Table XX we reproduce some values of diffusion coefficients for hydrogen in palladium, summarized by Barrer (1).

TABLE XX

Diffusion constants of H in Pd, $D = D_0 \exp\left(-Q/RT\right)$

Method	D cm.^{2} sec.$^{-1}$	Author
Time lag	$2.5\times10^{-1}\exp\left(-10{,}100/RT\right)$	Barrer (1, 20, 22)
Rate of absorption and desorption .	$5.4\times10^{-3}\exp\left(-5{,}740/RT\right)$	Jost and Widmann (87, 88)
Rate of absorption .	$2.6\times10^{-2}\exp\left(-7{,}400/RT\right)$	Tammann and Schneider (142)
E.M.F. of wire . . .	$7.4\times10^{-1}\exp\left(-7{,}200/RT\right)$	Coehn and Specht (40)

Jost and Widmann (87, 88) measured the rate of absorption and desorption of hydrogen and of deuterium by palladium using two different spheres of 15 and of 30 mm. diameter, respectively. To avoid disturbances by phase boundary reaction, the surfaces of the spheres were coated with palladium black, to increase the rate of the reaction H_2 (or D_2) gas $\rightarrow H$ (or D) dissolved in palladium. Since there is very good agreement between observed rates of sorption and theoretical curves, computed by means of eq. [1.176], p. 46, it was assumed that the influence of phase boundary reactions had been practically eliminated.

The sphere hung in a glass tube, heated by an electric furnace, which could be connected either to a vacuum pump or to a series of storage vessels with hydrogen or deuterium at various pressures, below 1 atmosphere. The rate of sorption or desorption was determined from the rate of pressure change, this being kept small compared with the absolute pressures involved. The gas bulbs of known volume were kept in a water thermostat; the maximum volume available, when all bulbs were connected, was 18 liters. For pressure measurements a quartz spiral manometer, of about $^1/_{25}$ mm. Hg sensitivity, and two differential manometers, filled with apiezon oil were available, one of these inclined to increase the sensitivity. The sensitivities were 3×10^{-3} and 6×10^{-3} mm. Hg. For experiments with fairly rapid change of pressure the oil manometers could not be used, on account of the time lag caused by the high viscosity of the oil.

Using for evaluation the equation

$$\frac{\bar{c}-c_f}{c_i-c_f} = \frac{6}{\pi^2} \sum_{n=1}^{n=\infty} \frac{1}{n^2} \exp\left(-n^2 t/\tau\right) \qquad \tau = r_0^2/\pi^2 D \qquad [7.32]$$

where $\bar{c}$ is the average concentration in the sphere, c_i and c_f are the initial and final concentrations, r_0 is the radius of the sphere and D the diffusion coefficient (cf. Chap. I, p. 46), the most rational procedure was as follows. By plotting $\log \dfrac{\bar{c}-c_f}{c_i-c_f}$ versus t, curves like that shown in Fig. 7-10 were obtained. From the slope of the almost straight part of the curve a preliminary value of τ was taken. Starting with this value a theoretical curve according to [7.32] was drawn, the value of τ was improved by trial and error until the whole curve fitted the experiments. As is seen from

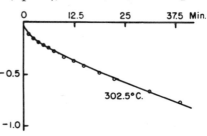

Fig. 7-10. Rate of absorption of hydrogen by palladium sphere, after Jost and Widmann. $\log_{10} \dfrac{\bar{c}-c_f}{c_i-c_f}$ versus time, c concentration of H in Pd.

Fig. 7-10 this agreement is very close, indicating that disturbances due to boundary reactions should be very small. The procedure, as outlined above, leads to better values of D than that based upon the evaluation of the straight part only, because, for higher values of t, pressure changes are very small, the most reliable experimental points being just those corresponding to the first curved part of the plot. Therefore points corresponding to $\log \dfrac{\bar{c} - c_f}{c_i - c_f} < -0.8$ were discarded in the evaluation.

The results obtained with H in a sphere for which $r_0 = 0.75$ cm. are as follows,

°C.	302.5.	248.5	192.5
$D_{obs.}$	3.95	2.43	1.21×10^{-5} cm.^{2} sec.$^{-1}$
$D_{calc.}$	4.02	2.38	1.21×10^{-5} cm.^{2} sec.$^{-1}$

The calculated values are given by

$$D = 5.95 \times 10^{-3} \exp\left(- 5{,}720/RT\right) \text{ cm.}^2 \text{sec.}^{-1}. \qquad [7.33]$$

The results for deuterium, of about 95 per cent purity, were as follows

°C.	302.5	192.5
$D_{obs.}$	3.01	0.97×10^{-5} cm.^{2} sec.$^{-1}$
D_H/D_D	1.31	1.25×10^{-5} cm.^{2} sec.$^{-1}$

Correcting for the fact that the deuterium employed was not 100 % pure, one obtains as an average for the ratio of the diffusion constants for hydrogen and deuterium

$$D_H/D_D \approx 1.31$$

which still is smaller than the ratio of the mean thermal velocities $\sqrt{2} = 1.41$.

Results with the larger sphere of 30 mm. diameter are similar, though they exhibit some systematic differences which cannot be due to the difference in diameter or to the experimental technique employed. From the very good agreement, within a single experiment, between observed and calculated values of $\log \dfrac{\bar{c} - c_f}{c_i - c_f}$ one may estimate that the accuracy achieved was about ± 2 per cent, while deviations between the two sets of experiments are much larger, viz. about 50 per cent. This difference cannot be due to accidental errors but must be attributed to differences in the properties of the palladium metal, caused either by the presence of small impurities, or by influences of methat chanical treatment. It is known from Tammann's (142) experiments diffusion in hard, rolled palladium is much faster than in soft, annealed metal. In the present experiments the metal had been annealed for a long time at temperatures above those of the experiments to be carried out. But even if any strain present in the metal had been removed by the treatment, the process of dissolution must have caused new strains. For, the lattice constant of palladium containing dissolved hydrogen is higher than that of pure palladium; the so called β-phase of the palladium hydrogen solid solution, containing about 1 atom of hydrogen per two atoms of the metal, has a lattice constant about 10 per cent higher than that of pure palladium.

It has been mentioned elsewhere (p. 307) that saturation of the 30 mm. sphere with hydrogen in the course of three weeks, up to a content of 6.06 l. hydrogen at N.T.P., corresponding to the composition $PdH_{0.54}$, resulted in rupture of the sphere. Other types of disturbances were observed incidentally. Thus a drop of the apparent diffusion constant of deuterium to about $1/4$ its original value could be traced to the leakage of a stopcock, $3/4$ per cent of air being present in the deuterium. This was probably a surface influence.

After the palladium sphere had been ruptured, of course, further measurements were impossible. It seems noteworthy, however, that the first experiments after this accident, which led to its detection, gave an apparent ratio of D_H/D_D only slightly above 1. The rate of diffusion in the hydrogen rich β-phase is certainly of the same order of magnitude as that in the α-phase.

The results obtained with the larger sphere can be represented by

$$D_H = 8.43 \times 10^{-3} \exp (- 5\ 720/R\,T) \text{ cm.}^2 \text{ sec.}^{-1}$$

$$D_D = 6.70 \times 10^{-3} \exp (- 5\ 720/R\,T) \text{ cm.}^2 \text{ sec.}^{-1}$$

the ratio D_H/D_D being somewhat smaller than in the former experiments. The higher values within the new set of experiments are somewhat more probable than the lower ones, owing to the greater number of single observations.

An unambiguous theoretical explanation of the results obtained, is impossible. The simplest kinetic theory of diffusion (cf. Chap. X, p. 417 ff.) suggests that D is proportional to the mean thermal velocity of the diffusing particles, giving for the ratio $D_H/D_D = \sqrt{2} = 1.41$, which, within the limits of error, seems compatible with the present results. However there should be a difference in zero point energies of hydrogen and of deuterium in the palladium lattice, favoring the diffusion of hydrogen and giving rise to a temperature dependent factor which should cause differences in the heats of activation for hydrogen and deuterium.

The transition state theory permits a theoretical treatment to be made agreeing with the above results, but this, however, seems unsatisfactory, because the magnitudes referring to the transition state simply have to be chosen in such a way as to fit the experiments. If one assumes that hydrogen, dissolved in palladium, occupies those interstitial sites in the face centred palladium lattice, which, when occupied, would give the rock salt lattice, hydrogen atoms on their way from one equilibrium position to the nearest one would have to pass through the centre of a tetrahedron composed of palladium atoms. Here the distance to the nearest palladium atoms is shorter than in the equilibrium position, and it might be possible that the vibration frequencies for the coordinates normal to the reaction coordinate are so much higher than in the normal state, that the contribution of these two degrees of freedom compensates that of the three degrees of freedom in the normal state.

VII. The rate of escape of emanation from solids

Only a fraction of the emanation, formed by the disintegration of radioactive substances within solids, is given off to the outside; the remainder is undergoing decay within the solid. The fraction which escapes depends on the grain size and temperature of the solid containing the radioactive substance. This was first tested by Rutherford (124), with emanation from thorium hydroxide, cf. also Kolowrat (91, 92, 93). The method has chiefly been developed and applied by O. Hahn (3), since 1923, cf. also Zimens (161—164). A thorough theoretical investigation of the rate of escape of emanation from solids is due to Flügge and Zimens (66).

Their calculations are based upon the following model. The solid is assumed to consist of homogeneous grains of spherical shape. The emission of a single grain is given by two contributions, a surface emission, ε_r, due to the fact that the newly formed atoms of emanation have a finite recoil range, R, allowing a certain fraction of the atoms, formed within a distance R from the surface, to escape to the outside, and a contribution of diffusion, ε_D, accounting for the emanation atoms passing through the surface by diffusion.

The emission of emanation is defined as the fraction of the emanation atoms, generated per unit time, which escape through the surface. Further, the establishment of a stationary state is assumed, i.e., we assume a constant concentration C of the parent substance within the grain, for instance of radium or of thorium X, and a stationary concentration c of the emanation within the grain. This stationary concentration is not completely determined by the constants of decay for the parent substance, Λ, and for the emanation, λ, but also depends on the rate of escape of the emanation from the grains. Consequently, we shall obtain a solution for the stationary state, independent of time, but depending on the distance r from the center of the grain, having a total radius r_0. For geometrical reasons, exactly one half of the emanation atoms, generated within the surface will escape, the other half being rejected back into the grain. Of the atoms formed within a shell of thickness R, the range of recoil, only a fraction $< 1/2$ will be able to escape. A simple geometrical reasoning leads to the following expression for the fraction of atoms, formed within a layer at r $(r > r_0 - R)$, which escape

$$q(r) = \frac{2r\,R - (r_0{}^2 - R^2) + r^2}{4\,R\,r}.$$ [7.35]

The total number of atoms, escaping by recoil, N_r, will be

$$N_r = c\,\varLambda\,4\,\pi \int_{r_0-R}^{r_0} q(r)\,r^2\,dr = C\,\varLambda\,\pi\left(r_0^2\,R - \frac{1}{12}\,R^3\right)$$ [7.36]

where $c\varLambda$ is the number of emanation atoms generated per cm.³ and second. Dividing by $^4/_3\,\pi\,r_0^3 c\varLambda$, the total number of emanation atoms formed per second, we obtain for the fraction, ε_r, which is emitted due to recoil

$$\varepsilon_r = \frac{3}{4}\frac{R}{r_0} - \frac{1}{16}\left(\frac{R}{r_0}\right)^3 \quad \text{for} \quad 2r_0 \geq R$$ [7.37]

the latter condition being necessary, because for grains of radius $r_0 < R/2$, every emanation atom will escape by recoil. Since R is of the order of magnitude of 10^{-6} cm., the equation holds down to about this grain size. For grains of radius sufficiently large compared with R, the second term in [7.37] may be neglected. One may easily derive the equations for grains of different shape.

The number of particles, leaving the grain per second by diffusion, is

$$N_D = -D\,4\pi\,r_0^2\,(\partial c/\partial r)_{r=r_0}.$$ [7.38]

Hence the concentration gradient in the surface must be determined. $c(r)$ must satisfy the differential equation

$$\partial c/\partial t = 0 = D\varDelta c + \varLambda C - \lambda c - \varLambda C q(r)$$ [7.39]

since we have assumed a stationary state. In [7.39], with $\varDelta$ Laplace operator, the first term is the contribution of diffusion, the second the rate of generation of the emanation, the third that of the decay of the emanation, while the last term represents the rate of escape due to recoil. $q(r)$ is given by [7.35] for $r_0 - R \leq r \leq r_0$, while for $r \leq r_0 - R$ we have $q = 0$.

The solution of the homogeneous differential equation is

$$c = \frac{a_1}{r} \sinh \sqrt{\frac{\lambda}{D}}\,r + \frac{a_2}{r} \cosh \sqrt{\frac{\lambda}{D}}\,r \quad \text{for} \quad 0 < r \leq r_0 - R$$ [7.40]

and, for $0 \leq r \leq r_0 - R$, a particular integral of the inhomogeneous equation is $c = \Lambda c / \lambda$, Thus one arrives at the integral for the inner region

$$c = \frac{\Lambda C}{\lambda} - \frac{c_0}{r} \sinh \sqrt{\frac{\lambda}{D}} \, r \qquad [7.41]$$

c_0 being a constant of integration. In the outer shell, $r_0 - R \leq r \leq r_0$, $q(r) \neq 0$, and the solution obtained is

$$c = \frac{\Lambda C}{4 \lambda R} \left\{ \frac{r_0^2 - R^2}{r} - \frac{2 D}{\lambda r} + 2 R - r \right\} + \frac{c_1}{r} \sinh \sqrt{\frac{\lambda}{D}} r + \frac{c_2}{r} \cosh \sqrt{\frac{\lambda}{D}} r \quad [7.42]$$

c_0, c_1, c_2 being integration constants which must be determined from the condition that c and $\partial c / \partial r$ are continuous at $r = r_0 - R$. The third condition is $c(r_0) = 0$, i.e., the emanation concentration in the surface is zero, provided that all the escaping emanation is carried off by a gas stream.

The emission coefficient, ε_d, is finally obtained in the form

$$\varepsilon_D = \frac{3}{2 \, y^2} \left\{ \frac{1}{x} - \frac{1}{x} \frac{\sinh y \, (1 - x)}{\sinh y} - 1 \right\}$$
$$+ \frac{3}{2 \, y} \left\{ \left(1 - \frac{x}{2} - \frac{1}{x \, y^2} \right) \coth y + \frac{1}{x \, y^2} \frac{\cosh y \, (1 - x)}{\sinh y} \right\}. \qquad [7.43]$$

Here the following dimensionless magnitudes have been introduced

$$x = \frac{R}{r_0}, \quad y = r_0 \sqrt{\lambda / D}. \qquad [7.44]$$

[7.43] is applicable when $2 r_0 > R$. Some simple limiting cases may be mentioned

$$y \, (1 - x) \gg 1 \quad \text{and} \quad y \gg 1$$

$$\varepsilon_d = \frac{3}{2 \, y^2} \left\{ (y - 1) \left[1 + \frac{1}{x \, y} - \frac{1}{x \, y} \exp \, (- x \, y) \right] - \frac{1}{2} x \, y \right\}, \qquad [7.45]$$

$$x \ll 1$$

$$\varepsilon_d = \frac{3}{y} [\coth y - 1/y], \qquad [7.46]$$

$$y > 3 \qquad\qquad\qquad y \gg 3$$

$$\varepsilon_d = \frac{3}{y} \left(1 - \frac{1}{y} \right) \quad \text{and} \quad \varepsilon_d = \frac{3}{y}. \qquad [7.47]$$

In the latter case the total emission is given by

$$\varepsilon = \varepsilon_r + \varepsilon_d = 3 \left(\frac{x}{4} + \frac{1}{y} \right). \qquad [7.48]$$

A graphical representation of [7.47] is found in the paper by Flügge and Zimens (66). The authors also discuss the mutual influence of the grains, because recoil atoms from one grain may enter a neighboring grain and stick there.

It is possible to determine ε_r and ε_d separately from experiments carried out with two different emanations, for instance with radon and with thoron. For experimental details we refer to the original paper.

From measured values of the emissivity, ε, we obtain values for x and y. Thus, finally, from [7.44] the radius r_0 of the grains and the diffusion coefficient D of the emanation within the grains may be determined. When radon and thoron are used, the following relations hold

$$x_{\mathrm{Rn}} = 0.69 \, x_{\mathrm{Tn}} \qquad y_{\mathrm{Tn}} = 77.8 \, y_{\mathrm{Rn}} \,. \qquad [7.49]$$

The range of the emanation recoil atoms is of the order of 3×10^{-6} cm. For small values of ε_D we obtain for D from [7.47]

$$D = r_0^2 \, \varepsilon_D \, \lambda / 9 \,. \qquad [7.50]$$

ε_d can only be measured if it is not negligibly small compared with ε_r. Thus we must have approximately $\varepsilon_D > 10^{-2} \, \varepsilon_r$, or, from eq. [7.47], neglecting the second term on the right

$$\varepsilon_D > \frac{3}{4} \frac{R}{r_0} 10^{-2} \quad \text{or} \quad D > 10^{-4} \, R^2 \, \lambda / 16 \,. \qquad [7.51]$$

For radon λ is equal to 2×10^{-6} sec.$^{-1}$. With an average range of $R \approx 3 \times 10^{-6}$ cm., we obtain

$$D > 10^{-22} \, \text{cm.}^2 \, \text{sec.}^{-1} \,. \qquad [7.52]$$

Thus diffusion coefficients can be measured which are smaller than most values accessible by other methods. The authors give a table from which D values, for different values of ε between 10^{-2} and 9×10^{-1}, and grain radii between 10^{-1} and 10^{-5}, may be derived.

Measurement of the temperature dependence of the emission leads to very interesting results, provided that influences due to a change of structure of the substances employed, have been eliminated by previous annealing. When $\log D$ or $\log y$ (cf. eq. [7.44]) is plotted versus $1/T$, one should obtain straight lines the slope of which gives an activation energy E. For CaO, $BaCO_3$ and $SrCO_3$ the emanation method gives E values between 30,000 and 60,000 cal./mol. In Fig. 7-11 we reproduce some values obtained by Cook (44) with Fe_2O_3. Here $\log y$ is plotted against $1/T$. It is seen that for sufficiently high temperatures a linear relationship is obtained, corresponding to

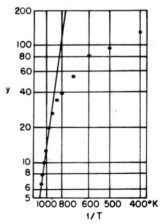

Fig. 7-11.
Rate of escape of emanation from Fe_2O_3, after Cook.

an energy of activation of the order of magnitude of 39,500 cal./mol. For lower temperatures deviations from the straight line relationship are considerable, being in the same direction as those encountered in measurements of electrolytic conductivity at low temperatures. The diffusion coefficients at low temperatures turn out to be much higher than the values gained by extrapolation from high temperatures, the temperature coefficient, at the same time, being much lower. We may explain the observations in the following manner. At high temperatures some type of disorder, present in equilibrium, is responsible for the observed diffusion. The exponential term, representing the dependence on temperature, contains an energy of disorder, E_1,* and an energy barrier, $\exp\left(-(E_1 + U)/RT\right)$. For the lowest temperatures under consideration, equilibrium of disorder is not established; disorder has been frozen in at some higher temperature, T_0, therefore the resulting exponential expression is

$$\exp\left(-E_1/RT_0\right)\exp\left(-U/RT\right)$$

the first term being a constant, the second one determining the dependence on temperature. In a transition region around T_0, equilibrium of disorder may be partly established, depending on the rate of cooling. In the experiments of Cook, quoted above, the temperature T_0 is of the order of magnitude of 960°K. The following diffusion coefficients have been calculated from Cook's observations

T °K	293	400	600	800	1000	1075
$D\,\mathrm{cm.^2sec^{-1}}$.	7.5×10^{-16}	1.5×10^{-15}	5×10^{-15}	2.3×10^{-14}	3.1×10^{-13}	1.2×10^{-12}

It is a serious disadvantage of the emanation method that it gives diffusion coefficients of a foreign substance only, those of the emanation within the lattice under consideration, and not diffusion coefficients of some component of the solid. It would be much more interesting to have data referring to the constituents of the lattice. Flügge and Zimens give the following estimate of coefficients of self diffusion, derived from values of the temperature T_0, at which equilibrium of disorder has been frozen out. T_0 is identical with Tammann's (141) so called "place exchange" temperature, a temperature for which the coefficient of self diffusion has become sufficiently large to allow of an average displacement of the order of magnitude of the lattice constant ($\sim 3 \times 10^{-8}$ cm.) within a reasonable time (10 to 10^3 sec.). Thus D_0 at T_0 will be of the order of magnitude

$$D_0 \approx (3 \times 10^{-8})^2 / 10^2 \approx 10^{-17} \text{ cm.}^2 \text{ sec.}^{-1}. \qquad [7.53]$$

* Or a fraction thereof (cf. Chap. II, p. 95 ff.).

Assuming that D may be represented*, within an accuracy of ± 2 in its common logarithm, by

$$D \approx 10^{-4} \left(\frac{E_0}{RT}\right)^{3/2} \exp\left(-E_0/RT\right) \qquad [7.54]$$

we obtain, by inserting D_0 and T_0 in [7.54], the equation for the determination of E_0

$$10^{-17} \approx 10^{-4(\pm 2)} \left(\frac{E_0}{RT_o}\right)^{3/2} \exp\left(-E_0/RT_0\right) . \qquad [7.55]$$

In the above example of Fe_2O_3 we thus find for E_0

$$E_0 \approx 66{,}000 \pm 9{,}000 \text{ cal./mol.} \qquad [7.56]$$

The heat of activation, determined in this way for self diffusion, is considerably higher than that for the diffusion of the emanation. If [7.55] is taken as the relation defining Tammann's T_0 we have

$$E_0 \approx (35 \pm 5)\,RT_0 . \qquad [7.57]$$

This estimate is consistent with other results. Tammann found, if T_m is the temperature of the melting point of salts and oxides, that $T_0 \approx 1/2\,T_m$, while for metals $T_0 \approx 1/3\,T_m$. In the case of Fe_2O_3 we have $T_0/T_m = 960/1838 = 0.52$ in agreement with Tammann's rule. For metals it follows with $T_0 \approx 1/3\,T_m$, that $E_0 \approx 11\,RT_m$, in agreement with a number of observations (cf. Chap. V, Tables XIV, XV).

Flügge and Zimens also have treated non stationary processes in emission of emanation for which we refer to the original paper.

REFERENCES

Monographs and Review Articles

1. Barrer, R. M., Diffusion in and through solids. Cambridge University Press, 1941.
2. Glasstone, S., Laidler, K. J., and Eyring, H., Theory of Rate Processes. McGraw Hill, New York 1941.
3. Hahn, O., Applied Radiochemistry. Cornell University Press, Ithaka, 1936.
4. McBain, J. W., Sorption of Gases by Solids. Routledge 1932.
5. Manegold, E., Kolloid-Z. 82, 26, 135, 269 (1938).
6. Manegold, E., Kolloid-Z. 83, 146, 299 (1938).
7. Mark, H., and Proskauer, E. S., The Science of Plastics. Vol. 1. Interscience Publishing Co., New York 1948.
8. Müller, F. H., Physik und Kolloidstruktur, in Houwink R., Chemie und Technologie der Kunststoffe, 2nd ed. Vol. 1, Leipzig, 1942.

* We do not consider the special temperature function, chosen by Flügge and Zimens, as justified, since it has been derived from Maxwell's distribution function for gases. But owing to the uncertainties entering the result anyway, there is no serious objection to the use of this formula as an approximation.

9. Smithells, C. J., Gases and Metals. Chapman and Hall, London 1937.
10. West, C. J., Kunz, W. B., and Sears, G. R., Permeability of Organic Materials to Gases. Appleton, Wisconsin 1948.

General Bibliography

11. Aiken, W. H., Doty, P. M., and Mark, H., *Modern Packaging* **45**, 137, 166/8 (1945).
12. Van Amerongen, G. J., Comm. No. 46. *Rubber-Stickling Rev. Gén. caoutchouc* **21**, 50 (1944).
13. Van Amerongen, G. J., *J. Applied Phys.* **17**, 972 (1946).
14. Van Amerongen, G. J., *J. Polymer Sci.* **2**, 381 (1947).
15. Andrew, J. H., Lee, H., Lloyd, H. K., and Stevenson, N., *J. Iron and Steel Inst.* **156**, 208 (1947).
16. Badum, E., and Leilich, K., Felten and Guillaume, Carlswerk Rundschau no. 22 (1938).
17. Barrer, R. M., *J. Chem. Soc. London* **1934**, 378.
18. Barrer, R. M., *Proc. Roy. Soc. (London)* **A 167**, 392 (1938).
19. Barrer, R. M., *Proc. Roy. Soc. (London)* **A 167**, 406 (1938).
20. Barrer, R. M., *Trans. Faraday Soc.* **35**, 628 (1939).
21. Barrer, R. M., *Trans. Faraday Soc.* **35**, 644 (1939).
22. Barrer, R. M., *Phil. Mag.* **28**, 148 (1939).
23. Barrer, R. M., *Trans. Faraday Soc.* **36**, 1235 (1940).
24. Barrer, R. M., *Trans. Faraday Soc.* **36**, 644 (1940).
25. Barrer, R. M., *Trans. Faraday Soc.* **38**, 322 (1942).
26. Barrer, R. M., and Ibbitson, D. A., *Trans. Faraday Soc.* **40**, 195 (1944).
27. Barrer, R. M., and Ibbitson, D. A., *Trans. Faraday Soc.* **40**, 206 (1944).
28. Barrer, R. M., and Jost, W., *Trans. Faraday Soc.* **45**, 928 (1949).
29. Barrer, R. M., and Riley, D. W., *J. Chem. Soc. London* **1948**, 133.
30. Barrer, R. M. and Skirrow, G. J., *J. Polymer Sci.* **3**, 549 (1948).
30a. Boger, R. F., *J. Applied Phys.* **20**, 540 (1949).
30b. Barrer, R. M., and Skirrow, G., *Rubber Chem. and Technol.* **22**, 427 (1949).
30c. Barrer, R. M., *Kolloid Z.* **120**, 177 (1951).
31. de Boer, J. H. and Fast, J. D., *Rev. Trav. Chim. Pays-Bas* **57**, 317 (1938).
32. Boggs, C. and Blake, J., *Ind. Eng. Chem.* **18**, 224 (1926).
33. Borelius, C. and Lindblom, S., *Ann d. Physik* **82**, 201 (1927).
34. Braaten, E. and Clark, G., *Proc. Roy. Soc. (London)* **A 153**, 504 (1936).
35. Bradley, R. S., *Trans. Faraday Soc.* **33**, 1185 (1937).
36. Brooks, S. C., *Ann. Rev. Physiol.* **7**, 1 (1943).
37. Brüning, H. and Sieverts, A., *Z. physik. Chem.* **A 163**, 409 (1933).
38. Carpenter, A. S., *Trans. Faraday Soc.* **43**, 529 (1947).
39. Carson, F., *Misc. Publ. U. S. Bur. Stand.* **M 127** (1937).
40. Coehn, A., and Specht, W., *Z. Physik* **62**, 1 (1930).
41. Coehn, A., and Jürgens, H., *Z. Physik* **71**, 179 (1931).
42. Coehn, A., and Sperling, K., *Z. Physik* **83**, 291 (1933).
43. Coehn, A., *Z. Elektrochem.* **35**, 676 (1935).
44. Cook, L. G., *Z. phys. Chem.* **B 42**, 221 (1939).
44a. Crank, J., and Park, G. S., *Trans. Faraday Soc.* **45**, 240 (1949); ibid. **46**, 684 (1950).
45. Custers, J. F. H., *J. Polymer. Sci.* **2**, 301 (1947).
46. Darken, L. S. and Smith, R. P., *Corrosion* **5**, 1 (1949).
47. Daynes, H., *Proc. Roy. Soc. (London)* **A 97**, 286 (1920).

48. Deeg, G. jr., *Bell Lab. Record* **25,** 227 (1947).
49. Deeg, G. jr., and Frosch, C. J., *A. S. T. M. Symposium on Plastics* **1944,** 47.
50. Deming, H. and Hendricks, B., *J. Amer. Chem. Soc.* **45,** 2857 (1923).
51. Doty, P. M., *J. Chem. Phys.* **14,** 244 (1946).
52. Doty, P. M., Aiken, W. H., and Mark, H., *Ind. Eng. Chem. Anal. Ed.* **16,** 686 (1944).
53. Doty, P. M., Aiken, W. H., and Mark, H., *Ind. Eng. Chem.* **38,** 788 (1946).
54. Duhm, B., *Z. Physik* **94,** 434 (1935).
55. Duhm, B., *Z. Physik* **95,** 801 (1935).
56. Dünwald, H., and Wagner, C., *Z. physik. Chem.* **B 24,** 53 (1934).
57. Eastwood, L. W., *Light Metal Age* **4,** 10 (1946).
58. Edwards, C. A., *J. Iron and Steel Inst.* **60,** 9 (1929).
59. Euringer, G., *Z. Physik* **96,** 37 (1935).
60. Ewell, R. H., *J. Applied Physics* **9,** 252 (1938).
61. Eyring, H., *J. Chem. Phys.* **4,** 283 (1936).
62. Farkas, A., and Farkas, F., *Proc. Roy. Soc. (London)* **A 144,** 467 (1934).
63. Farkas, A., *Trans. Faraday Soc.* **32,** 1667 (1936).
64. Fast, J. D., *Philips techn. Rundschau* **6,** 369 (1941).
65. Fischer, Ch., and Müller, F. H., *Kolloid-Z.* **101,** 43 (1942).
66. Flügge, S., and Zimens, K. E., *Z. physik. Chem.* **B 42,** 179 (1939).
67 a. Grün, F., *Rubber Chem. and Technol.* **22,** 316 (1949). (Diffusion in rubber)
67. Gillespie, L. J. G., and Downs, W. R., *J. Amer. Chem. Soc.* **61,** 2496 (1939).
68. Haegel, J., *Helv. Chim. Acta* **27,** 1669 (1944).
69. Hagen, H., and Sieverts, A., *Z. physik. Chem.* **A 165,** 1 (1933).
70. Ham, W. R., *J. Chem. Phys.* **1,** 476 (1933).
71. Ham, W. R., *J. Chem. Phys.* **7,** 903 (1939).
72. Ham, W. R., *Am. Soc. Metals* **25,** 536 (1937).
73. Ham, W. R., and Rast, W., *Am. Soc. Metals* **26,** 885 (1938).
74. Ham, W. R., *Phys. Rev.* **55,** 1137 (1939).
75. Ham, W. R., and Bennett, F. D., *Phys. Rev.* **59,** 939 (1941).
76. Harris, L., Jost, W., and Pearse, R. W. B., *Proc. Nat. Acad. Sci. U. S. A.* **19,** 991 (1933).
77. Hauffe, K., *Z. anorg. Chem.* **257,** 279 (1948).
78. Hauser, P. M., and McLaren, A. D., *Ind. Eng. Chem.* **40,** 112 (1948).
79. Heckter, M., *Glastechn. Ber.* **12,** 156 (1934).
79 a. Heering, H., Puell, H., and Drewitz, I., *Kunststoffe* **38,** 49 (1948). (Water-vapor permeability of cable-sheath materials)
80. Herrmann, D. B., *Bell. Lab. Record* **13,** 45 (1934).
81. Hey, M. H., *Min. Mag.* **24,** 99 (1935).
82. Hey, M. H., *Phil. Mag.* **22,** 492 (1936).
83. Houwink, J. R., *Ind. Plastiques* **3,** 409 (1947).
84. Houwink, R., *Verfkroniek* **20,** 172 (1947).
85. Johnson, F. and Larose, P., *J. Amer. Chem. Soc.* **46,** 1377 (1924).
86. Jouan, R., *J. phys. Radium* **7,** 101 (1936).
87. Jost, W. and Widmann, A., *Z. physik. Chem.* **B 29,** 247 (1935).
88. Jost, W. and Widmann, A., *Z. physik. Chem.* **B 45,** 285 (1940).
89. King, G., *Trans. Faraday Soc.* **41,** 479 (1945).
90. Kline, G., *Bur. Stand. J. Res.* **18,** 235 (1937).
91. Kolowrat, L., *Le Radium* **4,** 37 (1907).
92. Kolowrat, L., *Le Radium* **6,** 321 (1909).
93. Kolowrat, L., *Le Radium* **7,** 266 (1910).
94. Korvezee, A. E., and Mol, E. A. J., *J. Polymer. Sci.* **2,** 371, 487 (1947).

95. Kuhn, W., Suhr, H., and Ryffel, K., *Helv. Phys. Acta* **14,** 497 (1941).
96. Laidler, K. J., and Shuler, K. E., *J. Chem. Phys.* **17,** 851 (1949).
97. Laidler, K. J., and Shuler, K. E., *J. Chem. Phys.* **17,** 856 (1949).
98. Levey, H., *Plastic Prod.* **11,** 52 (1934).
98a. Levi, D. L., *Trans. Faraday Soc.* **42,** 152 (1946). (Entropy and energy of diffusion. Diffusion of H_2O through solids)
99. Liempt, van, J. A. M., *Rec. Trav. chim. Pays-Bas* **57,** 871 (1938).
100. Lombard, V., *Compt. Rend. Acad. Sci. Paris* **177,** 116 (1923).
101. Lombard, V., and Eichner, C., *Bull. Soc. Chim. France* **53,** 1176 (1933).
102. Lombard, V., Eichner, C., and Albert, M., *Bull. Soc. Chim. France* **4,** 1276 (1937).
103. Luhr, O., and Harris, L., *Phys. Rev.* **45,** 843 (1934).
104. Lowry, H., and Kohman, G., *J. Phys. Chem.* **31,** 23 (1923).
105. Melville, H. W., and Rideal, E. K., *Proc. Roy. Soc. (London)* A **153,** 89 (1936).
106. Michel, A., Bénard, J., and Chaudron, G., *Bull. Soc. Chim. France* **12,** 336 (1945).
106a. Morton,T. H., *Textil Rundschau* **4,** 39 (1949). (Diffusion of dyes in cellulose)
107. Muckenthaler, H., *Phys. Z.* **35,** 851 (1934).
108. Müller, F. H., *Phys. Z.* **42,** 48 (1941).
109. Müller, F. H., and Fischer, C. H., *Naturwiss.* **30,** 604 (1942).
110. Müller, F. H., *Kolloid-Z.* **100,** 355 (1942).
111. Müller, F. H., *Kolloid-Z.* **105,** 16 (1943).
112. Newitt, D. M., and Weale, K. E., *J. Chem. Soc. London* **(1948)** 1541.
112a. Newkirk, T. F., and Tooley, F. V., *J. Am. Ceram. Soc.* **32,** 272 (1949). (Permeability of glasses)
113. Nowak, P., *Kunststoffe* **34,** 120 (1944).
114. Phillips, A., and Skinner, E. N., *Trans. Amer. Inst. Min. Met. Eng.* **143,** 301 (1941).
115. Post, C., and Ham, W. R., *J. Chem. Phys.* **6,** 598 (1938).
116. Post, C., and Ham, W. R., *J. Chem. Phys.* **5,** 913 (1937).
117. Rayleigh, Lord., *Proc. Roy. Soc. (London)* A **156,** 350 (1936).
118. Rayleigh, Lord., *Proc. Roy. Soc. (London)* A **163,** 377 (1937).
119. Reitlinger, S. A., *J. Gen. Chem. USSR.* **14,** 420 (1944).
120. Reitlinger, S. A., *Rubber Chem. Techn.* **19,** 385 (1946).
121. Richardson, O., Nicol, J., and Pornell, T., *Phil. Mag.* **8,** 1 (1904).
122. Riehl, N., *Kolloid-Z.* **106,** 201 (1944).
122a. Riehl, N., and Waschiczek, K., *Z. anorg. Chem.* **253,** 45, 54 (1945). (Diffusion through semipermeable membranes)
123. Rouse, P. E., *J. Amer. Chem. Soc.* **69,** 1068 (1947).
124. Rutherford, E., *Physik. Z.* **2,** 429 (1901).
125. Ryder, *Electr. J.* **17,** 161 (1920).
126. Sager, T. P., *Bur. Stand. J. Res.* **25,** 309 (1940).
127. Seeliger, K. E., *Naturwiss.* **30,** 461 (1942).
128. Shuler, K. E., Dames, C. A., and Laidler, K. J., *J. Chem. Phys.* **17,** 860 (1949).
129. Sieverts, A., *Z. physik. Chem.* **88,** 114 (1914).
130. Sieverts, A., and Danz, W., *Z. physik. Chem.* B **34,** 158 (1936).
131. Sieverts, A., and Danz, W., *Z. physik. Chem.* B **38,** 46, 61 (1937).
132. Sieverts, A., and Zapf, G., *Z. physik. Chem.* A **174,** 359 (1935).
133. Simons, J. H., *J. Phys. Chem.* **36,** 652 (1932).
134. Simons, J. H., and Ham, W. R., *J. Chem. Phys.* **7,** 899 (1939).

134a. Simril, V. L., and Herschberger, A., *Modern Plastics* **27,** 97 (1950). (Permeability of polymer films to organic vapors)

135. Smithells, C. J., and Ransley, C. E., *Proc. Roy. Soc. (London)* **A 150,** 172 (1935).

136. Smithells, C. J., and Ransley, C. E., *Proc. Roy. Soc. (London)* **A 152,** 706 (1935).

137. Smithells, C. J., and Ransley, C. E., *Proc. Roy. Soc. (London)* **A 157,** 292 (1936).

138. Spencer, L., *J. Chem. Soc. London* **123,** 2124 (1923).

139. Schulze, W. M. H., *Kunststoff Technik* **10,** 249 (1940).

140. Schupp, P. O., *Siemens Veröfftl. Nachrichtentechnik* **10,** 27 (1940).

141. Tammann, G., *Z. angew. Chem.* **39,** 869 (1926).

142. Tammann, G. and Schneider, J., *Z. anorg. allgem. Chem.* **172,** 43 (1928).

143. Taylor, R., Herrmann, D., and Kemp, A., *Ind Eng. Chem.* **28,** 1255 (1936).

144. Taylor, N. W., and Rast, W., *J. Chem. Phys.* **6,** 612 (1938).

145. Thomas, A. M., and Gent, W. L., *Proc. Phys. Soc.* **57,** 324 (1945).

146. Tiselius, A., *Z. physik. Chem.* **A 169,** 425 (1934).

147. Tiselius, A., *Z. physik. Chem.* **A 174,** 401 (1935).

147a. Tolliday, J. D., Woods, E. F., and Hartung E. J., *Trans. Faraday Soc.* **45,** 148 (1949). (Membrane Permeability)

148. Tiselius, A., *J. Phys. Chem.* **40,** 233 (1936).

149. T'sai, Liu Sheng, and Hogness, T. R., *J. Phys. Chem.* **36,** 2595 (1932).

150. Ubbelohde, A. R., *Proc. Roy. Soc. (London)* **A 159,** 295, 306 (1937).

151. Urry, W., *J. Amer. chem. Soc.* **54,** 3887 (1932).

152. Urry, W., *J. Amer. chem. Soc.* **55,** 3242 (1933).

153. Veith, H., *Wiss. Veröfftl. Siemens Werkstofjk.* **1940,** 318.

154. Vieweg, R., and Gast, T. H., *Kunststoffe* **34,** 117 (1944).

155. Wagner, C., *Z. physik. Chem.* **A 159,** 459 (1932).

156. Ward, R., *Am. Inst. Min. Met. Engrs. Techn. Publ. Nr.* 1832 (1945).

157. Weyl, A. W., *Bull. inst. verre* No. 6, 1 (1947).

158. Wheeler, T. S., *Trans. Nat. Inst. Sci. India* **1,** 333 (1938).

159. Wustner, H., *Ann. Physik* **46,** 1095 (1915).

160. Wynne-Jones, W. F., and Eyring, H., *J. Chem. Phys.* **3,** 492 (1935).

161. Zimens, K. E., *Z. physik. Chem.* **B 37,** 231 (1937).

162. Zimens, K. E., *Z. Elektrochem.* **44,** 590 (1938).

163. Zimens, K. E., *Z. physik. Chem.* **A 191,** 1, 95 (1942).

164. Zimens, K. E., *Z. physik. Chem.* **A 192,** 1 (1943).

165. Zwolinski, B. J., Eyring, H., and Reese, C. E., *J. Phys. & Colloid Chem.* **53,** 1426 (1949). (Diffusion and membrane permeability)

CHAPTER VIII

MOBILITY OF IONS IN SOLID AND MOLTEN METALS AND ALLOYS

I. Transfer of matter in solid metals

At first sight it may seem rather meaningless to ask if there is an electrolytic component of conduction in alloys. If we have a wire of a pure metal which carries an electric current J, there is no possibility of determining whether a very small fraction n (transference numbers for metal ions at room temperature are in most cases certainly smaller than 10^{-10} by many orders of magnitude) of the current is due to a movement of metal ions in the wire. If, however, we bring

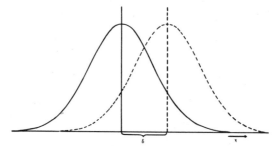

Fig. 8-1. Distribution of radioactive tracer, originally at $x = 0$, without electric field (solid line) and with field (dashed line).

some radio-active tracer atoms into a very thin layer perpendicular to the current, Fig. 8-1, we might be able to detect a minute electrolytic component of the current. So far, an experiment of this type has not yet been carried out. Of course, it should be attempted at a temperature as close to the melting point as possible. Without an electric current, one should observe after some time a distribution of the tracer atoms such as that in Fig. 8-1, where the origin of the coordinate system coincides with the centre of the layer which originally contained the radioactive atoms, and which might be marked mechanically. The resulting distribution is given by an error curve (cf. Chap. I). In the case of a sufficiently strong electric current, one might observe a distribution, shifted toward that given by the full curve of Fig. 8-1, which would allow of a calculation of the average displacement of a tracer atom in the electric field. If carried out properly, such an experiment should give a shift of the curve, though perhaps only a very slight one. Of course the movement of the centre of gravity of the tracer atoms must coincide with that of the bulk of the metal atoms.

If we wish to observe effects due to a displacement of metal atoms in a wire of pure metal, we must provide some frame of reference.

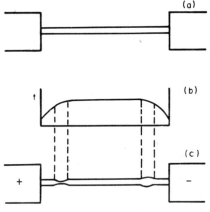

Fig. 8-2. Transfer in pure metal, after Schwarz. (a) Experimental arrangement, (b) Temperature distribution, (c) Change in diameter of wire in case of mobility of positive ions in metal.

When we stretch a thin wire between sufficiently heavy electrodes, Fig. 8-2a, heating the wire by a rather strong electric current, we have the situation as sketched in Fig. 8-2b. The middle of the wire is at a uniform, high temperature (which is not determined by heat conduction to the electrodes, but only by conduction through the surrounding gas, and eventually by convection and by radiation), sufficient for self diffusion to become observable. If now a displacement of particles takes place in the electric field, the result might be a decrease of mass of the wire near the one cold end, coupled with a corresponding increase near the other end. This is shown in Fig. 8-2 c, in the same sense as is to be expected for positively charged metal particles moving in an electric field.

An estimate still gives very small values for an effect of this type, if existing at all. There are observations, reported by Johnson (24, 25) which might be due to a transfer of metal ions in an electric field. Tungsten wires, heated by an alternating current retained a smooth surface, while heating by direct current resulted in structural change of the surface which was definitely assymmetrical with respect to the direction of the current. In addition, ...'' in silhouette the wire looks to be budding toward the negative terminal'' ... Johnson concludes from these observations that tungsten ions migrate towards the cathode. Wires of Ta, Mo, Pt, Fe and Ni also showed, upon being heated by direct current, in vacuo, a change in surface structure, not observed with alternating current. K. Schwarz (4) carried out a series of experiments with incandescent bulbs. 3 carbon filament, and 8 metal filament, 1 amp. bulbs were connected to a d.c. source of 150 volts (instead of 110), resulting in burning-out within 48 hours. With the exception of one carbon filament and two metal filaments, destroyed near the middle, in all other bulbs the filament was broken within about 0.5 to 1.5 mm. from the positive electrode. This would have been expected if positive metal ions had been migrating away from the positive electrode.

It cannot be stated unambiguously whether these observations are due to a migration of metal ions within the volume of the wires or due to surface migration, as suggested by Johnson. Schwarz's experiments might rather indicate a volume effect.

If the explanation of these experiments with pure metals still remains uncertain, there can be no doubt as to the interpretation of observations with alloys. Effects are most pronounced with interstitial mixed crystals where the dissolved component is not a metal but may be considered to have quasi-metallic properties, as in the case of the solid solutions of hydrogen, carbon, nitrogen and boron in metals. With the exception of nitrogen these components migrate toward the cathode, as seen from Table I, taken from Schwarz (4).

TABLE I

Transfer in solid metals
[after Schwarz (4) and Seith (5)].

System	1st component atom per cent	$t\ °C$	1st component migrates towards	$u\ \dfrac{cm.^2}{sec\ Volt}$	t_I	Author
H-Pd	37	10—72	cathode	0.4—2.7		Coehn, Specht (14)
Pd-Au	29	900	cathode		1.6×10^{-11}	Jost, Linke (27)
Cu-Au	62	1000	cathode		7.4×10^{-11}	Nehlep, Jost, Linke (34)
Au-Pb	0.04	200	anode		10^{-10}	Seith, Etzold (50)
	0.04	290	anode		1.54×10^{-9}	Schwarz, Stokkert (47)
C-Fe	4.5	1000	cathode	2×10^{-5}	1.6×10^{-6}	Seith, Kubaschewski (51)
N-Fe	—	1000	anode	3×10^{-5}		Seith, Daur (52)
B-Fe	—	1040	cathode	10^{-5}		Seith, Daur (52)
Ni-Fe			no effect			Seith, Daur (52)
Po-Ag	*	350	anode			Schwarz (4)
Th-W	*	450	anode cathode			Johnson (24)

* Po and Th on surface.

The migration of hydrogen in palladium was first proved by Coehn and co-workers (12, 13, 14, 15, 16). They obtained values for the mobility of protons in the palladium solid solution of the order of magnitude of 10^{-5} cm./sec. per volt/cm., at temperatures varying between 20 and 72°C. This mobility is, by more than one power of ten, smaller than that calculated from the rate of diffusion of hydrogen in palladium, as observed by Duhm (17, 18)* within this temperature range, corresponding to an effective charge of the protons of about 1/25. On

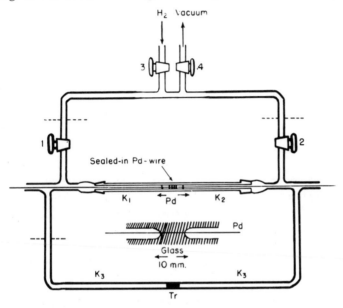

Fig. 8-3. Wandering of protons in Pd wire in electric field. Experimental arrangement of Wagner and Heller. K_1, K_2, K_3 Glass capillaries, between K_1 and K_2 sealed-in Pd wire, shown enlarged below.

account of the interaction of protons and electrons it is not surprising to find an effective charge < 1. It should be borne in mind, however, that the diffusion coefficients as observed by Duhm, are considerably higher than those obtained by means of extrapolation from the measurements of other observers. Wagner and Heller (61) thoroughly reinvestigated the transport of protons in palladium in an electric field. They used a palladium wire of 0.1 mm. diameter, sealed in a capillary of thermometer glass for a length of 10 mm. (Fig. 8-3). At either end the palladium wire was wielded to gold wires of 0.3 mm. diameter. Both sides of the capillary were connected by means of a

* cf. also Franck (20) and Herzfeld and Goeppert-Mayer (21).

second capillary, of 0.00723 cm.² cross section. The system could be evacuated and filled with hydrogen. Now in the middle of the connecting capillary a droplet of naphthalene monobromide had been inserted. Therefore, if due to the electric current hydrogen was transported through the sealed-in part of the wire, this could be measured from the displacement of the droplet within the capillary. A shift of 1 mm. corresponds to 7.23×10^{-4} cm.³, i.e., at atmospheric pressure, to 6×10^{-8} g. atoms of hydrogen transported. With sufficiently symmetrical construction of the apparatus and precautions against air drafts it was possible to avoid fluctuations of the drop by more than ± 0.5 mm. Thus the sensitivity of the apparatus should correspond to about 3×10^{-8} g. atoms of hydrogen. Experiments were carried out with a current of 0.2 amp., which corresponds to a calculated temperature rise of the wire, compared with its surrounding, of only about 2°C. The results thus obtained are listed in Table II.

TABLE II

Electrolytic transport of hydrogen in palladium
(after Wagner and Heller (61))

Temperature: furnace	180°C.	237°C.
wire	182°C.	240°C.
Current, amp.	0.2	0.2
Time of experiment, days	55	20
Average movement of droplet mm./day . .	2.36 ± 0.06	3.56 ± 0.15
Transport number t_{H+}	0.79×10^{-6}	1.19×10^{-6}

From these values, the authors calculate the following transference numbers for protons: $n_H = 0.79 \times 10^{-6}$ at 182°C., and 1.19×10^{-6} at 240°C.

Since it can be concluded from magnetic measurements (3, 6, 7, 35, 57, 58) that hydrogen in palladium is present predominantly in the form of protons and electrons, the concentration of protons may be equated to that of hydrogen atoms. Thus it is possible to evaluate the mobility of protons from transference numbers and the known conductivity, and to compare it with the values obtained from diffusion measurements (28, 29). The results, thus obtained, are seen in Table III.

The mobilities derived from transference measurements and diffusion measurements agree within an order of magnitude; the comparatively small differences may be due to

a) neglecting the influence of the electron atmosphere and the interaction of electrons and cations,

b) neglecting the electrophoretic effect (55).

TABLE III

Evaluation of transference experiments in the system Pd/H
After Wagner and Heller (61)

Temp. °C	t_{H+}	x_H	σ_{Pd}	$\dfrac{\sigma_{Pd+H}}{\sigma_{Pd}}$	u_{P+}	D	u_{H+} (from D)
182	0.79×10^{-6}	0.028	6.02×10^4	0.93	1.46×10^{-4}	1.05 to 1.48×10^{-5}	2.7 to 3.8×10^{-4}
240	1.19×10^{-6}	0.020	5.38×10^4	0.95	2.80×10^{-4}	2.16 to 3.06×10^{-5}	4.9 to 6.9×10^{-4}
References		(53)	(22) (23)	(11)		(28, 29)	

t_{H+} = measured transference numbers for H^+

x_H = gram atoms of H per gram atom of Pd in palladium metal

σ_{Pd} = conductivity of pure Pd in Ohm^{-1} cm.$^{-1}$

σ_{Pd+H} = conductivity of Pd saturated with hydrogen of 1 atm.

u_{H+} = mobility of protons, [cm./sec. per Volt/cm.] calculated from the preceding values

D = measured values of D, differing as to the state of the palladium used ("soft" or "hard")

u_{H+} (from D) = values of u_H^+ calculated from D as listed in the preceding column.

De Boer and Fast (10) investigated the transfer of oxygen in solid solutions of zirconium and oxygen. Zirconium takes up oxygen and nitrogen in considerable quantities (9), without change in the crystal structure. Even with an oxygen content of about 40 atom per cent, only one hexagonal lattice is found (19). Since the volume increase found experimentally from density measurements is in agreement with that calculated from the increase in lattice constant, it follows that all the oxygen taken up is contained on interstitial sites, like hydrogen in palladium. From the fact that solution equilibrium is readily obtained one may conclude that oxygen in zirconium has a rather high mobility.

A zirconium wire of 260 microns in diameter and 100 mm. length was heated electrically inside a glass bulb. While it was heated by alternating current it was allowed to absorb 5 atom per cent of oxygen. After this it was heated in vacuo to 1650°C. for homogenization. Then, in an atmosphere of pure neon, the wire was heated by direct current for 8 hours to a temperature of 1640°C. The potential drop obtained was 1 volt/cm. From the way the wire was glowing one could see that some change had taken place. At the beginning of the experiment the wire had been glowing uniformly over its total length. At the end of the experiment its temperature increased from the negative pole to the positive one, due to a corresponding change in resistance. X-ray examination confirmed this result, the dimensions of the lattice cell increasing from the negative to the positive terminal, indicating an increase of oxygen content in the same direction. No effect was obtained in a wire heated by passing alternating current. The results were confirmed by measuring the resistance of several parts of the wire, before direct current had been applied and after passing direct current for two different time intervals. The effect so obtained was quite marked. Thus it has been proved that oxygen in zirconium moves in an electric field as a negative ion.

Carbon, dissolved in iron, has been shown by Seith and Kubaschewski (51) to migrate toward the cathode when an electric field is applied. The effect may be observed quite easily. An iron wire of low carbon content, having a diameter of 1.5 mm., was coated with copper. For a length of 10 mm. the coating was removed, and the carbon content of these unprotected parts was allowed to increase to 1 per cent by heating the wire for about two hours to 960°C. in an atmosphere of coal gas.

Then the wires were heated in vacuo by passing an electric current of 25 amp., corresponding to an electric field strength of about 0.1 volt/cm. The temperature, thus attained, was about 1000°C. Microscopic examination, after the wires had been ground and etched, showed that carbon had been transferred by the electric current, while in a.c.-heated wires only a symmetrical diffusion could be observed. The movement occurs in the same sense as positively charged particles would migrate, i.e. in the direction toward the cathode. The mobility of carbon in iron, at 1000°C., derived from these experiments, is on the average 2×10^{-5} cm./sec., in a field of 1 volt/cm.

Similar results were obtained with nitrogen in iron (52). The technique employed was almost identical with that used in the carbon-iron measurements, viz. copper coating of the wires, dissolving the copper over part of their length, nitriding the wire in an atmosphere of ammonia. In a second run nitrided wires of 1 cm. length were welded to nitrogen free wires at both ends. The analysis was the same as with carbon. The mobility was determined to be 0.3×10^{-5} cm./sec. in a field of 1 volt/cm., at 1000°C. Contrary to the behaviour of carbon, nitrogen migrated toward the anode, corresponding to the movement of a negativily charged ion.

The measurement of a transfer of matter in purely metallic alloys was attempted independently by the author (26, 27, 34) and by Seith (49, 50, 51, 52).

In the system gold-lead, chosen by Seith (49, 50), the mobility of the gold atoms is remarkably high, as is known from diffusion measurements (cf. Chap. V, p. 238 and Table VI). This fact and the very poor solubility of gold in lead, about 0.05 per cent at temperatures above 200°C., suggest that we have to deal here with an interstitial type of mixed crystal. Seith and Etzold (49) worked at a temperature of 200 to 220°C. where the diffusion constant of gold in lead is about $\geqq 2 \times 10^{-7}$ cm.² sec.$^{-1}$ (36). On account of the low solubility of gold in lead, a concentration of only 0.04 per cent gold in lead could be used. Rods of this alloy, 6 mm. in diameter, were heated by a current of 220 amp., and during a time interval of several months. A total of 430,000 amp. hours was passed through a rod. At the end of the experiments, discs of the rod were turned off, beginning from either end, and the gold concentration in the discs was determined analytically. Without exception, it was found that gold had moved toward the anode, 2×10^{-6} g. atoms of gold having been transported by 1.5×10^{9} coulombs. This corresponds to a transport number for gold of 10^{-10}. No effect was observed if alternating current was used.

In the systems, chosen by the author, extreme conditions were necessary in order to obtain observable effects, on account of the smallness of the diffusion constants. Alloys of gold with palladium and with copper were employed. Temperatures were chosen as close to the melting point of the alloys as possible. In the first experiments with a gold-palladium alloy of 18.1 weight per cent of palladium, wires of 0.05 mm. diameter were used. It was desirable to increase the current to almost the maximum that could be borne without melting of the alloy. Since now rather slight fluctuations of the voltage were sufficient to cause a melting of the wire, 20 wires, each of 50 mm. length, were used in series. Thus the major part of the wires served just as fuses to save a few ones, still surviving after several months. These were analysed by taking Debye-Scherrer pictures. The experiments, carried out with a current density of 60,000 amp. per cm.² at about 1000°C., showed after two months of electrolysis a definite effect, corresponding to a transfer of palladium to the cathode. The final experiments were carried out with wires of 0.1 mm. diameter, heated with a current density of 25,000 amp./cm.² to 900°C. Of twenty wires, thus heated in series, several survived a period of as much as 18 months. Five of these were finally analysed, their average time of heating being 15 months and 13 days. The amount of palladium, transferred to the cathode, was found to be on the average 1.4×10^{-6} g. $\approx 1.3 \times 10^{-8}$ g. atom per wire. With a current of 2 amp. for the above stated time a total of 8×10^{7} amp.sec. = 830 Faraday passed through the wires. This gives a transference number at 900°C. for palladium of 1.6×10^{-11}.

Since, in contrast to electrolytes, it is not absolutely necessary that an amount of gold, equivalent to that of palladium, has been transferred in the opposite direction, i.e. toward the anode, we cannot conclude with certainty that a definite amount of gold or of palladium has been transported. We definitely know, however, the concentration changes in the neighborhood of the electrodes. These may have been brought about by a transfer of the above mentioned amount of palladium or by an equivalent transfer of gold in the opposite direction, or by some intermediate transfer of either one. It would even be conceivable that gold and palladium had migrated in the same direction, the current of one component being so much greater than that of the other one as to bring about the observed concentration change (cf. Schwarz's results with wires of pure metals).

Definite statements would be possible if one could claim that the local number of lattice points was conserved. In the case of an interstitial mixed crystal, as with carbon in iron and probably with gold in lead, this must almost certainly be true, the main component, which determines the number of lattice sites or of interstitial sites, not participating in movement. In substitution mixed crystals this need not be true, though it might be so*.

With the alloy copper-gold, containing 35 weight per cent of copper, experiments were carried out at $\sim 750°C$. Wires of 0.1 mm. diameter were used, glowing in an atmosphere of hydrogen. Due to the high heat conductivity of hydrogen, a current of 3.2 amp. could be applied, corresponding to a current density of 41,000 amp./cm.^{2}, in spite of the comparatively low melting point of the alloy. Again 20 wires in series were used. Four wires out of those surviving a 3 months period of heating were chosen for x-ray analysis. Besides an assymmetrical concentration distribution, relative to the electrodes, a symmetrical decrease of the gold concentration toward the middle of the wire was found, apparently due to evaporation. Thus an average of the lattice constant after the experiment was calculated for each of the wires, and the evaluation was based upon the deviations from this average. The concentration changes, thus obtained, correspond to a transfer of about 1.9×10^{-8} g. atoms of copper, provided the concentration change is due to a migration of the copper only. An amount of electricity equal to 260 Faraday having been transferred, one calculates a transference number for the copper of 7.4×10^{-11} at ca. 1000°K. With respect to the relative participation of copper and gold in the transport of electric charge, the above remarks must be borne in mind. The change in concentration corresponds to a migration of copper to the cathode, therefore, if gold had migrated solely, it must have moved toward the anode.

Schwarz and Stockert (47) used the same method, electrolysis in an atmosphere of hydrogen, with wires of a lead-gold alloy. Besides reproducing the effect, as first observed by Seith and Etzold, they

---

* Cf. the experiments of Smigelskas and Kirkendall, Chap. III and V, p. 159, 255.

were able to observe its temperature dependence, in accordance with that of the diffusion coefficient.

A transfer of metals, adsorbed on the surface of other metals, has been proved by Johnson (25) for thorium on tungsten, and by Schwarz (46) for polonium on silver. In the latter case, the effect is quite striking, and can be made visible by the immediate action of the radioactive radiation on the photographic plate (radiographs).

II. Transfer of matter in molten metals

There are many more results available on the transfer in molten alloys (1, 2), especially in amalgams, than there are for transfer of matter in solid alloys. The first reliable results are due to G. N. Lewis (33) and collaborators. They employed a glass capillary of inverted V shape in order to avoid errors caused by convection currents. Electric field strengths of several hundredths of a volt/cm. could be applied, sufficient to obtain a movement of sodium and potassium toward the anode. The transference numbers observed, defined as g. atoms of metal transported per 1 Faraday, are 0.29×10^{-6} and 2.93×10^{-6} for sodium amalgam of 0.57, and 3.24 atom per cent of sodium, and 3.56×10^{-6} for potassium amalgam of 2.16 atom per cent of K.

It is to be expected that in dilute solutions transference numbers are proportional to the concentration, as is observed, approximately, with the sodium amalgam. Kremann (30) and co-workers, since 1923, have carried out an extensive series of experiments on the electrolysis of molten alloys. The alloys were electrolyzed in capillaries of about 1 mm. diameter and 200 to 500 mm. length, current densities were of the order of a few hundred amp./cm.², corresponding to electrical field strengths between 0.02 and 0.1 volt/cm. Since the capillaries used were straight and horizontal, considerable remixing must have occurred due to convection currents, as pointed out by Schwarz (4). Density differences, produced by electrolysis, are by no means small, rising up to several units in density. In Table IV results obtained by Kremann, are reproduced. From this table it is seen which component migrates toward the cathode and what maximum concentration difference between cathode and anode has been produced by the current. The effects are rather large, ranging up to 75 per cent.

K. Schwarz (4, 39, 41, 42, 44) published a series of investigations dealing with transference numbers in alloys. By using rather long capillaries, bent several times to preclude convection currents, cf. (8), he was able to achieve a fairly high degree of accuracy. We reproduce a few results in Table V. He also measured diffusion potentials of

TABLE IV

Transfer in molten alloys, after Kremann
(taken from Schwarz (4))

Alloy	°C.	concentration per cent	Component, migrating towards cathode	Concentration change, per cent
Ag-Al . . .	900	50—80 Al	Al	15
Ag-Bi . . .	—	30 Ag	Ag	3
Ag-Cu-Sn .	1000	—	Ag + Cu	13
Ag-Pb . . .	1000	30—50	Ag	8
Ag-Sb . . .	—	40	Ag	5
Ag-Sn . . .	—	16 Ag	Ag	2.5
Al-Cu . . .	1050	50	Al, Cu ? ? ?	—
Al-Sn . . .	800—1600	40	Al	8
Al-Au . . .	700	9 Au	Al	0.4
Al-Fe-Sn .	660	—	Fe	—
Au-Bi . . .	680	50	Au	2
Au-Pb . . .	450	50	Au	3
Au-Sb . . .	400	50	Au	14
Be-Cu-Fe. .	1050	10 Be	Be (Fe)	—
Bi-Cd . . .	—	25—75	Cd	65
Bi-Pb . . .	240—400	60	Pb	42
Bi-Sn . . .	200, 300	25—88	Sn	40
Bi-Cu-Sn. .	1000	—	Cu	—
Ba-Hg . . .	—	0.0—2.7	Hg	—
		2.7—100	Ba	
Ca-Hg . . .	280	2 Ca	Ca	0.65
Cd-Hg . . .	300	50	Cd	35
Cd-Pb . . .	300	40	Cd	30
Cd-Sn . . .	300	25—75	Cd	6
Cu-Sn . . .	1000	50	Cu	20
Cu-Pb-Sn .	1000	1 Pb	Cu	10
Cu-Pb-Zn .	1000	—	Cu, Zn	—
Fe-P. . . .	1400	11 P	—	0.0
Hg-K . . .	240	0,0—2,5	Hg	—
		2,5—100	K	—
Hg-Li . . .	—	—	Li	—
Hg-Na . .	240	0.0—1.5	Hg	—
	—	1.5—100	Na	—
K-Na . . .	100	50	K	—
Na-Pb . . .	370	10	Na ? ?	—
Hg-Na-Sn .	240	1—5 Sn, 40 Na	Sn, Na	—
Pb-Sn . . .	350	60	Sn	10
Sb-Zn . . .	500	20—60	Zn	75
Sn-Zn . . .	400	50	Zn	12

Further investigated without success: Ag-Zn, Ag-Cd, Ag-Cu, Al-Mg, Al-Sb, Al-Zn, Bi-Sb, Bi-Zn, Cu-Zn, Cu_2S-PbS, FeS, Pb-Sb, Pb-Zn.

TABLE V

Measurement of transport numbers by eletrolysis of amalgams, at 26°C., after Schwarz (4)

Element	Faradays used	Increase in metal conc. at anode*	Transport number t_{Me}	$\dfrac{t_{Me}}{x}$	Mole fraction x
Na ..	36.0	0.355	-0.98×10^{-6}	-7.7×10^{-5}	0.0128
Na ..	69.5	0.70	-1.01×10^{-6}	-7.6×10^{-5}	0.01330
K ...	59.1	1.31	-2.23×10^{-6}	-1.96×10^{-4}	0.01136
K ...	63.9	1.04	-1.63×10^{-6}	-2.20×10^{-4}	0.00740

* Expressed in c. c. $\dfrac{n}{10}$ acid, used in titration.

amalgams against pure mercury (4, 40), cf. (38), (without an electrolyte in the ordinary sense of the term). The existence of such potentials had been assumed by Lewis, Adams and Lanman (33).

The mobilities of metals in amalgams are of the same order of magnitude as those of the corresponding ions in aqueous solution, cf. Tab. VI. Schwarz (4, 45) has developed several methods for a direct determination of these mobilities.

TABLE VI

Electrolytic migration in amalgams at 25°C., after Schwarz (4)

Dissolved metal	$\dfrac{t_{Me}}{x}$	u cm./hour	Valence	Diffusion coef. cm.² sec.⁻¹	Author
Li	7.5×10^{-5}	0.41	1	0.92×10^{-5}	
Na	-7.8×10^{-5}	-0.43	1	0.86×10^{-5}	Schwarz (42)
K	-2.3×10^{-4}	-1.3	1	0.71×10^{-5}	
Cs	-7.9×10^{-4}	-4.3	1	0.63×10^{-5}	
Ag	4.0×10^{-4}	2.2	2	1.11×10^{-4}	Schwarz (44), Schwarz and Stockert (48)
Au	2.7×10^{-4}	1.5	2	0.73×10^{-5}	Schwarz (41)
Mg	6.3×10^{-4}	3.5	2	—	Schwarz, unpubl.
Ca	—	< 0.2	2	—	
Zn	7.7×10^{-4}	4.2	2	2.4×10^{-5}	Schwarz (40)
Cd	6.4×10^{-4}	3.5	2	2.0×10^{-5}	Schwarz (39, 45)
Tl	$< 1 \times 10^{-5}$	0.0	1	1.18×10^{-5}	
Pb	$< 1 \times 10^{-5}$	0.0	1	2.08×10^{-5}	Schwarz (40)
Bi	-5.2×10^{-4}	-2.9	0	1.5×10^{-5}	
Sn	3.5×10^{-4}	1.9	2	2.09×10^{-5}	
Ga	5.2×10^{-4}	2.9	—	—	Schwarz, unpubl.

While for low concentration there is a proportionality between transference number and concentration, for higher concentrations considerable deviations from proportionality have been observed.

From Kremann's (31, 32) measurements it appears that a maximum for the transference number is often observed in the neighborhood of 50 atom per cent. This is not quite unexpected, because for the transference number, referred to the second component, a linear increase with concentration is also to be expected in dilute mixture. This would suggest an expression for the transport number of the form $\sim N\,(1-N)$, if N is the atomic fraction of one of the two components, giving a maximum at $N = 0.5$. But there are more striking deviations. As first found by Kremann (32), the observed effect may even change its sign with increasing concentration. Such change of sign, for instance, has been found with the amalgams of sodium, potassium and barium, the change being observed at quite low concentrations, i.e., a few weight per cent of the metal in mercury. With sodium amalgam the change of sign coincides with the composition of the compound $NaHg_7$. In all the cases mentioned, the dissolved metal migrates toward the anode at the lowest concentrations while for higher concentrations migration is directed toward the cathode.

A theoretical treatment of transfer in metals has been attempted by Skaupy (54, 55, 56), Wagner (59, 60) and by Schwarz (43). A rough estimate may be obtained as follows. If diffusion constants for the metal under consideration are known, one can calculate the mobility of these particles. Ascribing a definite electrical charge to the atoms in the alloy or the amalgam, we may calculate the partial conductivity due to the movement of these ionized atoms in the alloy. This partial conductivity, divided by the total conductivity gives, to a first approximation, the order of magnitude of the transference number to be expected. There is some uncertainty, however, as to the effective charge to be attributed to the atoms in the alloy, but this uncertainty does not affect the order of magnitude.

In a quantitative treatment, considering the migration of either component, Wagner (59, 60) arrives at an equation for the transport number t_2' of the dissolved metal (assuming a dilute solution)

$$\frac{t_2}{N_2} = \frac{96,500}{300}\,\frac{z_2\,D_2 - z_1\,D_1}{\sigma}\,\frac{N e}{R T}\,\frac{d_1}{A_1}, \qquad [8.1]$$

where N_2 = mole fraction of the dissolved metal, z_1 and z_2 are the numbers of elementary charges, e, on components 1 and 2, σ is the conductivity of the pure component 1, D_1 is the coefficient of self diffusion of pure component 1, D_2 is the coefficient of mutual diffusion, d_1 the density of component 1, and A_1 is the atomic weight of 1.

Eq. [8.1] is at least in qualitative agreement with observations. For instance, in the system, cadmium dissolved in mercury, Schwarz (4), Table VI, has found

$$\frac{t_2}{N_2} = + 6.4 \times 10^{-4} \text{ at } 25^0 \text{ C.} \qquad [8.2]$$

We assume that $z_1 = z_2 \approx 2$, D_2 (measured by von Wogau (62)) is 2×10^{-5} cm.^{2} sec.$^{-1}$ at $25°C$. If we further assume that D_1, so far not determined experimentally, is of the same order of magnitude as D_2, which is certainly the case, we have

$$| D_2 - D_1 | \lesssim D_2$$

and with the values $\sigma = 10^4$ Ohm^{-1}cm.$^{-1}$, $e = 4.77 \times 10^{-10}$ e. s. u., $N = 6.02 \times 10^{23}$, $R = 8.31 \times 10^7$ erg./deg., $T = 298°K.$, $d_1 = 13.6$ and $A_1 = 200.6$, we finally obtain as limiting value for the transport number

$$| t_2/N_2 | \lesssim 10^{-3}. \qquad [8.3]$$

[8.3] agrees in order of magnitude with [8.2]. Since for other amalgams the values entering eq. [8.1] are of the same order of magnitude as those for Cd, transference numbers should be of the same order of magnitude, as actually is the case. For negative values of t_2, i.e., migration of the dissolved atoms to the anode, one has to assume $z_2 D_2 < z_1 D_1$. Indeed, for Na, K, Ba, with negative t_2, observed diffusion coefficients in mercury are comparatively small, $\sim 6 \times 10^{-6}$ cm.^{2} sec.$^{-1}$ at $10°C.$, while for Cd at the same temperature D is $\sim 1.6 \times 10^{-5}$ cm.^{2} sec.$^{-1}$. Of course, the values of z_1 and z_2 are quite uncertain but they do not affect the order of magnitude of the calculated effect.

K. Schwarz (43), arrives at an equation, not very different from that of Wagner, by assuming that the density of electric charge is the determining factor. To obtain his equation, the expression $z_2 D_2 - z_1 D_1$ in Wagner's formula is to be replaced by $D_2 \left(\dfrac{z_2}{v_2} - \dfrac{z_1}{v_1} \right)$, where v_1 and v_2 are the specific volumes of the two constituents. Schwarz finds reasonable agreement between theory and observation. In a discussion of Schwarz's theory, which, of course, gives results of the same order of magnitude as that of Wagner, Wagner (60), arrives at the conclusion that his theory might be preferable for solid alloys, while that of Schwarz might be more applicable to liquid alloys.

REFERENCES

Monographs and Review Articles

1. Kremann, R., Elektrolyse geschmolzener Legierungen, Samml. chem. u. chem.-techn. Vorträge **28**, 347. Stuttgart, 1926.

2. Kremann, R., Elektromotorische Kräfte, in P. Walden and C. Drucker Handb. allgem. Chem. Vol. VIII, p. 597. Leipzig, 1931.
3. Mott, N. F., and Jones, H., The theory of the properties of Metals and Alloys. Oxford, 1936.
4. Schwarz, K., Elektrolytische Wanderung in flüssigen und festen Metallen. Leipzig, 1940.
5. Seith, W., Diffusion in Metallen (Platzwechselreaktionen). Berlin, 1939.

General Bibliography

6. Aharoni, J., and Simon, F., Z. physik. Chem. **B 4,** 175 (1929).
7. Biggs, H. F., Phil. Mag. (6), **32,** 131 (1913).
8. Le Blanc, M., and Jäckh, R., Z. Elektrochem. **35,** 395 (1929).
9. De Boer, J. H., and Fast, J. D., Rec. trav. chim. Pays-Bas **55,** 459 (1936).
10. De Boer, J. H., and Fast, J. D., ibid. **59,** 161 (1940).
11. Brüning, H., and Sieverts, A., Z. physik. Chem. **A 163,** 409 (1933).
12. Coehn, A., Naturwiss. **16,** 183 (1928).
13. Coehn, A., Z. Elektrochem. **35,** 767 (1929).
14. Coehn, A., and Specht, W., Z. Physik **62,** 1 (1930).
15. Coehn, A., and Jürgens, H., Z. Physik **71,** 179 (1931).
16. Coehn, A., and Sperling, K., Z. Physik **83,** 291 (1933).
17. Duhm, B., Z. Physik **94,** 434 (1935).
18. Duhm, B., Z. Physik **95,** 801 (1935).
19. Fast, J. D., Metallwirtschaft **17,** 641 (1938).
20. Franck, J., Nachr. Ges. Wiss. Göttingen. Math. Phys. Kl. II, No. 44 (1933).
21. Herzfeld, K. F., and Goeppert-Mayer, M., Z. physik. Chem. **B 26,** 203 (1934).
22. Holborn, L., Ann. Physik (4), **59,** 145 (1919).
23. Jäger, W., and Diesselhorst, H., Wiss. Abh. d. Physik-techn. Reichsanstalt **3,** 269 (1900).
24. Johnson, R. P., Phys. Rev. **53,** 766 (1938).
25. Johnson, R. P., Phys. Rev. **54,** 459 (1938).
26. Jost, W., Z. angew. Chem. **45,** 544 (1932).
27. Jost, W., and Linke, R., Z. physik. Chem. **B. 29,** 127 (1935).
28. Jost, W., and Widmann, A., Z. physik. Chem. **B 29,** 247 (1935).
29. Jost, W., and Widmann, A., Z. physik. Chem. **B 45,** 285 (1940).
30. Kremann, R., Ortner, H., and Markl, R., Monatshefte Chem. **44,** 401 (1923).
31. Kremann, R., Vogrin, A., and Scheibel, H., Monatshefte Chem. **57,** 323 (1931).
32. Kremann, R., Korth, B., and Schwarz, E. I., Monatshefte Chem. **56,** 16 (1930).
32a. Kubaschewski, O., and Reinartz, K., Z. Elektrochem. **52,** 75 (1948).
33. Lewis, G. N., Adams, E. Q., and Lanman, E. H., J. Amer. Chem. Soc. **37,** 2656 (1915).
34. Nehlep, G., Jost, W., and Linke, R., Z. Elektrochem. **42,** 150 (1936).
35. Oxley, A. E., Proc. Roy. Soc. (London) **A 101,** 264 (1922).
36. Roberts-Austen, W. C., Phil. Trans. Roy. Soc. London **A 187,** 404 (1896).
37. Scarpa, O., Rend. R. Acad. Linc. (IX, 6a), **1,** 11, 1007 (1929).
38. Scarpa, O., Mem. R. Acad. d'Italia, Class. fis. e nat. **1,** No. 5 (1930).
39. Schwarz, K., Z. physik. Chem. **A 154,** 245 (1931).
40. Schwarz, K., ibid. **A 156,** 227 (1931).
41. Schwarz, K., ibid. **A 161,** 231 (1932).
42. Schwarz, K., Z. Elektrochem. **39,** 550 (1933).
43. Schwarz, K., Z. physik. Chem. **A 164,** 223 (1933).

44. Schwarz, K., *Monatshefte Chem.* **66,** 218 (1935).
45. Schwarz, K., *Z. Elektrochem.* **44,** 648 (1938).
46. Schwarz, K., ibid. **45,** 712 (1939).
47. Schwarz, K., and Stockert, R., *Z. Elektrochem.* **45,** 464 (1939).
48. Schwarz, K., and Stockert, R., *Monatshefte Chem.* **68,** 383 (1936).
49. Seith, W., and Etzold, H., *Z. Elektrochem.* **40,** 829 (1934).
50. Seith, W., and Etzold, H., ibid. **41,** 122 (1935).
51. Seith, W., and Kubaschewski, O., ibid. **41,** 551 (1935).
52. Seith, W., and Daur, Th., ibid. **44,** 256 (1938).
53. Sieverts, A., and Danz, W., *Z. physik. Chem.* **B 38,** 46 (1937).
54. Skaupy, F., *Z. physik. Chem.* **58,** 560 (1907).
55. Skaupy, F., *Verh. dtsch. physikal. Ges.* **16,** 156 (1914).
56. Skaupy, F., ibid. **18,** 252 (1916).
57. Svensson, B., *Ann. Physik* (5) **18,** 299 (1933).
58. Vogt, E., *Ann. Physik* (5) **14,** 1 (1931).
59. Wagner, C., *Z. physik. Chem.* **B 15,** 347 (1932).
60. Wagner, C., ibid. **A 164,** 231 (1933).
61. Wagner, C., and Heller, G., ibid. **B 46,** 242 (1940).
62. von Wogau, M., *Ann. Physik* (4) **23,** 345 (1907).

CHAPTER IX

SURFACE REACTIONS OF METALS, FORMATION OF PROTECTIVE LAYERS AND RELATED REACTIONS

I. General remarks

Many metals react with gases such as oxygen, the halogens, sulfur and hydrogen sulfide at high temperatures, and some even at room temperature.

As Pilling and Bedworth (173) have pointed out, two groups of phenomena may be distinguished. In the first, the oxide or other compound formed has a volume smaller than that of the reacting metal. In this case a porous layer of oxide or other compound is formed and the attacking gas still reaches the reacting surface through the pores. The porous layer may slow down the rate of attack somewhat, but it does not actually prevent the gas from coming into contact with the metal, consequently no really protective surface layer is formed. Such phenomena are exhibited, for instance, in the oxidation of alkali, and alkaline earth, metals. We shall not deal with this topic

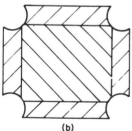

(a)   (b)

Fig. 9-1. Oxidation of copper a and of "Widia "-metal (W - C - Co - Ti hard metal) b, schematically after Scheil.

here, since there are no reactions involved which proceed within solids.

In the second group, the volume of the compound formed is larger than that of the reacting metal and a protective surface layer, free from pores, may be formed. Even here the reaction does not come to a complete stop after the surface layer has been formed, but in the absence of pores the reaction can continue only as a result of a diffusion process occurring within this surface layer. This is a very slow process compared with the passage of gas through porous material. Furthermore, if the reaction does continue by means of such a diffusion process, the protecting surface layer increases in thickness, thus impeding more and more the attack of the gas. In Table I, taken from Seith (19), we give the ratio of the densities of oxides and the corresponding metals.

While Pilling and Bedworth's rule is usually a sufficient criterion as to the formation of a protective layer, there may be exceptions. Scheil (198) has shown that it may be possible to decide from the shape of the tarnished layer whether a coherent protective layer can be formed or not. In Fig. 9-1 Scheil's results are seen. In the case of

TABLE I

Relative densities of oxides, $d_{metal} = 1$

metal	Li	Na	K	Rb	Cs	Mg	Ca	Ba
d_{oxide}/d_{metal}	0.57	0.58	0.65	0.46	0.86	0.85	0.69	0.71
metal	Cu	Zn	Cd	Al	Tl	Ce	Sn	Pb
d_{oxide}/d_{metal}	1.71	1.44	1.19	1.38	1.11	1.24	1.31	1.40
metal	Sb	Cr	W	Mn	Fe	Ni	Co	Pd
d_{oxide}/d_{metal}	1.50	1.97	3.50	1.75	2.23	1.64	1.78	1.60

copper, where a protective layer is formed, the sharp edges of the original metal block disappear, the protective layer growing around edges and corners. Fig. 9-1b shows the oxide layer growing separately on each surface upon "Widia" metal (W, C, Co, Ti).

II. Parabolic law

We shall first assume that diffusion through the layer of oxide or other compound formed is the rate determining step in a tarnishing reaction*. If we choose the increase of the thickness of the layer x as a measure for the reaction velocity, then we have

$$dx/dt = k/x . \qquad [9.1]$$

The rate of increase of the layer will be inversely proportional to the thickness of the layer, because the concentration-gradient in the layer will be proportional to $1/x$, provided we have a quasi-stationary state. The constant k is proportional to the diffusion coefficient.

---

* This is often the case, but the rate of reaction at some interface may also become important.

Integration of [9.1] yields

$$x^2 = 2kt \qquad [9.2]$$

if for $t = 0$ the thickness of the layer is zero. This "quadratic" law, first derived by Tammann (207), has often been observed. We shall consider a more general group of reactions in this section. Obviously it is not essential, for the above law of growth of a surface layer, that the attacking agent be a gas. It could be a liquid, or even another solid, see Fig. 9-2. If a new solid layer III is formed between two components I and II, of which I is supposed to be solid while II is in any state of aggregation then we may expect the laws [9.1] and [9.2]

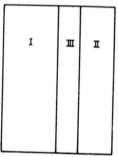

to hold. The rate of growth of the layer III will be given by [9.2] provided that diffusion in III is the rate determining step. Thus, for instance, I may consist of metallic silver while II is liquid sulfur. Or we may have the formation of a complex compound from its components, for instance Ag_2HgI_4 from AgI and HgI_2, the first compound representing the layer III, the two simple compounds corresponding to I and II.

Fig. 9-2. Type of reaction, treated in this chapter: I solid reacting component, II attacking agent (gas, liquid or solid). III protective layer of reaction product, assumed to be solid.

Analogous is the formation of spinels, such as $MgO \cdot Al_2O_3$ from the components MgO and Al_2O_3, or the formation of silicates such as $MgO + MgSiO_3 = Mg_2SiO_4$. In all these cases we have a scheme similar to that of Fig. 9-2. Therefore we may expect that within a certain range of conditions diffusion through the newly formed compound will determine the speed of the reaction.

There is no general answer to the question as to what is diffusing in this layer. In the case of tarnishing reactions in the strict sense it would seem almost obvious that the gaseous component, oxygen, sulfur, or halogen would diffuse through the protective layer. This had been generally assumed until C. Wagner (237, 243) gave strong evidence that the diffusing component need not to be identical with the attacking agent.

Several methods have been used in the investigation of tarnishing reactions. The thickness of the layer formed may be estimated from interference colours (206, 207, 208, 87, 129, 73, 13). For not too thin layers it may be determined directly by weighing. If the reaction is continued until all of the metal has been transformed into oxide or another compound, then measurement of the electrical resistance indicates with great accuracy the moment when all of the metal has been used up (188, 237). The decrease of the concentration of the gas may also be chosen as a measure of the reaction (175, 176).

III. The reaction of silver with sulfur

In the case of the reaction $2\,Ag + S = \alpha\text{-}Ag_2S$ (stable above 179 °C) Wagner carried out the following instructive experiment, Fig. 9-3.

Against the lower open end of a glass tube (Fig. 9-3) two cylinders each consisting of compressed polycrystalline Ag_2S, were in close contact followed by a piece of silver sheet. The tube was filled with molten sulfur. Now, if the usual assumptions were true, sulfur should diffuse through the two silver sulfide cylinders, forming new sulfide at the interface silver sulfide/metallic silver. Thus the weight of the lower silver sulfide cylinder should increase. The quantitative experiment, however, showed the opposite to be true (see Table II). The tarnishing constant, listed in the last column of the table, is defined by the following equation

$$dn/dt = kq/x .\qquad [9.3]$$

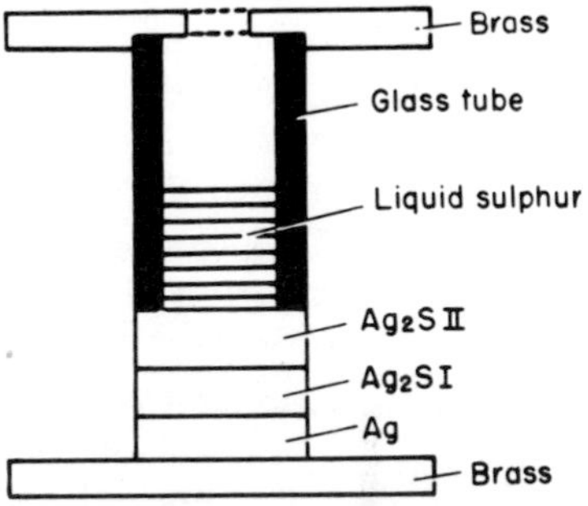

Fig. 9-3. Reaction of silver with liquid sulfur, after Wagner.

Here n, in gram equivalents, is the quantity of silver sulfide formed, q is the cross section of the system and x the thickness of the layer of compound formed. [9.3] is equivalent to [9.1], but the constant k thus defined is of different dimensions from that defined by equation [9.1], viz. gram equivalents sec.$^{-1}$ cm.$^{-1}$.

There is quite conclusive evidence that in these experiments silver, and not sulfur, has migrated through the sulfide layer. Now it is known that in $\alpha\text{-}Ag_2S$ silver ions have a great mobility. There had

TABLE II

Tarnishing experiments carried out by Wagner (237) with the system silver-sulfur at 220°C. (cross section $q = 0.12$ cm.^{2})

No	time seconds	change in weight(mg) of silver	sulfide cylinder I	sulfide cylinder II	height of sulfide cylinder cm.	tarnishing constant k eq. sec.$^{-1}$ cm.$^{-1}$
1	3600	− 108	+ 3	+ 117	0.61	1.4×10^{-6}
2	3600	− 137	+ 1	+ 135	0.77	2.3×10^{-6}
3	3600	− 84	+ 1	+ 96	0.65	1.2×10^{-6}
4	3600	− 108	+ 2	+ 126	0.60	1.4×10^{-6}
5	3600	− 121	+ 5	+ 131	0.58	1.5×10^{-6}
				average		1.6×10^{-6}

arisen considerable difficulty in reconciling the observed conductivity and transference numbers of silver ions in Ag_2S with the mobilities of silver ions estimated from diffusion experiments (in the system Ag_2S and Cu_2S, cf. p. 199). Wagner's (237) tarnishing experiments gave the clue to an understanding of the former discrepancies.

The observed facts cannot be explained by movement of silver ions alone, because it is connected with a transport of electrical charge in one direction, not compensated by an equivalent transport of charge of the opposite sign. The charge of the opposite sign, of course, cannot be transported by sulfur ions. For, if sulfur ions should move from the sulfur to the silver, the difficulty would only be increased. Moreover such a movement is incompatible with the results listed in Table II and is also in contradiction to the transference numbers observed.

Hence there remains only the alternative, that metallic silver has moved upwards to the sulfur in the form of silver ions and free electrons, migrating through the silver sulfide crystal.

Now, anticipating the results of Wagner's (237) exact theory of tarnishing processes, we are able to give a simple electrochemical

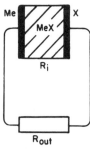

Fig. 9-4. Substitute circuit for reaction according to preceding figure.

picture of this reaction. There is a certain analogy between these corrosion processes in gases and the normal corrosion processes in electrolytic solutions (10, 121). To the free energy of the reaction

$$2\,Ag + S = Ag_2S$$

corresponds a certain electromotive force. This may be either calculated from thermodynamic data or, with certain precautions, measured directly (186). Let us consider as a substitute circuit the galvanic cell of Fig. 9-4, having an inner, electrolytic resistance R_i, given by the electrolytic component of the conductivity of Ag_2S

$$R_i = x/[q(t_1 + t_2)\sigma] \qquad [9.4]$$

where x is the thickness, q the cross section of the α-Ag_2S layer, σ the conductivity, t_1 and t_2 the transference numbers of cations and anions [since there exists a transference number t_3 for the electrons, the sum $(t_1 + t_2)$ is $\neq 1$ and may even be very small compared with 1]. We further assume that this cell is closed by an outer metallic circuit of resistance R_{out}, corresponding to the electronic component of the conductivity of α-Ag_2S

$$R_{out} = x/[qt_3\sigma] . \qquad [9.5]$$

Then the current flowing in the circuit of Fig. 9-4 will be

$$I = E/(R_i + R_{out}) = Eq\,(t_1 + t_2)t_3\sigma/x . \qquad [9.6]$$

To convert the electric current into the equivalent current of matter (i.e., equivalents transported per second), [9.6] must be divided by the electrochemical equivalent 96,500 coulomb/equivalent. Thus

$$dn/dt = E\,q\,(t_1 + t_2)\,t_3\sigma/96{,}500\;x = kq/x\;.\qquad\qquad [9.7]$$

Here k is the tarnishing constant

$$k = (t_1 + t_2)\,t_3 E\,\sigma/96{,}500\;.\qquad\qquad [9.8]$$

[9.8] is identical with the value provided by the exact theory, see p. 383. Since σ, t_1, t_2, and t_3 depend on the partial pressure of sulfur which varies from the sulfur to the silver side of the sulfide layer, appropriate averages of these values must be chosen.

In our case t_2 is negligibly small, $t_3 \approx 1$, and for $t_1\sigma$ a safe estimate may be obtained as follows. From measured diffusion coefficients of Cu^+ ion in Ag_2S and transference numbers of both cations in the mixed crystal used the coefficient of self diffusion for Ag^+ ions can be calculated. From the value of these at a temperature of 220°C. one obtains $t_1\sigma = 0.8$ to 2 Ohm^{-1} cm.$^{-1}$. E is approximately 0.2 Volt. The value for the tarnishing constant, thus computed, is

$$k_{calc} = (2 \text{ to } 4) \times 10^{-6} \text{ equivalents sec.}^{-1}\text{ cm.}^{-1}$$

which is to be compared with the observed value of 1.6×10^{-6}. The agreement is quite satisfactory, especially if we consider that this is essentially an absolute calculation of a rate of reaction. Before reviewing Wagner's (237) theory of tarnishing reactions we shall have to deal briefly with the electric conduction of α-Ag_2S in order to remove all possible objections to the above argument.

The conductivity of α-Ag_2S is of the order of magnitude of 500 to 800 Ohm^{-1} cm.$^{-1}$ (27, 128, 135, 222, 223). In spite of this high conductivity, exhibiting all symptoms of electronic conduction, Tubandt (221) has found a transference number for the silver ions equal to 1.000, indicating pure electrolytic conduction by silver ions. On the other hand, measurements of diffusion coefficients of copper ions in silver sulfide, as mentioned above, and of transference numbers of Cu^+ and Ag^+ ions in mixed crystals of silver sulfide with cuprous sulfide permit a calculation of the coefficient of self diffusion of silver ions in silver sulfide (cf. p. 147). From these measurements the conductivity of silver sulfide can be calculated independently, giving as a maximum 1 per cent of the conductivity measured directly. This corresponds to a transference number for the silver ions in silver sulfide of less than 1 per cent. Since Tubandt's measurements of the transference numbers had been carried through with great care, the removal of this discrepancy met with considerable difficulty.

Tubandt's measurements of transference numbers had been carried out with the conventional arrangement, see Fig. 9-5, the silver iodide being inserted between cathode and silver sulfide in order to prevent metal dendrites from growing through the solid electrolyte. Now Wagner's explanation of Tubandt's results is as follows. In the arrangement of Fig. 9-5, for each equivalent of electrical charge transported, not one equivalent of silver ions has migrated through the silver sulfide (as is definitely the case through the silver iodide), but only a small fraction of an equivalent, about 1 per cent, in accordance with Wagner's estimate of the transference number. Consequently at the interface AgI/Ag_2S an amount of sulfur, has been freed, corresponding to about 99 per cent of the electrical charge transferred. But as soon as sulfur is freed at the interface AgI/Ag_2S we have exactly the conditions for a tarnishing reaction, as sketched in Fig. 9-2 viz. a

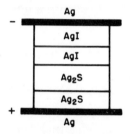

Fig. 9-5. Transference experiment with Ag_2S, after Tubandt.

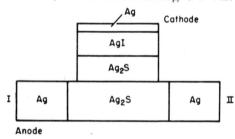

Fig. 9-6.
Transfer experiment with Ag_2S, after Wagner.

layer of silver sulfide between sulfur and metallic silver. Hence now the tarnishing process sets in, carrying exactly the silver deficit from the silver electrode to the interface AgI/Ag_2S. Thus in the end actually one equivalent of silver has been transferred per equivalent of electrical charge. But only about 1 per cent of it is due to the electric current, the remainder to the induced tarnishing reaction.

Wagner was able to verify this experimentally in the following way. He repeated Tubandt's transfer measurements with the arrangement shown in Fig. 9-6. The silver piece I is made the anode while the symmetrically located piece II is not connected to the electric circuit. Thus, if only changes due to normal electrolysis occur, silver metal II should be found unchanged after an experiment. If, however, tarnishing reactions between the interface AgI/Ag_2S and the silver metal determine the quantity of silver transported, then the silver pieces I and II, on account of their symmetrical arrangement, should decrease equally in weight. This is exactly what Wagner has observed. Thus the above assumptions are proved in every detail.

Reinhold (188, 191) has extended Wagner's measurements of the reaction of sulfur with silver. Besides confirming Wagner's results he found some new features of the process. His experiments with liquid sulfur are in accordance with those of Wagner, for the temperature region from 200 to 400°C. and also for the β-modification of silver sulfide, stable below 179°C. But above 179°C. the reaction proceeds much more slowly with sulfur vapor than with liquid sulfur. Furthermore, under these conditions the rate of growth of the silver sulfide layer is almost independent of the thickness of the layer. At 196°C. two experiments with a variation of the thickness of the layer by a factor 5 gave almost identical reaction velocities. Thus the rate of diffusion through silver sulfide does not determine the observed speed. This must be governed by the reaction of sulfur vapor at the interface vapor/Ag_2S. In the temperature region just above the transformation point of Ag_2S (179°C.) the reaction velocity is almost proportional to the vapor pressure of sulfur. So far no explanation of the mechanism has been given. In the reaction of hydrogen sulfide with silver, which is by 2 to 4 powers of ten slower than the reaction with liquid sulfur, a boundary reaction at the interface Ag_2S/gas must be the rate determining step also. The mechanism of this reaction has not been cleared up either.

For the corresponding reaction of copper with sulfur cf. (85, 88, 208). Still further anomalies are observed with the system $Ag/Ag_2Te/Te$. We reproduce a few experiments of Reinhold and Seidel (191), Table III.

TABLE III

Formation of Ag_2Te from the elements at 270°C. Between the tellurium and the silver there are three cylinders of Ag_2Te, each of 1,1 cm. height

	Change in weight after		
	1 hour	4 hours	15 hours
Te Ag_2Te I	+ 0.1288 g	+ 0.2577 g	+ 0.4608 g
Ag_2Te II	-- 0.0616	— 0.1731	— 0.2292
Ag_2Te III	— 0.0682	— 0.0762	— 0.2286
Ag	0.0000	0.0119	— 0.0503

Several characteristic points are seen from this Table. The reaction between the tellurium and the silver telluride starts long before there is any appreciable reaction between the silver and the silver telluride. Of course, a reaction like that observed at the end of the first hour is possible only if the component Ag_2Te is stable within a considerable range of composition. For new silver telluride of non - stoichiometric composition is formed by loss of silver from the original silver telluride.

Reaction of silver with the silver telluride is not observed until the silver telluride has lost part of its silver content amounting to 0.06 to 0.07 g. Ag per 2 g. of Ag_2Te. It may be assumed that the rate of reaction of solid silver with solid silver telluride determines to some extent the observed overall speed. This velocity is different for rolled, hard material and for soft, annealed silver metal, the latter being much more reactive. Further, both electrical conductivity of Ag_2Te and diffusion of cations in Ag_2Te depend strongly on its composition.

IV. The reaction of silver and copper with halogens

Copper iodide is probably the first substance for which the dependance of electronic conductivity on the partial pressure of the electronegative component has been observed, Baedeker (27, 30). With rising partial pressure of iodine there is a very marked increase in the conductivity of CuI. "Pure" CuI, i. e., the compound kept as free from iodine as possible, is a poor conductor at low temperatures, the conduction being at least partially electrolytic. CuI above $\sim 300°C.$ exhibits strong electrolytic conductivity, with a negligible electronic component (there are three phases of CuI known, α-, β-, γ-CuI, with transition points at $402°C.$ ($\gamma \rightarrow \beta$) and $440°C.$ ($\beta \rightarrow \alpha$)). The tarnishing of copper in iodine vapor has been investigated by Wagner and Nagel (168). The tarnishing constant, as defined above, was found to be

$$k = 3.34 \times 10^{-10} \text{ equivalents cm.}^{-1} \text{sec.}^{-1} \text{ at } 195°C.$$

At 200°C. and at an iodine pressure of 46 mm. Hg the transference number of the Cu^+-ions was found to be 2.7×10^{-6} (the overwhelming part of the conduction being electronic), the corresponding conductivity is 66 $Ohm^{-1} cm.^{-1}$. By means of eq. [9.8], Wagner calculated for k

$$k = 3,8 \times 10^{-10} \text{ equivalent cm.}^{-1} \text{sec.}^{-1}$$

in remarkable agreement with the observed value.

In the case of silver + chlorine, bromine, or iodine, a theoretical prediction, beyond that of a limiting value, is impossible because measurements of transference numbers for electrons in the corresponding compounds could not be made. These transference numbers must be rather small, probably less than 10^{-3}. Conversely, in these cases measurements of the tarnishing reactions provide a means of calculating the electronic conductivity.

Reinhold (191) measured the reaction of silver with iodine and found for the tarnishing constant

$$k = 4 \times 10^{-9} \exp(-600/T) \text{ equivalents cm.}^{-1} \text{sec.}^{-1}.$$

In order to derive this constant from other known data on AgI one has to assume a value of 10^{-4} for the transference number of the electrons. Since Tubandt's transfer measurements (219, 220), which are of a high accuracy, give $n_{Ag} = 1.000$ with an error of less than 10^{-3}, the assumption of $n_{el} = 10^{-4}$ is at least not in contradiction with other measurements.

Evans and Bannister (80) have shown that the parabolic law of film growth also holds for the reaction of silver with iodine in solution in such liquids as hexane, ether, carbon tetrachloride, over the temperature range 0 to 35°C. They consider diffusion of iodine molecules through pores or along grain boundaries as being the most probable mechanism, contrary to that responsible at higher temperatures.

The data obtained by Wagner (243) for the reaction of silver with bromine are reproduced in Table IV, (cf. also 208, 139). Wagner

TABLE IV

Rate of tarnishing of silver in bromine vapor

temp. °C.	tarnishing constant eq. cm^{-1}. sec.$^{-1}$ $k \times 10^{10}$		$\dfrac{k\ (0.09\ \text{atm. Br}_2)}{k\ (0.23\ \text{atm. Br}_2)}$
	0.09 atm. Br$_2$	0.23 atm. Br$_2$	
200	0.23	0.38	0.61
250	0.53	0.91	0.58
300	0.96	1.78	0.54
350	1.21	2.32	0.52
400	1.15	2.27	0.50

measured the tarnishing constant for several temperatures and two different bromine pressures. The square root of the ratio of the two bromine pressures employed is 0.62, approximately equal to the corresponding ratio of the tarnishing constants. This is in agreement with theoretical predictions since the electronic conductivity of AgCl or AgBr should increase as the square root of the halogen pressure (cf. p. 388, 372). As in the case of silver iodide, transference numbers of the electrons are not known and the results of the tarnishing reactions may be used for computation of the electronic transference numbers, (Table V). Wagner tried to test the predictions concerning the electronic conductivity by measuring the conductivity of AgBr at 200° C. without bromine and in the presence of 0.23 atm. of bromine vapor. In the latter case the conductivity was increased by 12 per cent above that obtained in pure nitrogen. This result at least does not contradict the conclusions drawn from Table V.

TABLE V

Partial conductivity (Ohm^{-1} cm.$^{-1}$) due to electrons, in AgCl and AgBr

temp. °C.	Conductivity in nitrogen		Electronic conductivity calc. from rate of tarnish.		Transference number of electrons	
	AgCl	AgBr	AgCl (1 atm. Cl$_2$)	AgBr (0.23 at. Br$_2$)	AgCl	AgBr
200	—	5.2×10^{-4}	—	9.0×10^{-5}	—	0.17
250	3.0×10^{-4}	3.2×10^{-3}	—	2.0×10^{-4}	—	0.06
300	1.5×10^{-3}	1.8×10^{-2}	3.7×10^{-5}	3.5×10^{-4}	0.02	0.02
350	6.5×10^{-3}	8.0×10^{-2}	1.5×10^{-4}	4.2×10^{-4}	0.02	0.005
400	2.6×10^{-2}	3.8×10^{-1}	3.4×10^{-4}	3.8×10^{-4}	0.01	0.001

V. Tarnishing reactions in oxygen*

Oxidation reactions of metals are the most important tarnishing reactions. These reactions, therefore, have been the subject of many investigations of which only those of fundamental interest will be

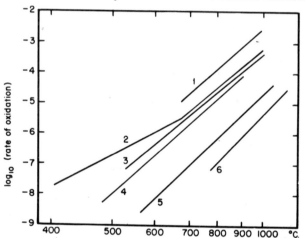

Fig. 9-7. Logarithm of rate of oxidation of several metals, after Dunn, rate expressed as: g.oxygen taken up per cm.^{2} of metal per hour. 1. Fe, 2. Cu, 3. Brass (95% Cu), 4. Brass (90%) Cu), 5. Brass (70% Cu), 6. Ni.

discussed here in any detail. To give an idea of the order of magnitude of the effects observed, we reproduce a diagram given by Dunn (66, 67), Fig. 9-7. In this diagram the speed of oxidation of several metals is shown, expressed in grams of oxygen, taken up per cm.^{2} per hour by the metal surface. In Table VI taken from Wagner,

* (1, 5, 6, 23, 246)

TABLE VI*

Rate of oxidation of several metals, after Wagner (23)

Metal Temperature	Oxidation constant ($g^2 \times cm.^{-4} \times h^{-1}$)						
	408°C.	500°C.	600°C.	700°C.	800°C.	900°C.	1000°C.
Cu in O$_2$ (173)	1.64×10^{-8}	1.93×10^{-7}	1.13×10^{-6}	5.86×10^{-5}	3.14×10^{-5}	1.27×10^{-4}	6.02×10^{-4}
Ni (electrolyte) in O$_2$ (173)					0.093×10^{-6}	0.76×10^{-6}	3.4×10^{-6}
Ni ("Grade A") in O$_2$ (173)						1.9×10^{-6}	6.8×10^{-6}
Fe (electrolyte) in O$_2$ (173)				0.17×10^{-4}	1.00×10^{-4}	6.5×10^{-4}	43×10^{-4}
Fe (Armco) in O$_2$ (173)					1.95×10^{-4}	10.1×10^{-4}	20.5×10^{-4}
Fe (Armco) in air (173)					1.06×10^{-4}	4.9×10^{-4}	
Co in air (70)				5.8×10^{-7}	3.3×10^{-6}	2.2×10^{-5}	7.4×10^{-5}
W in air (78)				1.61×10^{-5}	$\sim 2 \times 10^{-4}$	$\sim 1.5 \times 10^{-4}$	4.61×10^{-3}
Zn in O$_2$ (173)	0.88×10^{-10}						
Al in O$_2$ (173)			0.30×10^{-10}				

* cf. footnote p. 352.

tarnishing constants for a number of metals for varying temperatures are given*. In many cases the "quadratic" or "parabolic" law of tarnishing has been observed, while in some cases the speed falls off with time, becoming smaller than calculated by the quadratic law. Tammann has represented such results by a law $t = a \, (\exp \, (b \, x) - 1)$, which, except for an early stage of the reaction (126), cannot be derived theoretically. It seems likely that this relation is incidental. Newly formed tarnish layers may occur in an unstable modification with high rate of diffusion, being slowly transformed into the stable modification of low diffusion coefficient. In special cases this assumption could be proved to be correct (82, 83, 84, 139, 205).

1. Oxidation of copper

If copper is oxidized at oxygen pressures below the equilibrium pressure for the formation of CuO a uniform film of Cu_2O is formed, its rate of growth obeying the quadratic law except for the very early stages of the reaction. This is by far the most thoroughly investigated tarnishing reaction (64, 92, 153, 173, 196, 197, 250). C. Wagner (64, 250) has treated this reaction both theoretically and experimentally, and was able to present a complete theory of the phenomena observed. Recently Bardeen, Brattain and Shockley (31) took up the problem again by means of radioactive copper. The results, thus obtained, are interesting in themselves, besides confirming Wagner's theory of oxidation, cf. (48).

Earlier measurements of Feitknecht (81) gave, for an oxygen pressure of 100 mm. Hg and 1000°C., a tarnishing constant (interpolated) of

$$k_{exp} = 7 \times 10^{-9} \text{ equivalent cm.}^{-1} \text{ sec.}^{-1}.$$

By means of [9.8] and the values $n_{Cu} = 9.4 \times 10^{-4}$ and $\sigma = 4.8$ Ohm^{-1} cm.$^{-1}$, determined by Wagner and Duenwald at 1000°C. and 8 mm. Hg of oxygen, and an electromotive force of 0.311 Volt measured for the corresponding galvanic cell by Treadwell (218), the following theoretical value is calculated

$$k_{calc} = 6 \times 10^{-9} \text{ equivalent cm.}^{-1} \text{ sec.}^{-1}$$

in remarkable agreement with the observed value.

Wagner and Gruenewald (250) very thoroughly investigated the oxidation of copper for various oxygen pressures at 1000°C. A small copper sheet of 0.3 mm. thickness and 5×10 mm^2 area was suspended from an horizontal quartz fibre outside the furnace. By measuring the

---

* Reaction constants in Table VI have been calculated from the equation $\left(\dfrac{\Delta m}{q}\right)^2 = k t$ where Δm = increase in mass during time t, and q = surface area.

deflection of this quartz fibre with a microscope Wagner and Gruenewald followed the reaction without interrupting the process of oxidation. The results thus obtained are reproduced in Fig. 9-8. Here the
mass increase per unit area is taken as abscissa, while the time t,
divided by the mass increase per unit area, is taken as ordinate. This
has been done for the following reason. From preliminary experiments
it was known that for early sta-
ges of the reaction anomalies
occur. Since the so called "quadratic" law would give infinite
reaction velocity for $t = 0$, it
is obvious, that during the early
stages of the reaction reactions
at phase boundaries cannot be
considered as infinitely fast
compared with the rate of diffusion through the oxide layer.
Thus these boundary reactions
may become rate determining.
One would expect, as a first
approximation, that for given
conditions this speed would be
constant, i.e.,

$$\Delta m/(t\,q) = k_i , \qquad [9.9]$$

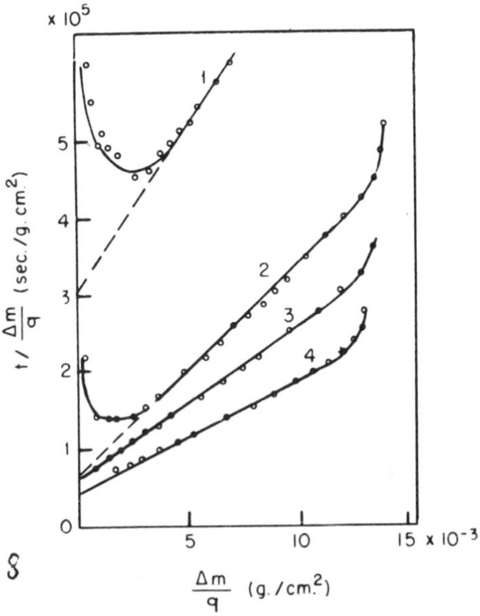

Fig. 9-8. Evaluation of oxidation experiments with copper at 1000°C, after Wagner. Abscissa: g. oxygen taken up per cm.²
metal surface, ordinate: time of oxidation
divided by preceding magnitude. 1. pO_2
$= 0.23$ mm. Hg, 2. $pO_2 = 1.71$ mm Hg,
3. $pO_2 = 11$ mm. Hg, 4. $pO_2 = 63$ mm. Hg.

where Δm is the mass increase,
q the area, k_i a velocity constant
for interface reaction. If both
processes, viz. reaction at an
interface and diffusion, proceed
with comparable speed, the "reaction resistivities" might be
expected to be additive (90), yielding

$$\Delta m/q\,k_i + (\Delta m/q)^2/k = t . \qquad [9.10]$$

[9.10] contains the quadratic law and the law for reaction at a phase
boundary as limiting cases. It is seen, that, if [9.10] holds, the representation of the experiments chosen in Fig. 9-8 should give a
straight line. Since this is not the case for small values of $\Delta m/q$*,
other causes must be responsible. From Fig. 9-9 it is seen that, for
the early stages, the reaction is autocatalytic, the speed increasing

* The deviation for large values of $\Delta m/q$ is trivial, due to the fact, that
all the metallic copper has been used up.

with time. Wagner and Gruenewald assume, that, as in other similar cases (22, 236), formation of nuclei might be responsible for this phase of the reaction.

For an evaluation of the experiments the linear portions of the curves of Fig. 9-8 have been used, see Table VII. Before dealing with the theoretical calculation, we give in Fig. 9-10 the dependence of the tarnishing constant k on the partial pressure of oxygen. With $(p_{O_2})^{1/7}$ as abscissa the values of k fit very closely to a straight line, indicating

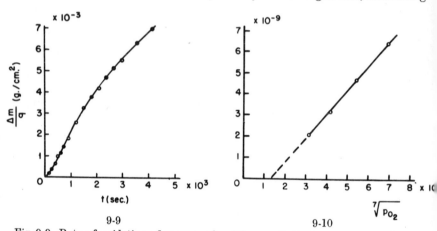

9-9

9-10

Fig. 9-9. Rate of oxidation of copper, after Wagner. Ordinate: g. oxygen taken up per cm.² of metal, abscissa: time.

Fig. 9-10. Oxidation constant of copper (ordinate: equivalent of oxygen, per cm. and sec., definition see text) versus 7 th root of oxygen pressure (atmospheres), after Wagner.

a dependence of k on the 7th root of the oxygen pressure. The constant k_i for phase boundary reaction varies rather slowly with oxygen pressure above $p = 2.25 \times 10^{-3}$ atm. For an increase of the pressure by a factor ~ 40, k_i increases by a factor 2.5. Below $p = 2.25 \times 10^{-3}$ atm. k_i falls off rather rapidly. For a decrease of pressure by a factor of $7:1$ k_i decreases as $3.5:1$. Wagner and Gruenewald suggest that for low oxygen pressures the reaction at the interface Cu_2O/O_2 might be rate determining, while for high oxygen pressures that at the interface Cu/Cu_2O might be the decisive step.

2. Experiments with radioactive copper

Bardeen, Brattain and Shockley (31) made use of a radioactive isotope of copper in studying its rate of oxidation. Radioactive copper, Cu^{64} with a period of decay of 12.6 hours, was deposited electrolytically on a copper blank. It then was oxidized in air at 1000°C. for 18 min.; only the active side was oxidized, the back being protected by another sheet of copper. After oxidation at 1000°C. the blank was

TABLE VII

Oxidation of copper at 1000°C. after Wagner and Gruenewald (250)

pO_2 Atm.	Copper deficit of Cu_2O, $y*$		Concentration difference for equilibrium at phase boundaries, $y^{II} - y^I$	Oxidation constant $k \left(\dfrac{\text{equivalents}}{\text{cm.} \times \text{sec.}} \right)$		Rate constant for phase boundary reaction $\left(\dfrac{\text{equivalents}}{\text{cm.}^2 \times \text{sec}} \right)$
	y^I for Cu_2O in equilibrium with Cu	y^{II} for Cu_2O in equilibrium with O_2		obs.	calc.	
3.0×10^{-4}	0.12×10^{-3}	0.40×10^{-3}	0.28×10^{-3}	2.0×10^{-9}	2.1×10^{-9}	0.4×10^{-6}
2.25×10^{-3}	0.12×10^{-3}	0.62×10^{-3}	0.50×10^{-3}	3.1×10^{-9}	3.4×10^{-9}	1.4×10^{-6}
1.45×10^{-2}	0.12×10^{-3}	0.91×10^{-3}	0.79×10^{-3}	4.5×10^{-9}	4.8×10^{-9}	2.1×10^{-6}
8.3×10^{-2}	0.12×10^{-3}	1.29×10^{-3}	1.17×10^{-3}	6.2×10^{-9}	6.6×10^{-9}	3.4×10^{-6}

* y g. atoms Cu deficit per mol Cu_2O.

kept at 500°C. for 5 min. and then quenched in liquid air. At 1000°C. Cu_2O only is formed, while at 500°C. a thin film of CuO is formed too, being less than 10 per cent of the total oxide layer. The thickness of the oxide layer was determined by the increase in weight of the copper, being 1.27×10^{-2} cm.

Then successive layers of oxide were removed by etching the oxidized face of the copper blank in nitric acid. Again the thickness of each of the sucessive layers was obtained from the weight of the remaining copper. The last (fourth) layer included some unoxidized copper. From the solution prepared from each layer the copper was precipitated as sulfide, and its activity determined by means of a Geiger-Mueller counter. The data obtained are reproduced in Tables VIII and IX.

TABLE VIII

Per cent of radioactive copper in successive layers as determined from tests of activity, after Bardeen, Brattain and Shockley (31)

Sample	Thickness of layer (from weight) cm. $\times 10^3$	Wt. of Cu tested mg.	Counts in 5 min.	Counts per min. per mg. corrected for background	Per cent of total activity in sample
1	1.6	21	218	1.2	22.5 ± 2
2	4.67	17	180	1.0	55.0 ± 6
3	3.48	27	155	0.45	17.5 ± 2.5
4*	3.00	27	108	0.11	5.0 ± 2.5

TABLE IX

Calculated and observed values of per cent of total activity in successive layers of oxide. ξ = fractional distance from metal to oxygen interface. $D = D_1 (\alpha + \xi)$ = self-diffusion coefficient for Cu^+ ions. Calculated values of activity are given for different values of α and for assumptions of both completed dissociation and no dissociation of centers composed of vacant Cu^+-ion sites and defect electrons, after Bardeen, Brattain and Shockley (31)

Sample	Range of ξ	Observed per cent	Calculated, per cent				Undissoc.
			Dissociated				
			$\alpha = 0$	0.1	0.25	0.50	$\alpha = 0$
1	0.77—1.00	22.5	21	20	18	17	18
2	0.50—0.77	55.0	54	52	50	46	48
3	0.22—0.50	17.5	21	22	23	25	26
4	0—0.22	5.0	4	6	9	12	8

* Including some of the underlying copper.

In order to discuss the results obtained by Bardeen, Brattain and Shockley, we have to give a brief survey of their theoretical treatment of the tarnishing process which is a slightly modified and simplified version of Wagner's theory. They start from the equations for the ionic and electronic currents respectively

$$J_{el} = -eD_{el}\,(\partial n_{el}/\partial x) + \sigma_{el}\,\partial\varphi/\partial x \qquad [9.11\text{a}]$$

$$J_{ion} = eD_v\,(\partial n_v/\partial x) + \sigma_{ion}\,\partial\varphi/\partial x \qquad [9.11\text{b}]$$

where J_{el} and J_{ion} are electron and ion currents, n_{el} and n_v are the numbers of defect electrons and of ionic vacancies per cm.[3], σ_{el} and σ_{ion} the corresponding conductivities, and φ the electrostatic potential. At 1000°C. $D_{el}/D_{ion} = \sigma_{el}/\sigma_{ion} = 2 \times 10^{-3}$, (from Wagner's measurements of transference numbers). Since electric neutrality requires $n_{el} = n_v$, each term on the right hand side of [9.11a] differs from the corresponding term of [9.11b] by the same factor, equal to the inverse transference number of the ions. Since no net current is flowing, $J_{el} = J_{ion}$, hence J_{el} must be the small difference of two large terms. This, on account of the proportionality of the single terms to those of eq. [9.11b], must also hold for eq. [9.11b]. But the terms, having the same sign in [9.11b], must add to twice the first term, i.e.,

$$J_{ion} = 2eD_v\,(\partial n_v/\partial x)\,. \qquad [9.12]$$

When D_v is independent of x, (D_v is the diffusion constant of the vacancies, not the average diffusion constant for all copper ions, which is smaller by a factor n_v/n, n being the total number of copper ions per cm.[3]), then $\partial n_v/\partial x$ must be constant throughout the layer. If by X we denote the thickness of the oxide layer for time t ($X = 0$ for $t = 0$), then

$$dX/dt = 2D_v/n \cdot \partial n_v/\partial x \qquad [9.13]$$

where n is the number of copper ions per cm.[3] Further

$$\partial n_v/\partial x = \Delta n_v/X \qquad [9.14]$$

if Δn_v is the difference in number of vacancies (or defect electrons) for cuprous oxide in equilibrium with Cu metal and with oxygen of given pressure respectively. Then the differential equation for the tarnishing process becomes

$$dX/dt = K/X \qquad K = 2D_v\,\Delta n_v/n \qquad [9.15]$$

$$X = \sqrt{2Kt} = 2\sqrt{D_v \times t\,\Delta n_v/n}\,. \qquad [9.16]$$

With Einstein's relation $e \cdot D_v = U_v kT$ (U_v, the mobility of the ions, as defined here, is connected with the mobility, as used elsewhere in this book, by $U = e\,u$), the transference number t_v of the vacancies, the total electrical conductivity σ, $U_v = \sigma \, t_v / e \, n_v$, K becomes

$$K = (2 \sigma \, t_v \, k \, T / e^2 n) \, (\Delta n_v / n_v) \, . \qquad [9.17]$$

The most obvious assumption is made with respect to the diffusion of radioactive copper, that Cu^+ ions move by jumping into Cu^+ vacancies. This gives a diffusion coefficient of Cu^+ ions equal to $D_1 = D_v \cdot n_v / v$. Of course an equivalent number of electrons is diffusing with the ions. Since we have to assume a quasi-stationary state in the oxide layer, we may put

$$n_v = n_{met} + x \Delta n_v / X \, , \qquad [9.18]$$

which means that the number of vacancies increases linearly with x from the value n_{met} in equilibrium with the metal to $n_g = n_{met} + \Delta n_v$ in equilibrium with oxygen. Since X depends on t, n_v, also must depend on t. By putting

$$D = D_0 + D_v \, (\Delta n_v / n) \, (x / X) \qquad [9.19]$$

cognizance is taken of a diffusion coefficient D_0 in the neighborhood of the metal, which may be due to the contribution by the n_{met} vacancies there, but which also might contain a term independent of the vacancy mechanism, for instance due to direct exchange of neighboring particles. In [9.19] X may be replaced by the value [9.16], derived for the tarnishing reaction, giving

$$D = D_0 + \tfrac{1}{2} \, (D_v \, \Delta n_v / n)^{1/2} \times (x / t^{1/2}) \, . \qquad [9.20]$$

The current of radioactive Cu^+-ions is given by two terms: the diffusion current $- D \, \partial c / \partial x$, if c is the concentration of radioactive copper, and a convective term $V c$, due to the current of copper ions toward the oxygen/oxide interface. The rate of change of the concentration of the radioactive copper thus becomes

$$\partial c / \partial t = - \partial / \partial x \, (- D \, \partial c / \partial x + V c)$$
$$= D \partial^2 c / \partial x^2 - (V - \partial D / \partial x) \, \partial c / \partial x \, . \qquad [9.21]$$

Since

$$V = d X / d t = (D_v \Delta n_v / n t)^{1/2} \qquad [9.22]$$

is the rate with which the interface oxygen/oxide moves away from the copper, comparison with [9.20] shows that

$$V = 2 \partial D / \partial x \, . \qquad [9.23]$$

Hence

$$\partial c / \partial t = D \partial^2 c / \partial x^2 - \partial D / \partial x \cdot \partial c / \partial x \, . \qquad [9.24]$$

There is a quasi-stationary solution of [9.24] of the form

$$c = 1 / t^{1/2} \cdot g \, (x / X) \qquad [9.25]$$

which is apparently suitable for the present purpose. It retains its shape as the layer increases in thickness, the total amount being kept constant. For c decreases with time exactly as X increases, i.e., proportional to $t^{-1/2}$, the integral $\int_0^X c\,dx$ being kept constant. Of course one has to assume that the diffusion of radioactive copper into the copper metal is negligible. This assumption is justified since, at 1000°C., D for Cu metal is approximately 10^{-9} cm.^{2} sec.$^{-1}$, compared to 10^{-7} for the self diffusion of copper in Cu_2O in equilibrium with air at 1000°C.

With the notation $\xi = x/X$, $D_1 = D_v \Delta n_v/n$, $\alpha = D_0/D_1$, we have

$$D = D_0 + D_1 \xi = D_1 (\alpha + \xi) \tag{9.26}$$

$$(\xi + \alpha)\, d^2g/d\xi^2 + (2\xi - 1)\, dg/\partial\xi + 2\,g = 0 \tag{9.27}$$

or

$$\frac{d}{d\xi}\left\{ [\xi + \alpha]\frac{dg}{d\xi} + 2[\xi - 1]g \right\} = 0. \tag{9.28}$$

[9.28] implies that the gradient of the function in brackets must vanish in the system of relative coordinates, as the condition for a quasi-stationary state. Since the current through the oxygen/oxide interface is zero, the expression in brackets must be zero

$$[\xi + \alpha]\, dg/d\xi + 2[\xi - 1]g = 0. \tag{9.29}$$

The integral of [9.29] is

$$g = \text{const}\, (\xi + \alpha)^{2(1+a)}\exp(-2\xi) \tag{9.30}$$

or

$$c(x,t) = \frac{A}{t^{1/2}}\left(\frac{x}{X} + \frac{D_0}{D}\right)^{2(D_0 + D_1)/D_1}\exp(-2x/X). \tag{9.31}$$

The fraction f of the total radioactive copper, contained between ξ_1 and ξ_2 is given by

$$f = \int_{\xi_1}^{\xi_2}(\xi + \alpha)^{2(1+a)}\exp(-2\xi)d\xi \Big/ \int_0^\cdot (\xi+\alpha)^{2(1+a)}\exp(-2\xi)\,d\xi. \tag{9.32}$$

The integral has been evaluated by means of tables for the incomplete Γ function. In Table IX observed values of f are compared with values calculated from [9.32] for $\alpha = 0, 0.1, 0.25$ and 0.5, and for complete dissociation of defect electrons and vacancies. Best agreement is obtained for $\alpha = 0$, but for $\alpha = 0.1$ agreement is still sufficient. Wagner and Gruenewald's results give the concentration of vacancies for cuprous oxide in equilibrium with copper as being smaller by a factor $1/14$ than for equilibrium with air at atmospheric pressure. Thus $\alpha = 0.07$, which is consistent with the above results.

Therefore Bardeen, Brattain and Shockley's results are in complete agreement with those of Wagner.

Experiments, similar to those of Bardeen, Brattain and Shockley (31) were performed by Castellan and Moore (48). Radioactive copper Cu^{64}, of 12.8 hours half-life, was plated on copper foils, 0.005 cm. thick. Then, strips, thus prepared, were allowed to oxidize at temperatures of 800, 900 and 1000°C., respectively, for times varying from 0.5 to 2 min. After oxidation successive layers of the oxide were etched in hydrochloric acid, and, after precipitation of the copper, the activity of each of the successive layers was determined by means of a Geiger counter. Results thus obtained are seen in the following tables X and XI, taken from Castellan and Moore. The experimental arrangement resembles very closely that of an infinitely thin layer of diffusing substance, brought upon the surface of a semi-infinite system. The resulting concentration distribution is given by an error curve (cf. Chap. I, p. 19)

$$c = \frac{s}{\sqrt{\pi D t}} \exp \left(-\frac{x^2}{4 D t} \right) \qquad [9.33]$$

TABLE X

Typical data showing the distribution of radioactivity in the different layers of Cu_2O. Layers are numbered beginning at the oxide-gas interface. Count is corrected for background, after Castellan and Moore (48)

| | 800° | | | 900° | | | 1000° | |
Layer No.	% total thick-ness	% total count	Layer No.	% total thick-ness	% total count	Layer No.	% total thick-ness	% total count
1	32	50	1	17	27	1	25	43
2	28	34	2	19	26	2	24	35
3	32	13	3	27	20	3	24	15
4	8	3	4	37	27	4	27	7

Total thickness: 1.12 × 10⁻³ cm. Total time: 120 sec.	Total thickness: 2.19 × 10⁻³ cm. Total time: 120 sec.	Total thickness: 2.12 × 10⁻³ cm. Total time: 30 sec.

1	33	55	1	21	34	1	34	58
2	43	35	2	24	38	2	33	32
3	24	10	3	26	20	3	22	7
4	—	—	4	29	8	4	11	3

Total thickness: 0.91 × 10⁻³ cm. Total time: 120 sec.	Total thickness: 2.36 × 10⁻³ cm. Total time: 120 sec.	Total thickness: 2.15 × 10⁻³ cm. Total time: 30 sec.

TABLE XI

Values of the Diffusion coefficient computed from the data of Table X by the use of eq. [9.34], after G. W. Castellan and W. J. Moore (48)

Layer No.	800°C. $D \times 10^{10}$	Layer No.	900°C. $D \times 10^{10}$	Layer No.	1000°C. $D \times 10^{10}$
1	11.8	1	48.5	1	145
2	9.5	2	49.6	2	120
3	9.4	3	65.2	3	122
1	6.6	1	52.9	1	137
2	7.4	2	40.3	2	128
1	10.7	3	38.2	3	130
2	8.4			1*	(145)
1	11.4			2*	(123)
2	9.1			3*	(115)
Average: 9.4 ± 1.3		Average: 49.1 ± 6.8		Average: 130 ± 7	

and the relative activity of a layer between $x = a$ and $x = b$ is obtained by integration with respect to the position coordinate x

$$f_{ab} = \frac{1}{s} \int_a^b c \, dx = erf\left(\frac{b}{2\sqrt{Dt}}\right) - erf\left(\frac{a}{2\sqrt{Dt}}\right). \qquad [9.34]$$

Here D is the diffusion coefficient and s either the concentration or the activity per cm.^{2} of the original deposit, depending on whether c is expressed as concentration or as activity. Diffusion coefficients, calculated by means of eq. [9.34], are found in Table XI. They can be represented by the formula

$$D = 0.0358 \exp\left(- 37\,000/R\,T\right) \text{ cm.}^2 \text{ sec.}^{-1} . \qquad [9.35]$$

The value calculated from electrical conductivity and from the transference number for 1000°C. is 260×10^{-10} cm.^{2} sec.$^{-1}$, about twice the experimental value of 130×10^{-10} cm.^{2} sec.$^{-1}$ The authors suggest that the difference might be ascribed to the fact that the measured value refers to the oxide during growth of the film. There might also be a considerable inaccuracy in the experimental value of the transference number, entering the calculations. For 1000°C. the value of D agrees within a few per cent with that of Bardeen, Brattain and Shockley. From the rather close agreement between energy of activation for diffusion and for oxidation, about 40 kcal., as determined by Pilling and Bedworth (173), the authors infer that Wagner's theory of oxidation must be essentially correct.

* Data of Bardeen et al. (31).

VI. Oxidation of iron

So far this most important of all tarnishing reactions has not been analyzed in all details like that of copper, but the experiments available at least do not contradict the ideas advanced so far. Observations with this reaction led Pfeil (170, 171) to the conclusion that diffusion of iron to the oxygen might be at least as important as the diffusion of oxygen through the tarnish layer.

A quantitative analysis is complicated by the fact that under the conditions of investigation several oxides of iron are formed, unlike the case of formation of Cu_2O. The following constitution of the tarnish layer may be expected

$$Fe/FeO/Fe_3O_4/Fe_2O_3 .$$

In addition some oxygen may diffuse into the iron. If the pressure of the attacking agent, air or water vapor* is sufficiently high for the formation of Fe_2O_3, then the possibility for the formation of the lower oxides is always present. The number of phases thus possible is not seriously restricted by the phase rule since never more than two phases coexist for a given oxygen partial pressure which decreases steadily from that outside to the value corresponding to equilibrium of Fe with FeO. Since during the course of the reaction equilibrium need not be established at the interfaces between different oxides and cannot be established rigorously if the reaction is to proceed with finite velocity, there might develop neighboring phases which in equilibrium could not coexist at all.

The amounts of the different phases formed during the steady state of oxidation is determined by their different rates of growth. It is not difficult to derive quantitative relations for this (91, 10, 127, 230, 231, 232, 233). The total rate of growth of the oxide layer may even become independent of the oxygen partial pressure (208, 211). The explanation of this observation, given by Fischbeck, is consistent with the general theory of tarnishing processes. This observation is possible only with partial pressures of oxygen sufficiently high for the formation of at least two different oxides. If the lower oxide (or one of several lower oxides) is the one with the highest speed of formation, its rate of growth is independent of the outside oxygen pressure, since there are constant oxygen partial pressures at the

---

* The oxygen pressure in water vapor has a definite value only for a given value of the hydrogen pressure, according to the eq. $p_{O_2} = K_p (p_{H_2O}/p_{H_2})^2$. Since during the reaction with iron the partial pressure of hydrogen may vary considerably, it is neccessary to add hydrogen at a well defined pressure to the water vapor, if experiments with a given oxygen pressure are to be carried out.

interfaces of the oxide with the next higher oxide and with the following lower oxide or the metal. A change of the outside oxygen pressure therefore can affect only the growth of the layer of the highest oxide present. But if, due to the low speed of its growth, the thickness of this layer is small compared to at least one other layer, a change in the growth rate of the layer does not affect appreciably the total rate of tarnishing.

G. Valensi (230—233) has given a comprehensive theoretical and experimental investigation of the formation of several oxides on the surface of a metal. This subject had previously been treated by Fischbeck (91) and a tentative theoretical treatment had been given by Jost (127).

Fischbeck (91) gives the following composition in a tarnish layer of iron, grown in water vapor above 570°C.

$$\alpha\text{-iron} \left| \begin{array}{c} \text{FeO with Fe content} \\ \text{varying from } 77.5 \text{ to} \\ 76\% \text{ (calc. } 77.74\% \text{ for} \\ \text{FeO)} \end{array} \right| \begin{array}{c} 98\% \text{ of the} \\ \text{whole layer} \end{array} \left| \begin{array}{c} Fe_3O_4 \, 2\% \\ \text{of layer} \end{array} \right| \begin{array}{c} Fe_2O_3 \\ 0.2\% \text{ of} \\ \text{the layer.} \end{array}$$

In accordance with the fact that the oxygen partial pressure must be higher at the interface FeO/Fe_3O_4 than at the interface Fe/FeO the iron content of the FeO layer increased by $1\frac{1}{2}$ per cent from the outside to the inside (close to the metal).

The mechanism of tarnishing cannot be considered as definitely proved in all details. There is, however, some evidence in favour of the Wagner mechanism. It is apparent that the tarnish layer is not growing in the direction toward the metal but in the opposite one. Foreign bodies present are occluded by the growing tarnish layer. This can hardly be interpreted otherwise than by a movement of iron from the metal toward the oxidizing gas. Since FeO crystallizes in a lattice with Fe-vacancies, corresponding to the oxygen surplus present, it seems quite conceivable that the rate of diffusion of Fe^{++}-ions might be sufficiently high to account for the observed rate of tarnishing.

The quantitative relation for the thickness of the oxide layer as a function of time is

$$t = a \, x + b \, x^2 \, . \tag{9.36}$$

Values for the increase in thickness of the tarnish layer (expressed by its weight in mg.) as a function of t are contained in Table XII, taken from Fischbeck. The agreement with values calculated by [9.36] is sufficient. This means that diffusion in the oxide layer is not the only rate determining step. Hence a reaction at an interface also comes into play (cf. p. 353) which well might be the reaction at the interface gas/highest oxide present (Fe_2O_3). This assumption, however,

TABLE XII

Oxidation of Fe by water vapor at 800°C. after Fischbeck (91)

Weight increase mg.	t (min.) obs.	t (min.) calc.
9.8	5.0	6.4
13.0	10	(10)
20.1	20	19.1
26.5	30	29
35.8	50	(50)

would not allow one to interpret Fischbeck's results for the oxidation of iron by nitric oxide. The rate of this reaction shows a pronounced discontinuity in the neighborhood of the transformation point of the iron. Of course, such an effect, depending on the transformation of the metal, can only be due to a reaction involving the metal itself, occuring at the boundary metal/lowest oxide present. Thus this might be the step responsible for the linear term in eq. [9.36]. There still remains a serious difficulty in the interpretation of Fischbeck's observations. If a discontinuity in the rate of oxidation is connected with a transformation of the metallic iron, then the discontinuity should occur at the transformation point of the iron and not at a temperature 40°C. above this point as observed by Fischbeck. There seems to be only one ready explanation for this fact. Iron in contact with NO might take up oxygen or nitrogen or both in sufficient quantity to raise the temperature of transformation, at least in a surface layer, by as much as 40°C.

With manganese Fischbeck found an analogous discontinuity in the rate of oxidation at the transformation point.

The oxidation of iron and the transformation of FeO has been studied by Chaudron (50, 51, 52, 53, 54, 162) by means of micro-photography.

VII. The oxidation of zinc

Wagner and Gruenewald (250) oxidized carefully polished zinc rods of 6 mm. diameter in pure oxygen and in 'technical' nitrogen, containing 2.19 per cent oxygen. Results obtained at a temperature of 400 °C. are given in Table XIII. The fluctuations of the results are rather high, which might be due to the fact that zinc oxide crystallizes hexagonally and the rate of diffusion might be strongly dependent

TABLE XIII

Oxidation of zinc at 400°C., after Wagner and Gruenewald (250)

No.	Gas	time t (hours)	zinc surface (cm.²)	weight increase Δm (g.)	oxidation constant $(\Delta m/q)^2/t$ (g.×cm.$^{-2}$)²/h	average
1		24	57.5	2.0×10^{-3}	0.50×10^{-10}	
2		24	57.3	2.0×10^{-3}	0.51×10^{-10}	
3		25	56.3	2.8×10^{-3}	0.98×10^{-10}	
4	Pure oxygen	24	56.1	1.9×10^{-3}	0.48×10^{-10}	0.72×10^{-10}
5		24	53.6	1.7×10^{-3}	0.42×10^{-10}	
6		24	57.2	2.6×10^{-3}	0.86×10^{-10}	
7		24	56.0	3.0×10^{-3}	1.19×10^{-10}	
8		24	56.3	2.6×10^{-3}	0.89×10^{-10}	
9		24	56.3	1.4×10^{-3}	0.26×10^{-10}	
10	N₂ containing 2.19% O_2	47.5	54.4	3.4×10^{-3}	0.82×10^{-10}	0.75×10^{-10}
11		24	56.7	2.8×10^{-3}	1.02×10^{-10}	
12		24	56.5	2.6×10^{-3}	0.88×10^{-10}	
13		24	56.8	2.2×10^{-3}	0.63×10^{-10}	

on the orientation of the crystals formed. In addition instable modifications of zinc oxide might first be formed, Finch and Quarrell (84), and then be transformed to the stable modification (cf. p. 367), during the course of the reaction.

There is no pronounced difference in the speed of oxidation for pure oxygen and 'technical' nitrogen. Pilling and Bedworth's vaiue for the reaction constant $(0.88 \times 10^{-10} \text{ g. cm.}^{-2})^2$ per hour at 400°C. and $p_{O_2} = 1$ atm. is in sufficient agreement with the above results.

The electronic conductivity of zinc oxide decreases with increasing oxygen pressure. Therefore it has been concluded, von Baumbach and Wagner (33), that at finite oxygen pressures zinc oxide always contains a small surplus of metallic zinc, being at least partly present in the form of Zn^{++}-ions and quasi-free electrons. This zinc excess is largest for zinc oxide in equilibrium with metallic zinc. A schematic representation of the situation is found in Fig. 9-11. Here the metal deficit is shown for cuprous oxide as well as the metal excess for zinc oxide. The zinc surplus at the interface oxide/oxygen, for all oxygen pressures

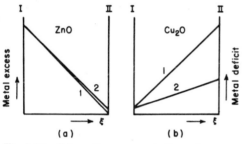

Fig. 9-11. Schematic representation of concentration change within ZnO and Cu_2O, after Wagner. 1. Interface metal/oxide, II. Interface oxide/oxygen, ξ position coordinate. ZnO: 1 pO_2 $= 1$ atm. Cu_2O: 1 $pO_2 = 0.1$ atm.; ZnO 2 pO_2 $= 0.01$ atm. Cu_2O 2 $pO_2 = 0.001$ atm. Varying metal excess in ZnO, varying metal deficit in Cu_2O.

between 0.01 and 1 atm. is very small compared with that at the boundary metal/oxide. This has been derived from measurements of the electronic conductivity (33). Thus a change of oxygen pressure within those limits has a negligible effect on the concentration gradient of zinc in zinc oxide. Consequently the rate of diffusion should be independent of the oxygen pressure, in accordance with the experiments.

VIII. Orientation in oxyde layers

If an oxide layer is crystallized, the orientation of the crystals may be influenced by the orientation of the crystals of the underlying metal, as observed by Mehl (157, 158). Such is the case with FeO on Fe-metal, also with Cu_2O growing upon a copper surface. If the compound formed crystallizes in a non-regular system of symmetry, different orientation of the crystals formed may cause a large dif-

ference in the speed of oxidation or other tarnishing processes, for the
rate of diffusion for different crystallographic orientations may vary
by several powers of ten. Definite observations of this effect, so far,
have not been reported, but there are indications that such influences
may come into play (cf. below). Preston and Bircumshaw (179) investigated the oxidation of liquid tin which was repeatedly oxidized
and reduced. They attributed the varying speeds, thus observed,
to different orientations of the SnO_2 crystals in the oxide layer. Finch
and Quarrell (83, 84) have observed that zinc oxide grows upon zinc
metal in a pseudomorphous hexagonal modification, the Zn-Zn
distance in the oxide being the same as in
the metal and smaller than in normal zinc
oxide. But the distance perpendicular to
the Zn-plane is larger than in stable ZnO.
Aluminum oxide, formed upon aluminum
at room temperature is amorphous (180),
while at higher temperatures an unstable
modification may be formed (43). X-ray
investigations of Cu_2O, grown upon Cu
were carried out by Thompson (217),
Mehl (157, 158), Preston and Bircumshaw
(178), Brueck (43), Thiessen and Schuetza
(215). Fig. 9-12 shows the oriented growth
of AgBr on Ag, after Schwab (201).

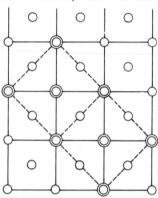

Fig. 9-12. Orientated growth of
AgBr upon Ag, after Schwab.
○ Ag-atoms of silver lattice;
double circles Ag-ions of AgBr
lattice.

J. Bénard (36, 38, 39) studied the influence of the condition of iron and copper on the oxidation at high temperatures.
The rate of oxidation of different planes of a single crystal of copper
was different at 900°C. decreasing in the order:

$$210 - 221 - 211 - 111 - 100 - 123 - 110.$$

IX. Temperature dependence of rate of oxidation

As far as the rate of tarnishing reactions is determined by diffusion
in a solid layer, a dependence on temperature may be expected similar
to that of diffusion, i.e., for not too large a range of temperature

$$k \approx \exp (-Q/RT),$$

as observed in some cases, cf. Dunn (66). It must be remembered,
however, that tarnishing is a rather complex process. There is diffusion
of at least one ion and of electrons; diffusion in several phases comes
into play if more than one oxide or other compound is formed; in
addition to which there may be reactions at phase boundaries. Finally

the concentration gradients, governing diffusion, are complex quantities themselves, being determined by the activity of the attacking agent and by equilibria between solid phases. Consequently, a simple temperature dependence of the net process generally cannot be expected.

X. Oxidation of alloys

The process of oxidation of alloys is even more complicated than that of pure metals. Here the less noble component may be oxidized preferentially; further the mutual solubility of the oxides generally will be different from that of the metals. There may result an increase of the concentration of the nobler component at the interface metal/oxide, causing diffusion in the metal phase, too. Besides, it now depends on the properties of more than one oxide, whether a protective surface layer be formed or not. Hence addition of a less noble component may increase the resistance of a metal toward oxidation if a coherent oxide layer of this component is formed. Such a layer is not necessarily formed at the outside of the tarnish layer, but also may arise between the main tarnish layer and the metal, depending on the mutual solubility of the oxides and the mobility of the metal ions and electrons within them. Thus, in the case of iron, Scheil and Kiwit (199, 200)) aluminum, silicon and chromium oxide are known to be enriched between the metal and the main oxide layer, reducing further oxygen attack. The rate of oxidation of iron may be reduced to a small fraction of its original value by the addition of a few per cent of aluminum. Similar results in case of copper are obtained with aluminum and beryllium, Froehlich (95). On the other hand, magnesium and zinc diffuse to the gas/oxide interface, forming a protective layer there.

Addition of a noble component may increase the oxidation of a given metal, if, for instance, with the alloy a porous oxide layer is formed while that of the pure metal was coherent.

Therefore general predictions as to the behavior of alloys toward oxidation are very difficult. During oxidation anomalous mixed crystals might be formed, Wagner (23), which are responsible for an increased rate of oxidation due to an increase of the rate of diffusion. As in mixed crystals of AgCl with $CdCl_2$ or $PbCl_2$ (cf. Chap. II, p. 94) bivalent ions are taken up by the cation lattice, an equivalent number of cation sites being unoccupied and increasing the mobility of the univalent cations, so analogous effects might occur with oxides. Thus in the oxidation of nickel-copper alloys mixed crystals of cuprous oxide and nickel oxide might be formed according to the scheme

$$\begin{array}{ccccccc}
Cu^+ & Cu^+ & Cu^+ & Cu^+ & Cu^+ & Cu^+ & Cu^+ \\
O^{--} & O^{--} & O^{--} & O^{--} & O^{--} & O^{--} & O^{--} \\
Cu^+ & Cu^+ & Ni^{++} & Cu^+ & Cu^+ & Cu^+ & Cu^+ & Cu^+
\end{array}$$

two Cu^+-ions being substituted by one Ni^{++}-ion and one vacancy. This would account for an increased mobility of the Cu^+-ions and for an increased rate of oxidation, as observed by Pilling and Bedworth (174), cf. also Froehlich (95), Dunn and Wilkins (70). In the oxidation of brass with low zinc content a mixture of copper oxides and zinc oxide is formed (66, 69), while with higher zinc content zinc oxide is formed preferentially, giving a coherent protective layer and reducing the rate of oxidation considerably*. Alloys with less than 10 per cent Zn form a dark oxide layer, while with more than 20 per cent of Zn a light oxide layer is formed consisting chiefly of ZnO.

Wagner and Gruenewald (250) investigated the oxidation of Ni-Au-alloys to test theoretical considerations on the oxidation of alloys. They found that gold increased the rate of oxidation of nickel. During oxidation, generally, the nobler component will be present in the oxide layer to a lesser degree than in the original alloy. In the case of the Ni-Au-alloy practically no gold could be detected in the oxide phase, while the metals form a continuous series of mixed crystals. Hence the course of the reaction will be determined not only by diffusion in the oxide layer, but also by diffusion in the metal. For, if practically no gold is oxidized, there always will be a surplus of gold at the oxide/metal interface, and gold must diffuse into the alloy. Without this diffusion the reaction might be stopped by the formation of a protective layer of gold between oxide and metal, provided that this layer is coherent. These processes have been discussed by several authors, Dunn, Froehlich, Pfeil, Portevin, Prétet and Jolivet, Scheil and Kiwit, Tammann and co-workers (69, 95, 170, 175, 199, 209, 210). Wagner concludes from a dimensional argument that even in this case the quadratic law of growth should hold, provided that diffusion in both the alloy and the oxide is the rate determining step. The experiments gave in some cases the quadratic law, while in others different relations were found.

The rate of diffusion of nickel within the nickel oxide should not be very sensitive toward the nickel content in the alloy at the interface (Ni, Au)/NiO. For the oxygen surplus in the oxide, equal to the metal deficit at the interface NiO/gas, practically determines the concentration gradient within the oxide layer, at least for a

* Analogous results were obtained by Wagner and Zimens (255) for the oxidation of Ni with added Cr or Mn.

nickel content of the alloy not below about 1 per cent. A schematic
picture of the concentration gradient of nickel is found in Fig. 9-13.
During the steady state of oxidation the nickel content in the surface of the alloy is determined by a condition of continuity: the diffusion current of nickel in the surface of the alloy must be equal to
the current of nickel consumed in the growing tarnish layer. For Ni
contents of the alloy at the interface alloy/oxide below 1 per cent,
the rate of diffusion in the alloy should become rate determining,
causing a sharp drop in the rate of oxidation of the alloy.

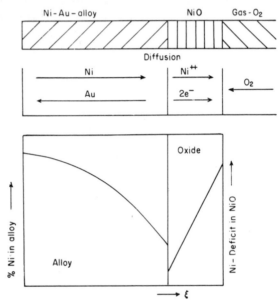

Fig. 9-13. Oxidation of Ni-Au alloy, after Wagner.

Contrary to expectation, addition of gold increased the speed of
oxidation of nickel. Since the quadratic law of growth was not obeyed
either, it seemed probable that no homogeneous tarnish layer had
been formed. A microscopic examination of the tarnish layer proved
this to be true. In the oxidation of copper-silver alloys there is an
enhancement of the reaction, due probably to metallic silver being
present in the reaction product $Cu_2O + Ag$, Leroux and Raub, (150).
In this case it has been assumed that the influence is due to the great
solubility of oxygen in silver and its high speed of diffusion therein. In
the case of the nickel gold alloy an analogous explanation fails since the
solubility of oxygen in gold is below the limits of experimental error.
Thus the results are best explained by the assumption that the oxy-

gen diffuses through pores present in the oxide layer though these pores are not visible under the microscope.

We have dealt at some length with these considerations because similar arguments will be necessary in other cases where mixed crystals are involved in reactions (cf. Uhlig (226, 227, 228, 229)).

While diffusion in oxide layers may be enhanced considerably compared with that of pure metals the opposite may occur in case of reactions of chlorine with alloys (253).

Wagner and Himmler (120 b, 253) investigated the reaction of silver with chlorine in the presence of lead and cadmium. Here the velocity of diffusion of electrons is the rate determining step, or more correctly the velocity of diffusion of defect electrons. Addition of lead or cadmium chloride to the silver chloride decreases the number of defect electrons, though it increases the number of cation vacancies. Thus it is to be expected that the reaction of chlorine with silver and added lead or cadmium should proceed more slowly than that of pure silver with chlorine. In pure silver chloride silver ion vacancies and interstitial silver ions are present in equal concentration, Wagner and Beyer (249), Koch and Wagner (136), see, however, Chap. II, p. 105. The rate of reaction of silver with chlorine was measured by determining the increase in weight of a piece of silver in a chlorine atmosphere. The tarnishing constant was calculated according to the formula

$$k = (1/t)\,(\Delta m/q)^2$$

where Δm is the increase in mass during time t, and q the surface area. During the tarnishing of a silver-lead alloy a sublimate was observed, assumed to be lead chloride. Hence another technique was finally adopted. Pure silver and chlorine were heated in sealed off glass tubes in the presence of solid lead chloride. Consequently the newly formed layer of silver chloride was saturated with respect to lead chloride, corresponding to the temperature of the experiments, 300°C. The following results were obtained.

1. In absence of lead chloride, at 300°C.

t (seconds)	3600	9000
$k \times 10^9$ gram.^{2} cm.$^{-4}$ sec.$^{-1}$	3.0	3.2

2. With $PbCl_2$ at 300°C.

t (seconds)	3960	4680	7200	7890	8220	10 800	13 500
$k \times 10^9$	1.31	0.97	1.37	1.38	0.85	2.05	1.92

The fluctuations of the results obtained in presence of lead chloride are much larger than those in experiments without lead. There is a slow increase with time, but on the average, the reaction velocity in the presence of $PbCl_2$ is reduced to about $1/2$ to $1/3$ its value without lead.

3. With cadmium chloride instead of lead chloride the following values were obtained

t (seconds)	3793	7222	8160	16 200
$k \times 10^9$	1.91	1.36	2.33	1.79

The influence of cadmium chloride, therefore, is similar to that of lead chloride. Hence the experiments confirm qualitatively the theoretical predictions. But the effect observed is much smaller than that predicted by theory.

In pure silver chloride the "lattice" concentrations (see p. 101) of silver holes and interstitial silver ions, $[Ag^+]_v$ and $[Ag^+]_i$ are given approximately by the ideal mass action law

$$[Ag^+]_v \, [Ag^+]_i = K. \qquad [9.37]$$

In a chlorine atmosphere the chloride takes up a small surplus of chlorine, equivalent to a silver deficit. This process may formally be described by the "chemical" equation

$$1/2\,(Cl_2)_{gas} + (el)_{latt} + (Ag^+)_i = (Ag^+)_{latt} + (Cl^-)_{latt} + (el)_{def} \qquad [9.38]$$

where (el) refers to electrons, and the subcripts to the gas phase, the lattice, the interstitial sites and to defect electrons respectively. Since the concentrations of all particles on lattice sites are constant, application of the ideal mass action law leads to

$$\sqrt{p_{Cl_2}} \times [Ag^+]_i/[el]_{def} = K_1. \qquad [9.39]$$

From [9.37] and [9.39]

$$[el]_{def} = (K/K_1)\sqrt{p_{Cl_2}}/[Ag^+]_v. \qquad [9.40]$$

As shown elsewhere (cf. p. 348) the rate of reaction of chlorine with silver is essentially determined by the rate of electron transfer through the chloride layer, proportional to the concentration of defect electrons at the interface chloride/chlorine. For pure silver chloride the concentration of silver ion vacancies is almost independent of the chlorine pressure, since the excess of chlorine, taken up by the silver chloride, is small compared with the concentration of vacancies and interstitial sites. Hence it follows from [9.40] that the rate of chlorination of pure silver is proportional to the square root of the chlorine pressure, as confirmed experimentally (cf. p. 349). It also follows from [9.40] that by increasing the concentration of silver ion vacancies the number of defect electrons is decreased, as it is by addition of $CdCl_2$ or $PbCl_2$ (137, 252). At 300°C solid AgCl dissolves up to 0.6 mol per cent of $PbCl_2$ and above 10 mol per cent $CdCl_2$. Ag^+-ions in the lattice are substituted by Cd^{++} or Pb^{++}-ions, equivalent number of silver ion sites being left unoccupied*. If the concentration (lattice concentration) of $PbCl_2$ or $CdCl_2$ is denoted by y, one obtains

$$[el]_{def} = (K/K_1)\sqrt{p_{Cl_2}}/y, \qquad [9.41]$$

provided that y is very large compared with the equilibrium concentration of $[Ag^+]_v$ in pure AgCl. Division of [9.41] by [9.40], applied for the same chloride pressure, with and without additional $PbCl_2$ or $CdCl_2$, gives

$$\frac{[el]_{def} \text{ (mixed crystal)}}{[el]_{def} \text{ (pure AgCl)}} = \frac{[Ag^+]_v \text{ (pure AgCl)}}{y}. \qquad [9.42]$$

Making use of the values given by Koch and Wagner (137) (cf. p. 153), one obtains for the ratio [9.42], which should also be the ratio by which additional $CdCl_2$ or $PbCl_2$ decreases the rate of tarnishing,

a) for equilibrium with solid $PbCl_2$

$$\frac{[Ag^+]_v \text{ (pure crystal)}}{y} \approx \frac{5.5\times10^{-4}}{6\times10^{-3}} \approx 0.1 , \qquad [9.43]$$

b) for equilibrium with solid $CdCl_2$

$$\frac{[Ag^+]_v \text{ (pure crystal)}}{y} \approx \frac{5.5\times10^{-4}}{0.10} \approx 0.0055 . \qquad [9.44]$$

The actual decrease found for the rate of reaction is much smaller than that predicted by [9.43] and [9.44]. Wagner and Himmler's work suggests that the lack of quantitative agreement between experiment and theory is due to the electrostatic interactions between the centres of disorder.

XI. Related reactions

We have dealt with the theory and the experiments on tarnishing processes at some length because the mechanism of these reaction is probably typical for a very large group of reactions of solids. We start with an example which has been investigated by Wagner (245, 136), viz. the formation of the complex salt Ag_2HgI_4 from the solid components AgI and HgI_2 (136). The picture, analogous to the tarnishing reactions, is

$$AgI/Ag_2HgI_4/HgI_2$$

i.e., Ag_2HgI_4 is formed at the interface between solid silver iodide and mercury iodide. For the reaction to continue it is necessary

---

* This holds better, the higher the concentrations of $CdCl_2$ or $PbCl_2$ in silver chloride, where interstitial silver ions no longer are present. At lower concentrations this relation is only approximately true, on account of the equilibrium of vacancies and interstitial ions, cf. p. 372.

that diffusion through the newly formed layer takes place. If again a quasi-stationary state is assumed, the concentration gradient within the layer of complex salt will be inversely proportional to the thickness of this layer, x, as is, consequently, the speed of formation of this layer too. Thus we arrive at our well known quadratic law

$$d x/d t = k/x \qquad x^2 = kt$$

(incomplete analogy with tarnishing reactions. A theoretical expression for k may also be derived analogous to that for tarnishing reactions (cf. p. 345, 383, 392).

The crystal structure of Ag_2HgI_4 has been investigated by Ketelaar (132, 133). Within the stability range of the α-phase (from 50 to 158°C.), the cations occupy a lattice in complete disorder, leaving a certain fraction of sites unoccupied. The compound shows a comparatively high ionic conductivity, in accordance with this structure, both the Ag^+-ions and the Hg^{++}-ions participating in the transport of electrical charge. The range of composition within which the complex salt is stable is extremely large, and in addition the two components show a marked mutual solubility. Steger (204) gives the following data, referring to 65°C.

1. AgI-HgI_2 mixed crystals, stable from 100 to 98 mol per cent of AgI.

2. Ag_2HgI_4-phase, stable from 88 to 51 mol per cent AgI.

3. HgI_2-AgI mixed crystals, stable from 8 to 0 mole per cent of AgI.

The experimental set-up, appropriate for the investigation of the reaction of formation of the complex compound, is obvious. Koch and Wagner (136) used pressed cylinders of the components and the compound, according to the scheme

$$AgI/Ag_2HgI_4/Ag_2HgI_4/HgI_2 \,,$$
$$1 \qquad 2 \qquad 3 \qquad 4$$

which were brought into contact and heated for 66 days to a temperature of 65°C. Before and after the experiment both the weight of the cylinders, as well as their silver content, were determined, the mercury content being derived from these data. The results of two experiments are reproduced in Table XIV. It is seen from this table, that the silver iodide and the mercury iodide end of the system have suffered an almost identical increase and decrease in mercury and silver content, as was to be expected. There are some minor discrepancies which need to be explained. If silver ions migrate from the silver iodide cylinder and are replaced by an equivalent number of mercury ions, one would expect a slight decrease in weight of this part of the system, due to the difference in the weight of an equivalent (Ag 107.88 and Hg 100.3). But actually a slight increase

TABLE XIV

Reaction: $2 AgI + HgI_2 = Ag_2HgI_4$ (65°C.) after Koch and Wagner (136)

	experiment III cylinders		experiment V cylinders	
	1 + 2	3 + 4	1 + 2	3 + 4
Original cylinders				
weight g	0.3280	0.3466	0.3256	0.3471
equivalents $Ag^+ \times 10^3$ . . .	1.044	0.362	1.037	0.365
equivalents $Hg^{2+} \times 10^3$ . . .	0.365	1.152	0.361	1.151
After reaction				
weight g	0.3289	0.3446	0.3267	0.3444
equivalents $Ag^+ \times 10^3$ . . .	0.881	0.526	0.868	0.529
equivalents $Hg^{2+} \times 10^3$ . . .	0.537	0.974	0.541	0.970
Change				
weight g	+ 0.0009	− 0.0020	+ 0.0011	− 0.0027
equivalents $Ag^+ \times 10^3$ . . .	− 0.163	+ 0.164	− 0.169	+ 0.164
equivalents $Hg^{2+} \times 10^3$ . . .	+ 0.172	− 0.178	+ 0.180	− 0.181
equivalents $(Ag^+ + Hg^{2+}) \times 10^3$ . .	+ 0.009	− 0.014	+ 0.011	− 0.017

reaction time 66 days = 5.7×10^6 sec.
height of single cylinder 0.1 cm.,
height Ag_2HgI_4 layer 0.2 cm.,
cross section 0.28 cm.²

is observed. Since neither a movement of iodine ions (transport number below 10^{-3}) nor of undissociated molecules seems possible, the observed effect was traced to an influence of the gas phase. The vapor pressure of HgI_2 is about 10^{-2} mm. Hg at 65°C., sufficient for an explanation of this disturbing effect. Though this impairs somewhat the quantitative reliability of the experiments, nevertheless the effects observed are quite certain, for a transport of silver iodide to the mercury iodide end of the system, as shown by the experiments, can only be due to diffusion of silver ions in exchange with mercury ions. From the data of Table XIV the following value for the reaction constant was derived

$$k = 2.1 \times 10^{-11} \text{ equivalents cm.}^{-1} \text{ sec.}^{-1}$$

k giving the number of equivalents of newly formed compound per cm.^{2} per second, if there exists a compound layer of 1 cm. thickness. The theoretical expression for the reaction constant is quite analogous to that for tarnishing processes and can be given in terms of the electromotive force E corresponding to the free energy of formation of the compound and an effective conductivity, corresponding to the galvanic cell discussed below. Thus one obtains (cf. p. 345, 383, 392)

$$k_{th} = E t_1 t_2 \sigma (c_1 + c_2)/[c_2 \, 96,500 \, (t_1 + t_2)] \qquad [9.45]$$

where t_1, t_2 are the transference numbers of silver and mercury ions, σ its conductivity, and c_1 and c_2 are the concentrations in equivalents per cm.^{3}. Wagner measured the electromotive force of the cell

$$\text{Pt/I}_2 \left| \begin{array}{c} \text{mixture of} \\ \text{AgI} + \text{Ag}_2\text{HgI}_4 \end{array} \right| \text{Ag}_2\text{HgI}_4 \left| \begin{array}{c} \text{mixture of} \\ \text{Ag}_2\text{HgI}_4 + \text{HgI}_2 \end{array} \right| \text{I}_2\text{/Pt}.$$

E was found to be 0.011 Volt. With the values given by Ketelaar ($t_1 = 0.94$, $t_2 = 0.06$, $\sigma = 1.44 \times 10^{-3} \text{Ohm}^{-1}\text{cm.}^{-1}$) one thus obtains for k

$$k_{calc} = 1.9 \times 10^{-11} \text{ equivalent cm.}^{-1} \text{ sec.}^{-1}.$$

The agreement between theory and experiment is remarkably good. Wagner suggested that many similar reactions might proceed by an analogous mechanism, for instance the formation of spinels

$$\text{MgO} + \text{Al}_2\text{O}_3 = \text{MgO} \cdot \text{Al}_2\text{O}_3 .$$

Here the order of the layers would be $\text{MgO/MgO} \cdot \text{Al}_2\text{O}_3/\text{Al}_2\text{O}_3$. It seems probable that in compounds of this type only the relatively small cations would diffuse (ionic radii Mg^{++} 0.78 Å, Al^{+++} 0.57 Å), while the oxygen ions (radius 1.32 Å) would hardly be expected to move. Such a mechanism is also suggested by the crystal structure of the spinels, viz. a cubic face-centred lattice of the oxygen ions, a lattice of the cations with random distribution of Mg^{++} and Al^{+++} ions.

A surplus of Al_2O_3 is possible by substitution of 3 Mg^{++} ions by two Al^{+++} ions and one vacancy. The scheme for the formation of a spinel would be as follows

	MgO	$MgO \cdot Al_2O_3$	Al_2O_3
Ionic diffusion		3 Mg^{++} →	
		← 2 Al^{+++}	
Phase boundary reactions	4 MgO		4 Al_2O_3
	− 3 Mg^{++}		− 2 Al^{+++}
	+ 2 Al^{+++}		+ 3 Mg^{++}
	= 1 $MgO \cdot Al_2O_3$		= 3 $MgO \cdot Al_2O_3$

An experimental proof would be much more difficult than in the case of Ag_2HgI_4, but might be attempted with thin sections, and radioactive tracers. In analogy to the above the formation of silicates might proceed as follows

	MgO	Mg_2SiO_4	$MgSiO_3$
		2 Mg^{++} →	
Ionic diffusion		← Si^{4-}	
Phase boundary reactions	4 MgO		4 $MgSiO_3$
	− 2 Mg^{++}		− Si^{4+}
	+ Si^{4+}		+ Mg^{++}
	= Mg_2SiO_4		= 3 Mg_2SiO_4

Examples are conceivable where the role of cations and anions might be the reverse of that encountered in the formation of Ag_2HgI_4. For instance

$$PbBr_2 + PbF_2 = PbBr_2 \cdot PbF_2$$

with the order of the layers $PbBr_2/PbBr_2 \cdot PbF_2/PbF_2$. Here a mobility of the anions seems rather probable (cf. p. 166). Of course there also may be cases where one type of anions and one type of cations are migrating, or where more than two species of ions are moving.

XII. Mechanism of double decompositions

Many reactions of powders, investigated by Hedvall (7, 8), Hüttig (9), Jander (124), and others, fall under this group. The explanations given for their mechanism seem hardly to be satisfactory. Hedvall explained reactions of the type

$$BaO + MgCO_3 = MgO + BaCO_3 ,$$

"acid exchange reactions", by a jumping of the CO_2 group from one oxide to the other. But this explanation could hold only for the very first stage of the reaction. Then a layer of the new compounds, of the right-hand side of the equation, must have been formed, separating the two compounds of the left-hand side. Therefore shortly after reaction has started any direct exchange between the reactants will be prevented.

An explanation of the mechanism of special reactions of this type has been given by Wagner (245). This explanation might prove as valuable for the further development of the theory of double decompositions in the solid phase, as Wagner's theory of tarnishing has become for an understanding of reactions of the type $A + B = AB$. Before turning to an attempt of a theoretical treatment of these processes, we shall review some experimental work.

The reaction

$$AgCl + Cu = CuCl + Ag,$$

the corresponding reactions with lead, and analogous reactions with silver bromide were examined in the following arrangement (245).

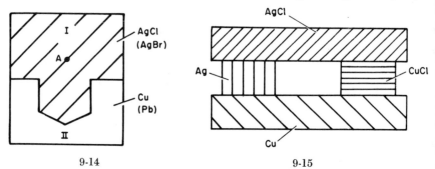

9-14   9-15

Fig. 9-14. Reaction of AgCl (AgBr) with Cu(Pb) after Wagner.
Fig. 9-15. Reaction of AgCl with Cu, schematic, after Wagner.

Into a lead or copper cylinder of 5 mm. diameter a central hole of 2 mm. diameter was drilled. Then silver chloride or bromide was pressed upon this cylinder, giving a piece of the shaded cross section of Fig. 9-14. The whole system was heated in an oxygen-free atmosphere for two days to 230°C. After the experiment the upper silver halide cylinder was broken off. Microscopic examination of the surface of fracture revealed the presence of silver fibers, still imbedded in halide. Even in the middle of the surface, i.e., in the neighborhood of point A, Fig. 9-14 and at a distance of about 1 mm. from the copper, silver crystals were detected. These observations, and others with reaction systems cut parallel to the axis, show that the arrangement of the reaction products is not according to the scheme

$$Cu/Ag/CuBr/AgBr,$$

but according to a scheme shown in Figs. 9-15, 9-16.

This scheme at once suggests an electrochemical explanation of the observed reactions. We have a galvanic cell

$$Cu / CuCl / AgCl / Ag.$$

The net effect of this cell is the dissolution of Cu at the interface Cu/CuCl and deposition of silver at the interface AgCl/Ag. The formation of CuCl and of Ag depend on chance, depending on where nuclei of these new phases are first formed. The galvanic cell is short circuited by the contact of copper with silver. The electromotive force of the corresponding cell has been measured by Haber and Tolloczko (111), giving 0.15 to 0.20 Volt. Of course, a quantitative calculation of the rate of reaction is not possible to the same degree of accuracy as that obtained for the rate of tarnishing processes, where there is a simple and definite geometrical arrangement. Here, on account of the lack of definiteness of the shape of the

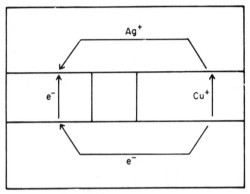

Fig. 9-16. Migration of ions and electrons in circuit of Fig. 9-15, after Wagner.

newly formed phases, only an estimate of the order of magnitude can be expected.

Again the theoretical formula, to be applied, is completely analogous to that for tarnishing processes. We shall make the assumption, (sufficiently correct for our present purpose) that the resistance of the electric circuit is chiefly due to that of the reaction products. If the new phases are formed according to the above scheme, their cross sections, q, will be proportional to their equivalent volumes, v_{Ag} and v_{CuCl}

$$q_{Ag} / q_{CuCl} = v_{Ag} / v_{CuCl} . \qquad [9.46]$$

If x is the thickness of the layer the resistance will be

$$R = \left[\frac{x}{q_{Ag}\, \sigma_{Ag}} + \frac{x}{q_{CuCl}\, \sigma_{CuCl}} \right] = \frac{x}{q} \left[\frac{1}{\sigma_{Ag}} \cdot \frac{v_{Ag} + v_{CuCl}}{v_{Ag}} + \frac{1}{\sigma_{CuCl}} \cdot \frac{v_{Ag} + v_{CuCl}}{v_{CuCl}} \right]. [9.47]$$

The reaction velocity, expressed as increase of the thickness x of the layer of reaction products with time, then becomes

$$\frac{dx}{dt} = \frac{v_{Ag}}{q_{Ag}} \frac{dn}{dt} = \frac{v_{CuCl}}{q_{CuCl}} \frac{dn}{dt} = \frac{1}{x} \frac{E}{F} \left[1 \Big/ \left\{ \frac{1}{\sigma_{Ag}\, v_{Ag}} + \frac{1}{\sigma_{CuCl}\, v_{CuCl}} \right\} \right] \qquad [9.48]$$

where n is the number of equivalents formed, and as usual, the reaction constant may be defined by

$$k = \frac{E}{F} \left[1 \Big/ \left\{ \frac{1}{\sigma_{Ag} v_{Ag}} + \frac{1}{\sigma_{CuCl} v_{CuCl}} \right\} \right] \qquad F = \text{Faraday constant}. \qquad [9.49]$$

Practically, the "reaction resistance" will be determined by that of the halide. With the values for 230°C.

$E = 0.15$ to 0.20 Volt, $\sigma_{CuCl} = 3 \times 10^{-4}$ Ohm^{-1} cm.$^{-1}$, $v_{CuCl} = 24$ cm.^{3}, we obtain

$$k = 1.3 \times 10^{-8} \text{ cm.}^2 \text{ sec.}^{-1}$$

and for $t = 2$ days $= 172\,800$ seconds, a value of x

$$x = \sqrt{2\,k\,t} \approx 7 \times 10^{-2} \text{ cm.} \qquad [9.50]$$

These values agree in order of magnitude with the observations, as the depth of the reaction zone was of the order of magnitude of the diameter of the central hole, 2 mm.

For the reaction

$$\text{Cu} + \text{AgBr} = \text{Ag} + \text{CuBr}$$

a sufficiently high reaction constant is calculated, though the electromotive force of the corresponding galvanic cell is 0.04 Volt only. The calculation of the reaction resistance is less certain than for the corresponding chloride reaction, because CuBr and AgBr form mixed crystals. The conductivity of pure CuBr at the reaction temperature of 230°C. is 3×10^{-4}, Reinhold and Schulz (190), increasing with increasing content of AgBr. But even with the lowest value of the conductivity for pure CuBr a thickness of the reaction layer of about 10^{-1} cm. is calculated, accounting for the observed depth.

For the reaction

$$2\,\text{AgCl} + \text{Pb} = 2\,\text{Ag} + \text{PbCl}_2$$

the following values are obtained for 230°C. (111, 130, 185)

$E = 0.5$ Volt, $\sigma_{PbCl_2} = 10^{-4}$, $\sigma_{PbCl_2\text{-AgCl mixed crystal}} = 4 \times 10^{-4}$ Ohm^{-1} cm.$^{-1}$, $v_{PbCl_2} = 24$ cm.^{3} per equivalent.

Thus a value of k is calculated

$$k_{calc} = 1.2 \times 10^{-8} \text{ to } 5 \times 10^{-8} \text{ cm.}^2 \text{ sec.}^{-1}$$

corresponding to a depth of the reaction zone, after two days, of

$$x = \sqrt{2\,k\,t} \approx 0.2 \text{ to } 0.4 \text{ cm},$$

again in sufficient agreement with observations.

Reactions such as the following

$$\text{Co} + \text{Cu}_2\text{O} = \text{CoO} + 2\,\text{Cu},$$

which also was investigated by Wagner (245) at 800°C., show some new features. The scheme for the reaction is analogous to that for the preceding ones, and the observations, too, are in agreement with this scheme. A different theoretical treatment is needed, however, on account of the different type of conductivity, encountered here. For all phases electronic conduction prevails. Therefore the rate determining factor will be the migration of the Co^{++} ions in the newly formed CoO phase (see Fig. 9-17, below). Since the same process is rate determining in the tarnishing reaction of cobalt, the necessary data may be obtained from measurements of the rate of oxidation of metallic cobalt. In our reaction an effective partial pressure of oxygen must be chosen, corresponding to that of the equilibrium with Cu and Cu_2O.

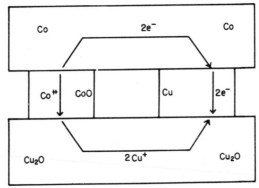

Fig. 9-17. Reaction of Co with Cu_2O, after Wagner.

For the experiments a tube of cuprous oxide was used, obtained by the oxidation of a copper tube. This tube of cuprous oxide was pressed between two pieces of cobalt. After 21 hours of heating to 800°C. the system was cut in two along its axis. Microscopic examination revealed the following. The cuprous oxide had completely disappeared, the tube consisting of an outside layer, predominantly CoO and an inside layer, predominantly of copper, though both layers were intermingled with traces of other phases. Unpublished experiments of Gruenewald gave a tarnishing constant of cobalt in pure oxygen at 1 atm. and 800°C. of 1.8×10^{-10} for electrolytic cobalt, while the values for technical cobalt, as used here, were much higher, viz 35×10^{-10} cm.^{2} sec.$^{-1}$. This would correspond to an oxide layer of 0.025 cm., formed within 21 hours. This should be the thickness of the reaction zone in the above experiments. But in spite of a much lower effective oxygen pressure, this thickness is still higher, probably on account of the formation of mixed crystals of CoO with Cu_2O, which might give a considerably increased ionic conductivity component, Koch and Wagner (137).

Results, qualitatively similar to the above, have also been obtained with the system $Fe + Cu_2O$.

Thus one may draw the general conclusion that, while the results for these double decompositions are not of such striking simplicity as those for tarnishing reactions and their analogues, these experiments are wholly consistent with the ideas developed by Wagner. Where a theoretical calculation has been possible, at least qualitative agreement has been achieved.

XIII. Powder reactions

Though definite statements about the mechanism of the vast class of powder reactions, as investigated by Hedvall (7, 8), Jander (124), and others are not possible, the most plausible explanation, advanced so far, is that of Wagner, based upon the above phenomena. Fig. 9-18 gives the scheme, by which the powder reaction

$$AgCl + NaI = AgI + NaCl$$

might proceed. It is seen that the electrical circuit, representing this reaction, is composed partly of the reaction products and partly of the reactants themselves. Thus the conductivity of the reactants might play a role in these reactions, as often pointed out by the observers. Such an influence could not at all be understood on the basis of a model giving simply successive layers of the reaction products between those of the reactants. Since powder reactions are often observed at comparatively low temperatures, ionic conduction due to irreversible disorder in the lattice or due to minute impurities might become of importance. In powders of very small grain size migration of ions might even occur relatively quickly compared with the speed of formation of nuclei and of transition reaction at phase boundaries. Thus such processes might play an important role in the complex course of reactions observed. For very small grains also migration of particles on surfaces may become important. Thus these principles might lead to an understanding of the embarassing complexity of the observations with powder reactions.

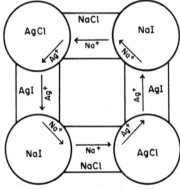

Fig. 9-18. Powder reaction of AgCl + NaI, after Wagner.

XIV. Wagner's theory of the rate of formation of protective films*

On p. 345 we gave the exact formula for the rate of formation of a surface film by substituting a galvanic cell of electromotive force, corresponding to the free energy of the reaction, closed by an outside resistance equal to that calculated for the electronic conductivity of the oxide layer, or other layer under consideration. Here we shall give the proof for this formula.

We shall use the following notations. t_1, t_2, and t_3 are the transference numbers of cations, anions and electrons, respectively, z_1, z_2 and z_3 are the corresponding valencies, i.e., the numbers of elementary positive charges, carried by a particle, consequently z_2 and $z_3 < 0$ and $z_3 = -1$. The reaction under consideration is essentially an electrochemical process. Therefore we have to deal with the currents of the three species, caused partly by a gradient in chemical potential and partly by the gradient of an electrical potential. If μ_i is the chemical potential of N particles i, N being Avogadro's number, the force acting on the average upon a particle i in the x-direction is

$$-\frac{1}{N}\frac{\partial \mu_i}{\partial x}.$$

If u_i is the mobility of particles of species i, i.e., the velocity obtained under the action of unit force, the velocity of these particles due to the gradient of the chemical potential will be

$$v_i = -\frac{u_i}{N}\frac{\partial \mu_i}{\partial x}.$$

The corresponding expression for the action of the electrical potential φ, with ε elementary charge, will be

$$- u_i z_i \varepsilon \, \partial\varphi/\partial x.$$

Hence the total current of the component i of concentration c_i for unit cross section will be

$$J_i = - c_i u_i \left\{ \frac{1}{N}\frac{\partial \mu_i}{\partial x} + z_i \varepsilon \frac{\partial \varphi}{\partial x} \right\}. \qquad [9.51]$$

The mobility u_i is derived in the usual way from the conductivity σ and the transference number t_i (cf. p. 139ff., 180)

$$u_i = \frac{300}{96,500}\frac{\sigma t_i}{\varepsilon |z_i| c_i}, \quad i = 1, 2, 3, \qquad [9.52]$$

where the factor 300 is introduced to convert practical units of voltage to absolute units, and 96,500 is Faraday's equivalent. Upon substituting [9.52] in [9.51] we obtain

$$J_i = \frac{300}{96,500}\frac{\sigma t_i}{|z_i|\varepsilon N}\left\{ -\frac{\partial \mu_i}{\partial x} - z_i N \varepsilon \frac{\partial \varphi}{\partial x} \right\}. \qquad [9.53]$$

* cf. (23, 237, 243, 250).

In the above equations the concentrations c_i are assumed to be given in equivalents per c. c. Electrical neutrality requires that equal amounts of positive and negative charge are transferred, consequently the current of positively charged particles, J_1, must be equal to that of the negatively charged particles, $J_2 + J_3$, and

$$J_1 - J_2 - J_3 = 0 \ . \tag{9.54}$$

The additional relation [9.54], together with the three eqs. [9.53] permits the elimination of the gradient of the electrical potential $\partial \varphi / \partial x$. From eqs. [9.53] and [9.54] we obtain

$$\frac{\partial \varphi}{\partial x} = -\frac{1}{\varepsilon N} \left\{ \frac{t_1}{|z_1|} \frac{\partial \mu_1}{\partial x} - \frac{t_2}{|z_2|} \frac{\partial \mu_2}{\partial x} - \frac{t_3}{|z_3|} \frac{\partial \mu_3}{\partial x} \right\} \tag{9.55}$$

which may be substituted in [9.53].

The μ_i for the three species of charged particles are not directly accessible to measurement. We may, however, eliminate the μ_i, also, by considering the equilibrium conditions. We write the chemical equations (making use of $|z_3| = 1$. Hence for the further calculations $|z_3|$ in eq. [9.55] also must be put equal to 1)

    a. 1 metal cation $+ |z_1|$ electrons $= 1$ metal atom

    b. 1 electronegative atom $X + |z_2|$ electrons $= 1$ X-anion,   [9.56]

and the corresponding equilibrium conditions

    a. $\mu_1 + |z_1| \mu_3 = \mu_{me}$ [9.57]
    b. $\mu_x + |z_3| \mu_3 = \mu_2$

where μ_{me} and μ_x are the chemical potentials of neutral Me and X. The Gibbs-Duhem equation provides an additional relation

$$n_{me} \, d \, \mu_{me} + n_x \, d \, \mu_x = 0 \tag{9.58}$$

where n_{me} and n_x are the molar concentrations of Me and of X. For stoichiometric composition we have $n_{me} : n_x = |z_2| : |z_1|$, and from eq. [9.58] we obtain

$$d \mu_x = - \left| \frac{z_2}{z_1} \right| d \mu_{me} \ . \tag{9.59}$$

By means of eqs. [9.55], [9.57], and [9.59] μ_1, μ_2, μ_3, and $\partial \varphi / \partial x$ may be eliminated from [9.53], thus giving finally

$$J_1 = \frac{300}{96,500} \frac{t_1 t_3 \sigma}{N \varepsilon} \left(-\frac{1}{|z_1|} \frac{\partial \mu_{me}}{\partial x} \right)$$

$$J_2 = \frac{300}{96,500} \frac{t_2 t_3 \sigma}{N \varepsilon} \left(\frac{1}{|z_1|} \frac{\partial \mu_{me}}{\partial x} \right) \tag{9.60}$$

$$J_3 = \frac{300}{96,500} \frac{(t_1 + t_2) t_3 \sigma}{N \varepsilon} \left(-\frac{1}{|z_1|} \frac{\partial \mu_{me}}{\partial x} \right)$$

and

$$J_{12} = |J_1| + |J_2| = \frac{300}{96,500} \frac{(t_1+t_2)\,t_3}{\varepsilon\,N} \frac{\sigma}{|z_1|} \left| \frac{\partial\,\mu_{me}}{\partial\,x} \right|. \qquad [9.61]$$

Wagner points out the remarkable symmetry of these final equation. The rate of reaction depends on the sum of the mobilities of anions and cations only, and the total mobilities of the ions and that of the electrons enter the result quite symmetrically. Because of [9.54] we may replace $\frac{1}{|z_1|} \partial \mu_{me}$ everywhere by $\frac{-1}{|z_2|} \partial \mu_x$, thus we may write instead of [9.61]

$$J_{12} = \frac{300}{96,500} \frac{(t_1+t_2)\,t_3}{\varepsilon\,N} \frac{\sigma}{|z_2|} \left| \frac{\partial\,\mu_x}{\partial\,x} \right|. \qquad [9.62]$$

For reasons of continuity J_{12} must be constant throughout the whole layer, while, in general, $\partial\mu_x/\partial x$, t_1, t_2, t_3 and σ will vary, on account of the variation of the composition of the layer from the side of the metal to that of the attacking agent. One may integrate [9.62] with respect to the coordinate x from the "inner" side, subscript i, i. e., the side of the layer which is in contact with the metal, to the outer side, subscript o, which is in contact with the attacking agent. Thus we obtain

$$J_{12}\xi = \frac{300}{96,500\,\varepsilon\,N} \left| \int_i^o (t_1+t_2)\,t_3\,\sigma\,\frac{d\mu_{me}}{|z_1|} \right|$$

$$= \frac{300}{96,500\,\varepsilon\,N} \left| \int_i^o (t_1+t_2)\,t_3\,\sigma\,\frac{d\mu_x}{|z_2|} \right| \qquad [9.63]$$

where ξ = the thickness of the layer.

This may be written, by introducing appropriate averages for t_1, t_2, t_3 and σ

$$J_{12}\,\xi = \frac{300}{96,500\,\varepsilon\,N} (\bar{t_1}+\bar{t_2})\,\bar{t_3}\,\bar{\sigma}\,\frac{(\mu_{me})_i - (\mu_{me})_o}{|z_1|}$$

$$= \frac{300}{96,500\,\varepsilon\,N} (\bar{t_1}+\bar{t_2})\,\bar{t_3}\,\bar{\sigma}\,\frac{(\mu_x)_o - (\mu_x)_i}{|z_2|}. \qquad [9.64]$$

The terms

$$\frac{(\mu_{me})_i - (\mu_{me})_o}{|z_1|} = \frac{(\mu_x)_o - (\mu_x)_i}{|z_2|}$$

are equal to the affinity of the reaction per equivalent, and may be expressed by the electromotive force E of the corresponding reversible galvanic cell (which can be measured directly only for negligible electronic conduction)

$$E = \frac{300}{\varepsilon\,N} \frac{(\mu_{me})_i - (\mu_{me})_o}{|z_1|} \qquad [9.65]$$

if E is measured in volts. Thus we have finally

$$J_{12} = \frac{1}{\xi} \left[\frac{(t_1 + t_2)\, \bar{t}_3\, \bar{\sigma}\, E}{96,500} \right] = \frac{k}{\xi} \qquad [9.66]$$

which is identical with the formula of p. 345.

XV. "Electronic disorder"*

Disorder in crystals may be of influence not only upon ionic conduction but also upon electronic conduction. Of course there exists no sharp borderline between ionic and electronic conductors. If the partial conductivity of the electrons, σ_{el}, is very large compared with that of the ions, we talk of an electronic conductor, and vice versa. But all transitions between these two limiting cases are possible, and actually do occur, even with the same substance, depending on outside conditions like temperature, gas pressure etc. For instance, CuI is an electronic semiconductor at low temperatures, its conductivity depending strongly on the vapor pressure of iodine, whereas the α-modification, stable above 400°C., is an ionic conductor of high conductivity, with negligible electronic component of conduction. But even very small components of electronic or ionic conduction may be of major importance for certain phenomena, as is seen from the above formulae for the rate of formation of protective layers, p. 383ff. If either the electronic or the ionic component of conduction were exactly zero the rate of those reactions would vanish.

In distinction to metals, semiconductors usually have a positive temperature coefficient of conductivity. The observed behaviour of conduction may be due to the fact that at the absolute zero of temperature no free electrons are present, while with rising temperature an increasing number of free electrons is formed, with absorption of energy, which contribute to conduction, in analogy with the interstitial ions in case of ionic conduction. One may write for this process

undisturbed crystal $\rightleftarrows$ quasi-free electron + defect electron.   [9.67]

By defect electron we mean a position with a deficit of one electron. In the classical corpuscular picture [9.67], for instance, might be interpreted in one of the following ways

$$Me^{n+} \rightleftarrows Me^{(n+1)+} + \text{electron}$$

or

$$X^{n-} \rightleftarrows X^{(n-1)-} + \text{electron}$$

---

* It is not the aim here to give a theory of semiconductors, for which the reader is referred to the literature (16, 20, 24).

where either a metal ion with n positive elementary charges has given off one electron, remaining itself $(n + 1)$ times positively charged, or a negative ion of n elementary charges has given off an elementary charge, remaining $(n - 1)$ times negatively charged. Not only the free electron may contribute to the conductivity, but the defect electron too. In the classical corpuscular picture it plays the same role for electronic conduction as an ion vacancy for ionic conduction. In accordance with this example, "motion" of a defect electron means that neighboring electrons jump into the gap provided by the defect electron. Therefore we have in the corpuscular picture

$$Me^{n+} + Me^{(n+1)+} \rightarrow Me^{(n+1)+} + Me^{n+} .$$
$$\searrow \text{electron} \nearrow$$

The consequences of this corpuscular model are preserved in the quantum mechanical theory of electronic conduction.

The quantum mechanical theory of metallic conduction leads to the following picture. There are certain energy bands for electrons in a crystal, i.e., regions of a finite energy interval, containing, on account of the Pauli exclusion principle, a finite number of quantum states in which electrons may be accommodated. A partially filled electron band gives rise to electronic conduction, as in metals. For, in order to contribute to conduction, an electron must gain a certain excess velocity in the direction of an applied electric field. This means that the electron must pass into another quantum state of slightly higher energy. This is always possible for electrons with energies not much below the upper limit of the energy of the electrons present, provided the electron band is only partially filled, i.e., there exist unoccupied quantum states of energy not much higher than that of the electrons in this band. If, however, the band is completely filled and separated from the following band by a finite gap in energy, then the electrons in this band cannot contribute to conduction. But if at sufficiently high temperature in thermal equilibrium some electrons are removed from the highest completely occupied energy band and are transferred to an higher empty energy band, then these transferred electrons as well as the holes left in the lower bands, i.e., the defect electrons, may contribute to conduction.

This is rather obvious for the electrons in the higher band. The defect electrons also contribute to conduction due to the fact that they provide unoccupied quantum states which may be occupied by electrons gaining energy in an applied electric field, thus contributing to conduction.

For our present purpose it is not necessary to make any explicit use of quantum theory. It is sufficient to know that by supplying energy we may transfer electrons into quasi-free states where they give rise to electronic conduction, and that there may exist defect electrons with properties corresponding to those of electrons (of opposite sign).

Since in semiconductors, contrary to metals, the number of quasi-free electrons and that of defect electrons are always small compared with that of the atoms or ions present, we may apply, to a certain approximation, the law of mass action upon the "reaction" formulated by eq. [9.67], thus obtaining

$$n_{el} \times n_{def\,el} = \text{const } [= f(T)] . \qquad [9.68]$$

Experience shows that it is to be considered an exception if semi-conduction in pure crystals of stoichiometric composition is due to a process such as [9.67]. Since the numbers of free electrons and of defect electrons are always very small compared with the number of lattice sites, even very small impurities may be of considerable influence if they are apt to increase or decrease the numbers of conducting particles. As we have seen before (Chap. II, p. 83ff) small deviations from the exact stoichiometric composition may be considered quite normal. There may be a surplus of the electropositive component Me or of the electronegative component X. The surplus may arise in three ways.

1. Substitution type. Some of the Me sites in the lattice are occupied by X-particles, or vice versa. Since we are dealing chiefly with ionic crystals, this type of disorder is extremely unlikely, and will not be further considered.

2. Interstitial type. The particles of the component which is present in excess are located on interstitial sites of the ordinary lattice, normally unoccupied.

3. Vacancy type. A relative surplus of one component arises by the fact that lattice sites of the other component remain unoccupied.

In an ionic lattice a surplus of one component may also be present in the form of ions. On account of the condition of electric neutrality a surplus of ions of one type is possible only if the additional charge is compensated by a corresponding change in the number of electrons. For instance, if Me atoms are added, we may have either

$$Me \rightarrow Me^{\nu+} + \nu \text{ electrons} \qquad [9.69]$$

or

$$X \rightarrow X^{\nu-} - \nu \text{ electrons}, \qquad [9.70]$$

i.e., an excess of an electropositive component will either produce a corresponding number of free electrons or decrease the number of defect electrons already present, while an excess of an electronegative component will increase the number of defect electrons or decrease accordingly the number of free electrons. Thus a surplus of either component may increase the conductivity as well as decrease it (cf. Wagner (238, 241), Gudden and Schottky (96)), depending on the mechanism of conduction prevailing in the compound under consideration.

We shall now consider the special case of cuprous oxide, because of its importance with respect to the rate of the oxidation reaction of copper. Cuprous oxide takes up an excess of oxygen, depending on oxygen pressure. The most probable mechanism is the formation of vacancies in the lattice of the copper ions, the surplus oxygen entering the normal lattice of the oxygen ions, for every oxygen molecule taken up by the cuprous oxide 4 free electrons being consumed. This may be written in form of the equation

$$O_2 \text{ (gas)} + 4 e^- \text{ (lattice)} = 2 O^{2-}\text{(lattice)} + 4 Cu^+ \text{ vacancies}$$
$$+ 4 e^- \text{ vacancies.} \qquad [9.71]$$

This equation is to be understood in the following way. Since the oxygen is being built-in on normal lattice sites, new lattice sites must be produced, thus the corresponding number of Cu^+-vacancies appear on the right hand side of the equation. It is not specified from what sites in the lattice the free electrons come. The most probable mechanism consists in the removal of electrons from Cu^+-ions, leaving them as Cu^{++}-ions, which then would represent electron vacancies. Application of the law of mass action to equation [9.71] gives

$$\frac{[Cu^+ \text{ vacancies}]^4 \, [e^- \text{ vacancies}]^4}{p_{O_2}} = \text{const}. \qquad [9.72]$$

where the quantities in brackets mean concentrations; the concentrations of lattice electrons and oxygen ions, being constant, have been incorporated into the constant. If there is no appreciable disorder except that caused by surplus oxygen, then the numbers of defect electrons and of Cu^+-vacancies must be equal, and it follows from [9.72] that

$$[Cu^+\text{-vacancies}] = [e^-\text{-vacancies}] = \text{const} \, p_{O_2}^{1/8}. \qquad [9.73]$$

If the electronic conduction of cuprous oxide is due to defect electrons, the conductivity should be proportional to the concentration of defect electrons, i.e., to the $1/8$-th power of the oxygen pressure. As we have seen already, cf. p. 354, the experimental results do not agree exactly with this theoretical prediction, but the observed law, $\sim p^{1/7}$, comes rather close to it. Of course the application of the ideal mass action law can be an approximation only. Deviations in the sense predicted by the Debye-Hückel theory seem quite probable. Wagner (64) points out that this influence works in a direction to improve the agreement between theory and experiment. Besides there may be a certain association of electron vacancies and Cu^+ vacancies. These associated centres of disorder would not play a role in the conduction mechanism, but they would, however, be responsible for absorption of oxygen.

Wagner and Dünwald (64) tested these ideas further by measuring the amount of oxygen taken up by cuprous oxide at varied oxygen pressures and temperatures. These measurements give at the same time the deficit of copper and therefore the concentration gradient of copper ions in the oxide layer during reaction of copper with oxygen. Wagner and Dünwald (64) determined the excess of oxygen by a gas volumetric method. They introduced a magnitude $\eta = \Delta y / \Delta \log p_{O_2}$, where y is the excess amount of oxygen, in gram atoms of oxygen per mol of Cu_2O, Δy is the change of this magnitude for a change $\Delta \log p_{O_2}$. They found for 1000°C. and $p_{O_2} \approx 30$ mm. Hg $\eta = 3 \times 10^{-4}$ g. atom O per mole Cu_2O, while for $p_{O_2} \approx 0.3$ mm. Hg $\eta \approx 1.6 \times 10^{-4}$. In the later experiments with Hammen (251) the content of Cu^{++} ions, present in cuprous oxide was titrated by means of $CrSO_4$ solution, after the substance had been dissolved in hydrochloric acid under an oxygen-free atmosphere. The values thus obtained differ somewhat from the previous results and are reproduced in Table XV. There is obtained a value of $\eta = 1.9 \times 10^{-4}$ at 1000°C. The authors consider this value the more reliable one. While for the above model the formula had been derived

$$y = K \, p_{O_2}^{1/8} \tag{9.74}$$

the empirical values correspond to a relation

$$y = \text{const } p_{O_2}^{1/5} . \tag{9.75}$$

In eq. [9.74] use has been made of the ideal mass action law, applied to the charged quasi-particles Cu^+ vacancies (equivalent to a negative charge) and defect electrons (equivalent to a positive charge). A certain improvement of the theory is possible by the introduction of activity coefficients calculated on the basis of the first approximation of the Debye-Hückel theory. Thus the authors write instead of [9.73] and [9.74]

$$[Cu^+ \text{ vacancies}] \, \bar{f} = [\text{defect electrons}] \, \bar{f} = \text{const } p_{O_2}^{1/8} \tag{9.76}$$

or

$$y \, \bar{f} = K \, p_{O_2}^{1/8} . \tag{9.77}$$

The Debye-Hückel theory gives $f = 0.5$ instead of 1 in the ideal case, and $- \log \bar{f} \sim \sqrt{y}$, thus

$$\frac{d \log y}{d \log p_{O_2}} = \frac{1/8}{1 + d \log f / d \log y} = \frac{1/8}{1 + 1/2 \log f} = 1/5.2 \tag{9.78}$$
$$\text{for } y = 0.83 \times 10^{-3} .$$

This result comes rather close to the empirical formula [9.75].

TABLE XV

Mobilities of defect electrons and Cu$^+$-vacancies in Cu$_2$O, after Wagner and Hammen (251)

Temperature °C.	p_{O_2} mm. Hg	y	σ Ohm^{-1} cm.$^{-1}$	t_{Cu}^+	u (el)$_v$ cm.$^2 \times$ sec.$^{-1}$ $\times$ Volt^{-1}	u (Cu$^+$)$_v$ cm.$^2 \times$ sec.$^{-1}$ $\times$ Volt^{-1}
1000	33	1.14×10^{-3}	7.4	5.2×10^{-4}	8.2	4.3×10^{-4}
1000	6.5	0.83×10^{-3}	6.0	5.2×10^{-4}	9.1	4.7×10^{-4}
1000	0.73	0.52×10^{-3}	4.5	5.2×10^{-4}	10.9	5.7×10^{-4}
900	6.5	0.54×10^{-3}	3.5	3.5×10^{-4}	8.2	2.9×10^{-4}
900	0.73	0.30×10^{-3}	2.6	3.5×10^{-4}	11.0	3.8×10^{-4}

$$u \text{ (el)}_v = \frac{\sigma \cdot (1 - t_{Cu}^+) \cdot v}{y \cdot 96500} \quad ; \qquad u \text{ (Cu}^+)_v = \frac{\sigma \cdot t_{Cu}^+ \cdot v}{y \cdot 96500}$$

t_{Cu}^+ = transference number of Cu$^+$ ions after Gundermann and Wagner (108)

σ = conductivity of Cu$_2$O, after Gundermann (109)

y = g. atom excess oxygen per mol Cu$_2$O

v = 12,2 cm.^{3} (equivalent volume of Cu$_2$O).

Since the concentrations of Cu^+ vacancies and of defect electrons now are known, it is possible to calculate the mobilities of these centres, from measured values of the conductivity and of the transference numbers of the Cu^+ ions. The results are listed in Table XV.

With the above theoretical and experimental results one obtains the equation for the speed of formation of an oxide layer on copper, as follows, Wagner and Grünewald (250),

$$k = \frac{300 \times \sigma(1)\, t_1\, v\, RT}{96{,}500 \times 2\, |z_2|\, \varepsilon\, N} \left\{ \left[\sqrt[v]{p_{O_2}} \right]_o - \left[\sqrt[v]{p_{O_2}} \right]_i \right\}. \qquad [9.79]$$

Here $\sigma(1)$ is the conductivity of cuprous oxide at unit pressure of oxygen, and the conductivity of Cu_2O has been written

$$\sigma(p) = \sigma(1) \sqrt[v]{\frac{p}{(p = 1\,atmos)}}.$$

The subscripts o and i refer to the outer (oxygen) and inner (metal) side of the cuprous oxide layer. The calculated values of Table VII are thus obtained and agree remarkably well with the observed values.

The deviations from stoichiometric composition of CuI with varying pressure of iodine and the dependence of the electric conductivity of CuI on the concentration of absorbed iodine atoms have been thoroughly investigated by Maurer (154). He used a magnetically operated quartz microbalance for the determination of the iodine excess. The density n of absorbed iodine atoms could be represented by an equation

$$n \sim p_{I_2}^{1/2}. \qquad [9.80]$$

The dependence on temperature was exponential, giving a heat of reaction of 0.24 electron volt per atom absorbed.

The electric conductivity was found to vary approximately as the $4/3^{th}$ power of the density of the absorbed iodine atoms

$$\sigma \sim n^{4/3}. \qquad [9.81]$$

XVI. The theory of the formation of addition compounds

We consider reactions of the type *

$$A + B \to AB$$

where the reaction product AB is formed in a continuous layer between the reactants A and B. The following theory is due to Wagner (244). We write, in complete analogy to the relations derived for the oxidation

* Here A and B are ionic compounds, having either the anion or the cation in common denoted by 3, while the diffusing particles are referred to as 1 and 2.

of metals and related processes for the flow of matter

$$\text{a.}\quad J_1 = -u_1 c_1 \left\{ \frac{1}{N} \frac{\partial \mu_1}{\partial x} + z_1 \varepsilon \frac{\partial \varphi}{\partial x} \right\}$$

$$\text{b.}\quad J_2 = -u_2 c_2 \left\{ \frac{1}{N} \frac{\partial \mu_2}{\partial x} + z_2 \varepsilon \frac{\partial \varphi}{\partial x} \right\} \qquad [9.82]$$

where u_1, u_2 are the mobilities, c_1, c_2 the concentrations (in equivalents per c.c.), μ_1, μ_2 the chemical potentials, φ the electric potential, and z_1 and z_2 the valencies of the ions 1 and 2.

Electric neutrality requires that the total rate of transport is zero, thus, after elimination of $\partial \varphi / \partial x$

$$J_1 = -J_2 = \frac{-1}{N \left[1/(z_1 c_1 u_1) + 1/(z_2 c_2 u_2) \right]} \left[\frac{1}{z_1} \frac{\partial \mu_1}{\partial x} - \frac{1}{z_2} \frac{\partial \mu_2}{\partial x} \right]. \qquad [9.83]$$

We introduce the chemical potentials μ_A and μ_B of the reacting compounds A and B, which are connected to μ_1 and μ_2 and the chemical potential μ_3 of the anions, common to A and B, by

$$\mu_A = \frac{1}{z_1} \mu_1 + \frac{1}{|z_3|} \mu_3 \qquad \mu_B = \frac{1}{z_2} \mu_2 + \frac{1}{|z_3|} \mu_3. \qquad [9.84]$$

The roles of the cations and anions may, of course, be reversed. Eq. [9.84] and the Gibbs-Duhem relation

$$c_1 \, d\mu_A + c_2 \, d\mu_B = 0$$

give

$$\frac{1}{z_1} \frac{\partial \mu_1}{\partial x} - \frac{1}{z_2} \frac{\partial \mu_2}{\partial x} = \frac{\partial (\mu_A - \mu_B)}{\partial x} = \frac{c_1 + c_2}{c_2} \frac{\partial \mu_A}{\partial x} = -\frac{c_1 + c_2}{c_1} \frac{\partial \mu_B}{\partial x}. \qquad [9.85]$$

[9.85] may be determined from the electromotive force of an appropriately chosen galvanic cell. The mobilities, as usual, can be derived either from coefficients of self diffusion, D_1 and D_2 for the two kinds of ions, or from electric conductivity σ and transference numbers t_1, t_2

$$u_i = D_i / kT \quad \text{or} \quad u_i = \frac{300}{96,500} \frac{t_i \sigma}{z_i \varepsilon c_i} \qquad i = 1, 2 \qquad [9.86]$$

where ε is the elementary charge. Thus the result may be written in the alternative forms

$$J_1 = -J_2 = -\frac{z_1 c_1 D_1 z_2 c_2 D_2}{z_1 c_1 D_1 + z_2 c_2 D_2} \frac{1}{RT} \frac{c_1 + c_2}{c_2} \frac{\partial \mu_A}{\partial x}$$

$$= -\frac{300 \, \sigma}{96,500} \frac{t_1 t_2}{t_1 + t_2} \frac{c_1 + c_2}{c_2 \varepsilon N} \frac{\partial \mu_A}{\partial x}. \qquad [9.87]$$

In either expression $\dfrac{c_1 + c_2}{c_2} \dfrac{\partial \mu_A}{\partial x}$ may be replaced by $-\dfrac{c_1 + c_2}{c_1} \dfrac{\partial \mu_B}{\partial x}$.

[9.87] refers to any value of the coordinate x across the layer of the reaction product. In order to obtain an expression containing the finite differences $\Delta \mu_A$ or $\Delta \mu_B$, we integrate our equation with respect to x over the thickness of the reaction layer, ξ, and have

$$|J_1| = |J_2| = \frac{1}{\xi}\left[\frac{\overline{z_1 c_1 D_1 z_2 c_2 D_2}}{z_1 c_1 D_1 + z_2 c_2 D_2}\left(\overline{\frac{c_1+c_2}{c_2}}\right)\frac{\Delta\mu_A}{RT}\right]$$

$$= \frac{1}{\xi}\left[\frac{300}{96,500}\left(\overline{\frac{t_1 t_2}{t_1+t_2}}\right)\sigma\left(\overline{\frac{c_1+c_2}{c_2}}\right)\frac{\Delta\mu_A}{\varepsilon N}\right] \qquad [9.88]$$

the bars indicating averaging. In the above derivation, as in the analogous calculations for the rate of oxidation etc., the assumption is implied that the range of concentration, within which the compound formed is stable, is not too wide. Otherwise the above equations would be approximations only. The terms in the brackets are identical with the reaction constant k (cf. p. 353), with the dimension equivalents per cm. per sec.

XVII. Some remarks concerning Wagner's theory and the paper of Bardeen, Brattain and Shockley

Wagner took care to give his formulae for the rate of formation of protective films in the most general form, making use only of magnitudes which normally are observable, such as gas pressure or chemical potential of metal and electronegative component. In the special case of cuprous oxide, due to the work of Wagner and others, we know the concentration of vacancies and of defect electrons. Hence in the resulting equations we may retain expressions pertaining to these magnitudes.

The short cuts which Bardeen, Brattain and Shockley (31) apply, mean in Wagner's notation, that in the equation for $\frac{\partial\varphi}{\partial x}$, t_2, the transference number of the anions, has been put equal to zero, thus

$$\frac{\partial\varphi}{\partial x} = -\frac{1}{\varepsilon N}\left\{\frac{t_1}{|z_1|}\frac{\partial\mu_1}{\partial x} - \frac{t_3}{|z_3|}\frac{\partial\mu_3}{\partial x}\right\}. \qquad [9.89]$$

If further the first term in the bracket is neglected, because $t_{cat} \ll t_{el}$, we have (with $t_3 \approx 1$)

$$\frac{\partial\varphi}{\partial x} \approx -\frac{1}{\varepsilon N|z_3|}\frac{\partial\mu_3}{\partial x} \qquad [9.90]$$

and the equation for the diffusion current becomes

$$J = -c_1 u_1\left\{\frac{1}{N}\frac{\partial\mu_1}{\partial x} - \frac{1}{N}\frac{\partial\mu_3}{\partial x}\right\}. \qquad [9.91]$$

Assuming the validity of the laws of ideal solution, we may write instead of [9.91]

$$J = -c_1 u_1 kT\left\{\frac{1}{c_1}\frac{\partial c_1}{\partial x} - \frac{1}{c_3}\frac{\partial c_3}{\partial x}\right\}. \qquad [9.92]$$

Now we might have written all the equations in terms of defect electrons instead of electrons. Then all equations would remain essentially the same with the exception that the signs of all terms referring to defect electrons would have to be reversed. Consequently [9.92] must be replaced by the equation

$$J = -c_1 D \left\{ \frac{1}{c_1} \frac{\partial c_1}{\partial x} + \frac{1}{c_3'} \frac{\partial c_3'}{\partial x} \right\}, \quad D = u_1 k T \qquad [9.93]$$

where the prime refers to defect electrons. Since the gradient of cations is due to the presence of vacancies which are also responsible for the defect electrons, both terms in the brackets are equal, giving the final expression

$$J = -2 D \frac{\partial c_1}{\partial x} \qquad [9.94]$$

which is identical with that used by Bardeen, Brattain and Shockley.

XVIII. Further investigations of oxidation reactions

Evans (74, 75, 76, 77, 79) has discussed the several possibilities for film growth on metal surfaces and has given theoretical explanations for the different laws of growth, found by Vernon (234).

The parabolic law is derived in the usual way. Taking into account cracking of the surface film, he arrives at a more general equation

$$\frac{dx}{dt} = \frac{k_2}{k_3 + k_4 x} \qquad [9.95]$$

which for $k_3 \ll k_4 x$ gives the parabolic law, while for $k_3 \ll k_4 x$ a rectilinear relation is obtained. In the case of blistering of the film, Evans suggests as the equation for film growth

$$\frac{dx}{dt} = \frac{k_2}{k_3} \exp(-k_5 x) \qquad [9.96]$$

or

$$x = k \log(k' t + k'') \qquad [9.97]$$

the logarithmic law.

Oxidation of metals, involving diffusion processes, may not only occur by the formation of surface films, but also in the interior of the metal, provided that a metal with high affinity for oxygen is dissolved in a base metal with sufficient solubility for oxygen (Fröhlich (95), Rhines (193), Meijering (159, 160, 161)). Thus, for instance, zinc and other metals, dissolved in copper may be oxidized (Fröhlich, Rhines), Mg in silver (Meijering and Druyvesteyn) etc.

Gulbransen and collaborators (97, 98, 99, 100, 101, 102, 103, 104, 105, 106, 107) carried out extensive studies of the formation of oxide films on metals, following the reaction by means of a microbalance, of about 3×10^{-7} g. sensitivity, and using electron diffraction (104, 172) and electron microscope methods for the investigation of thin oxide films. He also gave a transition state theory of the formation of thin oxide films on metals (99).

Above a certain thickness and within definite pressure and temperature ranges, the parabolic law is obeyed in the oxidation of electrolytic iron, stainless steel and copper

$$s^2 = k\,t \qquad [9.98]$$

where s is the weight of oxide, formed per cm.^{2} in time t. The validity of this relation is seen from Fig. 9-19.

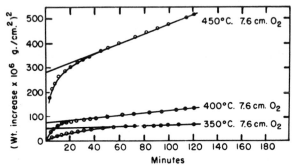

Fig. 9-19. Oxidation of electrolytic iron, after Gulbransen.

Rate constants and diffusion constants are seen from Table XVI.

TABLE XVI

Parabolic Rate Constants and Diffusion Constants, after Gulbransen (99)

	$t°$C.	$\dfrac{1}{T} \times 10^3$	k (g./cm.^{2})^2/sec.	D_0 cm.^{2}/sec.
Iron	350	1.605	2.63×10^{-15}	3.70×10^{-9}
7.6 cm. O$_2$	400	1.486	8.98×10^{-15}	3.35×10^{-9}
$E = 22.600$	450	1.383	$33.4 \ \times 10^{-15}$	3.66×10^{-9}
Stainless Steel . . .	550	1.215	0.55×10^{-15}	0.66×10^{-9}
7.6 cm. O$_2$	600	1.145	$1.7 \ \times 10^{-15}$	0.68×10^{-9}
$E = 29.600$	650	1.083	3.52×10^{-15}	0.60×10^{-9}
Copper	139	2.426	2.86×10^{-15}	4.65×10^{-4}
15.2 cm. O$_2$	169	2.26	$23.4 \ \times 10^{-15}$	5.44×10^{-4}
$E = 24.900$				

For molybdenum (106) and tungsten (105) the parabolic law has been observed, also, within a temperature range from 250 to 450°C. and from 400 to 500°C., respectively, while for magnesium (100) a linear relation holds above 475°C.

For aluminum the parabolic law could be observed within the temperature range from 350 to 450°C. Numerical values are seen from Table XVII.

TABLE XVII

Parabolic rate constants k and diffusion constants, entropies, energies, and free energies of activation for the oxidation process, after Gulbransen and Wysong (107)

Material	t °C.	k cm.^{2}/sec.	D_0 cm.^{2}/sec.	ΔS^* cal./ mol·deg	E^* kcal./ mol	$T \Delta S^*$ kcal./ mol	ΔF^* kcal./ mol
Aluminum, Nr. 4 polished	350	4.7×10^{-16}	2.47×10^{-8}	-25.6	22.8	16.0	38.8
	400	2.34×10^{-15}	3.08×10^{-8}	-25.4	22.8	17.0	39.9
	450	5.29×10^{-15}	2.2×10^{-8}	-26.2	22.8	19.0	41.8
Aluminum, Nr. 1 polished	350	1.7×10^{-16}	0.815×10^{-8}	-27.9	22.8	17.3	40.1
	400	1.08×10^{-15}	1.38×10^{-8}	-26.9	22.8	18.0	40.8
	450	2.01×10^{-15}	0.80×10^{-8}	-28.0	22.8	20.2	43.0
	475	7.53×10^{-15}	1.72×10^{-8}	-26.6	22.8	19.9	42.7
Iron	350	1.2×10^{-15}	5.48×10^{-8}	-24.6	22.6	15.3	37.9
	400	4.09×10^{-15}	4.68×10^{-8}	-24.6	22.6	16.5	39.1
	450	15.25×10^{-15}	5.52×10^{-8}	-24.5	22.6	17.7	40.3

For the theory of oxidation of aluminum and related phenomena cf. especially Mott (16), Cabrera and Mott (46a).

REFERENCES

Monographs and review articles

1. Barrer, R. M., Diffusion in and through solids. Cambridge 1941.
2. Cohn, G., *Chem. Rev.* **42**, 527 (1948).
3. Evans, U. R., *J. Iron Steel Inst. (London)* **149**, 67 (1944).
4. Evans, U. R., *J. Chem. Soc.* **1946**, 207.
5. Evans, U. R., Metallic Corrosion, Passivity and Protection 2nd edit. Arnold, London 1946.
6. Fischbeck, K., *Z. Elektrochem.* **39**, 316 (1933).
6a. Garner, W. E., *Science Progress*, **33**, 209 (1938). (Reactions in solids)
7. Hedvall, J. A., Reaktionsfähigkeit fester Stoffe. Leipzig 1938.
8. Hedvall, J. A., Umwandlung und Katalyse fester Stoffe in G. M. Schwab: Handbuch der Katalyse Vol. VI, p. 578. Wien 1943.
8a. Hedvall, J., *Z. anorg. allgem. Chem.* **258,** 180 (1949). (Reactions in solids, survey)
9. Huettig, G., Zwischenzustände bei Reaktionen im festen Zustand in G. M. Schwab: Handbuch der Katalyse, Vol. VI, p. 318. Wien 1943.
10. Jost, W., Diffusion und chemische Reaktion in fester Stoffen. Steinkopff, Leipzig and Dresden 1937.
11. Justi, E., Leitfähigkeit und Leitungsmechanismus fester Stoffe. Vandenhoeck and Ruprecht, Göttingen 1948.

12. Manning, M. F., and Bell, M. E., *Rev. Mod. Phys.* **12**, 215 (1940).
13. Masing, G., Article in: Die Korrosion metallischer Werkstoffe. Edited by C. Bauer, O. Kröhnke and G. Masing, Vol. I, p. 97 (1936).
14. Meyer, W., Z. *Elektrochem.* **50**, 274 (1944).
15. Mott, N. F., *Nature* **145**, 996 (1940).
16. Mott, N. F., and Gurney, R. W., Electronic Processes in Ionic Crystals. Oxford Univ. Press, 1940; 2nd ed. 1948.
16a. Mott, N. F., *Rept. Progr. Phys.* **6**, 186 (1940).
17. Pittsburgh International Conference on Surface Reactions. Corrosion Publishing Company, Pittsburgh 12, Pa. 1948.
18. Review of Oxidation and Scaling of Heated Metals. Ed. by the Department of Scientific and Industrial Research. H. M. Stationary Office, London 1935.
19. Seith, W., Diffusion in Metallen (Platzwechselreaktionen). Springer, Berlin. 1939.
20. Seitz, F., Modern Theory of Solids. McGraw Hill, New York 1940.
21. Seitz, F., and Johnson, R. P., *J. Applied Phys.* **8**, 84, 186, 246 (1937).
22. Volmer, M., Kinetik der Phasenbildung. Steinkopff, Leipzig 1939.
23. Wagner, C., Handbuch der Metallphysik, Vol. I, 2, Leipzig 1940.
24. Wilson, A. H., The Theory of Metals. Cambridge 1936.

General Bibliography

25. Andruschenko, N. K., and Dankov, P. D., *Doklady Akad. Nauk USSR* **62**, 353 (1948).
26. Arkharov, V. I., *Bull. Acad. Sci. USSR Cl. Sci. techn.* **1946**, 127.
27. Baedeker, K., *Ann. Physik* (4) **22**, 749 (1907).
28. Baedeker, K., *Ann. Physik* **29**, 556 (1909).
29. Baedeker, K., *Physik. Z.* **9**, 431 (1908).
30. Baedeker, K., *Physik. Z.* **13**, 1080 (1912).
31. Bardeen, J., Brattain, W. H., and Shockley, W., *J. Chem. Phys.* **14**, 714 (1946).
32. Baukloh, W., and Reif, O., *Metallwirtsch.* **14**, 1055 (1935).
33. von Baumbach, H. H., and Wagner, C., *Z. physik. Chem.* B **22**, 199 (1933).
34. Bénard, J., *Bull. soc. chim. France* **11**, 327 (1944).
35. Bénard, J., *J. chim. phys.* **44**, 266 (1947).
36. Bénard, J., Pittsburgh International Conference on Surface Reactions. Corrosion Publishing Company, Pittsburgh, Pa. 1948, p. 167 Influence of the condition of iron and copper on oxidation at high temperatures.
37. Bénard, J., and Coquelle, O., *Rev. métal.* **43**, 113 (1946).
38. Bénard, J., and Coquelle, C., *Rev. métal.* **44**, 82 (1947).
39. Bénard, J., and Talbot, J., *Rev. métal.* **45**, 78 (1948).
39a. Bénard, J., *Bull. soc. chim. France* **1949**, D 89.
39b. Bénard, J., and Moreau, J., *Rev. métal* **47**, 317 (1950). (Oxidation of Fe-Ni alloy)
40. Bircumshaw, L. L., and Preston, G. D., *Phil. Mag.* (7), **25**, 769 (1938).
41. Bozorth, R. M., *J. Am. Chem. Soc.* **49**, 969 (1927).
42. de Broukère, L., *J. Inst. Metals* **71**, 131 (1945).
43. Brueck, L., *Ann. Physik* (5), **26**, 233 (1936).
44. Burns, R. M., Pittsburgh International Conference on Surface Reactions. Corrosion Publishing Company, Pittsburgh, Pa., 1948, p. 1, Properties of Metallic Surfaces.

45. Burwell, B. L., and May, T. P., Pittsburgh International Conference on Surface Reactions. Corrosion Publishing Company, Pittsburgh, Pa., 1948. p. 10. The Measurement of Permeability Characteristics of Anodic Films in Aluminum.

46. Cabrera, N., *Rev. métal.* **45**, 86 (1948), *Phil. Mag.* **40**, 175 (1949).

46a. Cabrera, N., and Mott, N. F., *Rept. Progr. Phys.* **12**, 163 (1949). (Theory of oxidation of metals)

47. Campbell, W. E., and Thomas, H. B., *Trans. Electrochem. Soc.* **91**, (1947) Preprint.

48. Castellan, G. W., and Moore, W. J., *J. Chem. Phys.* **17**, 41 (1949).

49. Championi, F. A., *Metal Ind. (London)* **72**, 440, 444, 463 (1948).

50. Chaudron, G., *Compt. rend.* **172**, 152 (1921).

51. Chaudron, G., *Ann. chim.* (9) **16**, 221 (1921).

52. Chaudron, G., *Bull. soc. chim. Belg.* **44**, 339 (1935).

53. Chaudron, G., *Metaux et Corrosion* **17**, 37, 155 (1942).

54. Chaudron, G., Pittsburgh International Conference on Surface Reactions. Corrosion Publishing Company, Pittsburgh, Pa., 1948, p. 165. Etude micrographique de l'oxydation du fer et des transformations du protoxyde de fer.

55. Chauvenet, G., *Compt. rend.* **207**, 360 (1938).

56. Chauvenet, G., *Compt. rend.* **209**, 886 (1939).

57. Chauvenet, G., and Valensi, G., *Compt. rend.* **205**, 317 (1937).

58. Chevenard, P., and Waché, X., Comm. tech. états et propriétés surface métaux, Journées états surface (Paris), Oct. 1945, 237.

58a. Chevenard, P., and Waché, X., *Rev. métal.* **45**, 121 (1948).

59. Czerski, L., *Roczniki Chem.* **17**, 436 (1937).

59a. Czerski, L., *Roczniki Chem.* **22**, 83 (1948).

59b. Czerski, L., *Roczniki Chem.* **23**, 19 (1949).

60. Dankov, P. D., Kochetkov, A. A., and Shishakov, N. A., *Bull. Acad. Sci. URSS Cl. Sci. Chim.* **1942**, 274.

61. Darken, L. S., and Smith, R. P., *Corrosion* **5**, 1 (1949).

62. Dravnieks, A., and McDonald, H. J., *Trans. Electrochem. Soc.* **93**, 177 (1948).

63. Dravnieks, A., and McDonald, H. J., *Trans. Electrochem. Soc.* **94**, 139 (1948).

33a. Dravnieks, A., and McDonald, H. J., *Iron Age* **164**, 78, 84 (1949).

33b. Dravnieks, A., and McDonald, H. J., *Ind. Gas* **27**, Nr. 12, 6 (1949).

34. Duenwald, H., and Wagner, C., *Z. physik. Chem.* **B 22**, 212 (1933).

65. Dumas, A., *Rev. métal.* **40**, 310, 343, 374 (1943).

66. Dunn, J. S., *Proc. Roy. Soc. (London)* **A 111**, 203 (1926).

67. Dunn, J. S., *Proc. Roy. Soc. (London)* **A 111**, 210 (1926).

68. Dunn, J. S., *J. Chem. Soc. (London)* **1929**, 1149.

69. Dunn, J. S., *Inst. Metals* **46**, 25 (1931).

70. Dunn, J. S., and Wilkins, F. J., Review of Oxidation and Scaling of Heated Metals. Edited by Department of Scientific and Industrial Research. H. M. Stationary Office, London 1935.

71. Eborall, R., and Ransley, C. E., *J. Inst. Metals* **71**, 525 (1945).

72. Emmett, P. H., Pittsburgh international Conference on Surface Reactions, Corrosion Publishing Company, Pittsburgh, Pa., 1948, p. 82, Studies of Metal Surfaces by low Temperature Gas Adsorption.

73. Evans, U. R., *Kolloid-Z.* **69**, 129 (1934).

74. Evans, U. R., *Trans. Faraday Soc.* **41**, 365 (1945).

75. Evans, U. R., *Trans. Electrochem. Soc.* **91**, Preprint Nr. 5 (1947).

76. Evans, U. R., *Métaux et Corrosion* **22**, 184 (1947).
77. Evans, U. R., Symposium on Internal Stresses in Metals and Alloys, Inst. Metals 1947.
78. Evans, U. R., *Corrosion* **4**, 149 (1948).
79. Evans, U. R., Pittsburgh International Conference on Surface Reactions, Corrosion Publishing Company, Pittsburgh, Pa., 1948, p. 71. The Mechanism of the Formation of Films on Metals.
80. Evans, U. R., and Bannister, L. C., *Proc. Roy. Soc. (London)* **A 125**, 370 (1929).
80a. Evans, U. R., Proc. Third Intern. Electrodeposition Conf. **1947**, 179.
81. Feitknecht, W., *Z. Elektrochem.* **35**, 142 (1929).
82. Finch, G. I., and Quarrell, E. G., *Nature* **131**, 877 (1933).
83. Finch, G. I., and Quarrell, E. G., *Proc. Roy. Soc. (London)* **A 141**, 398 (1933).
84. Finch, G. I., and Quarrell, E. G., *Proc. Phys. Soc. (London)* **46**, 148 (1934).
85. Fischbeck, K., *Z. anorg. allgem. Chem.* **154**, 261 (1926).
86. Fischbeck, K., *Z. anorg. allgem. Chem.* **165**, 46 (1927).
87. Fischbeck, K., *Z. Elektrochem.* **37**, 593 (1931).
88. Fischbeck, K., *Z. Metallkunde* **24**, 313 (1932).
88a. Fischbeck, K., *Z. Elektrochem.* **39**, 318 (1933). ("Reaction" and "diffusion" resistance)
89. Fischbeck, K., and Dorner, O., *Z. anorg. allgem. Chem.* **181**, 372 (1929).
90. Fischbeck, K., Neundeubel, L., and Salzer, F., *Z. Elektrochem.* **40**, 517 (1934).
91. Fischbeck, K., and Salzer, F., *Metallwirtsch.* **14**, 733, 753 (1935).
92. Foote, H. W., and Smith, E. K., *J. Am. Chem. Soc.* **30**, 1344 (1908).
93. Friedmann, H., and Birks, L. S., *Rev. Sci. Instr.* **17**, 99 (1946).
94. Fritsch, O., *Ann. Physik* (5) **22**, 375 (1935).
95. Froehlich, K. W., *Z. Metallkunde* **28**, 368 (1936).
95a. Garner, W., Gray, T. J., and Stone, F. S., *Proc. Roy. Soc. (London)* **A 197**, 244 (1949).
95b. Gray, T. J., *Proc. Roy. Soc. (London)* **A 197**, 314 (1949).
96. Gudden, B., and Schottky, W., *Z. tech. Physik* **16**, 323 (1935).
97. Gulbransen, E. A., *Trans. Electrochem. Soc.* **81**, 327 (1942).
98. Gulbransen, E. A., *Trans. Electrochem. Soc.* **82**, 375 (1942).
99. Gulbransen, E. A., *Trans. Electrochem. Soc.* **83**, 301 (1943).
100. Gulbransen, E. A., *Trans. Electrochem. Soc.* **87**, 589 (1945).
101. Gulbransen, E. A., *Trans. Electrochem. Soc.* **91**, (1947) preprint.
102. Gulbransen, E. A., *Rev. métal.* **45**, 181 (1948).
103. Gulbransen, E. A., and Hickman, J. W., *Am. Inst. Mining Met. Engrs. Inst. Metals Div. Metals Technol.* **13**, Techn. Publ. Nr. 2068 (1946).
104. Gulbransen, E. A., Phelps, R. T., and Hickman, J. W., *Ind. Eng. Chem.* **18**, 640 (1946).
105. Gulbransen, E. A., and Wysong, W. S., *Am. Inst. Mining Met. Eng. Inst. Metals, Div. Metals Technol.* **14**, Techn. Publ. Nr. 2224 (1947).
106. Gulbransen, E. A., and Wysong, W. S., *Am. Inst. Mining Met. Eng. Inst. Metals, Div. Metals Technol. Publ.* Nr. 2226 (1947).
107. Gulbransen, E. A., and Wysong, W. S., *J. Phys. Chem.* **51**, 1087 (1947).
107a. Gulbransen, E. A., *Rev. métal.* **45**, 181, 287 (1948).
107b. Gulbransen, E. A., and Andrew, K., Pittsburgh International Conference on Surface Reactions **1948**, 222; *J. Phys. & Colloid Chem.* **53**, 690 (1949).

107c. Gulbransen, E. A., *Ind. Eng. Chem.* **41**, 1385 (1949).
107d. Gulbransen, E. A., and Andrew, K. F., *J. Metals* **1**, Nr. 10 Trans. 741 (1949).
108. Gundermann, J., Hauffe, K., and Wagner, C., *Z. physik. Chem.* **B 37**, 148, 155 (1937).
109. Gundermann, J., unpublished.
109a. Gurnick, R. S., and Baldwin, W. M., Jr., *Trans. Am. Soc. Metals Preprint* Nr. 9 (1949).
110. Gwathmey, A. T., Pittsburgh International Conference on Surface Reactions, Corrosion Publishing Company, Pittsburgh, Pa., 1948, p. 66. The Preparation of Single Crystals for the Study of Surface Reactions.
110a. Gwathmey, A. T., and Benton, A. F., *J. Chem. Phys.* **8**, 431 (1940); *J. Phys. Chem.* **44**, 35 (1940); ibid. **46**, 969 (1942).
111. Haber, F., and Tolloczko, A., *Z. anorg. allgem. Chem.* **41**, 407 (1904).
111a. Hauffe, K., and Gensch, Chr., *Z. physik. Chem.* **195**, 116 (1950).
111b. Hauffe, K., and Pschera, K., *Z. anorg. allgem. Chem.* **262**, 147 (1950).
111c. Hauffe, K., and Vierk, A. L., *Z. physik. Chem.* **196**, 160 (1950).
111d. Hauffe. K., and Gensch, Ch., *Z. physik. Chem.* **195**, (1950); (Reaction of bromine with silver alloys) *Z. physik. Chem.*, in print, (Rate of oxidation of Zn alloys); Neunhoeffer, O., and Hauffe, K., *Z. anorg. Chem.* **262**, 300 (1950). (Reaction of sulfur with FeAs and $FeAs_2$)
112. Hedvall, J. A., Ekwall, G., and Dahr, K., *Arkiv Kemi, Mineral, Geol.* **18 A**, Nr. 11 (1944).
113. Hedvall, J. A., and Joenson, O., *Naturwissenschaften* **29**, 726 (1941).
114. Hickman, J. W., Pittsburgh International Conference on Surface Reactions Corrosion Publishing Company, Pittsburgh, Pa., 1948, p. 142. Investigations of gas-metal reactions by reflection electron diffraction.
115. Hickman, J. W., *Iron Age* **162**, (1948).
116. Hickman, J. W., *Am. Inst. Mining Met. Eng. Techn. Publ.* Nr. 2483 (1948).
117. Hickman, J. W., and Gulbransen, E. A., *Am. Inst. Mining Met. Eng. Inst. Metals Div. Metals Technol.* **13**, *Techn. Publ.* Nr. 2069 (1946).
118. Hickman, J. W., and Gulbransen, E. A., *Am. Inst. Mining Met. Eng. Techn. Publ.* Nr. 2144 (1947).
119. Hickman, J. W., and Gulbransen, E. A., *Am. Inst. Mining Met. Eng. Techn. Publ.* Nr. 2372 (1948).
120. Hickman, J. W., and Gulbransen, E. A., *Am. Inst. Mining Met. Eng. Techn. Publ.* Nr. 2391 (1948).
120a. Hickman, J. W., *Am. Inst. Mining Met. Eng Inst. Metals Div. Metals Technol.* **15**, Nr. 8, *Tech. Publ.* Nr. 2483 (1948).
120b. Himmler, W., *Z. Metallkunde*, in print, 1950.
121. Hoar, T. P., and Price, L. E., *Trans. Faraday Soc.* **34**, 867 (1938).
122. Holmesland, P. B., *Kong. Norske Vidensk. Selsk. Forh.* **12**, 129 (1940).
123. Horn, L., *Z. Metallkunde* **36**, 142 (1944).
123a. Horn, L., *Z. Metallkunde* **40**, 73 (1949).
123b. Jagitsch, R., *Arkiv Mineral. Geol.* **1**, 65, 85 (1949). (Geologic diffusion)
124. Jander, W., see Jost (10) and Wagner (247).
125. Iitaka, I., and Miyake, S., *Nature* **137**, 457 (1936).
126. Jost, W., Diffusion und chemische Reaktion in festen Stoffen, p. 31-33.
127. Jost, W., Diffusion und chemische Reaktion in festen Stoffen, p. 166 ff.
128. Jost, W., *Z. physik. Chem.* **B 16**, 129 (1932).
129. Jung, G., *Z. physik. Chem.* **119**, 111 (1926).
130. Katayama, M., *Z. physik. Chem.* **61**, 566 (1908).

131. Keller, F., and Edwards, J. D., Pittsburgh International Conference on Surface Reactions. Corrosion Publishing Company, Pittburgh, Pa., 1948, p. 202. The Behavior of Oxide Films on Aluminum.
132. Ketelaar, J. A. A., Z. Kristallogr. 87, 436 (1934).
133. Ketelaar, J. A. A., Z. physik. Chem. B 30, 53 (1935).
134. Ketelaar, J. A. A., Trans. Faraday Soc. 34, 874 (1938).
135. Klaiber, F., Ann. Physik (5) 3, 229 (1929).
136. Koch, E., and Wagner, C., Z. physik. Chem. B 34, 317 (1936).
137. Koch, E., and Wagner, C., Z. physik. Chem. B 38, 295 (1938).
138. Kochetkow, A. A., Bull. Acad. Sci. USSR Cl. Sci. Chim. 1944, 390.
139. Kohlschütter, V., and Krähenbühl, E., Z. Elektrochem. 29, 570 (1923).
140. Kornilov, I. I., and Shpikel'man, A., C. R. Acad. Sci. USSR 53, 805 (1946).
141. Kornilov, I. I., and Shpikel'man, A., C. R. Acad. Sci. USSR 54, 511 (1946).
142. Krichevskii, I. R., and Khazunova, N. E., J. phys. Chem. USSR 19, 676 (1945).
143. Krupkowski, A., and Balicki, S., Acad. Ann. Sci. techn. Varsovie 4, 242 (1937).
144. Krupkowski, A., and Balicki, S., Ann. Acad. Sci. techn. Varsovie 5, 130 (1938).
145. Krylowa, T. N., Bull. Acad. Sci. USSR Cl. Sci. Techn. 1938, 89.
146. Kubaschewski, O., Z. Metallkunde 39, 218 (1948).
146a. Kubaschewski, O., and Schneider, A., J. Inst. Metals 75, 403 (1949).
146b. Kubaschewski, O., and Speidel, H., J. Inst. Metals 75, 417 (1949).
147. Kunze, E., Arch. Eisenhüttenw. 18, 57 (1944).
148. Laidler, K. J., Pittsburgh International Conference on Surface Reactions, Corrosion Publishing Company, Pittsburgh, Pa., 1948, p. 51. The Mechanism of some Elementary Surface Reactions.
149. Leontis, T. E., and Rhines, F. N., Am. Inst. Mining Met. Eng. Inst. Metals Div. Metals Techn. 13, Nr. 4 Technol. Publ. Nr. 2003 (1946).
150. Leroux, J. A. A., and Raub, E., Z. anorg. allgem. Chem. 188, 205 (1930).
151. Leslie, W. C., and Fontana, M., Pittsburgh International Conference on Surface Reactions. Corrosion Publishing Company, Pittsburgh, Pa., 1948, p. 172. Mechanism of the Rapid Oxidation of High Temperature, high Strength Alloys.
152. Lustman, B., Metal progress 50, 850, 860 (1946).
153. Lustman, B., and Mehl, R. F., Metals Technol. 8, Techn. Publ. Nr. 1317 (1941).
153a. Lustman, B., Steel 120, 68, 116 (1947).
153b. Masing, G., Naturwissenschaften 32, 333 (1944).
154. Maurer, R. J., J. Chem. Phys. 13, 321 (1945).
155. McAdam, D. J. jr., and Geil, G. W., J. Res. Nat. Bur. Stand. 23, 63 (1939).
156. McAdam, D. J. jr., and Geil, G. W., J. Res. Nat. Bur. Stand. 28, 593 (1942).
157. Mehl, R. F., McCandless, E. L., and Rhines, F. N., Nature 134, 1009 (1934).
158. Mehl, R. F., McCandless, E. L., and Rhines, F. N., Trans. Am. Inst. Mining Met. Eng. 125, 531 (1937).
159. Meijering, J. L., Pittsburgh International Conference on Surface Reactions. Corrosion Publishing Company, Pittsburgh, Pa., 1948, p. 101. Some Aspects of Internal Oxidation in Silver, Copper, Nickel and Iron Alloys.
160. Meijering, J. L., Proc. Phys. Soc. (London) 1948.

161. Meijering, J. L., and Druyvesteyn, M. J., *Philips Res. Rept.* **2**, 81, 260 (1947).
161a. Meijering, J. L., *Rept. Conf. on Strength of Solids* (Univers. Bristol) July 1947, 140.
162. Michel, A., Bénard, J., and Chaudron, G., *Bull. soc. chim. France* **11**, 175 (1944).
163. Miyake, S., *Sci. Pap. Inst. physic. chem. Res. (Japan)* **29**, 167 (1936).
164. Mott, N. F., *Trans. Faraday Soc.* **35**, 1175 (1939).
165. Mott, N. F., *Trans. Faraday Soc.* **36**, 472 (1940).
166. Mott, N. F., *Trans. Faraday Soc.* **43**, 429 (1947).
166. Mott, N. F., *Trans. Faraday Soc.* **43**, 429 (1947).
167. Mott, N. F., *J. chim. phys.* **44**, 172 (1947).
167a. Mott, N. F., *Bull. soc. chim. France* **1949**, D 84.
168. Nagel, K., and Wagner, C., *Z. physik. Chem.* **B 25**, 71 (1934).
169. Orlov, A., and Smirnov, A., *Acta physicochim. USSR* **22**, 225 (1947).
170. Pfeil, L. B., *J. Iron and Steel Inst.* **119**, 501 (1929).
171. Pfeil, L. B., *J. Iron and Steel Inst.* **123**, 237 (1931).
172. Phelps, R. T., Gulbransen, E. A., and Hickman, J. W., *Ind. Eng. Chem. Analyt. Edit.* **18**, 391 (1946).
173. Pilling, N. B., and Bedworth, R. E., *J. Inst. Metals* **29**, 529 (1923).
174. Pilling, N. B., and Bedworth, R. E., *Ind. Eng. Chem.* **17**, 372 (1925).
175. Portevin, A., Prétet, E., and Jolivet, H., *Rev. métal.* **31**, 101, 186, 219 (1934).
176. Portevin, A., Prétet, E., and Jolivet, H., *J. Iron Steel Inst. (London)* **130**, 219 (1934).
177. Preston, G. D., *Phil. Mag.* (7) **26**, 65 (1938).
178. Preston, G. D., and Bircumshaw, L. L., *Phil. Mag.* (7) **20**, 706 (1935).
179. Preston, G. D., and Bircumshaw, L. L., *Phil. Mag.* (7) **21**, 686 (1936).
180. Preston, G. D., and Bircumshaw, L. L., *Phil. Mag.* (7) **22**, 654 (1936).
181. Price, L. E., and Thomas, G. J., *J. Inst. Metals* **63**, 253 (1938).
182. Price, L. E., and Thomas, G. J., *J. Inst. Metals* **63**, 357 (1938).
183. Raub, E., and Engel, M., *Mitt. Forsch. Inst. Edelmetalle staatl. Höh. Fachsch. Schwäbisch-Gmünd* **1939**, 1.
184. Raub, E., and von Polaczek-Wittek, A., *Z. Metallkunde* **34**, 275 (1942).
185. Reinhold, H., *Z. anorg. allgem. Chem.* **171**, 181 (1928).
186. Reinhold, H., *Z. Elektrochem.* **40**, 361 (1934).
187. Reinhold, H., and Bräuninger, H., *Z. physik. Chem.* **B 41**, 397 (1938).
188. Reinhold, H., and Möhring, H., *Z. physik. Chem.* **B 28**, 178 (1935).
189. Reinhold, H., and Möhring, H., *Z. physik. Chem.* **B 38**, 221 (1937).
190. Reinhold, H., and Schulz, H., *Z. physik. Chem.* **A 164**, 241 (1933).
191. Reinhold, H., and Seidel, H., *Z. Elektrochem.* **41**, 499 (1935).
192. Reinhold, H., and Seidel, H., *Z. physik. Chem.* **B 38**, 245 (1937).
193. Rhines, F. N., *Am. Inst. Mining Met. Eng. Inst. Metals Div. Metals Technol.* **7**, Nr. 2, Techn. Publ. Nr. 1162 (1940).
194. Rhines, F. N., *Corrosion and Material protection* **4**, Nr. 2, 15 (*J. Corrosion* 3—8) (1947).
195. Rhines, F. N., Johnson, W. A., and Anderson, W. A., *Am. Inst. Mining Met. Eng. Inst. Metals Div. Metals Technol.* **8**, Nr. 7 Techn. Publ. Nr. 1368 (1941).
196. Roberts, H. S., and Smyth, F. H., *J. Am. Chem. Soc.* **42**, 2582 (1920).
197. Roberts, H. S., and Smyth, F. H., *J. Am. Chem. Soc.* **43**, 1061 (1921).
197a. Robertson, W. D., and Uhlig, H. H., *J. Electrochem. Soc.* **96**, 27 (1949).

198. Scheil, E., Z. Metallkunde 29, 209 (1937).
199. Scheil, E., and Kiwit, K. K., Arch. Eisenhüttenw. 9, 405 (1935/6).
200. Scheil, E., and Kiwit, K. K., Z. Metallkunde 29, 209 (1937).
201. Schwab, G. M., Z. physik. Chem. B 51, 245 (1942).
202. Smirnov, A., J. exp. theor. Phys. USSR 14, 46 (1944).
203. Smirnov, A., Acta physicochim. USSR 22, 162 (1947).
204. Steger, A., Z. physik. Chem. 43, 595 (1903).
205. Steinheil, A., Ann. Physik (5) 19, 465 (1934).
206. Tammann, G., Z. anorg. allgem. Chem. 111, 78 (1920).
207. Tammann, G., Z. anorg. allgem. Chem. 124, 25 (1922).
208. Tammann, G., and Koester, W., Z. anorg. allgem. Chem. 123, 196 (1922).
209. Tammann, G., and Bredemeier, H., Z. anorg. allgem. Chem. 136, 337 (1924).
210. Tammann, G., and Rienaecker, W., Z. anorg. allgem. Chem. 156, 261 (1926).
211. Tammann, G., and Schroeder, E., Z. anorg. allgem. Chem. 128, 179 (1923).
212. Terens, H. N., Bull. soc. chim. France (5) 5, 589 (1938).
213. Terens, H. N., Bull. Soc. chim. France (5) 6, 664 (1939).
214. Terens, H. N., Compt. rend. 226, 905 (1948).
215. Thiessen, P. A., and Schuetza, H., Z. anorg. allgem. Chem. 233, 35 (1937).
216. Thiessen, P. A., and Schuetza, H., Z. anorg. allgem. Chem. 243, 32 (1939).
217. Thompson, G. P., Proc. Roy. Soc. London A 128, 649 (1930).
218. Treadwell, W. D., Z. Elektrochem. 22, 414 (1916).
219. Tubandt, C., and Eggert, S., Z. anorg. allgem. Chem. 110, 196 (1920).
220. Tubandt, C., and Eggert, S., Z. anorg. allgem. Chem. 115, 105 (1921).
221. Tubandt, C., Eggert, S., and Schibbe, G., Z. anorg. allgem. Chem. 117, 1 (1921).
222. Tubandt, C., and Reinhold, H., Z. physik. Chem. Bodenstein Festband, p. 874 (1931).
223. Tubandt, C., and Reinhold, H , Z. Elektrochem. 37, 589 (1931).
224. Tubandt, C., and Reinhold, H., Z. physik. Chem. B 24, 22 (1934).
225. Tubandt, C., Reinhold, H., and Neumann, A., Z. Elektrochem. 39, 227 (1933).
226. Uhlig, H. H., Am. Inst. Mining Met. Eng. Techn. Publ. Nr. 1121 (1939).
227. Uhlig, H. H., Trans. Electrochem. Soc. 85, 207 (1944).
228. Uhlig, H. H., Am. Inst. Mining Met. Eng. Techn. Publ. Nr. 2243 (1947).
229. Uhlig, H. H., and Wulff, J., Am. Inst. Mining Met. Eng. Techn. Publ. Nr. 1050 (1939).
230. Valensi, G., Compt. rend. 203, 1252, 1354 (1936).
231. Valensi, G., Journées sur la corrosion des métaux, Paris 1947.
232. Valensi, G., Métaux et Corrosion (1948).
233. Valensi, G., Pittsburgh International Conference on Surface Reactions. Corrosion, Publishing Company, Pittsburgh, Pa., 1948., p. 156. Theoretical and Experimental Investigations about Conjugated Formation of Several Layers in Dry Corrosion.
233a. Valensi, G., Rev. métal. 45, 205 (1948).
234. Vernon, W. H. J., Chem. Ind. 1943, 314.
235. Vernon, W. H. J., Akeroyd, E. I., and Stroud, E. G., J. Inst. Metals 65, (1939) Advance Copy.
236. Volmer, M., Z. Elektrochem. 35, 555 (1929).
237. Wagner, C., Z. physik. Chem. B 21, 25 (1933).
238. Wagner, C., Z. physik. Chem. B 22, 181 (1933).

239. Wagner, C., Z. physik. Chem. **B 21**, 42 (1933).
240. Wagner, C., Z. Elektrochem. **40**, 364 (1934).
241. Wagner, C., Z. tech. Physik **16**, 327 (1935).
242. Wagner, C., Z. angew. Chem. **49**, 735 (1936).
243. Wagner, C., Z. physik. Chem. **B 32**, 447 (1936).
244. Wagner, C., Z. physik. Chem. **B 34**, 309 (1936).
245. Wagner, C., Z. anorg. allgem. Chem. **236**, 320 (1938).
246. Wagner, C., Trans. Faraday Soc. **34**, 851 (1938).
247. Wagner, C., Z. Elektrochem. **47**, 696 (1941).
248. Wagner, C., Pittsburgh International Conference on Surface Reactions. Corrosion Publishing Company, Pittsburgh, Pa., 1948,p. 77. Reactions of Metals and Alloys with Oxygen, Sulphur, and Halogens at High Temperature.
249. Wagner, C., and Beyer, J., Z. physik. Chem. **B 32**, 113 (1936).
250. Wagner, C., and Gruenewald, K., Z. physik. Chem. **B 40**, 455 (1938).
251. Wagner, C., and Hammen, H., Z. physik. Chem. **B 40**, 197 (1938).
252. Wagner, C., and Hantelmann, P., J. Phys. & Colloid Chem. **54**, 426 (1950).
253. Wagner, C., and Himmler, W., unpublished.
254. Wagner, C., and Zimens, K. E., Acta chim. Scand. **1**, 539 (1948).
255. Wagner, C., and Zimens, K. E., Acta chim. Scand. **1**, 547 (1948).
255a. Wagner, C., Corrosion and Material Protection **5**, Nr. 5, 9—11 (J. Corrosion 1—4) (1948).
256. Wilkins, F. J., and Rideal, E. K., Proc. Roy. Soc. London **A 128**, 394 (1930).
257. Winterbottom, A. B., Pittsburgh International Conference on Surface Reactions. Corrosion Publishing Company, Pittsburgh, Pa., 1948. p. 91. Optical Determination of Thin Films on Reflecting Bases in Transparent Environments.

CHAPTER X

DIFFUSION IN GASES

I. Experimental methods

It would be beyond the scope of this book to attempt a theoretical treatment of diffusion in gases. First this would absorb considerable space, not because the theory of diffusion in gases is more complicated than that for condensed phases but because it is much more advanced and elaborated, and secondly there are excellent monographs available on the kinetic theory of gases (2, 5, 7, 8, 9). Therefore we shall emphasize the experimental methods of determining diffusion constants in gases and give only a collection of theoretical formulae for practical applications.

As has been mentioned before, diffusion constants in gases are of the order of magnitude of $1—10^{-1}$ cm.^{2}/sec. at N.T.P. This can be estimated from measurements of viscosity or heat conduction (especially as viscosity measurements are much easier than measurements of diffusion coefficients), on the basis of the kinetic theory of gases (cf. the formulae p. 421). The mean displacement of a gas molecule during one second, therefore, is of the order of magnitude of 1 cm. An experimental arrangement, adequate for the measurement of gas diffusion, which suggests itself consists of a rather long tube of not too large diameter, separated into two halves by means of a stopcock of bore equal to the diameter of the tube, cf. Chap. I. The tube must be kept vertical, with the heavier component in the lower half of the tube. After each half of the tube has been filled with a different gas or with gas mixtures differing in concentration, an experiment is started by opening the stopcock. Since convection may cause considerable error in diffusion measurements, the temperature of the tube must be kept quite constant over its whole length, although in some experiments it has been considered advantageous to maintain a slight vertical temperature increase, of the order of magnitude of a few tenths of a degree over a tube length of the order of magnitude of 1 meter, in order to preclude convection. We shall give some details of apparatus actually applied to measurements of diffusion in gases, and shall reproduce some results, thus obtained.

The method of the tube, divided into two halves, has been applied with slight modifications since Loschmidt's (86, 87) and Stefan's (111, 112, 113) earliest measurements. The effective boundary for the division of the tube is the one end of the bore of the stopcock, if a stopcock is used for the connection of both parts of the tube. Therefore, at the beginning of an experiment the stopcock must be filled with one component. A very elaborate apparatus, employing this principle, has been described by v. Obermayer (97). The only fundamental improvement, introduced later, is the elimination of the stopcock by the use of two ground discs, rotating upon each other, each connected to one tube, Fig. 10-1. Following its use in measurements of diffusion coefficients in liquids (Wogau (145), Cohen and Bruins (34)), Boardman and Wild (20) and Braune and Zehle (23) employed this method for the measurement of diffusion in gases. The total length of the diffusion tube in those experiments was of the order of magnitude of 1 meter, later experimenters worked with similar lengths. v. Obermayer and other early experimenters employed gun barrels for this purpose. The diameter of v. Obermayers's tube was 13 mm., while Loschmidt had worked with a tube of 26 mm. diameter. Since Loschmidt's experiments gave results which are consistently higher, by up to 6 per cent, than those of v. Obermayer, one may suspect that these experiments with the wider tube were influenced by convection currents. Therefore it seems advisable to use narrow tubes which are kept in a good thermostat. If slight temperature variations seem unavoidable, care should be taken that the temperature increases from bottom to top (within very narrow limits of

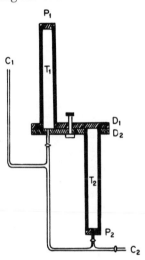

Fig. 10-1. Modern form of gas diffusion apparatus (Boardman and Wild). Diffusion tubes T_1 and T_2 connected by disc D_1 rotating upon disc D_2, with connections for evacuating, filling and analysing.

course). The time necessary for one experiment is of the order of magnitude of about 10 minutes up to about 2 hours, for conditions not very far from N.T.P.

An integral of the diffusion equation for the above boundary conditions is given in Chap. I, p. 45. v. Obermayer (97) has computed tables which still may be of value for a quick evaluation of corresponding experiments, though they require tubes of the same length as his apparatus, but they can be adapted to measurements with different tube lengths.

The accuracy achieved in these early experiments of v. Obermayer seems comparatively high. The fluctuations in D are of the order of magnitude of 1 per cent only.

One aim of these measurements had been to find the correct law for the temperature dependence of D. Since all theories lead to a relation of the form $D = f\eta/\rho$, where f is a factor of order unity, η the viscosity coefficient and ρ the density, varying at constant pressure as T^{-1}, the temperature dependence of D ought to be greater than that of the viscosity by a factor T^{+1}, which, within the limits of error, was v. Obermayer's result.

Loschmidt (87) gave in his experiments the first proof for the relation, derived from the kinetic gas theory, for the pressure-dependence of D. D, like the mean free path, should be inversely proportional to the gas pressure. In Table I we list some results obtained by Loschmidt for several gas pairs.

TABLE I

Dependence of diffusion coefficient on pressure, after Loschmidt (87)

Gas pair	D cm.²/sec.	$t°$C.	p mm. Hg	$\dfrac{Dp}{760}$
CO_2—Air	0.1653	17.6	751	0.163
CO_2—Air	0.3376	15.2	364	0.162
CO_2—Air	0.4139	15.7	309	0.164
CO_2—H_2	0.6142	12.8	757	0.612
CO_2—H_2	0.9184	15.4	510	0.616
H_2—O_2	0.8012	11.4	748	0.790
H_2—O_2	1.1718	15.8	512	0.791

A series of investigations was carried out at Halle under the direction of Dorn, cf. Lonius (83), in order to determine the dependence of the diffusion coefficient on the concentration ratio of the two inter-diffusing gases (R. Schmidt (104), 1904, O. Jackmann 1906, R. Deutsch 1907, A. Lonius 1909 (83)). As in v. Obermayer's experiments, the Maxwell-Loschmidt method of the vertical tube, divided by a stopcock, was employed.

To show the accuracy obtained, we reproduce a series of measurements in the system $N_2 - O_2$, taken from Jackmann, Table II.

In the earlier experiments by R. Schmidt (104) and by Jackmann, cf. Lonius (83), an attempt had been made to determine the concentration-dependence of the diffusion coefficient in the following manner. The diffusion tube had been divided by a second stopcock at $x = 3/2\, l$ into three parts (where l is the length of one half of the tube). The evaluation of the experiments suffers from the same inaccuracy as

TABLE II

Diffusion in N_2-O_2 mixtures, after Jackmann (see Lonius (83))

$t°C.$	p mm. Hg	D cm.^{2}/sec.
11.8	756.5	0.2031
11.7	758.7	0.2042
13.1	756.5	0.2004
12.4	755.7	0.2025
12.7	760.8	0.2040
	average	0.2028

the evaluation of experiments by means of the Kawalki tables for varying D, cf. Chap. V, p. 215. The authors were able, however, to detect a concentration dependence of D and to determine its magnitude qualitatively. We mention this explicitly because the same procedure has been chosen in many other cases, giving qualitatively correct results, but, of course, no results of quantitative value.

R. Schmidt (104) and Lonius (83) determined the dependence on concentration more correctly by using gas mixtures of different concentrations instead of the pure components. This method, if applied to sufficiently narrow concentration intervals, is both correct and convenient (cf. the discussion Chap. I, p. 4), i.e. more convenient than an evaluation of experiments over a wide range of concentrations by means of Boltzmann's method (21) (cf. Chap. I, p. 31).

The results of Lonius (83), which showed a variation of the diffusion coefficient with concentration of up to 8 per cent, will be discussed below (p. 423).

A review of methods, and results, of diffusion measurements has been given by Trautz (121, 122, 123, 124, 125), but much of the theoretical discussion is inadequate.

Boardman and Wild (20) investigated the diffusion of pairs of gases with molecules of equal mass and very similar molecular properties. The results, therefore, should not differ much from self diffusion. The experimental arrangement, used by the authors, is shown in Fig. 10-1. It follows Cohen and Bruins' (34) method; two copper tubes of 13 mm. diameter being connected to two circular brass discs. Details are seen from the figure. The temperature of the apparatus was kept at 16°C., in a cellar of constant temperature, the temperature of the upper tube being approximately 0.3° above that of the lower one

We give a survey of the results, reduced to 15°C. and 760 mm. Hg.

Diffusion coefficients for 15°C. and 760 mm. Hg.

Gas pair	$N_2 - CO$	$N_2O - CO_2$	$H_2 - N_2$	$H_2 - CO_2$	$N_2 - CO_2$
D_{12} cm.^{2}/sec.	0.211	0.107	0.743	0.619	0.158

Under certain assumptions it is possible to calculate the coefficients of self diffusion for H_2, N_2, and CO_2 from the data for inter-diffusion of the three pairs of gases, by a method due to Lord Kelvin, cf. p. 426.

Braune and Zehle (23) used a similar experimental arrangement for the measurement of the diffusion coefficients of the mixtures DCl—HCl, DBr—HBr, which must be very close to the coefficients of self diffusion.

Harteck and Schmidt (58) studied the self diffusion in hydrogen, by measuring the diffusion of para-hydrogen in normal hydrogen. Experiments at room temperature, carried out by the conventional

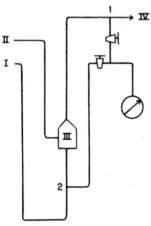

Fig. 10-2. Harteck's flow method for diffusion measurement. Normal hydrogen entering at I, parahydrogen at II, analysis for para-hydrogen at 1 and 2.

Maxwell-Loschmidt technique, gave a diffusion coefficient of 1.28 cm.² per sec., reduced to N.T.P. Further, they measured, though with less accuracy, the diffusion over a wide range of temperatures, by means of a streaming method, devised by Hertz (64). The principle of the method is seen from Fig. 10-2. Normal hydrogen is flowing with known velocity through a capillary I. Para-hydrogen, entering through capillary II is admixed with the normal hydrogen in the small mixing volume III, the mixture being pumped off at IV. Para-hydrogen diffuses backwards from II, against the streaming normal hydrogen, and at 2 its concentration can be determined by means of a test capillary, while at 1 the concentration of the streaming mixture can be analyzed.

If we choose the direction from III to 2 as that of the positive x-axis, the differential equation for our problem may be written (cf. Chap. I, p. 46)

$$\partial c/\partial t = D\,\partial^2 c/\partial x^2 + v\,\partial c/\partial x \qquad [10.1]$$

where v is the streaming velocity of hydrogen, the second term on the right representing the change of concentration due to convection. In the stationary state there is no change of concentration with time, consequently

$$0 = D\,\partial^2 c/\partial x^2 + v\,\partial c/\partial x \qquad [10.2]$$

which gives a solution

$$c = c_0 \exp\left(-v[x - x_0]/D\right). \qquad [10.3]$$

Here c_0 and x_0 are the concentration and position coordinate at III, Fig. 10-2, x, c, refer to point 2.

If $x - x_0$, v, c and c_0 have been measured, D may be calculated from [10.3]. Measurements were carried out between the freezing point of water and 20°K., with the following results.

Diffusion coefficients of para-hydrogen in hydrogen.

Temp.°K.	273	85	20.6
D cm.²/sec.	1.26	0.172	0.00816

For the factor f in the relation

$$D_{11} = f\eta/\rho$$

an average of $f = 1.32$ is obtained. Here D_{11} is the coefficient of selfdiffusion, η the viscosity and ρ the density, cf. p. 418, 427, 430.

As mentioned before (p. 8), the evaporation of a volatile liquid contained at the bottom of an open cylinder, communicating with the atmosphere, may be used for the determination of diffusion coefficients of vapors in air (or in other gases). The first quantitative experiments on this subject were carried out by Stefan (111, 112, 113) who used narrow tubes (of diameter between 0.64 and 6.16 mm.), filled with a volatile liquid (such as ether, carbon disulfide). The experiments were not seriously disturbed by convection currents, as is seen from the consistency of the results obtained. In particular, there is no difference beyond the limits of error for the 0.64 and the 6.16 mm. tubes. From table III it is seen that the rate of evaporation is inversely proportional to the height of air through which the vapor must diffuse, as is a consequence of Fick's first law of diffusion for a quasi-stationary state.

TABLE III

Evaporation measurements with ether in a tube of 6.16 mm. diameter at 747 mm. Hg and 22°C.

Falling of the ether level (measured from the open end of the tube)	within a period of
from 9 mm. to 11 mm.	9 min. 50 seconds
,, 14 ,, ,, 16 ,,	14 ,, 55 ,,
,, 19 ,, ,, 21 ,,	19 ,, 45 ,,
,, 24 ,, ,, 26 ,,	24 ,, 40 ,,
,, 34 ,, ,, 36 ,,	34 ,, 15 ,,
,, 44 ,, ,, 46 ,,	44 ,, 15 ,,

The average depths of the level, below the open end of the tube, are 10, 15, 20, 25, 35, 45 mm. respectively, giving the ratios 2 : 3 : 4 : 5 : 7 : 9. Dividing the above listed times for evaporation of a

TABLE IV

Diffusivities of some organic compounds in air at 1 atmosphere (evaporation method)

Substance	Temperature °C.	$D \dfrac{cm.^2}{sec.}$	Author
Isopropyl alcohol	30	0.101	Gilliland (49)
n Butyl alcohol	30	0.088	,,
sec. Amyl alcohol	30	0.072	,,
Ethyl acetate	30	0.089	,,
Chlorobenzene	30	0.075	,,
Toluene	30	0.088	,,
Aniline	30	0.075	,,
Chloropicrine	25	0.088	Klotz and Miller (77)
Phosgene	0	0.095	,, ,,
Cyanogen chloride	0	0.111	,, ,,
Hydrogen cyanide	0	0.173	,, ,,

cf. also the measurements of Winkelmann, Landolt-Börnstein, Tabellen, Hauptwerk I p. 249.

TABLE V

Diffusion coefficients D_0, measured by evaporation method, reduced to 0°C and 760 mm. Hg, corrected and calculated by Trautz and Müller (123) according to $D_0 = D_T \, (T_0/T)^n$

Gases	D_0 cm.^{2}/sec.	Author
H$_2$O—CO$_2$	0.1384	Winkelmann (138, 139, 140, 141, 142)
H$_2$O—air	0.219	,,
H$_2$O—H$_2$	0.747	,,
Ethyl alcohol—CO$_2$	0.0686	,,
Ethyl alcohol—air	0.099	,,
Ethyl alcohol—H$_2$	0.377	,,
Ethyl ether—CO$_2$	0.0541	Hansen (57)
Ethyl ether—air	0.0786	,,
Ethyl ether—H$_2$	0.299	,,
Benzene—O$_2$	0.0797	Trautz and Ludwig (122)
Benzene—H$_2$	0.318	,, ,,
Carbon tetrachloride—O$_2$ . . .	0.0636	Trautz and Müller (124)
Carbon tetrachloride—H$_2$ . . .	0.293	Trautz and Ries (125)
Acetone—H$_2$	0.361	Trautz and Müller (124)
Mercury—N$_2$	0.1190	Mullaly and Jacques (95)
Iodine—N$_2$	0.070	,, ,,
Iodine—air	0.0692	Topley and Whytlaw-Gray (118)

2 mm. layer by these numbers we obtain

$$4' \, 55'', \quad 4' \, 58'', \quad 4' \, 56'', \quad 4' \, 54'', \quad 4' \, 55''$$

respectively. The good constancy of these figures shows that the rate of evaporation is inversely proportional to the height of the air layer, within the limits of experimental error.

The method has later been employed by a large number of workers with minor modifications (49, 52, 55, 77, 82, 88, 95, 118, 122, 124, 125, 126, 138). Results obtained by this method for a number of vapors are listed in Tables IV, V.

TABLE VI

Diffusion of metal vapors in gases at room temperature and 760 mm. Hg measured by an optical method

Metal vapor	Gas	Temperature ^{0}C	$D \dfrac{cm.^2}{sec.}$	Author
Na	N_2	15	20.4	van der Held, Miesowicz (60)
Hg	H_2	0	0.53	Spier (109)
Hg	N_2	0	0.14	,, (110)
Cd	N_2	0	0.17	,, (110)

For results of diffusion of alkali metal vapors examined by Becker (18), Wilson (135), Weiss (133), Davis (38), Symon (116), Ginsel and Ornstein (51) cf. van der Held and Miesowicz (60) and Landolt-Börnstein Tabellen Ergänzungsband II a p. 201.

TABLE VII

Diffusion of radon gas mixtures at 15°C. and 760 mm Hg after Hirst and Harrison (71)

Radon-air	H_2	He	Ne	A
0.120	0.476	0.351	0.217	0.092

The diffusion thermo-effect, investigated by Clusius and Waldmann (32), after earlier work of Dufour (39, 40), may also be used to determine diffusion coefficients, as shown by Waldmann (129, 130, 131)

II. Some results of the elementary kinetic theory of gases

We do not aim at giving a survey of the kinetic theory of gases, for which we refer to a number of excellent monographs (5, 6, 7, 8, 9), especially to Chapman and Cowling's (2) book on "The Theory of non-uniform Gases".

Here we shall list a number of elementary relations only which are of value in calculations in reaction kinetics and for rough estimates of diffusion coefficients. In addition some of these relations are used in the elementary treatment of diffusion in condensed phases.

The magnitudes of primary interest to us are the velocity of the gas molecules and their mean free path, i.e., the average distance travelled between two consecutive collisions. The correct expression for the mean square velocity is easily obtained by elementary methods, equating the gas pressure to the momentum transferred by the impact of the molecules upon the wall. One has

$$p = 1/3 \, n m \overline{v^2} = 1/3 \, \rho \overline{v^2} \qquad [10.4]$$

where n is the number of molecules per c.c., m the mass of a molecule and $\rho = nm$ the density of the gas. Inserting numerical values one obtains for the square root of the mean velocity values of the order of magnitude of some hundred meters per second. The square root of the mean square velocity is larger than the mean velocity of the gas molecules, on account of their velocity distribution (Maxwell's distribution law). Multiplication of [10.4] by the volume V in which N molecules are contained (N = Avogadro's number) gives

$$p V = 1/3 \, N m \overline{v^2} = 1/3 \, M \overline{v^2} = R T \qquad [10.5]$$

where R is the gas constant (in absolute units, 8.315×10^7 ergs/degree) and M the molecular weight. Therefore, the total kinetic energy of one mole of gas is

$$1/2 \, M \overline{v^2} = 3/2 \, R T. \qquad [10.6]$$

The number, dn, of molecules in unit volume, with velocity components between v_x and $v_x + dv_x$, v_y and $v_y + dv_y$, v_z and $v_z + dv_z$, respectively where v_x, v_y, v_z are the rectangular components of the velocity, is given by

$$dn = f(v_x v_y v_z) \, dv_x \, dv_y \, dv_z$$
$$= n \left(\frac{m}{2 \pi k T} \right)^{3/2} \exp \left(- \frac{m [v_x^2 + v_y^2 + v_z^2]}{2 k T} \right) dv_x \, dv_y \, dv_z \qquad [10.7]$$

Maxwell's distribution law of the velocities.

If we are interested only in the number of molecules with velocities between v and $v + dv$, irrespective of the direction of velocity, we obtain from [10.7], with $v^2 = v_x^2 + v_y^2 + v_z^2$, and by introducing polar coordinates in velocity space, volume element $v^2 \sin \theta \, dv \, d\theta \, d\varphi$, and integrating with respect to θ and φ over all directions

$$dn = 4 \pi n \, (m/2 \pi k T)^{3/2} \exp \left(- m v^2 / 2 k T \right) v^2 dv. \qquad [10.8]$$

Although for a specified direction the most probable velocity is zero, on account of equation [10.7], there exists a finite value of maximum probability for the velocity irrespective of direction, as seen from [10.8]. This most probable value is

$$v_{max} = \sqrt{\frac{2\,k\,T}{m}}$$ [10.9]

while the average velocity is

$$\bar{v} = \sqrt{\frac{8\,k\,T}{\pi m}}.$$ [10.10]

For the square root of the mean square velocity we had obtained, eqs. [10.5] and [10.6]

$$\sqrt{\overline{v^2}} = \sqrt{\frac{3\,k\,T}{m}}.$$ [10.11]

Therefore the ratio of these values is

$$\sqrt{\overline{v^2}}/\bar{v} = \sqrt{3\pi/8} = 1.086.$$ [10.12]

The mean free path of a molecule depends on the concentrations of all molecules present, and on their velocities. If the molecules can be treated as rigid elastic spheres the effective collision diameter for two molecules of diameters σ_1 and σ_2, respectively, is $\sigma_{12} = (\sigma_1 + \sigma_2)/2$. If we consider a gas molecule 1 moving with very great speed among identical molecules which can be considered as being at rest, then an elementary argument leads to the limiting value for the free path

$$\lambda(\infty) = \frac{1}{n\,\pi\,\sigma^2}.$$ [10.13]

If the other molecules are not at rest but move with velocities as given by Maxwell's law, one obtains for the mean free path

$$\lambda = \frac{1}{\sqrt{2}\,n\,\pi\,\sigma^2} = 0.707/n\,\pi\,\sigma^2.$$ [10.14]

To obtain the mean free path λ_1 of molecules 1, moving in a mixture of molecules 1, 2, 3, ... of densities n_1, n_2, n_3... molecules per c.c., with masses m_1, m_2, m_3 ..., eq. [10.14] must be replaced by the following

$$\lambda_1 = 1/\pi\{n_1\,\sigma_1^2\,\sqrt{2} + n_2\sigma_{12}^2\sqrt{1+m_1/m_2} + n_2\sigma_{13}^2\sqrt{1+m_1/m_3} + \cdots\}$$ [10.15]

where $\sigma_{12} = (\sigma_1 + \sigma_2)/2$, $\sigma_{13} = (\sigma_1 + \sigma_3)/2$, ...

The mean free path $\lambda(v)$ of a molecule 1 with velocity v, moving among molecules 1 with average velocity $\bar{v}$, is given as function of $v/\bar{v}$ in Table VIII, taken from Chapman and Cowling (2).

TABLE VIII
Mean free path as function of velocity

$v/\bar{v}$	0	0.25	0.5	0.627	0.886	1.0	1.535	2	3	5	∞
$\lambda(v)/\lambda(\infty)$	0	0.345	0.641	0.765	0.961	1.026	1.213	1.288	1.355	1.392	1.414

The limiting values for $v/\bar{v} = 0$ and $= \infty$ can be obtained by elementary considerations.

If the mean free path λ were independent of the velocity, a free path l would have the relative probability $\exp(-l/\lambda)$. The actual value differs from this expression, cf. Jeans (7) and Chapman and Cowling (2).

After collision with another molecule a given molecule, on the average, will not have lost the whole of its velocity component in the original direction, as implied by elementary theories of transport phenomena, but it will still retain a velocity component in this direction. The theory permits the calculation of a persistence ratio (depending on the speed of the molecule), equal to the ratio of the mean velocity component after collision to the velocity before collision. This persistence ratio for molecules 1, moving with speed v_1 and colliding with molecules 2 of mass m_2, can be evaluated accurately for rigid elastic spheres. It varies between $M_1 - M_2/3$ and M_1 as v_1 varies between 0 and ∞. Here the abbreviations are used $M_1 = m_1/(m_1 + m_2)$ and $M_2 = m_2/(m_1 + m_2)$. It is obvious that in the limiting case $m_1/m_2 \to \infty$ the persistence ratio tends towards unity. For collisions between equal molecules the persistence ratio varies between 1/3 and 1/2. For the mean persistence ratio ω of molecules 1, averaged over all values of the velocity v_1 an expression is obtained (cf. Chapman a Cowling (2))

$$\omega = \frac{1}{2} M_1 + \frac{1}{2} M_1^2 \, M_2^{-1/2} \log\left[\left(M_2^{1/2} + 1\right)\Big/ M_1^{1/2}\right]. \qquad [10.16]$$

The mean persistence ratio is zero for $m_1/m_2 = 0$ and increases to unity for $m_1/m_2 \to \infty$; its value for collisions of like molecules is 0.406.

We shall deal briefly with the elementary theory of diffusion in gases, in spite of its obvious shortcomings, because in the theory of diffusion in liquids and solids one must make use of similar approximations. In addition, analogous considerations are indispensible in problems of reaction kinetics.

We consider a binary gas mixture with a concentration gradient in the direction of the x-axis, causing a diffusion flow in this direction. We shall make use of the simplification that one third of all molecules move parallel to the x-axis, and accordingly one third parallel to the y-axis and one third parallel to the z-axis, a simplification which, incidentally, gives correct results in the calculation of the gas pressure. A surface of unit area, perpendicular to the x-axis, will be crossed during one second by

$$1/6 \, n_1 \, \bar{v}_1$$

molecules 1, moving in the direction of the positive x-axis. Here n_1 is the number of molecules per c.c., $\bar{v}_1$ their average velocity. If the concentration varies in the direction of the x-axis, the above expression will be slightly changed, giving different numbers of molecules crossing the surface of reference in the positive and in the negative x-directions. The molecules, crossing the surface, had their last collision in a distance of approximately the mean free path apart from this surface. If the surface of reference is situated at $x = x_0$, the molecules crossing the surface in the positive x-direction, will come from a plane at $x_0 - \lambda_1$, and their number will be

$$\frac{1}{6} \bar{v}_1 \left(n_1 \right)_{x_0 - \lambda_1} = \frac{1}{6} \bar{v}_1 \left(n_1 - \lambda_1 \frac{\partial n_1}{\partial x} \right)$$

while the number of molecules, crossing this surface in the opposite direction will be given, to the same approximation, by

$$\frac{1}{6} \bar{v}_1 \left(n_1 \right)_{x_0 + \lambda_1} = \frac{1}{6} \bar{v}_1 \left(n_1 + \lambda_1 \frac{\partial n_1}{\partial x} \right).$$

The surplus of molecules, moving per second in the positive direction, by definition equal to the diffusion current $J_1 = - D_{12} \dfrac{\partial n_1}{\partial x}$, is accordingly given by the difference of the above expressions

$$J_1 = - \frac{1}{3} \lambda_1 \bar{v}_1 \frac{\partial n_1}{\partial x} \qquad [10.17]$$

and consequently the coefficient of diffusion must be

$$D_{12} = \frac{1}{3} \lambda_1 \bar{v}_1 . \qquad [10.18]$$

The above expression is a very rough approximation. If the molecules are not moving parallel to one of the axes, but with random distribution of directions of velocity, one obtains for the number of molecules which cross unit area per second

$$\frac{1}{4} n_1 \bar{v}_1$$

instead of the approximate value $\dfrac{1}{6} n_1 \bar{v}_1$. Further one has to consider that the molecules, crossing the surface at $x = x_0$, do not come exactly from a distance λ_1, therefore λ_1 must be replaced by $\lambda_1 \varphi_1$, φ_1 being a factor of order unity. Thus one obtains, instead of [10.18], as expression for the diffusion coefficient

$$D_{12} = \frac{1}{2} \lambda_1 \bar{v}_1 \varphi_1 \qquad [10.19]$$

where a refined theory would have to provide the value of the factor φ_1.

Since the pressure in the gas is supposed to be constant, and consequently $\frac{\partial n_1}{\partial x} = -\frac{\partial n_2}{\partial x}$, the corresponding expression for the diffusion coefficient of the second component must be

$$D_{12} = \frac{1}{2} \lambda_2 \bar{v}_2 \varphi_2 \qquad [10.20]$$

equal to that of the first one, eq. [10.19]. It is obvious that this equality can only be obtained on account of the factors φ_1 and φ_2, and, therefore, equation [10.18] cannot be correct because it does not contain such a factor.

If the two components 1 and 2 become identical, we obtain the coefficient of self diffusion

$$D_{11} = \frac{1}{2} \lambda \bar{v} \varphi_{11} \qquad [10.21]$$

where φ_{11} is again a factor of order unity. In certain cases it is possible to observe diffusion processes approaching self diffusion very closely (cf. p. 409ff), for instance if one component is an isotope of the other, or a compound where one isotope has been replaced by another; besides there exist (approximate) methods for an indirect determination of coefficients of self diffusion (cf. p. 426).

Though there exist methods for the determination of molecular dimensions, independent of the measurement of transport processes in gases, the values of σ entering the equation for diffusion (through λ), are most adequately determined from measurements of transport phenomena, for instance, from viscosity or heat conduction of gases which are more easily measured than the rate of diffusion.

From a consideration of transport of momentum one obtains in a way strictly analogous to the above for the coefficient of viscosity of a gas η (ϱ density)

$$\eta = \frac{1}{2} \varphi \varrho \bar{v} \lambda. \qquad [10.22]$$

If the factor φ, of order unity, were known, the mean free path and consequently the diameter σ could be determined from [10.22]. Without a rigorous theory one can determine λ and σ only approximately, by putting $\varphi = 1$. From [10.21] and [10.22] we obtain the relation between viscosity and the coefficient of self diffusion

$$D_{11} = f \eta / \rho \qquad [10.23]$$

where the factor $f = \frac{\varphi_{11}}{\varphi}$ is again of the order of unity, and must be determined by a more refined theory.

For heat conduction one obtains accordingly

$$\varkappa = \frac{1}{2} \varrho \, \varphi_\varkappa \, \lambda \, \bar{v} \, c_v \qquad\qquad [10.24]$$

where $\varkappa$ is the thermal conductivity of the gas, c_v its specific heat, and $\varphi_\varkappa$ a new factor of order unity. $\varkappa$ and η are interrelated by

$$\varkappa = f' \eta c_v \qquad\qquad [10.25]$$

f' being a numerical factor.

For problems of reaction kinetics the number of collisions of a gas molecule per second is of importance. The number of collisions of a molecule 1 with molecules 2 in a binary gas mixture is given by

$$N_1 = 2 \, n_2 \, \sigma_{12}^2 \left\{ \frac{2 \, \pi \, kT \, (m_1 + m_2)}{m_1 \, m_2} \right\}^{1/2} \qquad\qquad [10.26]$$

where n_2 is the number of molecules 2 per c.c. Consequently, the total number of collisions of molecules 1, of number n_1 per c.c., with molecules 2 per second is given by

$$N_{12} = 2 \, n_1 \, n_2 \, \sigma_{12}^2 \left\{ \frac{2 \, \pi \, kT \, (m_1 + m_2)}{m_1 \, m_2} \right\}^{1/2}. \qquad\qquad [10.27]$$

For the number of collisions between like molecules one obtains from [10.27]

$$N_{11} = \frac{1}{2} \, 4 \, n_1^2 \, \sigma_1^2 \left\{ \frac{\pi \, kT}{m_1} \right\}^{1/2} \qquad\qquad [10.28]$$

a factor 1/2 being inserted because otherwise every collision would be counted twice. The number of collisions of one molecule 1 with molecules of the same kind is twice the expression [10.28], divided by n_1.

In reaction kinetics we may have competition of a surface process with a volume process, and, therefore, may be interested in the computation of the reaction probability of a molecule while it is diffusing onto some surface. The probability for reaction of a molecule with other molecules in the gas volume is proportional to the number of collisions encountered before the molecule reaches the wall. The factor of proportionality usually contains an exponential term $\exp(-E/RT)$ where E represents an energy of activation. If we content ourselves with approximate results we may start with the formula for the mean square displacement, $\overline{\Delta x^2} = 2 \, Dt$, and insert for t the value we obtain by considering the number of collisions during time t. During time t the molecule has travelled a path of length $t \times v$, if v is its mean velocity, and this length, divided by the mean free path λ gives the number of collisions, N_{12}, consequently

$$t = N_{12} \lambda / v . \qquad\qquad [10.29]$$

With this value of t we obtain

$$\overline{\Delta x^2} = 2\, D N_{12} \lambda / v \qquad\qquad [10.30]$$

and

$$N_{12} = \overline{\Delta x^2} v / 2\, D \lambda . \qquad\qquad [10.31]$$

If we introduce, as further approximations, $D = \frac{1}{2}\lambda v$, and replace $\overline{\Delta x^2}$ by Δx^2, we finally have

$$N_{12} \approx \left(\frac{\Delta x}{\lambda}\right)^2 \qquad\qquad [10.32]$$

neglecting a factor of order unity. The result implies that the free path of the molecules under consideration is predominantly determined by collisions with the reacting molecules. A more accurate treatment gives instead of [10.32]

$$N_{12} = \frac{3\pi}{4} \frac{\overline{\Delta x^2}}{\lambda^2} . \qquad\qquad [10.33]$$

III. Some results of the accurate theory

The theory of non-uniform gases, as given by Chapman (2, 25, 26, 27, 28, 29) and Enskog (3, 41, 42, 43, 44) is accurate insofar as it permits an exact solution of the equations for transport phenomena in gases, based upon certain molecular models. But, so far, the choice of these models is not entirely free. They must be of spherical symmetry, and, therefore, an exact treatment of polyatomic molecules and the consideration of an exchange of internal energy of the molecules with kinetic energy of translation during collisions is excluded (with one exception, see below). But within the limits, thus imposed, the theory is quite general, the solutions being obtained as successive approximations to the correct values. The molecules may be considered as rigid elastic spheres, as rigid elastic spheres with a central field of force (Sutherland's model (115)), as point centres of force, with the special case of Maxwellian molecules, i.e., centres of force repelling each other by a force inversely proportional to the fifth power of the distance, a case which permits an easy evaluation of certain integrals, etc. The highest accuracy of the results thus obtained, is therefore to be expected for monatomic gases.

It has been possible (Pidduck (101)) to treat a model of rough spheres, giving an interchange of energy of rotation and translational kinetic energy during collision.

We shall not attempt at giving any account of the theory itself, which is based upon Boltzmann's fundamental integral equation. The best treatment is found in Chapman and Cowling's (2) monograph, which we shall follow in our presentation of some results of practical importance.

The first approximation to the coefficient of diffusion in a binary mixture $[D_{12}]_1$ for the model of rigid elastic spheres is

$$[D_{12}]_1 = \frac{3}{8 (n_1 + n_2) \sigma_{12}^2} \left\{ \frac{kT (m_1 + m_2)}{2 \pi m_1 m_2} \right\}^{1/2} . \qquad [10.34]$$

For molecules treated as point centres repelling each other with a force $\varkappa_{12} r^{-\nu}$ the corresponding expression is

$$[D_{12}]_1 = \frac{3}{8 n A_1 (\nu) \Gamma \left(3 - \dfrac{2}{\nu - 1} \right)} \left\{ \frac{kT (m_1 + m_2)}{2 \pi m_1 m_2} \right\}^{1/2} \left\{ \frac{2 kT}{\varkappa_{12}} \right\}^{2/(\nu - 1)} \qquad [10.35]$$

where $n = n_1 + n_2$.

Numerical values of the magnitude $A_1 (\nu)$ are found in table II p. 517. $\Gamma \left(3 - \dfrac{2}{\nu - 1} \right)$ is the Gamma function for the argument $\left(3 - \dfrac{2}{\nu - 1} \right)$. For $\left(3 - \dfrac{2}{\nu - 1} \right)$ equal to an integer, i, one has $\Gamma (i) = (i - 1)!$ For ν ranging from 2 to ∞, $\Gamma \left(3 - \dfrac{2}{\nu - 1} \right)$ varies between 1 and 2, and the product $A_1 (\nu) \Gamma \left(3 - \dfrac{2}{\nu - 1} \right)$ is always smaller than 2. $\left(\dfrac{2 kT}{\varkappa_{12}} \right)^{1/(\nu - 1)}$ is of the dimension of a reciprocal length. Hence a comparison of eqs. [10.35] and [10.34] shows that in the final result, the model of point centres, repelling one another by an inverse power of the distance, $1/r^\nu$, is equivalent to using a temperature-dependent effective collision diameter σ_{eff}

$$\sigma_{eff} = \sqrt{A_1 (\nu) \Gamma \left(3 - \frac{2}{\nu - 1} \right)} \left(\frac{\varkappa_{12}}{2 kT} \right)^{1/(\nu - 1)} . \qquad [10.36]$$

For Sutherland's model the expression is obtained

$$[D_{12}]_1 = \frac{3}{8 n \sigma_{12}^2} \left\{ \frac{kT (m_1 + m_2)}{2 \pi m_1 m_2} \right\}^{1/2} \bigg/ \left\{ 1 + \frac{S_{12}}{T} \right\} \qquad [10.37]$$

where S_{12} is Sutherland's constant, related to the law for the attracting force, but usually determined empirically from the temperature-dependence of the diffusion coefficient (or rather of that of the viscosity). Eq. [10.37], like [10.35] can be interpreted as giving a temperature dependent collision diameter

$$\sigma_{eff} = (\sigma_{12})_\infty \sqrt{1 + \frac{S_{12}}{T}} . \qquad [10.38]$$

Since most collision diameters for pure gases, σ_1, σ_2, have been determined from viscosity measurements, and since these measurements often are represented by Sutherland's formula, care must be taken that in the computation of D_{12} the effective diameter, valid for the specified temperature under consideration, is really used, and not the considerably smaller limiting value $(\sigma_{12})_\infty$ for $T \to \infty$. Pidduck's model for rough elastic spheres, allowing for an exchange between rotational and translational energy, leads to the equation

$$[D_{12}]_1 = \frac{3}{8 n \sigma_{12}^2} \left\{ \frac{kT (m_1 + m_2)}{2 \pi m_1 m_2} \right\}^{1/2} \frac{K_0 + K_1 K_2}{K_0 + 2 K_1 K_2} \qquad [10.39]$$

where $K_1 = 4 I_1/m_1 \sigma_1^2$, $K_2 = 4 I_2/m_2 \sigma_2^2$, $(m_1 + m_2) K_0 = m_1 K_1 + m_2 K_2$, and I_1 and I_2 are the moments of inertia of the molecules 1 and 2. This model gives no additional temperature-dependence of the coefficient of diffusion, but it increases the effective collision diameter above the value for smooth rigid elastic spheres, thus decreasing the value for $[D_{12}]_1$.

$[D_{12}]_1$, for any of the models considered, is independent of the concentration-ratio of the mixture. The dependence on concentration, as it has actually been found, though of moderate magnitude only, enters through the second approximation, $[D_{12}]_2$.

The second approximation is already rather complicated, containing a number of numerical factors derived from integrations for the special models adopted (2). Only in Maxwell's case, for molecules repelling each other with a force proportional to the inverse fifth power of the distance, do the results for higher approximations remain simple, being identical with the first approximation $[D_{12}]_1$, and strictly independent of the concentration ratio.

With the model of rigid elastic spheres simple expressions are obtained only for the limiting cases where the concentration of one component is very small compared with that of the other, i.e. for $n_1/n_2 \to 0$ or for $n_2/n_1 \to 0$. The ratio of the diffusion coefficients for these limiting cases is, to a second approximation

$$\frac{[D_{12}]_{2\, n_2 = 0}}{[D_{12}]_{2\, n_1 = 0}} = \frac{1 - m_2^2/[13 m_2^2 + 30 m_1^2 + 16 m_1 m_2]}{1 - m_1^2/[13 m_1^2 + 30 m_2^2 + 16 m_1 m_2]}. \qquad [10.40]$$

[10.40] gives as a maximum value for the ratio $[D_{12}]_{2\, n_2 = 0}/[D_{12}]_{2\, n_1 = 0}$ 13/12, for $m_1/m_2 \to 0$, equivalent to a change in the diffusion coefficient of $8^1/_3$ per cent. Though this difference increases for higher approximations, up to 13.2 per cent, Chapman and Cowling suggest that for actual gases — not rigid elastic spheres — the variation should be considerably smaller. In the experiments of Lonius (83) etc. (cf. p. 408ff.) the most extreme variation actually found was about 8 per cent. In Table IX, taken from Chapman and Cowling, the results of Lonius and others are listed, together with theoretical values for $[D_{12}]_2$, calculated by Chapman and Cowling for H_2–CO_2, and He–A. The theoretical values are not calculated independently of the experiments, the value of the first approximation, $[D_{12}]_1$, entering into the result, being determined from the experiments in such a way as to obtain the best average agreement. The agreement, thus obtained between observed and calculated values, for the dependence on concentration seems quite satisfactory.

TABLE IX

Variation of D_{12} with concentration, taken from Chapman and Cowling (2)

Pair of gases	n_1/n_2	D_{12} (obs.)	$[D_{12}]_2$ (calc.)	Observer
First gas H$_2$ . . . . . }	3	0.594	0.589	Deutsch
Second gas CO$_2$ . . . }	1	0.605	0.617	,,
	1/3	0.633	0.628	,,
First gas He . . . . . }	2.65	0.678	0.689	Lonius
Second gas A . . . . }	2,26	0.693	0.694	,,
	1.66	0.696	0.697	R. Schmidt
	1	0.706	0.706	,,
	0.477	0.712	0.714	Lonius
	0.311	0.731	0.719	,,

IV. The dependence of the diffusion coefficient on temperature and pressure

Within the range of validity of the ideal gas laws one has at constant temperature: $n \sim p$, and at constant pressure: $n \sim 1/T$. Consequently each of the equations for $[D_{12}]_1$ gives a dependence of the diffusion coefficient on pressure, for constant T, according to $1/p$. This has been tested experimentally by Loschmidt, cf. Table I, p. 408.

Of course, the proportionality of D with $1/p$, and, correspondingly, the independence of the viscosity η on pressure, must cease to be valid as soon as we are dealing with compressed gases beyond the range of validity of the ideal gas laws. Thorne (117) succeeded in extending Enskog's method to a gas mixture at high density. The coefficient of diffusion of a binary gas mixture, D_{12}, is given to the first approximation by

$$D_{12} = [D_{12}]_1/\chi_{12} \qquad [10.41]$$

where $[D_{12}]_1$ is the former value of the first approximation for ideal gases. χ_{12} is defined by

$$\chi_{12} = 1 + \frac{\pi}{12} n_1 \sigma_1^3 \left(8 - \frac{3\,\sigma_1}{\sigma_{12}} \right) + \frac{\pi}{12} n_2 \sigma_2^3 \left(8 - \frac{3\,\sigma_2}{\sigma_{12}} \right) + \cdots \qquad [10.42]$$

So far no diffusion measurements with highly compressed gases seem to have been performed. But for estimates of the rate of diffusion under such conditions use should be made of the above equation. To give an idea of the magnitude of the effect of high pressure on transport phenomena we reproduce in Table X some data of the viscosity of nitrogen at 50°C., from measurements of Michels and Gibson (93), together with calculated values, taken from Chapman and Cowling (2).

TABLE X

Viscosity of nitrogen at high pressure

Pressure (atmospheres) .	15.37	104.5	320.4	541.7	742.1	965.8
$\eta \times 10^6$ calc.	181	205	266	348	418	492
$\eta \times 10^6$ obs.	191.3	208.8	273.7	350.9	416.3	491.3

While for ideal gases the viscosity is independent of pressure, the variation with pressure in the above experiments is considerable, though of opposite sign to that of the diffusion coefficient. The agreement between theory and experiment is remarkable; the theory, however, is not the same as the above mentioned theory for the dependence of the rate of diffusion on pressure.

In order to give an estimate of the effect of pressure on diffusion we have calculated the dependence of the coefficient of self diffusion of nitrogen on pressure for $t = 50°C$. In this case the equation for χ reduces to $(\sigma_1 = \sigma_2 = \sigma_{12})$

$$\chi_{11} = 1 + \frac{5\pi}{12} n_1 \sigma_1^3 . \qquad [10.43]$$

We obtain for the ratio $D_{12}/[D_{12}]_1$ as function of p:

p (atmospheres)	1	15.37	104.5	320.4	541.7	742.1	965.8
$D_{12}/[D_{12}]_1$	1	0.975	0.86	0.70	0.62	0.58	0.55

For the ratio of the diffusion coefficient at p atmospheres to that at $p = 1$ atmosphere we obtain, for the same pressures

1   0.064   0.0084   0.0026   0.0016   0.0013   0.0011

It seems doubtful whether eqs. [10.42] and [10.43], containing only the first member of a series, will give a sufficient approximation for the highest pressures listed.

As might be expected, there is no longer proportionality between D and η/ρ. η/ρ varies by about $1 : 200$ in a region where D varies by $1 : 900$. This result seems quite satisfactory, since in liquids D is proportional to $1/\eta$, and dense gases might in some respect show a behaviour intermediate between that of a dilute gas and that of a liquid.

Due to the proportionality of n to $1/T$, for constant p, eq. [10.34], p. 421 for rigid elastic spheres gives the temperature-dependence of D, as $T^{3/2}$. The other models lead to a stronger dependence of D on T. For molecules repelling each other by a force proportional to $1/r^{\nu_{12}}$ a temperature-dependence is obtained, varying between $T^{3/2}$ and T^2. The expression, obtained from eq. [10.35]. p. 421 is

$$D_{12} \sim T^{3/2 + s} \qquad [10.44]$$

where s is connected with the exponent ν_{12} of the law of force by

$$s = \frac{2}{\nu_{12} - 1}. \qquad [10.45]$$

This gives, for rigid elastic spheres, $\nu_{12} = \infty$, $s = 0$, $D_{12} \sim T^{3/2}$, in accordance with the former result. For Maxwellian molecules, $\nu_{12} = 5$, $s = \frac{1}{2}$, therefore $D_{12} \sim T^2$. For actual gases ν_{12} should not be smaller than 5, therefore the exponent of the temperature should lie between 1.5 and 2, provided that the approximation of the molecules as point centres of repulsive force is a sufficient approximation.

The experiments of v. Obermayer, discussed on p. 407, were undertaken chiefly in order to obtain improved values for the exponent in the law for the temperature dependence. We reproduce in Table XI s-values taken from Chapman and Cowling (2) obtained

TABLE XI

Exponent s of eq. [10.44], and exponent ν_{12} of force law, calculated by Chapman and Cowling from v. Obermayer's diffusion measurements, together with the values ν_1, ν_2 for the individual gases (from viscosity)

Gases	s	ν_{12}	ν_1	ν_2
Air—CO_2 . .	0.468	5.3	8.46	5.6
H_2—O_2 . . .	0.255	8.8	11.3	7.6
CO_2—N_2O . .	0.550	4.6	5.6	6.15
CO_2—H_2 . . .	0.242	9.3	5.6	11.3
O_2—N_2 . . .	0.292	7.9	7.6	8.8

from v. Obermayer's results, with values of the exponent ν_{12} of the force law, derived by means of equation [10.45], and for comparison the exponents ν_1 and ν_2 of the individual gases, calculated from measured viscosities.

The value ν_{12} should not be very far from the average of ν_1 and ν_2. If the observed discrepancies prove to be real it might be due to the fact that the model used does not resemble closely enough actual di- and polyatomic molecules.

V. Self diffusion

Self diffusion in the strict sense of the word, viz. diffusion of a selected group of particles within a medium of exactly equal particles, is unobservable. One can, however, obtain results approaching self diffusion very closely, by using gas mixtures of components with very similar properties, e.g. N_2 and CO, by using isotopes as indicators for diffusion measurements (provided the mass ratio of the isotopes or of the molecules containing the isotopes is sufficiently close to unity), finally by using para-hydrogen as one component diffusing in normal hydrogen (58). The last example, probably, gives the best approximation to self diffusion.

There are several reasons why self diffusion is of some interest. When it is possible to carry out measurements closely approaching self diffusion one certainly has to deal with a diffusion coefficient sufficiently independent of concentration. Therefore, all difficulties are avoided, which would otherwise arise from the necessity of taking into account the dependence on concentration if precision measurements are to be obtained. Further, for self diffusion one obtains the simplest theoretical expressions, containing properties of one kind of molecule only. In particular one has a rigorous relation between self diffusion and viscosity. In the case of a binary gas mixture, one can derive collision diameters from the viscosity data, and compute the coefficient of interdiffusion of these components by means of these diameters, which involves the assumption that the collision diameter for different molecules is the arithmetic mean of that of the pure components, an assumption correct only for rigid elastic spheres.

Lord Kelvin (84) gave an indirect method for the determination of coefficients of self diffusion in gases. The accuracy of this method, however, depends on the theoretical formula employed for the calculation of interdiffusion in binary gas mixtures. If diffusion coefficients D_{12}, D_{23} and D_{31} for the three binary mixtures of the three components 1, 2 and 3 have been measured, then collision diameters can be computed, assuming the model of rigid elastic spheres. For this model the following relations hold

$$\sigma_{12} = \frac{1}{2}(\sigma_1 + \sigma_2), \ \ \sigma_{23} = \frac{1}{2}(\sigma_2 + \sigma_3), \ \ \sigma_{31} = \frac{1}{2}(\sigma_3 + \sigma_1).$$

Therefore it is possible to compute the individual values σ_1, σ_2 and σ_3. By means of these collision diameters, using again the model of rigid elastic spheres, we can compute the three coefficients of self diffusion. Though the result, thus obtained, depends on the equation adopted, it well may be that the error entering the result is considerably smaller than that encountered in an absolute computation of the coefficients of self diffusion by means of the same equation.

Experimental results for mixtures of N_2 and CO, and for CO_2 and N_2O, by Boardman and Wild (20), have been discussed before (p. 409).

Coefficients of self diffusion, calculated by Chapman and Cowling (2) by Kelvin's method are listed in Table XII.

TABLE XII

Coefficients of self diffusion (at N.T.P.), from Chapman and Cowling (2)

| Combination of gases used | Coefficient of self diffusion, D_{11} cm.^{2}/sec. | | | |
	H_2	O_2	CO	CO_2
H_2—O_2—CO .	1.24	0.191	0.179	—
H_2—O_2—CO_2 .	1.30	0.182	—	0.107
H_2—CO—CO_2	1.34	—	0.170	0.105
O_2—CO—CO_2	—	0.193	0.176	0.101
Mean	1.29	0.189	0.175	0.104

The agreement between the values, obtained from different combinations of gases, is rather satisfactory. The authors further compared the coefficients of self diffusion thus obtained with the corresponding viscosities, Table XIII.

TABLE XIII

Coefficients of self diffusion and viscosity, after Chapman and Cowling (2)

Gas	D_{11}	$\rho \times 10^6$	$\eta \times 10^7$	$D_{11}\,\rho/\eta$	3 A
H_2 . . .	1.29	89.9	850	1.37	1.39
O_2 . . .	0.189	1429	1926	1.40	1.46
CO . . .	0.175	1250	1665	1.31	1.45
CO_2 . . .	0.104	1977	1380	1.49	1.52

As mentioned above (p. 418), D_{11} should be proportional to the ratio η/ρ, the factor of proportionality being of order unity and depending on the gas model employed. The rigid-sphere model gives as first approximation

$$[D_{11}]_1 = \frac{3}{8\,\pi\,\sigma^2}\left\{\frac{k\,T}{\pi\,m}\right\}^{1/2} = \frac{6}{5}\frac{[\eta]_1}{\rho} \qquad [10.46]$$

and therefore a factor 1.20 if, for η, the corresponding first approximation is taken. The first approximation, not specialized for rigid elastic spheres gives

$$[D_{11}]_1 = 3A\,[\eta]_1/\rho\;.$$

In the following table, taken from Chapman and Cowling (2), values of the numerical factor A are given, for the model of point centres, repelling one another by a force $\sim 1/r^\nu$.

$\nu =$	5	7	9	11	15	∞
$A =$	0.517	0.493	0.478	0.465	0.449	0.4

Therefore, for rigid elastic spheres, $(\nu = \infty)$, the numerical factor is $3A = 1.20$. The calculated values for $3A$, contained in the last column of Table XIII, p. 427, have been computed for exponents ν equal to 11.3, 7.6, 8.75 and 5.6, respectively, obtained from viscosity measurements. Since for these values the model of point centres has been used, while in the evaluation of D_{11} that of rigid elastic spheres, $(\nu = \infty)$, had to be employed, complete agreement between calculated and observed values of $3A$ hardly can be expected.

Harteck and Schmidt (58) (cf. p. 410/1) give, for hydrogen, $D_{11} = 1.28$ cm.^{2}/sec. at N.T.P., equal to 1.36 η/ρ, and $\nu = 12$.

As has been emphasized before, since self diffusion in the strict sense of the word is unobservable, all results obtained are either very close experimental approximations or results of calculations making use of special models. The quantum theory of collisions (cf. Mott and Massey (10)) leads to anomalies in the case of collisions between identical particles. Massey and Mohr (91) find that in this case the cross section for self diffusion is twice the classical value. This result does not refer to the above experimental values, because these observed values are not the unobservable values, treated by quantum theory, but values based upon classical theory, derived on the assumption that from values of diffusion of non-identical particles with very similar properties a value for self diffusion may be calculated or extrapolated. It may even be that, for self diffusion in the strict sense, instead of the quantum laws for scattering of identical particles, the quantum laws for distinguishable particles should be applied. For, with the exception of monatomic molecules at not too high temperatures, two polyatomic molecules colliding will usually differ in their quantum states (cf. the above treated example of ortho- and para-hydrogen) and, therefore, cannot be considered as identical (Halpern and Gwathmey (56)). In such cases the above derived values of the coefficients of self diffusion might well approach the unobservable true values of self diffusion.

In Table XIV we list some experimental values of diffusion coefficients and collision diameters, for pairs of different molecules calcu-

TABLE XIV

Coefficients of diffusion, collision diameters and collision diameters for pure components (from viscosity), taken from Chapman and Cowling (2)

Gases	D_{12} cm.^{2}/sec. at. N.T.P.	$\sigma_{12} \times 10^8$ cm.	$^1/_2 (\sigma_1 + \sigma_2) \times 10^8$ (from visc.)
He—A	0.641	2.61	2.92
H_2—D_2	1.20	2.46	2.74
H_2—O_2	0.697	2.94	3.17
H_2—N_2	0.674	3.01	3.24
H_2—CO	0.651	3.05	3.25
H_2—CO_2	0.550	3.30	3.68
H_2—CH_4	0.625	3.14	3.44
H_2—SO_2	0.480	3.52	4.11
H_2—N_2O	0.535	3.35	3.70
H_2—C_2H_4	0.625	3.53	3.84
O_2—N_2	0.181	3.45	3.69
O_2—CO	0.185	3.41	3.69
O_2—CO_2	0.139	3.73	4.12
CO—N_2	0.192	3.44	3.76
CO—CO_2	0.137	3.83	4.20
CO—C_2H_4	0.116	4.38	4.36
CO_2—N_2	0.144	3.74	4.19
CO_2—CH_4	0.153	4.08	4.39
CO_2—N_2O	0.096	4.30	4.65
H_2—Air	0.611	—	—
O_2—Air	0.178	—	—
CO_2—Air	0.138	—	—
CH_4—Air	0.196	—	—

lated from diffusion coefficients, for single components taken from viscosity measurements.

Hirschfelder, Bird and Spotz (69, 70) have evaluated the integrals, entering the expressions for diffusion, thermal diffusion, viscosity and heat conductivity, as given by Chapman and Cowling (2), assuming that the energy of attraction is inversely proportional to the sixth power of the distance and the energy of repulsion is proportional to the twelfth power of the distance. Coefficients of self diffusion, compared, with theoretical values are contained in the following Table XV. Transport properties in gases also have been calculated by Amdur (14, 15, 16).

TABLE XV

Coefficient of self diffusion D measured and calculated by Hirschfelder, Bird and Spotz (70)*, viscosity η, $f = D \times \rho/\eta$ (ρ density) and Sutherland constant C

Gas	Temp. °K.	$D \frac{cm^2}{sec.}$ experimental	calculat. (HBS)	$\eta \times 10^4$ g./cm. sec.	f	C °K.	Author (of experimental work)
Hydrogen (para-hydrogen	273	1.285 ± 0.0025	1.243	0.844	1.37 ± 0.05	80	Harteck-Schmidt (58)
into ortho-hydrogen)	85	0.172 ± 0.008	0.167	0.377	1.32 ± 0.06		,,
	20.4	0.00816 ± 0.0002	0.01043	0.086	1.28 ± 0.02		,,
Deuterium into hydrogen	288	1.24					Heath, Ibbs and Wild (59)
Neon	293	0.473 ± 0.002	0.491	3.111	1.27 ± 0.006	60	Groth-Sussner (54)
Argon	326.7	0.212 ± 0.002	0.213	2.435	1.30	115	Hutchinson (73, 74)
	295.2	0.180 ± 0.001	0.178	2.240	1.32 ± 0.01		,,
	273.2	0.158 ± 0.002	0.154	2.104	1.34		,,
	194.7	0.0833 ± 0.0009	0.0820	1.555	1.34		,,
	90.2	0.028 ± 0.0010	0.0178	0.765	2.1		,,
Krypton	294.0	0.09 ± 0.004	0.093	2.485	1.30 ± 0.06	210	Groth-Harteck (53)
Xenon	292.1	0.0443 ± 0.002	0.055	2.260	1.24 ± 0.06	290	,,
Nitrogen	293	0.200 ± 0.008	0.198	1.747	1.48		Winn (136)
Methane ($p = 60$ mm.Hg)	292	26.32 ± 0.73	26.38	1.097	1.33		Winn-Ney (137)
Hydrogen chloride	295.0	0.1246	0.127	1.438	1.33		Braune-Zehle (23)
Hydrogen bromide	295.3	0.0792	—	1.858	1.43		,,
Uranium hexafluoride	303	$D \times \rho = 234 \pm 9 \times 10^{-6}$ g./cm.×sec	—		1.31		Ney-Armistead (96)
($p = 10$ mm. Hg)							

* All values of D are corrected to 760 mm. Hg except methane and uranium hexafluoride

VI. Diffusion in multicomponent mixtures

As discussed elsewhere (Chap. I and XII, p. 489ff.) in general a coupling between different irreversible processes is to be expected. If such a coupling exists for diffusion in mixtures of more than two components a concentration gradient present for two components may cause a diffusion flow of other components of uniform concentration distribution. Hellund (61, 62) has extended Enskog's theory to mixtures of more than two components. He defines as "osmotic" diffusion in a gas that diffusion which would occur in a tube containing one gas of constant density (the "solvent"), due to the existence in the tube of two or more gases of varying concentrations (the "solute") which would themselves diffuse on account of the concentration gradients. In an experiment where a long tube is separated in the middle by a diaphragm and one gas is present in both sections, at the same pressure, while two different gases are placed in the two sections, but at equal partial pressures, diffusion of the uniformly distributed first component will occur when the diaphragm is removed. This case has been treated theoretically by Hellund.

To give an idea of the effects possible, we quote a few values of Hellund's numerical results for the ternary mixture $H_2(1)$, $CH_4(2)$ and $CO_2(3)$. CO_2 is supposed to be the solvent gas. The number densities (numbers of molecules per c. c.) are all chosen equal and of such magnitude that the total pressure is 1140 mm. Hg at 0°C. The experimental values of the three diffusion coefficients for the binary mixtures are: $D_{12} = 0.625$, $D_{23} = 0.153$ and $D_{31} = 0.538$. In the section of the tube which originally contained H_2 and CO_2 a rise of the CO_2 partial pressure with time up to a maximum of 68.2 mm. Hg, and of course a subsequent fall, will be observed. For a theoretical treatment cf. Curtiss and Hirschfelder (37).

REFERENCES

Monographs and review articles

1. Boltzmann, L., Vorlesungen über Gastheorie, Leipzig 1896/98.
2. Chapman, S., and Cowling, T. G., The Mathematical Theory of Non-Uniform Gases. Cambridge University Press, London 1939.
3. Enskog, D., The kinetic theory of phenomena in fairly rare gases. Dissertation Upsala 1917.
4. Gaede, W., in Auerbach-Hort, Handbuch d. physikalisch-techn. Mechanik, Vol. VI. Leipzig 1927.
5. Herzfeld, K. F., Kinetische Theorie der Wärme. Braunschweig 1925.
6. Herzfeld, K. F., Freie Weglänge u. Transporterscheinungen in Gasen; in: Eucken-Wolf, Hand- u. Jahrbuch der chem. Physik, Vol. 3 Part 2, Leipzig 1939.

7. Jeans, J. H., Dynamical Theory of Gases. Cambridge 1925.
7a. Jeans, J. H., An Introduction to the Kinetic Theory of Gases, Cambridge University Press, 1940.
8. Kennard, E. H., Kinetic Theory of Gases. McGraw Hill, New York 1938.
8a. Landolt-Börnstein, Zahlenwerte und Funktionen, Vol. I. 1. Springer, Berlin 1950, p. 326ff., 373ff.
9. Loeb, L. B., The Kinetic Theory of Gases. McGraw Hill, New York 1934.
10. Mott, N. F., and Massey, H. S. W., The Theory of atomic collisions. Oxford University Press, 1933.
10a. Waldmann, L., Transporterscheinungen in Gasen (Transport phenomena in gases); in: *Fiat, Review of German Science* (1939—1946), Physics of Liquids and gases, Senior Author E. Kappler. Dieterich, Wiesbaden 1948.

General Bibliography

11. Alexander, P., *J. Sci. Instruments* **23,** 11 (1946).
12. Amdur, I., *J. Chem. Phys.* **4,** 339 (1936).
13. Amdur, I., *Phys. Rev.* **72,** 642 (1947).
14. Amdur, I., *J. Chem. Phys.* **15,** 482 (1947).
15. Amdur, I., *J. Chem. Phys.* **16,** 190 (1948).
16. Amdur, I., *J. Chem. Phys.* **17,** 100 (1949).
16a. Amdur, I., Kells, M., C., and Dayenport, D. E., *J. Chem. Phys.* **18,** 1676 (1950). (Collision cross sections of hydrogen and deuterium)
17. Avery, D. G., and Witty, R., *Proc. Phys. Soc. (London)* **59,** 1016 (1947). (Diffusion pump.)
18. Becker, A., *Heidelberger Akad.* **A 7** (1911).
19. Benigar, J., *Wien. Ber.* **62,** 687 (1870).
20. Boardman, L. E., and Wild, N. E., *Proc. Roy. Soc. (London)* **A 162,** 511 (1937).
21. Boltzmann, L., *Wied. Ann.* **53,** 959 (1894).
22. Bradley, R. S., Evans, M. G., and Whytlaw-Gray, R. W., *Proc. Roy. Soc. (London)* **A 186,** 368 (1946).
23. Braune, H., and Zehle, F., *Z. physik. Chem.* **B 49,** 247 (1941).
24. Brookfield. K. J., Fitzpatrick, H. D. N., Jackson, J. F , Matthews, J. B., and Moelwyn-Hughes, E. A., *Proc. Roy. Soc. (London)* **A 190,** 59 (1947).
25. Chapman, S., *Phil. Trans. Roy. Soc.* **A 211,** 433 (1912).
26. Chapman, S., *Phil. Trans. Roy. Soc.* **A 216,** 279 (1916).
27. Chapman, S., *Phil. Trans. Roy. Soc.* **A 217,** 115 (1917).
28. Chapman, S., and Hainsworth, W., *Phil. Mag.* **48,** 593 (1924).
29. Chapman, S., and Hainsworth, W., *Phil. Mag.* **5,** 630 (1928).
30. Chapman, S., and Cowling, T. G., *Proc. Roy. Soc. (London)* **A 179,** 159 (1941).
31. Clausing, P., *Ann. Phys.* (5) **7,** 489, 569 (1930).
32. Clusius, K., and Waldmann, L., *Naturwiss.* **30,** 711 (1942).
33. Clusius, K., *Helvetica Phys. Acta* **22,** 135 (1949).
34. Cohen, E., and Bruins, H. R., *Z. physik. Chem.* **103,** 349 (1923).
35. Coward, H. F., and Georgeson, E. H. M., *J. Chem. Soc. London* **1937,** 1085.
36. Cowling, T. G., *Phil. Mag.* **33,** 61 (1942).
37. Curtiss, C. H., and Hirschfelder, J. O., *J. Chem. Phys.* **17,** 530 (1949).
38. Davis, G. E., *Phys. Rev.* **24,** 383 (1924).
39. Dufour, L., *Arch. sci. phys. nat., Genève* **45,** 9 (1872).
40. Dufour, L., *Pogg. Ann.* **148,** 490 (1873).
41. Enskog, D., *Physik. Z.* **12,** 56, 533 (1911).
42. Enskog, D., *Ann. Physik* **38,** 731 (1912).

43. Enskog, D., *Arkiv för Matem., Astronomi och Fysik* Vol. **16,** Nr. 16 (1921).
44. Enskog, D., *Kungl. Svenska Vetenskapsak. Handl.* **63,** Nr. 4 (1921).
45. Estermann, I., Foner, S. N., and Stern, O., *Phys. Rev.* **71,** 25 (1947).
46. Fuchs, N., *Phys. Z. Sowjetunion* **6,** 224 (1934).
47. Furry, W. H., *Am. J. Phys.* **16,** 63 (1948).
48. Gaede, W., *Ann. Physik* **46,** 357 (1915).
49. Gilliland, E. R., *Ind. Eng. Chem.* **26,** 681 (1934).
50. Gilliland, E. R., and Sherwood, T. K., *Ind. Eng. Chem.* **26,** 516, 1093 (1934).
51. Ginsel, L. A., and Ornstein, L. S., *Z. Phys.* **84,** 276 (1933).
51a. Gorynuova, N. A., and Kuvshinsky, E. V., *J.Techn. Physics USSR* **18,** 1421 (1948). (Cyclohexane, chloroform, acetone)
52. Gribojedoff, S., *Journ. Soc. phys. chim. Russ.* **25,** 36 (1893).
53. Groth, W., and Harteck, P., *Z. Elektrochem.* **47,** 167 (1941).
54. Groth, W., and Sussner, E., *Z. physik. Chem.* **193,** 296 (1944).
55. Guglielmo, G., *Atti Acad. Torino* **17,** 54 (1881), **18,** 93 (1882).
56. Halpern, O., and Gwathmey, E., *Phys. Rev.* **52,** 944 (1937).
57. Hansen, G., Dissertation Jena 1907.
58. Harteck, P., and Schmidt, H. W., *Z. physik. Chem.* **B 21,** 447 (1933).
59. Heath, H. R., Ibbs, T. L., and Wild, N. E., *Proc. Roy. Soc. (London)* **A 178,** 380 (1941).
60. Held van der, E. F. M., and Miesowicz, M., *Physica* **4,** 559 (1937).
61. Hellund, E. J., *Phys. Rev.* **57,** 319, 328 (1940).
62. Hellund, E. J., *Phys. Rev.* **57,** 737 (1940).
63. Hellund, E. J., *Phys. Rev.* (2) **57,** 743 (1940).
64. Hertz, G., *Z. Physik* **19,** 35 (1923).
65. Hickman, K. C. D., *J. applied Phys.* **11,** 303 (1940).
66. Hickman, K. C. D., and Sandford, C. R., *Rev. Sci. Instruments* **1,** 140 (1930).
67. Hickman, K. C. D., and Sanford, C. R., *J. Phys. Chem.* **34,** 637 (1930).
68. Hickman, K. C. D , *J. Franklin Inst.* **221,** 383 (1936).
69. Hirschfelder, J. O., Bird, R. B., and Spotz, E. L., *J. Chem. Phys.* **16,** 968 (1948).
70. Hirschfelder, J. O., Bird, R. B., and Spotz, E. L., *Chem. Rev.* **44,** 205 (1949).
71. Hirst, W., and Harrison, G. E., *Proc. Roy. Soc. (London)* **A 169,** 573 (1939).
72. Hogerton, J. F., *Chem. Met. Eng.* **52,** Nr. 12, 98 (1945).
73. Hutchinson, F., *Phys. Rev.* **72,** 1256 (1947).
74. Hutchinson, F., *J. Chem. Phys.* **17,** 1081 (1949).
75. Jaeckel, R., *Z. Naturforsch.* **2a,** 666 (1947).
76. Jaffé, G., *Phys. Rev.* (2) **59,** 652 (1941).
77. Klotz, I. M., and Miller, D. K., *J. Am. Chem. Soc.* **69,** 2557 (1947).
78. Kohler, M., *Z. Physik* **124,** 772 (1947).
79. Kohler, M., *Z. Physik* **124,** 757 (1947).
80. Kohler, M., *Z. Physik* **127,** 41 (1950).
81. Langmuir, J., *Phys. Rev.* (1) **6,** 48 (1916).
82. Le Blanc, M., and Wuppermann, G., *Z. physik. Chem.* **91,** 143 (1916).
83. Lonius, A., *Ann. Physik* (4) **29,** 664 (1909).
84. Lord Kelvin, *Baltimore Lectures,* p. 295.
85. Lorentz, H. A., *Proc. Amsterdam Acad.* **7,** 438, 585, 684 (1905).
86. Loschmidt, J., *Wien. Ber.* **61,** 367 (1870).
87. Loschmidt, J., *Wien. Ber.* **62,** 468 (1870).
88. Mack, E., *J. Am. Chem. Soc.* **47,** 2468 (1925).

89. Mackenzie, J. E., and Melville, H. W., *Proc. Edinburgh* **52**, 337 (1932); **53**, 255 (1933).
90. McMurtrie, R. L., and Keyes, F. C., *J. Am. Chem. Soc.* **70**, 3755 (1948).
91. Massey, H. S. W., and Mohr, C. B. O., *Proc. Roy. Soc. (London)* **A 141**, 434 (1933).
92. Matricon, M., *J. de physique* **3**, 127 (1932).
93. Michels, A., and Gibson, R. O., *Proc. Roy. Soc. (London)* **A 134**, 288 (1931).
94. Mullaly, J. M., *Nature* **113**, 711 (1924).
95. Mullaly, J. M., and Jacques, H., *Phil. Mag.* (6) **48**, 1105 (1924).
96. Ney, E. P., and Armistead, F. C., *Phys. Rev.* **71**, 14, 138 (1947).
97. Obermayer, A. von, *Wien. Ber.* **81** (II), 1102 (1880).
98. Obermayer, A. von, *Wien. Ber.* **85** (II), 147, 748 (1882).
99. Obermayer, A. von, *Wien. Ber.* **87** (II), 188 (1883).
100. Obermayer, A. von, *Wien. Ber.* **96**, (II), 546 (1887).
101. Pidduck, F. B., *Proc. London Mathem. Soc.* (2) **15**, 89 (1915).
102. Pollard, W. G., and Present, R. D., *Phys. Rev.* **73**, 762 (1948).
102a Present, R. D., and de Bethune, A. J., *Phys. Rev.* **75**, 1050 (1949).
103. Roe, G. M., *Phys. Rev.* **60**, 468 (1941).
103a Rowlinson, J. S., *J. Chem. Phys.* **17**, 101 (1949).
104. Schmidt, R., *Ann. Physik* (4) **14**, 801 (1904).
105. Schuhmeister, J., *Wien. Ber.* (II) **78**, 603 (1879).
106. Schwartz, F. A., *Phys. Rev.* **68**, 145 (1945).
107. Senftleben, H., *Phys. Z.* **34**, 835 (1933).
108. Smith, A. S., *Ind. Eng. Chem.* **26**, 1167 (1934).
109. Spier, J. L., *Physica* **6**, 453 (1939).
110. Spier, J. L., *Physica* **7**, 381 (1940).
111. Stefan, J., *Wien. Ber.* (II) **68**, 385 (1874).
112. Stefan, J., *Wien. Ber.* (II) **98**, 1418 (1889).
113. Stefan, J., *Ann. Physik* (3) **41**, 725 (1890).
114. Summerhays, W. E., *Proc. phys. Soc.* **42**, 218 (1930).
115. Sutherland, W., *Phil. Mag.* (5) **36**, 507 (1893).
116. Symon, F. J., *Proc. Roy. Soc. Edinburgh* **46**, 15 (1925).
117. Thorne, H. H., cf. Chapman, S., and Cowling, T. G., The Mathematical Theory of Non-Uniform Gases. Cambridge 1939, p. 292.
118. Topley, B., and Whytlaw-Gray, R., *Phil. Mag.* **4**, 873 (1927).
119. Townsend, J. S., *Trans. Roy. Soc. London* **A 193**, 129 (1899).
120. Townsend, J. S., *Trans. Roy. Soc. London* **A 195**, 259 (1900).
121. Trautz, M., *Ann. Physik* (5) **18**, 816 (1933).
122. Trautz, M., and Ludwig, O., *Ann. Physik* (5) **5**, 887 (1930).
123. Trautz, M., and Müller, W., *Ann. Physik* (5) **22**, 329, 333 (1935).
124. Trautz, M., and Müller, W., *Ann. Physik* (5) **22**, 353 (1935).
125. Trautz, M., and Ries, W., *Ann. Physik* (5) **8**, 163 (1931).
126. Vaillant, P., *J. de Phys.* (5) **1**, 877 (1911).
126a Verschaffelt, J. E., *Bull. classe sci. Acad. Roy. Belg.* **34**, 500 (1948).
126b Verschaffelt, J. E., *Bull. classe sci. Acad. Roy. Belg.* **35**, 293 (1949).
127. Wagner, C., *Z. physik. Chem.* **A 192**, 85 (1943).
128. Waitz, K., *Wied. Ann.* **17**, 201, 351 (1879).
129. Waldmann, L., *Z. Physik* **124**, 2 (1947).
130. Waldmann, L., *Z. Physik* **124**, 30 (1947).
131. Waldmann, L., *Z. Physik* **124**, 175 (1947).
132. Wall, F. T., and Kidder, G. A., *J. Phys. Chem.* **50**, 235 (1946).
133. Weiss, R., *Heidelberger Akad.* **A 17**, 40 (1914).

134. Wertenstein, L., *Proc. Cambr. Phil. Soc.* **23,** 578 (1927).
135. Wilson, H. A., *Phil. Mag.* **24,** 118 (1912).
136. Winn, E. B., *Phys. Rev.* **74,** 698 (1948).
137. Winn, E. B., and Ney, E. P., *Phys. Rev.* **72,** 77 (1947).
138. Winkelmann, A., *Wied. Ann.* **22,** 1, 152 (1884).
139. Winkelmann, A., *Wied. Ann.* **23,** 203 (1884).
140. Winkelmann, A., *Wied. Ann.* **26,** 105 (1885).
141. Winkelmann, A., *Wied. Ann.* **33,** 445 (1888).
142. Winkelmann, A., *Wied. Ann.* **36,** 92 (1889).
143. Wintergerst, E., *Ann. Physik* (5) **4,** 323 (1930).
144. Witty, R., *J. Sci. Instruments* **22,** 201 (1945).
145. Wogau, M. von, *Ann. Physik* (4) **23,** 345 (1907).
146. Wretschko, A., *Wien. Ber.* **62,** 575 (1870).
147. Yang, L. M. *Proc. Roy. Soc. (London)* A **198,** 94 (1949). (Theory of diffusion)

CHAPTER XI

DIFFUSION IN LIQUIDS

I. General remarks

The technique of measuring diffusion coefficients in liquids is in principle the same as that employed with gases. Diffusion coefficients in liquids are smaller than those in gases at N.T.P. by at least four powers of ten. Differences in the experimental set up, to be used with liquids, compared with that employed with gases, are largely due to this fact. A certain concentration distribution, obtained with a given apparatus, is essentially a function of x^2/Dt, if x refers to the linear dimensions of the apparatus, and if D and t are diffusion coefficient and time, respectively. With linear dimensions kept constant a decrease in diffusion coefficient by 4 powers of ten would involve an increase in time of observation by the same factor 10^4. Hence, if one is interested in not extending the time of observation beyond that necessary for gases one is forced to use diffusion apparatus of only 10^{-2} the size of those employed with gases. Thus one arrives at linear dimensions of the order of magnitude of 1 cm., or in some special arrangements, even less. Though it is possible to work with diffusion cells of about this size, one may be compelled by the method of analysis available to increase the dimensions of the cell, and consequently to deal with much longer times of observation. If normal chemical analysis has been chosen, as has been the case especially in the earlier work on diffusion in liquids, it may be necessary to increase the linear dimensions by as much as a factor 10, thus increasing the time of observation by a factor 100. If, on the other hand, appropriate physical methods of analysis are available, dimensions of 1 cm., or in some cases even less, may be quite sufficient.

II. Measurements in stationary or quasi-stationary states

As in other cases, the arrangements for measuring diffusion coefficients in liquids may be divided into two main groups. In the first group diffusion in a stationary or quasi-stationary state is observed, where the diffusion flux can be observed, given by Fick's first law

$$J = -D \, \partial c/\partial x . \qquad [11.1]$$

In [11.1] J is the diffusion flow, D the diffusion coefficient, which may depend on the concentration c, and x is a position coordinate measured perpendicularly to the surface to which the diffusion flow has been referred. A determination of D involves the measurement of J and of $\partial c/\partial x$.

The second group comprises all experiments with a given initial distribution of concentration, $c = \varphi(x, 0)$ at $t = 0$, if we consider a linear system, depending on one position coordinate, x, only. The method of measurement consists of a determination of $\varphi(x, t)$, the concentration distribution at a certain time t. By means of Fick's second law

$$\partial c/\partial t = D\,\partial^2 c/\partial x^2 \qquad [11.2]$$

for D independent of concentration, or

$$\partial c/\partial t = \partial/\partial x\,(D\,\partial c/\partial x) \qquad [11.3]$$

for concentration-dependent D, one must usually calculate the concentration distribution for a given t, taking into account the initial and boundary conditions. The comparison of the theoretical and experimental distribution permits the calculation of D. In case of concentration-dependent D, eq. [11.3], special methods for evaluation are available (cf. Chap. I, p. 31).

The first method, from a mathematical point of view, is the simpler one, especially if D depends on concentration. An experimental arrangement for the measurement of J and of $\partial c/\partial x$ is shown, schematically, in Fig. 11-1. Two large containers, I and II, containing solutions of different concentration, c_I and c_{II}* are connected by means of a comparatively narrow tube III, of known diameter r

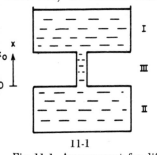

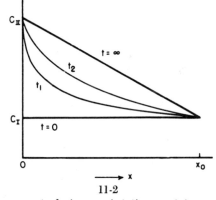

11-1   11-2

Fig. 11-1. Arrangement for diffusion measurements during quasi-stationary state.
Fig. 11-2. Establishment of stationary state in connecting tube of Fig. 11-1. Concentration distribution for $t = 0$, t_1, t_2, ∞.

* c_I often will be chosen equal to zero, the upper container being filled with the pure solvent.

and length l. After a certain time lag, which may be calculated by the methods of Chap. I and which may be rather long, of the order of magnitude of many days, a steady state will be established, cf. the concentration distributions as shown in Fig. 11-2. If care is taken that in each container a uniform concentration is maintained (by means of convection), varying but slowly with time, one has

$$\partial c/\partial x \approx \frac{-\Delta c}{l} = \frac{c_I - c_{II}}{l} \qquad [11.4]$$

and

$$J = \frac{s}{\Delta t\,\pi\,r^2} \qquad [11.5]$$

where s is the increase in content of the diffusing substance within the upper container during time Δt. If s and Δt have been determined experimentally, and if r, l, and c_I and c_{II} are known, (and supposed to remain essentially constant during the course of an experiment), D may be calculated by means of equation [11.1]. For certain refinements in the calculation see below, p. 441 ff.

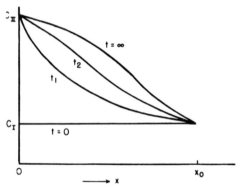

If D depends on concentration the stationary concentration distribution (corresponding to $t = \infty$) is not linear, as in Fig. 11-2, but is given by some other curve, Fig. 11-3 (cf. Chap. I, p. 15, 16). Application of eqs. [11.4] and [11.5] to this case gives, not a true diffusion coefficient, but an average (integral) diffusion coefficient, valid for a finite concentration interval. Since the true, differential diffusion coefficient is given by

Fig. 11-3. Concentration distribution if D depends on concentration, for $t = 0$, t_1, t_2, ∞.

$$D = - J \,\Big|\, \partial c/\partial x \qquad [11.6]$$

while the integral diffusion coefficient $\overline{D}$ for the concentration interval from c_I to c_{II} is given by

$$\overline{D} = - J \,\Big|\, \left(\frac{c_I - c_{II}}{l} \right). \qquad [11.7]$$

D and $\overline{D}$ are connected by

$$\overline{D} = \frac{1}{c_{II} - c_I} \int_{c_I}^{c_{II}} D \, dc. \qquad [11.8]$$

As seen from [11.6], D is inversely proportional to the concentration gradient $\partial c/\partial x$, and may be determined as function of x and of c, if c has been measured as function of x. Thus the determination of differential diffusion coefficients, D, pertaining to definite concentrations, c, depends on the measurement of the concentration distribution during the steady state. Such measurements have been carried out by means of optical methods or by density measurements, by weighing a suspended sphere at several heights within the tube III.

The method of the stationary diffusion flow is the oldest method employed in quantitative measurements of diffusion coefficients, but it has not found in recent experimental work the consideration it probably deserves, except in McBain's (206, 207) and Northrup's (220) diaphragm method, working with quasi-stationary diffusion (cf. p. 443).

A. Fick (96) founded his diffusion law upon experimental observations carried out under the conditions of a stationary, constant concentration gradient, in complete analogy to the much later measurements with gases by the evaporation method. A vertical tube, open at both ends and filled with solvent or solution, is connected at its bottom end with a reservoir of solution, and reservoir and tube are placed into a large water container, the upper open end of the tube ending underneath the water surface. Thus convection in the outer water container and within the reservoir of solution helps to establish uniform concentration distribution. For in the water reservoir a comparatively heavy solution is being formed in the upper part, sinking toward the bottom by gravity, while the concentration at the lower end of the tube within the container decreases, and the more dilute solution is being replaced by the original solution from the upper parts of it. After equilibrium has been established, the concentration gradient is constant within the tube, provided the diffusion coefficient does not depend on concentration, and is known from the concentration in the reservoir and from the length of the tube. The amount of substance, diffusing during a certain time, is determined by an analysis of the outside water. The establishment of a stationary state and the linearity of the concentration distribution can be tested by density measurements at different heights within the tube (see above). Though the method in this form is somewhat clumsy, it still might be useful. With solutes of not too high solubility one might replace the reservoir of solution by the solid solute, in contact with the bottom end of the diffusion tube. If c_0 is the concentration at the lower end of the tube, l the length of the tube with cross section q, and s the amount of substance which has diffused during the steady state within time t the diffusion coefficient is given by

$$D = sl/(qc_0t). \qquad [11.9]$$

Clack (66) succeeded in developing the method of stationary diffusion to a high degree of accuracy. His early apparatus was similar to that used by Fick, the container with the solution being suspended from a balance by a fine wire, and being immersed into a large container with solvent or a more dilute solution. Thus from the observation of the rate of loss of weight with time it was possible to see whether a stationary state had been obtained, and from the uniform loss of weight during steady diffusion the integral diffusion coefficient could be determined. The time, necessary for the establishment of the steady state was rather long, up to 14 days. This can be reduced if a shorter diffusion tube is employed, while at the same time the diameter of the tube must be reduced in order to avoid disturbances caused by convection near the ends of the tube. Later, Clack improved his method considerably by measuring the concentration distribution within the tube connecting both containers. For this purpose the cylindrical tube was replaced by a channel of rectangular cross section with plane parallel windows, allowing optical determination of concentrations. By employing Wiener's (329) method concentration gradients could be determined immediately. The deflection z of a light beam, passing through a cell of thickness a is given by

$$z = ab \, dn/dy , \qquad [11.10]$$

cf. Fig. 11-7. Thus, if n is known as function of the concentration, measurement of the vertical displacement z of the light beam for several values of y, at once gives dc/dy as function of y, on account of the relation

$$dn/dy = (dn/dc) \cdot (dc/dy) . \qquad [11.11]$$

In Fig. 11-4 measured values of the concentration gradient are reproduced. It is seen that dc/dy, and consequently the diffusion coefficient, may vary considerably with height, and therefore with concentration.

In Clack's final arrangement the measured values of dc/dy could not be taken immediately for the computation of D, for the following reason.

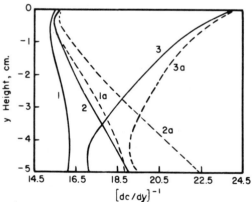

Fig. 11-4. Reciprocal concentration gradients, $[dc/dy]^{-1}$ measured by Clack, for $t = 18.5°C$. 1. NaCl, 2. KCl, 3. KNO$_3$ (1a, 2a, 3a corrected curves, cf. text).

In order to obtain a steady diffusion flow Clack filled the lower container of his apparatus with a concentrated solution in contact with the solid salt. During the course of an experiment this salt is dissolved and diffuses out of the container, its volume being replaced by a corresponding amount of solution. Consequently there is a flow of solvent of direction opposite to that of the diffusion flow. Since diffusion must be referred to the solution as frame of reference, which coincides with the container only in the absence of any convection current, a correction for this flow must be introduced.

If J_1 is the steady flow of dissolved salt, in grams per second and square centimeter, and if J_0 is the flow of water in the opposite direction, and qs the net loss of weight of the container, where q is the cross section of the diffusion channel, we have

$$s = J_1 - J_0 .$$ [11.12]

If qs' grams of salt are dissolved per unit time, of density ρ', its volume s'/ρ' being replaced by concentrated solution of concentration c'' and density ρ'', this volume will contain s_1 grams of salt

$$s_1 = \frac{s' \, c''}{\rho'}$$ [11.13]

and s_0 grams of water

$$s_0 = \frac{s' \, \rho''}{\rho'} - s_1 = \frac{s'}{\rho'} (\rho'' - c'') .$$ [11.14]

The amount s' of salt dissolved per unit time and unit cross-section must either be contained in the newly formed solution or must diffuse away, thus

$$s' = s_1 + J_1 , \quad s' \left(1 - \frac{c''}{\rho'} \right) = J_1$$ [11.15]

and correspondingly for the water

$$s_0 = J_0 , \quad \frac{s'}{\rho'} (\rho'' - c'') = J_0 .$$ [11.16]

Upon dividing [11.16] by [11.15] we find

$$J_0/J_1 = (\rho'' - c'')/(\rho' - c'') = \zeta$$ [11.17]

and from [11.12] and [11.17]

$$J_1 = s + J_0 = s/(1 - \zeta),$$ [11.18]

where $\zeta = J_0/J_1$. ζ is known from eq. [11.17], and J_1 may be calculated from the observed loss of weight s by means of [11.18]. The flux J_1 of salt is given by

$$J_1 = c_1 v_1$$ [11.19]

where c_1 is the concentration of the salt, v_1 the average velocity of the salt molecules relative to the apparatus, c_1 and v_1 being functions of the position, their product, however, being constant. Accordingly we have for the flux of water

$$J_0 = c_0 v_0 \qquad [11.20]$$

where again J_0 is constant while the single magnitudes on the right vary with the height y. Thus the flux of salt, relative to the solvent is

$$J = c_1 (v_1 + v_0) = J_1 + c_1 v_0 = - D \, dc/dy . \qquad [11.21]$$

At the top, where $c_1 = 0$, $c_0 \approx 1$, we have from [11.20]

$$v_0 \approx J_0 \qquad [11.22]$$

and at a level where the salt concentration is c_1, the water concentration $c_0 = \rho - c_1$, if ρ is the density of the solution, we have

$$v_0 = J_0/c_0 = J_0/(\rho - c_1). \qquad [11.23]$$

Thus from [11.21] with [11.23] and [11.17]

$$D = - \frac{J_1 + c_1 v_0}{\partial c/\partial y} = - \frac{J_1}{\partial c/\partial y} \left[1 + \frac{c_1 \zeta}{\rho - c_1} \right]. \qquad [11.24]$$

The values of dc/dy, divided by the expression $\left(1 + \dfrac{c_1 \zeta}{\rho - c_1} \right)$ are the corrected values, as shown in Fig. 11-4.

K. Schwarz (276) made use of the method of stationary diffusion for the determination of diffusion coefficients in amalgams, Fig. 11-5. From his arrangement it is not seen whether he had sufficient convection in the lower container to avoid a decrease of dissolved metal near the diffusion tube, which would give too low diffusion coefficients. In addition there may have been disturbances due to flow in the capillaries, as in Clack's experiments (66). At present, the most important application of the method of (quasi)stationary diffusion is the Northrup-McBain diaphragm cell (Northrup and Anson (220), McBain and Liu (207), cf. especially Gordon (122), who has given a very thorough critical review of the diaphragm cell method and its theory.) In order to avoid disturbances by convection and to maintain a sufficiently high concentration gradient, two volumes containing solutions of different concentrations are separated by a porous diaphragm of sintered glass. A diffusion cell, as used by McBain and Dawson (206) is seen in the following Fig. 11-6. The diaphragm is usually of a thickness of a few millimeters, the diameters of the pores being of the order of magnitude of 10^{-3} to 10^{-4} cm. An experiment is set up in such a way that a concentration gradient arises in the diaphragm only. Complete mixing within either container is achieved by placing the more concentrated, heavier solution into the upper container, and the diluted solution (or the pure solvent) into the lower one. Thus an equalization of concentration differences is established by the action of gravity. Equalization may be enhanced by mechanical stirring, with glass spheres of appropriate density, touching the upper and lower surfaces of the diaphragm (Hartley and Runnicles (137)). The recessity for stirring in the diaphragm cell has been shown by Stokes (296).

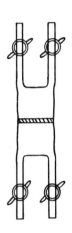

The theory of the diaphragm cell, on the assumption of a quasi- stationary state and for constant diffusion coefficient, has been given in Chap. I, p. 11, for equal volumes of both containers. In case of unequal volumes, V' and V'', with concentration c' and c'', one has the differential equations for the change dc of concentration in either container within time dt:

Fig. 11-5. Apparatus used by Schwarz for measuring diffusion coefficients in amalgams.

11-5   Fig. 11-6. Diaphragm cell, McBain and Dawson.   11-6

a. $V'\,dc' + (Dq/\delta)\,(c' - c'')\,dt = 0$

b. $V''\,dc'' + (Dq/\delta)\,(c'' - c')\,dt = 0$ [11.25]

where D is the diffusion coefficient, q the effective cross-section of the diaphragm and δ its thickness. From [11.25] a) and b) we obtain

$$\frac{d\,(c' - c'')}{c' - c''} + \beta\,D\,dt = 0$$ [11.26]

where the cell factor β now has the value

$$\beta = \frac{q}{\delta}\left(\frac{1}{V'} + \frac{1}{V''}\right).$$ [11.27]

Eq. [11.26] gives, on integration

$$\log\frac{(c' - c'')_f}{(c' - c'')_o} = -\,\beta\,D\,t$$ [11.28]

which is the analogue to eq. [1.42], p. 11. Here the subscripts f and o refer to the final, and initial states respectively.

The assumption of a quasi-stationary state has been discussed elsewhere (p. 11). It implies that the establishment of an almost linear concentration distribution within the diaphragm, (in case of concentration-independent D), is a quick process compared with the rate of change of concentration in the containers. Barnes (35) has treated the problem of the diaphragm cell without the assumption of a quasi-stationary state. He thus obtained additional terms in the equation describing the rate of change of concentration in either container. These additional terms, however, are quite negligible under ordinary conditions, as might be expected.

But there arise two other problems which need a careful consideration. First the calibration of the diffusion cell, necessary because the effective cross-section of the diaphragm is not known; second the dependence of the diffusion coefficient on concentration. For calibration, diffusion of salts has generally been used, and since diffusion coefficients of electrolytes show a marked dependence on concentration, both problems are related. This question has been discussed very thoroughly by Gordon (122) and by Hartley and Runnicles (137). Gordon arrives at the result that Cohen and Bruins' (1a,71) value for the diffusion of KCl in water must not be used for calibration, and he suggests as best values at 25°C. for the diffusion of 0.1 n KCl into dure water

$D = 1.838 \times 10^{-5}$ cm.^{2}/sec. for small concentration change, and
$D = 1.830 \times 10^{-5}$ cm.^{2}/sec. for a change in the difference of concentration
of both containers by about 50 per cent.

The relation between the differential diffusion coefficients and the integral value obtained by the diaphragm cell method, and the more complicated problem of deriving differential diffusion coefficients from measured integral diffusion coefficients has also been dealt with by Gordon (120, 122).

III. Non-stationary diffusion measurements

For non-stationary measurements a definite initial distribution of concentration must be established and the resulting distribution at some later time t must be measured. In measurements with liquids a linear arrangement has almost exclusively been used. Therefore we shall always assume in the following that we have a diffusion column of constant cross section, extended in the x direction, and with concentration varying with the position coordinate x only. If c_1 is the higher concentration, corresponding in most cases to a higher density of the solution or mixture, c_0 a lower concentration, often $c_0 = 0$, then the initial distribution aimed at, usually, will be such that up to a certain height h_1, $c = c_1$, while for $x > h_1$, $c = c_0$, for $t = 0$. Both solutions should be divided by a sharp interface, without any zone of mixing at the beginning of an experiment. Since a slight mixing can hardly be avoided, the height of the diffusion cell should be large compared with the dimensions of the zone of mixing present at the beginning, if accurate measurements are to be obtained. For hydrodynamic reasons it is usually not difficult to obtain a rather sharp interface by letting the heavier solution flow underneath the lighter one. This may be done by means of a fine capillary reaching through the light solution or the solvent down to the bottom of the diffusion cell, or by a tube attached to the lower end of the cell. With liquids of very small density differences it may be advisable to cool the heavier solution slightly below the temperature of an experiment, before filling the diffusion cell.

For cells of rather small height, which are preferable if the time necessary for an experiment is to be kept sufficiently short, even a very slight mixing may lead to errors which are not negligible. In such cases it may still be possible to correct for the initial mixing and to obtain quite good values of the diffusion coefficient. In principle there are two methods for correction. The first, to the knowledge of the author never applied so far, would consist of measuring the initial distribution at an arbitrary time $t = 0$, by an adequate physical method of analysis, and to evaluate the experiment by means of a solution of the diffusion equation, adapted to this given initial distribution. This is possible by means of the mathematical methods discussed in Chap. I.

The method, usually employed for correction, consists of assuming that the concentration distribution due to mixing before the beginning of an experiment resembles rather closely the concentration distribution obtained by diffusion within a certain time Δt. This additional time Δt is determined by trial and error in such a way that observations, with different times of diffusion give consistent results if this time Δt is added to the actual time of an experiment (129a, 156, 203).

The experimental method to be chosen depends largely upon the analytical methods available. In the following we shall deal with the most common types of diffusion apparatus, without aiming at any completeness. Reports on diffusion in liquids have been given by Fürth (7), Williams and Cady (24), Duclaux (4), Neurath (18), Cohn and Edsall (2), Harned and Owen (12), Harned (11), Bridgman and Williams (59), Geddes (8), Longsworth (198, 201).

For measurement of non-stationary diffusion one may use an arrangement quite similar to that described for stationary diffusion, p. 439. If a cylinder, closed at its bottom and containing a solution, is placed in a large vessel, filled with the solvent up to a level slightly above the top end of the cylinder, then the concentration at the top end of the cylinder will be zero to a sufficient degree of approximation, the substance diffusing out of the cylinder being carried to the bottom of the outer vessel by gravity. The solution of the diffusion equation for this case is derived from eq. [1.136], Chap. I, p. 36. If either the concentration distribution within the cylinder, or the total amount of substance which has entered the outer vessel by diffusion, or the amount of substance which has remained within the cylinder, has been determined experimentally, then it is possible to calculate the diffusion coefficient. Of course one must know the height and diameter of the diffusion cylinder, and the initial concentration of the solution. The oldest measurements thus carried out are those of Beilstein (41) and of Graham (125)*. The method may be improved; for instance it has been used as a micro method. The underlying assumption in evaluation, that D is independent of concentration, may be tested by determining the concentration distribution within the cylinder. As pointed out elsewhere, in case of a diffusion coefficient varying with concentration, it is the simplest and most advisable method to work with concentration differences sufficiently small so that a concentration dependence of D may be neglected and differential diffusion coefficients may be determined immediately. However, this is possible only if sufficiently accurate methods of analysis are available.

The most conventional method of measuring diffusion coefficients in liquids consists of establishing a discontinuous concentration distribution at $t = 0$, as discussed above. The vertical diffusion cell may be of any shape in cross section, usually either cylindrical, or, especially for optical methods of analysis, of rectangular shape. The mathematical equations to be used for evaluation differ for the two cases where the concentration change has not yet reached the upper and lower boundaries of the diffusion cell, and where it has reached these boundaries. In the former case the simpler solutions for an infinite system are applicable, in the latter one the solutions for finite systems must be used (cf. Chap. I, p. 35ff.). If D varies with concentration and Boltzmann's (51) method must be applied for evaluation, it is necessary to avoid concentration changes near the boundaries.

The older method, as employed by Graham (125), may still be useful in certain cases. A cylindrical vessel is filled with a known amount of solvent, then, by means of a capillary reaching almost to the bottom of the vessel, a known amount of solution is carefully brought underneath the solvent. Unless a physical analysis is possible within the diffusion cell itself, the solution must be separated at the end of an experiment into a number (at least two) of layers of known height. These layers need not be equal, but it is convenient to take all of them of the same height. Graham chose 16 layers of equal height in his experiments. He obtained this by withdrawing liquid from the

* Cf. also Bruins (60, 61).

top, using a pipette of exactly 1/16 of the volume of the cell. The single layer is analyzed chemically, or the solute content is determined after evaporation of the solvent, or any suitable physical method of analysis is chosen. The separation of the original diffusion column into a number of layers has also been attained by displacing appropriate volumes of the solution by a heavier liquid, like mercury, the solution being withdrawn through a tube connected to the upper end of the cell. An apparatus of this type has been used by Scheffer (272) and by Svedberg (301).

Stefan's (291) tables for the evaluation of diffusion measurements are adapted to Graham's method, 16 layers of equal height being analyzed. But these tables may be adapted to other subdivisions of the diffusion column, especially to four layers of equal height in the form given by Kawalki (158) (cf. Chap. I, p. 63).

The original discontinuous concentration distribution also may be obtained by filling two vertical tubes or cells of equal cross section with solutions of different concentrations, and by bringing them into contact at the beginning of an experiment. This method was first applied to the diffusion in liquids by Schuhmeister (274). The experimental set up is the same, in principle, as that shown in Chap. X, p. 407 for the diffusion of gases. Two tubes, usually, but not necessarily of equal length, are cemented into two glass or metal discs, the one sliding or rotating upon the other. After the tubes have been filled separately, they are brought into contact, the one exactly above the other. At the end of an experiment, the two tubes are moved apart and the content is withdrawn for analysis*.

This method has been considerably improved (cf. for instance v. Wogau (331)), especially by Cohen and Bruins (1 a, 71), who were able to obtain a high degree of accuracy in their measurements. Their apparatus is adapted to the evaluation by means of Kawalki's tables, with four layers of equal height. They used a set of six glass discs, thoroughly ground and rotating around a common axis. The four inner ones contained circular holes, representing the diffusion cell when brought into alignment. Actually three cells were contained in a single set of glass discs. By turning the discs around their axis, the main holes may be brought into exact alignment at the beginning of an experiment, or they may be separated at the end of it and they may be connected to auxiliary small holes for filling or draining. In the experiments the lowest hole contained a solution at the beginning, while the three upper ones were filled with the pure solvent. The

---

* In this connection Fürth's (105, 110) and Lamm's (172, 186) cell, where upper and lower parts are divided by a slide, should be mentioned. Cf. also Neurath (218), Claesson (67).

precision of these experiments is among the highest so far obtained, the error being less than 0.3 per cent.

The results, obtained by Cohen and Bruins with aqueous solutions of electrolytes, refer to comparatively high concentration differences, and, therefore, are integral diffusion coefficients for a not too well defined concentration range (owing to the assymmetry inherent in the arrangement according to Kawalki's tables), cf. the discussion by Gordon (122) and by Hartley and Runnicles (137).

By making use of adequate physical methods of analysis one can determine the concentrations and their rate of change with time for every cross section of a diffusion cell without interrupting an experiment. Many methods have been applied for this purpose, for instance measurement of absorption of light (Ullmann (316), Fürth (105, 106)), of the index of refraction, of the density (by means of the displacement of small floating bodies of known density) etc. An elegant micromethod for the determination of diffusion coefficients of coloured substances has been developed by Fürth (110, 113). Total reflection of light has been used in a micromethod by Zuber (334, 335), Sitte (286) and Dean (79).

Measurement of the index of refraction may lead to erroneous results, if not properly applied, due to the deflection of a light beam passing through a medium of varying index of refraction, (Stefan (290), Wiener (329)). But the same effect may none the less be very valuable in measuring the rate of diffusion.

A beam of light, passing through a medium of varying index of refraction, is deflected even if it passes perpendicularly to the gradient of the index of refraction, Fig. 11-7. If we replace the medium of continuously varying index of refraction by one consisting of a number of thin layers, each of height Δy, the index of refraction, n, increasing by Δn, as one passes from one layer to the succeeding one from top to bottom, we have the situation as shown in Fig. 11-7. The deflection of the light beam, as it passes from one layer to the next one, is given by the law of refraction.

$$\sin \varphi / \sin (\varphi + \Delta \varphi) = (n + \Delta n)/n \approx \sin \varphi /(\sin \varphi + \cos \varphi \, \Delta \varphi) \quad [11.29]$$

where the meaning of the angles introduced is seen from Fig. 11-7. Hence

$$- (\operatorname{ctg} \varphi) \, \Delta \varphi \approx \Delta n/n . \quad [11.30]$$

If x is the coordinate in the direction of the incident light beam, perpendicular to the direction, y, of the gradient of the index of refraction, then we have, Fig. 11-7.

$$\Delta y = \Delta x \operatorname{ctg} \varphi$$

and

$$\frac{\Delta \varphi}{\Delta x} \approx -\frac{\Delta n}{n \Delta y}.$$ [11.31]

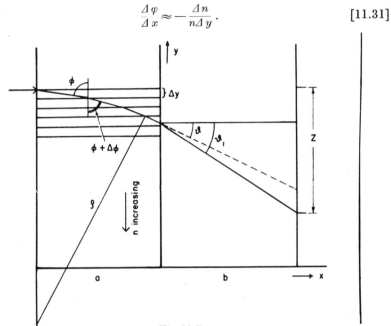

Fig. 11-7.
Deflection of light passing through a layer with varying index of refraction (cf. text).

Thus we obtain for the radius of curvature of the deflected light beam, Fig. 11-7, $\rho = 1/(d\varphi/dx)$, by passing to the limit $\Delta y \to 0$

$$\rho = -n/(dn/dy) = -n \left| \left(\frac{dn}{dc} \cdot \frac{dc}{dy}\right).$$ [11.32]

Fig. 11-7 corresponds to $dn/dy < 0$, consequently $\rho > 0$. If n is known as function of the concentration, c, it is possible to calculate dc/dy from [11.32] by means of observed values of the deflection of light.

Wiener (329) made use of this effect for the measurement of diffusion coefficients. A narrow slit, inclined toward the vertical at an angle of 45 degrees is illuminated by a monochromatic light source, Fig. 11-8. By means of a lens of long focal length an image of the slit is produced at a distance of several meters.

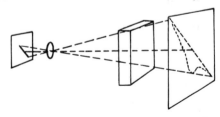

Fig. 11-8. Experimental arrangement for Wiener's method, schematic.

Without a diffusion cell a magnified image of the slit is obtained, Fig. 11-9. If now a diffusion cell of rectangular cross section with

plane parallel glass windows is placed between lens and screen, the
image is distorted, as shown in Fig. 11-10 according to the variation
of the concentration gradient within the solution. Since the concentration gradient must vanish at the upper and lower boundaries
of the diffusion column, the deflection, there, must vanish too. For
the deflection of the light beam on the screen the relation is obtained
from [11.32]

$$Z = ba\, n/\rho = ba\, dn/dy \qquad\qquad [11.33]$$

when a is the thickness of the diffusion cell and b the distance cell-
screen, Fig. 11-7 (making obvious assumptions, such as that $b \gg a$).

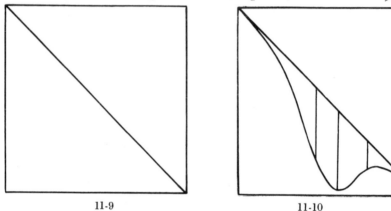

11-9   11-10

Fig. 11-9. Image of inclined slit, without concentration gradient.
Fig. 11-10. Image of inclined slit, with concentration gradient.

As long as the diffusion column may be considered as infinite
(i.e., as long as concentration differences have not yet reached the
boundaries of the system) the resulting concentration distribution at
time t is given by (cf. Chap. I, p. 20)

$$c = \frac{c_0}{2}\left[1 - erf\left(\frac{y}{2\sqrt{Dt}}\right)\right] \qquad\qquad [11.34]$$

provided that the diffusion coefficient is independent of concentration,
and the initial concentration distribution has been given by

$$c = c_0 \text{ for } y < 0, \text{ and } c = 0 \text{ for } y > 0.$$

Consequently the concentration gradient is given by an error curve

$$\frac{\partial c}{\partial y} = -\frac{c_0}{2\sqrt{\pi Dt}}\, \exp\left(-y^2/4\, Dt\right). \qquad\qquad [11.35]$$

If the index of refraction is a linear function of the concentration,
one obtains from eq. [11.35]

$$dn/dy = \frac{n_0 - n_1}{2\sqrt{\pi Dt}}\, \exp\left(-y^2/4\, Dt\right) \qquad\qquad [11.36]$$

where n is the index of refraction at a point y, n_0 the index of refraction of the original solution, and n_1 the index of refraction of the pure solvent (or of the less concentrated solution, if the above initial conditions are replaced by $c = c_1$ for $x > 0$, with $c_1 < c_0$). Since Wiener's method gives dn/dy for every value of y, this magnitude being proportional to the deflection of the light beam, the image obtained for the inclined slit is, directly, the error curve [11.36], distorted only by the transformation to a coordinate system with axes at an angle of 45°.

Wiener's method has been improved by Thovert (309, 311). Instead of using an illuminated inclined slit the image of which is

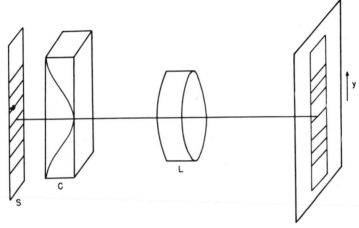

Fig. 11-11. Lamm's scale method, schematic. S scale, L lens, C diffusion cell (with concentration gradient shown), to the right distorted image of scale.

produced by means of a spherical lens, Thovert uses a point source of light, a collimator lens and a cylindrical lens with horizontal axis, to give an horizontal line as image on the screen. Masking the front of his diffusion cell by a slit, inclined at 45°, he obtains the vertical deflections, caused by the vertically varying gradient of the index of refraction within the cell, at different positions of the horizontal image on the screen. Thus the Gaussian curve for dn/dx can be photographed immediately.

The method has been employed by Lamm (172, 15, 22) in the form of the so-called scale method, cf. also (27, 304). A scale, S Fig. 11-11, is photographed through the diffusion cell, containing a solution of uniform concentration, thus giving a scale of reference on a photographic plate. If the scale is photographed again during a diffusion experiment, a distorted image of the scale is obtained, Fig. 11-11.

The distortion is due to the presence of a varying concentration gradient, and, therefore, of a varying deflection of light beams, passing at different heights through the diffusion cell. If the photograph is taken with sufficiently small aperture, every line of the scale refers to a well defined height in the diffusion cell. Therefore, if the deflection of the lines on the plate, relative to the image of the undistorted scale is measured by means of a comparator, dn/dy as function of y can be obtained. For the quantitative evaluation the constants of the optical system used must be determined, in order to convert deflections into gradients of the index of refraction.

Besides the scale method Lamm (172) also used the so-called slit method which is a special form of the schlieren method. The principle is shown in Fig. 11-12. Light from an illuminated slit S_1 passes through

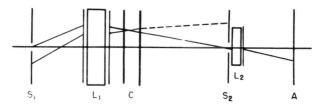

Fig. 11-12. Lamm's slit method.

a lens L_1 and a cell C to form an image on a second slit S_2. The cell is observed by means of a telescope, consisting of a lens L_2 and an ocular at A. Only if there is no deflection due to a concentration gradient in the cell does the light from the first slit pass through the second slit S_2. If there is a concentration gradient, varying with height, a shifting of the first slit in vertical direction is necessary to let the deflected light pass through the second slit, every position of the first slit corresponding to a definite concentration gradient and therefore to a definite height of the cell. Thus it is possible to measure the deflection of light as a function of the vertical position coordinate.

Several modifications of the schlieren method have been used for the determination of diffusion coefficients (Tiselius (312), Philpot (243), Longsworth and McInnes (204), Moore and White (212)). The method has proved very valuable, especially in the form of Longsworth's schlieren scanning method (204). We shall give below some details of schlieren methods, as far as use has been made of the interference phenomena connected with this arrangement.

Interference methods are among the most sensitive ones employed in measuring diffusion coefficients in liquids. One may classify two groups of such methods, depending on whether

a. interference phenomena are used for a local determination of the index of refraction, and consequently of the concentration, or

b. the interference phenomenon caused by the zone of varying concentration in the diffusion cell itself is being used for measuring the rate of diffusion.

The methods of group b. are the more ingenious ones and probably are adaptable to give a considerable improvement in the technique of measuring diffusion coefficients, both with respect to the speed with which an experiment may be performed, and with respect to the accuracy obtainable.

Application of interference methods to the determination of concentrations in a diffusion experiment is comparatively easy, and eventually a commercial type of liquid interferometer may be adapted to this purpose. It is not possible to observe the very early stages of diffusion by this method, because the concentration gradient during this period is very high and the concentration varies markedly already in the comparatively narrow regions, necessary for the interferometric determination. On the other hand, methods of group b. are especially suitable for measurements during the initial stages.

Interferometric concentration determinations have been used by Calvet and Chevalerias (65), and by Rögener (263, 264) in the author's laboratory, both employing a Young type of interferometer in connection with a twin diffusion cell, in Rögener's experiments the double slit of the interferometer being perpendicular to the concentration gradient, in Calvet's experiments parallel to it, Fig. 11-13, cf. also (219).

 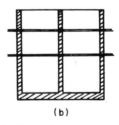

(a)   (b)

Fig. 11-13 a. Twin diffusion cell with vertical double slit, used by Calvet and Chevalerias for interferometric diffusion measurements. b. Twin diffusion cell with horizontal double slit, used by Rögener.

In Rögener's experiments two sets of interference fringes are obtained, that produced by the uniform solution (or solvent) in the comparison cell serving as reference mark. If the double slit is placed in such a way that the light coming from the upper slit passes through the pure solvent (or solution of lower concentration) in the upper part of the diffusion cell, the displacement of the interference fringes is a measure of the difference in refractive index, and therefore in concentration, at the position of the lower slit, with respect to the pure solvent or solution of lower concentration. During measurement the diffusion cell is raised vertically by means of a micrometer screw, and thus the concentration can be determined for various heights. As soon as the upper slit comes into a region where concentration changes have taken place, the change in refractive index, at the position of the upper slit, must be added to the difference between the two slits, as measured directly. This is possible because the distance between the slits and the vertical displacements of the cell are known.

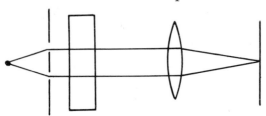

In Calvet's arrangement a system of interference patterns is ob-

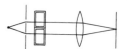

Fig. 11-14.
Interferometric arrangement, used by Rögener.

Fig. 11-15. Interferometric arrangement of Calvet, plan.

tained which represents for every value of the height the difference of index of refraction in the diffusion cell toward the comparison cell. If this pattern is photographed a representation of the concentration distribution within the cell is obtained. Rögener (265), used his apparatus in such a way. Calvet and Chevalerias use a different form of recording on a rotating drum, see below.

The complete optical arrangement for both methods is shown in Figs. 11-14 and 11-15.

11-16   11-17

Fig. 11-16. Interference fringes in Calvet's experiments, schematic.
Fig. 11-17. Interference fringes in Calvet's experiments.

If monochromatic light is used, as was the case in both types of experiments, the interference pattern, corresponding to a definite height in Calvet's experiments, would consist of a series of equidistant fringes, Fig. 11-16. Passing to an adjacent layer of slightly different concentration in the diffusion cell, one observes a set of fringes, slightly shifted in comparison with the first set, Fig. 11-16. Thus the system of interference fringes has the shape as shown in Fig. 11-17, being vertical for a region of vanishing concentration gradient, and deviating further from the vertical the higher the concentration gradient. In Calvet's experiments a part of this pattern, corresponding to a narrow vertical slit, is photographed on a continuously rotating drum. The picture, thus obtained, cf. Fig. 11-18, is essentially a system of curves $c =$ const. in a $(y \sim t)$ coordinate system, the trace of each fringe representing a curve $c =$ const., as a function of y and t. From this an $y \sim c$ plot for a constant value of t may be obtained.

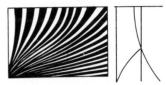

Fig. 11-18. Recording of interference pattern (left) in Calvet's experiments, through vertical slit (right).

The interference phenomenon, produced by a zone of diffusion, in a liquid was first observed by Gouy (124) who also gave a qualitative explanation. In Fig. 11-19, after Longsworth (203), the scheme of the optical arrangement is shown. Light from an horizontal slit S in the focal plane of a lens L_1 passes through a cell C, and a second lens L_2

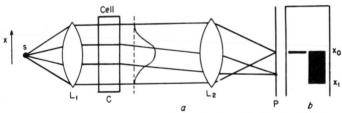

Fig. 11-19. Gouy's interference method, after Kegeles and Gosting. To the right of diffusion cell the concentration gradient is shown, with maximum in the middle.

produces an image of the slit on the screen P, Fig. 11-19. If the focal lengths of the two lenses are equal, an image of the slit in its original size is obtained, neither distorted nor deflected as long as the concentration within the cell is uniform. If there exists a concentration gradient within the cell, as shown in Fig. 11-19, (the higher concentration and the higher index of refraction being at the bottom), light beams passing the cell are deflected downwards, and are deflected to a different degree depending on the value of the coordinate x at which they pass the cell. Light, passing near the top or near the bottom of the cell, where the concentration gradient vanishes, forms an image of the slit at the original position x_0, while light from regions with non-vanishing concentration gradient, gives an image below x_0. To the curve for dc/dx, as shown in Fig. 11-19, there corresponds a maximum of dc/dx in the middle of the cell, and therefore light beams passing through the middle of the cell exhibit maximum deflection, giving an image at x_1. Consequently, the originally sharp image of the slit is now extended into a rectangle, Fig. 11-19. The vertical extension is greater, the higher the concentration gradient, i.e., the narrower the zone of diffusion, the distance $x_0 x_1$ being inversely proportional to the extension of the diffusion zone. Simultaneously an interference phenomenon occurs, due to the difference in length of the optical path for rays deflected at different heights of the cell. The system of interference fringes is shown schematically in Fig. 11-20.

Fig. 11-20. Scheme of interference fringes, corresponding to Fig. 11-19.

Recently Kegeles and Gosting (160) succeeded in giving a quantitative theory of this interference method, suitable for an evaluation of diffusion measurements. Longsworth (203) has tested this method experimentally, obtaining diffusion coefficients with an average deviation of 0.15 per cent only, cf. also (122a, 123).

Philpot's interference method is very similar to the preceding one, described in a paper by Coulson, Cox, Ogston and Philpot (73), cf. (235). The latter succeeded in the rapid determination of diffusion coefficients with a high degree of accuracy, first by employing this interference method, and second by using a diffusion cell which gives a very sharp initial boundary between solvent and solution, as suggested by Svensson (303).

The scheme of the diffusion cell used is seen in Fig. 11-21. Solution and solvent enter through the lower and upper of the three tubes at the side of the cell, leaving it through a horizontal slit and the middle tube. At the beginning of an experiment the flow through all three of the tubes is stopped simultaneously.

Among measurements of other physical properties, used in diffusion experiments, those of electrolytic conductivity have proved most successfulol, in the determination of diffusion coefficients of electrolytes.

An arrangement employed by Harned (132, 133) is shown in Fig. 11-22. In a diffusion cell of insulating material of rectangular cross-section two pairs of electrodes are introduced at heights ξ and $h - \xi$, where h is the height of the cell. The solution of the one-dimensional diffusion equation with the boundary condition

$$\frac{\partial c}{\partial x} = 0 \text{ for } x = 0 \text{ and } x = h$$

may be expressed in the form (cf. Chap. I, p. 35)

$$c = c_0 + \sum_{n=1}^{\infty} A_n \cos \frac{n\pi x}{h} \exp\left(-\frac{n^2 \pi^2 Dt}{h^2}\right) \qquad [11.36]$$

where the coefficients must be determined in accordance with the initial conditions. The measurement of the difference of conductivity at two levels, situated symmetrically with respect to the center of

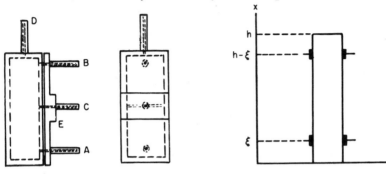

Fig. 11-21. Diffusion cell of Coulson, Cox, Ogston, Philpot, schematic.
Fig. 11-22. Diffusion cell for electrolytes, after Harned and French.

the cell, at heights ξ and $h - \xi$ amounts to a determination of the difference of concentrations at these heights, given by eq. [11.36]. Thus

$$c(\xi) - c(h - \xi) = 2 A_1 \cos \frac{\pi \xi}{h} \exp\left(-\frac{\pi^2 Dt}{h^2}\right)$$
$$+ 2 A_3 \cos \frac{3\pi\xi}{h} \exp\left(-\frac{9\pi^2 Dt}{h^2}\right)$$
$$+ 2 A_5 \ldots \ldots \ldots \ldots \ldots$$
$$+ \ldots \ldots \ldots \ldots \ldots \ldots \qquad [11.37]$$

Here, due to choosing the symmetrical arrangement of the electrodes only the odd terms of the Fourier series have been retained. This can be further simplified by choosing for ξ the special value $\xi = h/6$

$$c(\xi) - c(h - \xi) = 2 A_1 \cos \frac{\pi}{6} \exp\left(-\frac{\pi^2 Dt}{h^2}\right) + 2 A_5 \ldots \ldots \ldots \qquad [11.38]$$

Since the series converges very rapidly for not too small values of t, usually only the first term of this series need be considered.

The diffusion cell of the Tiselius (312) type was constructed from lucite and consisted of two symmetrical parts, the one sliding upon the other. The error of the first determinations of diffusion coefficients by this method was about 0.9 per cent, which was later reduced to about 0.1 per cent.

Ultrasonic sound has been applied to diffusion analysis in liquids by Kannuna (157).

Measurement of diffusion in molten alloys and in amalgams is possible by methods similar to those used with other liquids, except for the optical methods. v. Wogau (331) used a set of glass discs with cylindrical holes, K. Schwarz (276) made use of the original Fick apparatus for stationary diffusion (cf. p. 439), Cohen (68, 70) worked with a potentiometric analysis; conductivity measurements were employed by Weischedel (324). Weischedel's arrangement corresponds to that of most measurements with gases, a vertical glass tube being divided into two halves by a stopcock of bore equal in diameter to that of the tube. At the ends of the tube and at six intermediate positions electrodes were fitted for conductivity measurements.

Diffusion measurements with molten alloys are in some respect easier than those with normal liquid mixtures because at the end of an experiment the whole system may be cooled and single layers for analysis can be obtained by simple mechanical means. At elevated temperatures, however, it is more difficult to maintain constant temperature over the whole length of the system than at ordinary temperatures. Thus errors due to convection may easily occur. It probably would be best, in such cases, not to aim at all at a perfectly constant temperature, but at a temperature distribution, rising within controlled limits from bottom to top of the system.

Some data, referring to diffusion in amalgams and in molten alloys, are reproduced in Tables XII, XIII, XIV p. 478/9.

Not many data are available on diffusion in molten salts. Estimates of ionic diffusion in molten salts are possible from conductivity measurements, cf. the discussion of such data by Biltz and Klemm (46), and Mulcahy and Heymann (216). Bloom and Heymann (49) investigated the electric conductivity of a number of molten salts and of their mixtures.

In liquid mixtures one might expect in some cases an increase of conductivity, in analogy to the results obtained with solid salts, for instance an increase in conductivity of NaCl by addition of $CdCl_2$, as in the solid phase with AgCl and added $CdCl_2$. But as far as can been seen from the measurements with this and similar systems, not extending above the melting point of the pure alkali halides, no such effect is apparent, deviation from additivity, if present, being negative[*]. This is easily explained by the formation of compounds like $CdCl_2 \cdot 2NaCl$ etc. which are known in the solid state as incongruently melting compounds.

---

[*] The conductivity of liquid NaCl below its melting point has been obtained by extrapolation from measurements carried out above the melting point.

IV. Theory of diffusion in liquids

While we possess an elaborate theory of diffusion in gases, and while the physical picture, underlying the theoretical treatment of diffusion in solids, is quite accurate, actual shortcomings in the theoretical results being due only to simplifications involved in the calculations, the theory of diffusion in liquids must be based upon incomplete pictures of the liquid state, and, therefore, it is less satisfactory.

After early attempts to treat liquids by van der Waals' theory of condensed gases had failed, most modern theories have been based upon a model of a quasi-crystalline structure of liquids. X-ray investigations (Prins (253, 254), Debye (83, 84), cf. (9)) have shown that the structure of liquids in microscopic regions is similar to that of a crystal. There is a tendency for particles in the immediate vicinity of a central particle under consideration to occupy sites which correspond to those of a regular crystal lattice; this tendency, however, decreases rapidly with increasing distance from the central particle. Observed intensities of x-rays, scattered by liquids, can be explained on this basis, and in the simplest cases, from the distribution of x-ray intensities radial distribution functions for particles, surrounding a central particle, can be derived.

For the statistical thermodynamical treatment of liquids this picture has been further simplified by replacing the quasi-crystalline structure by that of an ordered crystal lattice. This procedure has proved rather successful in the theoretical treatment of liquid mixtures. It seems less justified to adopt the same picture for the treatment of kinetic phenomena of liquids (viscosity, diffusion), because here it is just the deviations from complete order which are of fundamental importance. But in most cases this picture had to be adopted, because it is the only way for a comparatively simple theoretical treatment. But the deviations from complete order, encountered in the case of liquids, are certainly of a somewhat different type from those present in solids, where the long range order of lattice structure is still preserved, if local imperfections are introduced, such as unoccupied lattice sites and interstitial particles. Thus a number of rather arbitrary assumptions must be introduced into the theoretical treatment of kinetic phenomena in liquids. In spite of these difficulties, the theory has been fairly successful. A survey of kinetic theories of liquids has been given by Frenkel (6) who stresses the limitations of every theory starting from the conception of a regular lattice structure of liquids. A theory of liquids, considered as a continuum containing holes of various sizes, and with a certain distribution function of sizes, in thermal equilibrium, has been given by Fürth (107, 108, 109, 111).

Recently Born (53, 54, 55), in a series of publications, has laid an exact foundation of the kinetic theory of liquids (cf. the survey given by Born (53)). He emphasizes the fact that all attempts at a theory of liquids, so far, suffered from a lack of physical accuracy even in the underlying picture, while it is Born's aim to establish at least the general equations rigorously, even if their solution necessitates the introduction of approximations, cf. also Kirkwood (164, 164a, 164b), Jaffé (151a). So far, Born's theory has not yet found practical application in the treatment of diffusion phenomena (cf.Yang (333)). He succeeded, however, in deriving preliminary results for viscosity and thermal conductivity (53, 55), which, formally, are similar to those derived on different lines by Guzman (130), Andrade (30, 30a), Eyring (10, 93) and co-workers, Ewell (94a, 94b), Fürth (109). It is, of course, possible to apply Born's results to diffusion processes in liquids if the validity of Stokes' law and the Nernst-Einstein relation, connecting mobility and diffusion coefficient, may be considered adequate. Without further proof, this may be assumed in the case of sufficiently large diffusing particles only.

It would be beyond the scope of this book to go into any details of Born's theory.

Frenkel (6, 99) emphasizes the facts supporting the assumption of a similarity between liquids and solids, much closer than that between liquids and compressed gases, at least in the vicinity of the melting point. The volume increase on melting is of the order of magnitude of 10 per cent only, in some cases it is less or may even become negative; the heat of fusion is of lower order of magnitude than the heat of evaporation. The latter fact is borne out most clearly by the approximate rules concerning the entropies of melting and of evaporation. For "normal" substances Trouton's rule gives for the entropy change connected with the evaporation of one mol of substance the order of magnitude of 20 cal. per degree, while the entropy change for melting of a mole of a simple substance is of the order of magnitude of 2 cal. per degree only (equal to the gas constant per mol, R). The specific heats, too, are very similar for liquids and solids, near the melting point.

The conception of disorder in a crystal leads to a certain understanding of the properties of a liquid, as far as it differs from a solid. The energy required for the production of a hole within a liquid, consisting of molecules (not of ions), is the same as that to be supplied for evaporation, provided that the size of the hole is equal to that of a molecule of the liquid*.

Therefore, the temperature function, giving the decrease in density of the liquid with rising temperature, as far as it is caused by the formation of holes within the liquid, is (approximately) the same as that giving the increase of vapor density with temperature, which is the Cailletet-Matthias' rule. Of course, in contrast to solids, a liquid may contain holes of any size, not only of size equal to that of the constituent particles, corresponding to the removal of one particle from a lattice point. The process of melting cannot be understood by considerations referring to the crystal only. The liquid phase differs from the solid by its greater free volume, by its greater energy, due to the volume increase, and by its greater entropy, due to the increase in number of configurations. Thus the Gibbs free energy of the liquid lies below that of the solid for temperatures above the melting point, while for temperatures below the melting point it is larger than that of the solid, for the melting point both being equal. At this temperature the finite increase in heat content of the liquid, above that of the solid, is exactly compensated by the term TS, due to the finite increase in entropy of the liquid.

The fluidity is due to the increase in free volume, permitting the movement of particles in the vicinity of vacancies, in a way similar to that discussed for diffusion in solids (cf. Chap. III, p. 135ff.). Since holes in a liquid may be of any size, and since no long range order is present in liquids, it is not possible to calculate the number of holes in a liquid without further (arbitrary) assumptions. Any calculation implies the determination of a distribution function for holes of different sizes. Fürth (108), introducing special assumptions arrives at a formula for the probability of holes in a continuous liquid, supposed to be spherical and of radius r

$$W(r)\,dr = C \exp\left(- \varepsilon/kT\right) r^6\,dr \qquad [11.39]$$

where the energy ε is given approximately by

$$\varepsilon = 4\pi r^2\sigma$$

with $\sigma =$ surface tension. The average radius of a hole becomes of the order of magnitude of $(kT/\sigma)^{1/2}$. Frenkel (6, 99), avoiding any special assumptions, puts

$$W(r)\,dr \approx \exp\left(- \varepsilon(r)/kT\right) \varphi(r)\,dr$$

---

* The energy to be supplied for the transportation of a particle out of the bulk of the liquid to infinite distance is twice the energy of evaporation (cf. Chap. II, p. 103). Condensation of the particle, thus removed, gives the energy of evaporation, therefore an energy gain of half the energy spent for the removal of the particle, thus leaving a "hole"-energy equal to the energy of evaporation.

$\varphi(r)$ being a function of the radius, r, of the hole. Putting $\varphi = \text{const.}$, and identifying ε with the surface energy of an hole of spherical shape, as above, he obtains the average values

$$\overline{\varepsilon(r)} = \frac{kT}{2} \qquad \overline{r} = \frac{1}{8\pi} \sqrt{\frac{kT}{\sigma}} \,. \qquad [11.41]$$

The value of the average radius, $\overline{r}$, obtained from [11.41], is of the order of molecular dimensions, 10^{-8} cm., but independent of the actual size of the molecules. Hence, the result derived on the basis of a crystalline structure of a liquid, may be rather near to the truth, as long as molecules are considered which are not too large.

As in the case of solids, formation of holes in a liquid, will cause a contribution to specific heat, which, at least, is not in disagreement with experimental facts.

The picture for diffusion in liquids, thus arrived at, does not differ essentially from that for solids, the only difference being a lower heat of activation in the case of liquids. In contrast to the case for solids, there exists a direct relation between viscosity and diffusion in liquids. The coefficient of diffusion is given by

$$D = u \, kT \qquad [11.42]$$

where u is the mobility of the particle under consideration, i.e., the stationary velocity acquired under the influence of unit force (1 dyne). The mobility for spherical particles, moving in a continuous liquid, is given by Stokes' formula

$$u = \frac{1}{6\pi\eta r} \qquad [11.43]$$

where η is the viscosity and r the radius of the particle. Though derived on the assumption of a continuous medium, eq. [11.43] is a fairly good approximation for not too small values of r. Therefore, a satisfactory theory of diffusion in liquids should allow of a calculation of the viscosity, also, and vice versa. It may be worth while to emphasize the fact that the relation between viscosity and diffusion constant in liquids is different from that for gases. In gases, viscosity and diffusion constant are proportional to each other, while in liquids they are inversely proportional to each other.

Is is not difficult to give an approximate expression for the coefficient of diffusion in a liquid on the basis of the "hole" theory of liquids. It is the exact analogue of the formula derived for diffusion in solids

$$D \approx f\frac{d^2}{\tau} \exp\left(-E/RT\right) \approx f \, dv \exp\left(-E/RT\right) \qquad [11.44]$$

where the exponential term is essentially the number of holes in the liquid (given as fraction of the number of particles present), d is the average distance travelled by a migrating hole, i.e., by a neighboring particle, jumping into the position of the hole, τ is the time necessary for a particle in the vicinity of a hole to move over the distance d. Thus d/τ may be interpreted as the velocity v of the diffusing particle. If we identify v with the average thermal velocity of a particle, of the order of magnitude of 10^4 cm. per second, then, with $d \approx 10^{-8}$ cm., the time τ becomes approximately 10^{-12} sec., of the order of magnitude of the time necessary for one oscillation of a particle about its instantaneous equilibrium position. E might differ from the energy necessary for the formation of a hole, by a comparatively small term, representing the height of an energy barrier, to be surmounted by a migrating particle. The numerical factor f would have to be derived by means of a more rigorous theory. Frenkel chooses $f = 1/6$, equivalent to the factor entering the expression for the mean square displacement for motion in three dimensions (cf. Chap. I, p. 30).

We shall not aim at giving a detailed account of the theory of viscosity. Since it is known experimentally, and since it can be proved theoretically for sufficiently large particles, that eqs. [11.42] and [11.43] connect viscosity and diffusion in liquids to an approximation which is better the larger the particles under consideration, substitution of [11.44] and [11.43] into [11.42] should give a correct expression for the viscosity of liquids. This is actually the case, as we shall see, though this argument cannot be considered to be a proof of the relation because it involves eq. [11.43], derived for a continuous medium only.

From eqs. [11.42], [11.43] and [11.44] we obtain for the viscosity, following Frenkel

$$\eta = \frac{kT\tau}{6\pi f r d^2} \exp (E/RT) = A \, \exp (E/RT) . \qquad [11.45]$$

Eq. [11.45] formally describes observed viscosities and is in agreement with expressions derived by other authors. As in a number of cases of diffusion in solids (cf. Chap. III, p. 149) eq. [11.45] gives the correct dependence of viscosity on temperature, but the factor outside the exponential may differ considerably from observed values*. These are by several orders of magnitude smaller than the values calculated from [11.45] with values of d comparable with the lattice distance of crystals. Frenkel (6) points out that this discrepancy can be removed as in the case of diffusion in solids (Jost (153), cf. Chap. III, p. 149), by a consideration of the influence of changes in volume, due either to temperature or to pressure variation, on the energy of activation. By putting

$$E = E_0 - \gamma RT$$

* Eyring's theory, however, gives better agreement, see below p. 467 ff.

he obtains

$$D \approx f \frac{d^2}{\tau} e^{\gamma} \exp\left(- E_0/R T\right) \qquad [11.46]$$

and for the factor A in the corresponding expression for the viscosity

$$A \approx \frac{k T \tau}{6 \pi f r d^2} e^{-\gamma} . \qquad [11.47]$$

If $e^{\gamma} \approx 100$ to 1000, i.e. $\gamma \approx 5 - 7$, agreement between theory and experiment may be obtained. This value of γ corresponds to a decrease in heat of activation by 10 to 15 cals. per mole per degree, caused by the thermal expansion of the liquid. This may be correlated with the effect of pressure on E, because a certain change in volume must have the same influence on E, whether it is due to a temperature decrease or to a pressure increase. The corresponding expressions are

$$E = E_0 - \beta \left(v - v_0\right) \qquad \frac{v - v_0}{v_0} = - \varkappa p \qquad E = E_0 + \beta \varkappa v_0\, p . \qquad [11.48]$$

Thus A depends exponentially on pressure

$$A = A_0 \exp\left(p/p_0\right) \qquad [11.49]$$

where

$$p_0 = \frac{R T}{\beta \varkappa v_0} \qquad [11.50]$$

and

$$p_0 = \frac{\alpha T}{\varkappa \gamma} \qquad [11.51]$$

where $\alpha =$ coefficient of thermal expansion.

A rise of pressure of magnitude p_0 corresponds to an e-fold increase in viscosity. Frenkel obtains, with

$$\alpha \approx 10^{-5} \text{ degree}^{-1}$$
$$1/\varkappa \approx 10^{12} \text{ dynes/cm.}^2$$
$$\gamma \approx 5$$
$$T \approx 300°\text{K}.$$

a value of the characteristic pressure

$$p_0 \approx 10^9 \text{ dynes/cm.}^2 \approx 1000 \text{ atmospheres.}$$

An increase of pressure to 10^4 atmospheres, therefore, should increase the viscosity by a factor $e^{10} \approx 10^4$. Correspondingly, the coefficient of diffusion should decrease by a factor 10^{-4}. This means that at a pressure of the order of magnitude of 10^4 atmospheres conditions for diffusion in a liquid should approach those of a solid crystal. Indeed, with the assumed value of $\alpha = 10^{-5}$, a pressure of 10^4 atmospheres should reduce the volume of the liquid by about 10 per cent, thus compensating closely for the volume increase of the same order of magnitude, connected with the transition from solid to liquid. The above formulae, of course, may be applied within a range of pressure only where a linear relation between pressure increase and volume decrease is sufficiently accurate.

The above argument is in accordance with Batschinski's rule (39), giving an empirical relationship between viscosity, η, of a liquid and its volume V, b being a constant, comparable to the b in van der Waals' equation of state. B is a second empirical constant, being approximately independent of temperature, like b

$$\eta = \frac{B}{V-b}. \qquad [11.52]$$

The physical meaning of Batschinski's rule is, essentially, that the viscosity of a liquid depends primarily on the free volume, i.e., the concentration of holes.

Frenkel emphasizes the fact that diffusion coefficients in liquids, in contrast to those in crystals, are all of about the same order of magnitude, 10^{-5} cm.^{2} sec.$^{-1}$, or smaller. This holds even for, different solvents and over a considerable range of temperature. Since the energies of activation, found empirically for diffusion in liquids, are much smaller than those for solid crystals, the variation of this energy, consequently, must be much smaller, also, as must the influence of temperature on the coefficient of diffusion. These facts are readily understood in the case of diffusion of dissolved large molecules where Stoke's law holds, and the viscosity of the solvent only enters into the formula for the mobility and the diffusion coefficient. Variations of the coefficient of diffusion due to variation of the radius are not large unless colloidal particles are considered. Even the movement of particles, comparable in size to those of the solvent, may be primarily determined by the properties of the solvent. For the migration of a foreign particle is largely determined by the formation and disappearance of holes in the surrounding liquid. These holes need not be of the size of the moving particle provided they permit a certain displacement.

The energy necessary for the formation of a hole may be estimated by putting it equal to the surface energy of an hole of equal size in a continuous liquid, $\varepsilon = 4\pi r^2 \sigma$, where σ is the surface tension. For $r = 10^{-8}$ cm., $\sigma = 80$ (water) and $\sigma = 400$ dynes/cm., one thus obtains $E = 2000$ and $= 10,000$ cals. per mole, respectively, which is of the right order of magnitude.

V. Electrical conductivity and viscosity of molten salts

Frenkel suggests the following relations for conductivity and viscosity of molten salts

$$\lambda = A \exp\left(-\Delta E_1/RT\right) \qquad [11.53]$$
$$\eta = B \exp\left(\Delta E_2/RT\right). \qquad [11.54]$$

Here it has been assumed that conductivity is chiefly due to the more mobile type of ion, usually the smaller cations, connected with an energy of activation ΔE_1, smaller than ΔE_2, the corresponding value for the less mobile ions. Frenkel assumes that the viscosity is mainly determined by the mobility of the less mobile ions, because in viscous flow of a molten salt both ions must move, the slower one being responsible for the observed rate. Thus an expression for the viscosity has been derived, containing the mobility of the slower ion. Consequently, the product $\lambda \eta$ can no longer be constant, because λ and η now refer to different processes. Now an expression

$$\lambda^m \eta = \text{const.} \qquad [11.55]$$

may be expected to be constant, independent of temperature, where

$$m = \Delta E_2 / \Delta E_1 \,.$$

A relation of this type, according to Frenkel (6, 100), has been found experimentally by Evstopiev (92), as seen from the following Table I, taken from Frenkel's monograph.

TABLE I

Exponents m of relation [11.55], as found by Evstopiev (92)

Substance	$NaNO_3$	KNO_3	AgBr	AgCl	Glass C 24	Glass N 3
m	1.23	1.23	7.59	5.26	1.55	7.17

As has been emphasized by Schwarz (275), considerable difficulties are encountered if one attempts to define transference numbers of ions in molten salts. Unlike the cases of dilute solutions or of solids, where either the solvent or the mechanical structure give a frame of reference for definition of transference numbers, no such frame of reference exists in the case of pure molten salts. After electrolysis one has no observable changes due to the existence of transference numbers, differing for the different types of ions. If one introduces, artificially, a frame of reference, by choosing suitable electrodes, one influences directly the apparent transport numbers, calculated with respect to this frame of reference. If, for instance, solid electrolytes are chosen as electrodes, which in one case allow the cations to pass, and in the other case the anions, one would observe a transference number of 1.00 for the cations and for the anions, depending on which type of electrode is chosen as frame of reference. Transference numbers, thus determined, obviously are not a property of the molten salt.

Even an attempt to create a frame of reference by the addition of a narrow layer of radioactive tracer ions, either of one type or of both types of ions, does not give any results. Consider an original distribution as given by the solid line in Fig. 11-23. After a certain time, due to diffusion, the concentration distribution of the tracer ions will be given by the dashed line in Fig. 11-23. In the absence of an electric field the center of gravity of this distribution coincides with that of the original distribution. It is impossible, however, to determine transference numbers from the observation of the distribution of radioactive ions in the presence of an electric field. All that could be observed, would be a relative displacement of the centres of gravity of radioactive ions of different type. The average movement

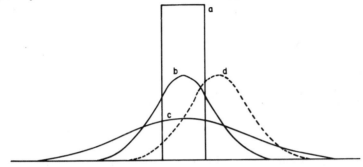

Fig. 11-23. Distribution of radioactive tracer ions in a liquid, a original distribution, b, c later distributions without electric field, d distribution if electric field has been applied.

of radioactive ions is not different from that of the bulk of ions of the same type. One may, however, determine self-diffusion constants for the different types of ions, present, by means of radioactive tracers, and one can define transference numbers in terms of the mobilities of the different types of ions, derived from these diffusion measurements.

VI. Eyring's treatment of diffusion in liquids

A detailed treatment of viscosity and diffusion of liquids, by means of the theory of absolute reaction rates, is due to Eyring (10, 93) and co-workers, (cf. Ewell (94 a, b), Hirschfelder, Stevenson and Eyring (146), Stearn, Irish and Eyring (289), and Powell, Rosevaere and Eyring (252, 266,) Kincaid, Eyring and Stearn (163)). The coefficient of diffusion may be written in the form (cf. the theory of diffusion in solids, Chap. III, p. 171)

$$D = d^2\varkappa \qquad [11.56]$$

where d is the distance between successive equilibrium positions of the diffusing particle, and $\varkappa$ is a rate constant for a unimolecular reaction, giving the number of times a molecule is leaving its equilibrium position per second. The theory of absolute reaction rates gives an expression for $\varkappa$ in the alternative forms (cf. Chap. III, p. 173)

$$\varkappa = \frac{kT}{h} \frac{f^*}{f} \exp\left(-\varepsilon_0/kT\right) \qquad [11.57]$$

and

$$\varkappa = \frac{kT}{h} \exp\left(\Delta S^*/R\right) \exp\left(-\Delta H^*/RT\right) \qquad [11.58]$$

depending on whether the statistical or the quasi-thermodynamic expressions are preferred. The magnitudes entering these equations are

f^* = partition function of the activated state (without contribution of the reaction coordinate, cf. Chap. III, p. 173)

f = partition function of the normal state

ε_0 = an energy of activation, per centre, at the absolute zero of temperature

ΔS^* = entropy of activation, per mole

ΔH^* = heat of activation, per mole.

In ε_0, ΔS^* and ΔH^* contributions of particles, surrounding the migrating molecule, may be contained, cf. (36a, 37, 38).

Thus one obtains for the diffusion coefficient

$$D = d^2 \frac{kT}{h} \frac{f^*}{f} \exp\left(-\varepsilon_0/kT\right) \qquad [11.59]$$

and

$$D = d^2 \frac{kT}{h} \exp\left(\Delta S^*/R\right) \exp\left(-\Delta H^*/RT\right). \qquad [11.60]$$

We obtain from [11.60] for the energy of activation, Q, as determined experimentally from the temperature-dependence of the diffusion coefficient, represented by the equation

$$D = A \exp\left(-Q/RT\right) \qquad [11.61]$$

$$Q = RT^2 \frac{d\log D}{dT} = \Delta H^* + RT. \qquad [11.62]$$

Consequently

$$\Delta H^* = Q - RT. \qquad [11.63]$$

By substituting this value into eq. [11.60] one has

$$D = d^2 e \frac{kT}{h} \exp\left(\frac{\Delta S^*}{R}\right) \exp\left(-Q/RT\right). \qquad [11.64]$$

An evaluation of f^*/f, or of the quasi-thermodynamic magnitudes in [11.60] or [11.64] is possible only by means of some arbitrary assumptions. The simplest model, used in the statistical treatment of a liquid, is the cage model (cf. 17, 94, 146, 193, 194, 195). Here a free volume v_f is attributed to a liquid-molecule, this molecule moving freely (i.e., with constant potential energy) within the cage, being reflected at the walls of the cage. Then the contribution to the partition function of the three translational degrees of freedom is the same as for a gas molecule, moving within a volume v_f, thus

$$f_{tr} = \frac{(2 \pi m k T)^{3/2}}{h^3} v_f . \qquad [11.65]$$

Contributions due to inner rotations and vibrations of the molecules may be neglected, if we consider them as equal for the normal state and for the activated state, because in this case they cancel in the ratio f^*/f. In the activated state, two degrees of translation must be considered only, the 'reaction' coordinate being treated separately, consequently

$$f_{tr}^* = \frac{(2 \pi m k T)}{h^2} v_f^{2/3} \qquad [11.66]$$

and we obtain for the diffusion coefficient from [11.59]

$$D = \frac{d^2}{v_f^{1/3}} \left(\frac{k T}{2 \pi m} \right)^{1/2} \exp (-E_0/R T) \quad E_0 = N \varepsilon_0 . \qquad [11.67]$$

Eq. [11.67] is of the form of observed diffusion coefficients, eq. [11.61]. For a quantitative comparison of [11.67] with experiment, an estimate of v_f and of E_0 is necessary. For a rigid molecular crystal lattice E_0 should be identical with the energy of vaporization (cf. Chap. II, p. 110). Comparison, however, of empirical Q values, derived from the temperature dependence of viscosity, which is very nearly the same as that for diffusion, (with opposite sign) with energies of vaporization ($\Delta E_{vap.} = \Delta H_{vap.} - R T$) reveals, that there is proportionality between the sets of values, but they are not identical. Powell, Rosevaere and Eyring (252) (cf. also Glasstone, Laidler and Eyring (10)) found, Fig. 11-24, that for non-metallic liquids on the average,

$$\frac{\Delta E_{vap}}{\Delta F_{visc}} \approx 2.45 , \qquad [11.68]$$

ΔF_{visc} = free energy of activation for viscosity .

For the ratio of ΔE_{vap} and the energy of activation ΔE_{visc} for viscosity, a ratio between 3 and 4 has been found, cf., however, Eirich and Simha (89). Thus it must be assumed that the size of the holes, formed within a liquid and responsible for viscous flow and for diffusion, is a fraction of the volume of the constituent molecules only. If in addition to the energy necessary for the formation of holes, an energy barrier of non-negligible height would have to be surmounted by migrating particles, the size of the hole would be still smaller.

In the case of metals the ratio $\Delta E_{vap}/\Delta E_{visc}$ is much higher, between 8 and 25, and even more. This fact has found a ready explanation

(Eyring et al. (10)). The energy of vaporization refers to the neutral metal atoms, while the units responsible for viscous flow and diffusion in liquid metals, are almost certainly the positive metal ions, which are much smaller than the neutral atoms. The energy of formation

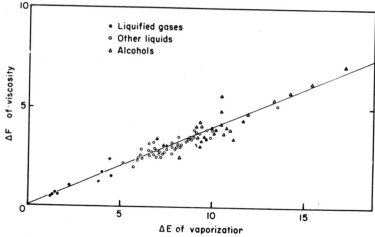

Fig. 11-24. Empirical relation between tree energy of activation in liquids, ΔF, and energy of evaporation, ΔE, Rosevaere, Powell and Eyring.

of an hole the size of an ion might approximately be smaller than that for formation of an hole the size of a neutral atom by a factor (volume of ion) / (volume of atom). Indeed, correction of the observed ratios of $\Delta E_{vap} / \Delta E_{visc}$ by a factor $(r_{ion} / r_{atom})^3$ gives values which lie within the same range as those for non-metallic liquids, Table II (taken from Eyring (10)).

TABLE II

Corrected ratio of energy of vaporization and activation for viscous flow

Metal	Average temp. °C.	ΔE_{vap} kcal.	ΔE_{vis} kcal.	$\dfrac{\Delta E_{vap}}{\Delta E_{vis}}$	$\dfrac{\Delta E_{vap}}{\Delta E_{vis}}\left(\dfrac{r_{ion}}{r_{atom}}\right)^3$
Na	500	23.4	1.45	16.1	2.52
K	480	19.0	1.13	16.7	3.41
Ag	1400	60.7	4.82	12.5	3.79
Zn	850	26.5	3.09	8.6	2.10
Cd	750	22.5	1.65	13.5	3.96
Ga	800	34.1	1.13	30.3	2.53
Pb	700	42.6	2.80	15.9	4.97
Hg	250	13.6	0.65	20.8	2.37
Hg	600	12.3	0.55	22.2	3.54
Sn	600	15.3	1.44	10.6	4.07
Sn	1000	14.5	1.70	8.ᵖ	3.30

An estimate of the free volume v_f may be obtained by various methods, one of which is the comparison of the velocity of sound in gases and in liquids, Kincaid and Eyring (161, 162). A sound wave, travelling within a liquid, must be propagated by the thermal motion of the constituent particles only over distances which are connected with the free volume, while it is propagated almost instantaneously over the distance occupied by the particles themselves, Fig. 11-25. Thus an estimate of the ratio $v_f^{1/3}/v^{1/3}$ may be obtained, where v is the average volume for one particle. Agreement between values for the free volume, obtained by different methods, is not very good. Since, however, the free volume enters into the results only as $v^{1/3}$, an uncertainty is not of very great importance (for a discussion of free volume cf. Fowler and Guggenheim (5), Kirkwood (165a)).

Fig. 11-25.
Estimate of free volume from propagation of sound in liquids, Eyring.

Eyring and co-workers (289) compared their theory with experiment by putting

$$d = (V/N)^{1/3} \qquad [11.69]$$

where V is the volume, occupied by N molecules. For the binary mixture of components 1 and 2 under consideration, the following mean values $d_{12} = (v_f)_{12}^{1/3}$ and $(\Delta E_{vap})_{12}$ were used

$$d_{12} = N_1 d_1 + N_2 d_2$$
$$(v_f)_{12}^{1/3} = N_1(v_f)_1^{1/3} + N_2(v_f)_2^{1/3}$$
$$(\Delta E_{vap})_{12}^{1/2} = N_1(\Delta E_{vap})_1^{1/2} + N_2(\Delta E_{vap})_2^{1/2}$$

where N_1 and N_2 are the mole fractions. Results, thus obtained, agree quite well with experiment, as seen from the following Table III.

TABLE III

Comparison of observed and calculated diffusion coefficients in the system Tetrabromethane-Tetrachlor-ethane, after Eyring and co-workers (10, 289)

Temp. °K.	$d^2 \times 10^{15}$ cm.²	$(v_f)_{12}^{1/3} \times 10^9$ cm.	ΔE_{vap} kcal.	$D \times 10^5$ cm.² sec.$^{-1}$ calc.	obs.
273.4	3.12	6.45	9.85	0.64	0.35
288.0	3.15	6.92	9.72	0.92	0.50
308.6	3.19	7.59	9.52	1.42	0.74
324.1	3.23	8.13	9.38	1.89	0.95

The energy of activation has been taken as equal to $\Delta E_{vap}/3$. It must be borne in mind that the theory contains several empirical elements, for instance, the relation between energy of activation and the energy of vaporization. In both cases agreement between theory and experiment is very good, also.

VII. Diffusion in non- ideal mixtures

As has been discussed elsewhere (Chap. III, p. 156) a dependence of the coefficient of diffusion, D, on concentration may be caused by two influences:

a. a change of mobility of the diffusing particle with concentration, and

b. deviations of the mixture from ideal behaviour.

It is assumed that the diffusion coefficient has been determined either from the application of Fick's first law

$$J = - D \frac{\partial c}{\partial x} \qquad [11.70]$$

or from Fick's second law, written for concentration dependent D, for unidimensional diffusion

$$\frac{\partial c}{\partial t} = \frac{\partial}{\partial x} \left(D \frac{\partial c}{\partial x} \right) . \qquad [11.71]$$

Now the Nernst-Einstein relation for the coefficient of diffusion, with Stokes' law for the mobility of spherical particles in a viscous liquid, gives the relation between viscosity and coefficient of diffusion

$$D \eta = \frac{k T}{6 \pi r} \qquad [11.72]$$

where r is the radius of the diffusing particles, considered as spheres. Empirical values for D ($C_2H_2Br_4/C_2H_2Cl_4$) and for $\varphi = 1/\eta$ of $C_2H_2Cl_4$ are seen in Fig. 11-26. A similar relation is obtained from the theory of absolute reaction rates

$$D \eta = f(r) . \qquad [11.73]$$

For the derivation of eq. [11.73] it is not necessary to assume that the diffusing particles are of dimensions large compared with those of the molecules of the solvent. [11.73], however, like all results derived on the basis of Eyring's theory, can be considered an approximation only. The right side of eq. [11.73] is not identical with that of eq. [11.72] but it will not be very different from it. In considering varying concentrations of a binary mixture, there may be some variation of the right term of [11.73], varying inversely as some effective average linear dimension of the two types of molecules involved. Consequently, the product $D\eta$, in such cases, may be expected to vary not more than the reciprocal of the average linear dimensions of the molecules.

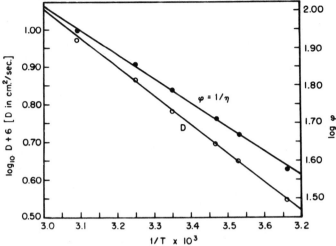

Fig. 11-26. Fluidity φ ($= 1/\eta$) and diffusion coefficient D in system $C_2H_2Cl_4 - C_2H_2Br_4$ after Cohen-Bruins, as function of temperature; logarithms of these magnitudes versus reciprocal temperature (slopes not quite identical).

This can be true, however, for ideal mixtures only. In case of deviations from ideality the relation is not fulfilled, as seen from Fig. 11-27, after Lemonde (192) and Rosevaere, Powell and Eyring (252, 266).

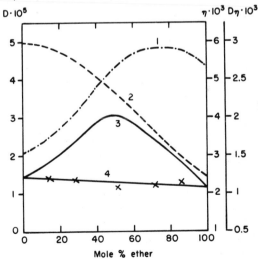

Fig. 11-27. Diffusion in (non-ideal) mixture of chloroform-ethyl-ether. 1 diffusion coefficient, 2 viscosity (H. Lemonde); 3 $D\eta$, 4 $D\eta \dfrac{\partial \log a}{\partial \log N}$ after Eyring and co-workers.

It has been shown before (cf. Chap. III, p. 156) that for non-ideal mixtures D should be replaced by

$$D = D_0 \frac{d \log a}{d \log c} = D_0 \left(1 + \frac{d \log \gamma}{d \log c} \right) \qquad [11.74]$$

where a is the activity, and γ is the activity coefficient. The coefficient D_0, thus defined, is independent of deviations from ideal behaviour, but may still depend on concentration, due to a dependence of mobility on concentration. Rosevaere, Powell and Eyring plotted corrected values

$$D_0 \times \eta = D \times \eta \left/ \frac{d \log a}{d \log c} \right. = D \times \eta \left/ \left(1 + \frac{d \log \gamma}{d \log c} \right) \right. \qquad [11.75]$$

as functions of concentration, Fig. 11-27. It is seen that these values fit a straight line fairly closely, giving a small linear dependence of $D_0 \times \eta$ on concentration.

VIII. Survey of experimental results

In the following Tables IV—XIV we give a survey of measured diffusion coefficients, for hydrocarbon mixtures, for diffusion of different substances in water, for molten salts, amalgams and molten metals. For an estimate of diffusion constants of electrolytes the Nernst (217) formula is quite sufficient. Measured values are therefore omitted here, except a few typical results, Table VII—X.

TABLE IV

Diffusion in 50 mole per cent liquid mixtures, after Trevoy and Drickamer (314). Diffusion coefficients $D \times 10^5$ (cm.^{2} sec.$^{-1}$) observed and calculated by the equation of Stearn, Irish and Eyring (289), the latter appearing in parentheses

Mixture	Temperature		
	25 °C.	45 °C.	65 °C.
Benzene-n-Heptane	2.47 (6.73)	3.40 (8.38)	4.32 (10.23)
Benzene-n-Decane	1.72 (5.04)	2.51 (6.43)	3.10 (8.01)
Benzene-n-Dodecane	1.40 (4.63)	—	—
Benzene-n-Hexadecane . . .	0.96 (4.45)	—	—
Benzene-n-Octadecane . . .	0.86 (4.52)	—	—
n-Heptane-n-Dodecane . . .	1.58 (4.31)	2.14 (5.56)	2.69 (7.06)
n-Heptane-n-Tetradecane . .	1.29 (4.09)	—	—
n-Heptane-n-Hexadecane . .	1.00 (4.18)	1.44 (5.41)	2.05 (6.89)
n-Heptane-n-Octadecane . .	0.92 (4.37)	—	—

TABLE V

Diffusion in Water

Values of D (cm.^{2} sec.$^{-1}$), observed and calculated, after Stearn, Irish and Eyring (289)

Solute	Concentration per cent	Temp. °C	$D_{obs.} \times 10^5$	Ratio $D_{obs.}/D_{calc.}$	Observer
Methanol . . .	0.25	18	1.37	3.5	Gerlach (117)
Ethanol. . . .	0.25	18	1.10	3.0	Gerlach (117)
Propanol . . .	0.25	18	0.98	2.8	Gerlach (117)
Butanol. . . .	0.25	18	0.88	2.6	Thovert (309, 311)
Amyl alcohol .	0.25	18	0.88	2.6	
Glycerol . . .	0.125*	20	0.83	2.3	Zuber (334)
Phenol	0.25	18	0.80	2.4	Thovert (309, 311)
Pyrogallol . .	0.25	18	0.66	2.0	Thovert (309, 311)
Urea	0.25*	20	1.18	3.1	Zuber (334)
Glucose	0.25	18	0.57	1.7	Thovert (309, 311)
Urethane . . .	0.25	18	0.87	2.6	Thovert (309, 311)
Acetylene . . .		18	1.76	4.5	Tammann and
Carbon dioxide.		18	1.46	4.0	Jessen (305)
Nitrogen . . .		18	1.62	4.1	
Hydrogen . . .		18	3.59	3.5	

* These concentrations are in moles per liter.

TABLE VI

Diffusion of iodine (0.1 normal solutions) in different solvents at 20°C., after Miller (211)

Solvent	$D \times 10^5$ cm.^{2} sec.$^{-1}$	$D \eta \times 10^{10}$ dyne
Heptane	2.386	1148
Benzene	1.670	1072
Carbon disulfide.	2.697	1010
Carbon tetrachloride	1.177	1128
Brombenzene	1.038	1176
Water	—	850
Methanol	1.572	960
Acetic acid.	—	1110
Ethyl acetate.	1.859	850

TABLE VII

An Experimental Test of Gordon's Relation* for Aqueous Sucrose Solutions, after Gosting and Morris (123)

$\bar{c}$ = average sucrose concentration

$\bar{c}$	$D \times 10^6$ cm.^{2} sec.$^{-1}$	η/η_0	$1 + c\dfrac{d\log\gamma}{dc}$	$D_0 \times 10^6$ cm.^{2} sec.$^{-1}$	
0.7507	5.170	1.019$_1$	1.007$_9$	5.227	
1.0011	5.148	1.025$_6$	1.010$_6$	5.224	
2.2521	5.049	1.059$_2$	1.024$_3$	5.221	24,95° C
3.7535	4.934	1.102$_0$	1.041$_2$	5.222	
5.2546	4.821	1.147$_4$	1.058$_8$	5.224	
0.2502	2.418	1.007$_0$	1.002$_9$	2.428	
1.2513	2.378	1.036$_2$	1.014$_5$	2.429	
2.2521	2.330	1.067$_0$	1.026$_4$	2.422	1,00°C.
3.2539	2.297	1.099$_6$	1.038$_6$	2.432	
4.2551	2.251	1.133$_8$	1.051$_1$	2.428	

* The equation, given by Gordon (120) and van Rysselberghe (267), is:

$$D = D_0\ \eta_0/\eta\ \left[1 + c\,\frac{d\log\gamma}{dc}\right],$$

where η_0 and η are the viscosities of the solvent and of the solution (cf. p. 474).

TABLE VIII

Observed and calculated* values of the differential diffusion coefficient of potassium chloride at 25°C., after Harned and Nuttall (133), cm.^{2}sec.$^{-1}$

c	$D \times 10^5$ observed	$D \times 10^5$ theoretical	$D_0 \times 10^5$
0.00000		1.9958	
0.00125	1.961	1.9605	1.996
0.00194	1.954	1.953	1.997
0.00325	1.943	1.943	1.996
0.00585	1.931	1.929	1.997
0.00704	1.924	1.925	1.995
0.00980	1.918	1.916	1.999

* By the equation of Onsager and Fuoss (237).

TABLE IX

$10^5 D$ at 18.5°C., after Gordon (120), cm.^{2} sec.$^{-1}$

m	KCl	NaCl	KNO$_3$
0.	1.694	1.354	1.645
0.05	1.559	1.246	1.483
0.10	1.535	1.227	1.428
0.20	1.522	1.214	1.37
0.50	1.540	1.219	1.29
1.00	1.604	1.243	
1.50	1.666	1.263	
2.00	1.723	1.273	

(m molality)

TABLE X

$10^5 D$ for hydrochloric acid at various temperatures,
after James and Gordon (152), cm.^{2} sec.$^{-1}$

c	10°	15°	25°	35°C.
0	2.16	2.48	3.14	3.87
0.02	2.05	2.35	2.97	3.66
0.05	2.02	2.33	2.93	3.61
0.20	2.05	2.35	2.98	3.65
0.35	2.11	2.40	3.06	3.77
1.00		2.68	3.58	

TABLE XI

Average diffusion coefficient D (cm.^{2} sec.$^{-1}$) of some high polymers

Solute	Solvent	Temperature	$D \times 10^7$	Oberserver
Edestin	Water	20°	3.18	Bevilacqua and others (45)
Tobacco mosaic virus . .	Water	20°	0.53	Lauffer (191)
Human tubercle bacillus polysaccharide	Water	20°	7.0—7.6	Bevilacqua and others (45)
Acid treated starch . .	Water		11.5	Beckmann and Rosenberg (40)
Cellulose Acetate. . . .	Acetone		5.4	,,
Polystyrene	Toluene		3.6	,,

TABLE XII. Diffusion of Molten Salts
Results of Harrison (134) and Höchberg (147), cf. Lorenz (16)

Diffusing substance	Diffusion medium	Temperature °C.	$D \times 10^5$ cm.^{2} sec.$^{-1}$
$AgNO_3$	KNO_3	360	4.56
$AgNO_3$	$NaNO_3$	330	4.57
AgBr	KBr	780	4.92
AgI	KI	720	4.63
$TlNO_3$	KNO_3	345	3.17
TlBr	KBr	770	4.28
TlI	KI	720	3.14
$NaNO_3$	KNO_3	360	5.22
KBr	KNO_3	360	3.01
KI	KNO_3	360	2.96
$Ba(NO_3)_2$	KNO_3	370	2.06
$Ba(NO_3)_2$	$NaNO_3$	360	3.71
$Sr(NO_3)_2$	KNO_3	360	2.81
$Sr(NO_3)_2$	$NaNO_3$	345	4.17

TABLE XIII. Diffusion in Amalgams (taken from Seith (19a))

Element	K. Schwarz (19, 276)		M. v. Wogau (331)		other authors		
	t °C.	$D \frac{cm.^2}{sec.} \times 10^5$	t °C.	$D \frac{cm.^2}{sec.} \times 10^5$	t °C.	$D \frac{cm.^2}{sec.} \times 10^5$	
Li	25	0.93	8.2	0.76			
Na	25	0.86	9.6	0.74			
K	25	0.71	10.5	0.61			
Rb			7.3	0.53			
Cs	25	0.64	7.3	0.52			
Ag	16	1.11					
Au	25	0.73			11	0.83	W. C. Roberts-Austen (261)
Tl	25	1.18	11.5	0.99			
Zn	25	2.4	11.5	2.52	20	1.5	F. Weischedel (324)
			99.2	3.35	15.0	2.42	G. Meyer (210)
Cd	25	2.0	8.7	1.68	15	1.8	G. Meyer (210)
			99.1	3.43	20	1.51*	E. Cohen and H. R. Bruins (70, 72)
					20	1.45**	E. Cohen and H. R. Bruins (70, 72)
Sn	25	2.1	10.7	1.77			
Bi	25	1.5					
Pb	25	2.1	9.4	1.74	15.6	1.59	G. Meyer (210)
			99.4	2.22			
Ba			7.8	0.60			
Sr			9.4	0.54			
Ca			10.2	0.62			

* $p = 1$ at.   ** $p = 1500$ at.

TABLE XIV
Diffusion in molten metals

	t°C.	$D \times 10^5$ cm.²/sec.	References
Mg in Al	700	7.54	N. A. Belosevsky (42)
Au in Bi.	500	5.22	W. C. Roberts-Austen (261)
Si in Fe	1480	2.4	M. Paschke and A. Hauttmann (239)
	1560	10.8	
ThB in Pb (Self-diff.)	343	2.55	J. Groh and G. v. Hevesy(128)
Au in Pb	500	3.7	W. C. Roberts-Austen (261)
Rh in Pb	500	3.52	
Pt in Pb.	490	1.95	
Ag in Sn	500	4.8	W. C. Roberts-Austen (261)
Au in Sn	500	5.37	
Pb in Sn	500	3.68	

REFERENCES

Monographs and Review Articles

1. Alexander, A. E., and Johnson, P., Colloid Science, Oxford Clarendon Press, 1940. Vol. I, Chap. X, Translational diffusion. p. 233ff.; Chap. XIV, Rotational diffusion, p. 380ff.
1a. Cohen, E., and Bruins, H. R., Ein Präzisionsverfahren zur Bestimmung von Diffusionskoeffizienten in beliebigen Lösungsmitteln. *Z. physik. Chem.* **103,** 349 (1923).
2. Cohn, E. J., and Edsall, J. T., Proteins, Amino Acids and Polypeptides Chapt. 18 and 21. New York 1943.
3. The Diffusion of Electrolytes and Macromolecules in Solution. *Ann. New York Ac. Sci.* **46,** 209 (1945).
4. Duclaux, J., Diffusion dans les liquides, Actualités scientifiques et industrielles, No. 349. Paris 1936.
4a. Edsall, J. T., Article rotatory diffusion in Advances in Colloid Science. Vol. I, Interscience Publishers, New York, 1942.
5. Fowler, R. H., and Guggenheim, E. A., Statistical Thermodynamics. Cambridge 1939 and 1949.
6. Frenkel, I., Kinetic Theory of Liquids. Oxford 1946.
7. Fürth, R., Article "Diffusion"; in: Auerbach, F., and Hort, W., Handb. physik. techn. Mechanik, Vol. 7, p. 635—739. Leipzig 1931.
7a. Fürth, R., *Science Progress* **37,** 202—218 (1949).
8. Geddes, A. L., Article "Determination of Diffusivity"; in: Weissberger, A., Physical Methods of Organic Chemistry, Vol. 1. New York 1949.
9. Gingrich, N. S., Diffraction of X-Rays by Liquid Elements. *Rev. Mod. Phys.* **15,** 90 (1943).

10. Glasstone, S., Laidler, K. J., and Eyring, H., The Theory of Rate Processes. New York and London 1941.
11. Harned, H. S., The Quantitative Aspect of Diffusion in Electrolyte Solutions. *Chem. Rev.* **40**, 461 (1947).
12. Harned, H. S., and Owen, B. B., The Physical Chemistry of Electrolyte Solutions. New York 1943. 2nd ed. New York 1950.
13. Höber, R., Physical Chemistry of Cells and Tissues. Philadelphia and London 1946.
14. Kuhn, A., Koloidchemisches Taschenbuch, 2nd edition, p. 21. Leipzig 1948.
15. Lamm, O., Article "Diffusion"; in: Bamann, E., and Myrbäck, K., Die Methoden der Fermentforschung, Vol. 1, p. 659. Leipzig 1941.
16. Lorenz, R., Raumerfüllung und Ionenbeweglichkeit, p. 207. Leipzig 1922.
17. Mayer, J. E., and Goeppert-Mayer, M., Statistical Mechanics, Sect. 141. New York 1940.
18. Neurath, H., The Investigation of Proteins by Diffusion Measurements. *Chem. Rev.* **30**, 357 (1942).
19. Schwarz, K., Elektrolytische Wanderung in flüssigen und festen Metallen, p. 57, 84. Leipzig 1940.
19 a. Seith, W., Diffusion in Metallen, Springer, Berlin, 1939.
20. Staverman, A. J., Cohaesie-Krachten in vloeibare Mengsels, Thesis. Amsterdam 1938.
21. Structure and Molecular Forces in Pure Liquids and Solutions, 65th General Discussion of the Faraday Society. *Trans. Faraday Soc.* **33**, 1 (1937).
22. The Svedberg, and Pedersen, K. O., The Ultracentrifuge. Oxford 1940.
23. Ulich, H., Article "Elektrische Leitfähigkeit, Flüssigkeiten und Lösungen"; in: Eucken-Wolf, Hand- u. Jahrb. chem. Phys., Vol. 6, part II B. Leipzig 1933.
23 a. Valkó, E., Kolloidchemische Grundlagen der Textilveredelung. Springer, Berlin, 1937. p. 355 ff. diffusion of dyes.
24. Williams, J. W., and Cady, L. C., Molecular Diffusion in Solution. *Chem. Rev.* **14**, 171 (1934).
24 a. Wagner, C., *J. Colloid Science* **5**, 85 (1950). (Periodic precipitation)

General Bibliography

25. Abegg, R., and Bose, E., *Z. physik. Chem.* **30**, 545 (1899).
26. Adamson, A. W., *J. Chem. Phys.* **15**, 762 (1947).
26 a. Adamson, A. W., Cobble, W., and Nielsen, J. M., *J. Chem. Phys.* **17**, 740 (1949).
27. Adler, F. T., and Blanchard, C. H., *J. Phys. Colloid Chem.* **53**, 803 (1949).
28. Altar, W., *J. Chem. Phys.* **5**, 577 (1937).
29. Andersson, K. J. I., *Nature* **143**, 720 (1939).
30. Andrade, E. N. da C., *Phil. Mag. J. Sci.* (7) **17**, 497, 698 (1934).
30 a. Andrade, E. N. da C., *Proc. Phys. Soc. (London)* **52**, 748 (1940).
31. Arrhenius, S., *Meddel. K. Vetenskapsakad. Nobelinst.* **3**, Nr. 20 (1916).
32. Asunmaa, S., *Ann. Acad. Sci. Fenn.* A **53**, Nr. 11 (1940).
32 a. Aten, A. H. W., jr., and von Dreve, J., *Trans. Faraday Soc.* **44**, 202 (1948).
33. Aulock, F. C., and Kothari, D. S., *Nature*, **153**, 777 (1944).
34. Aulock, F. C., and Kothari, D. S., *Proc. Cambridge Phil. Soc.* **41**, 180 (1945).
35. Barnes, C., *Physics* **5**, 4 (1934).

36. Barrer, R. M., *Trans. Faraday Soc.* **35**, 644 (1939).
36 a. Barrer, R. M., *Trans. Faraday Soc.* **38**, 322 (1942).
37. Barrer. R, M., *Trans. Faraday Soc.* **39**, 48, 59 (1943).
38. Barrer, R. M., *Trans. Faraday Soc.* **39**, 237 (1943).
39. Batschinski, A. J., *Z. physik. Chem.* **84**, 643 (1913).
40. Beckmann, C. O., and Rosenberg, J. L., *Ann. New York Ac. Sci.* **46**, 329 (1945).
41. Beilstein, F., *Ann. Chem. Pharm.* **99**, 165 (1855).
42. Belosevsky, N. A., *Chem. Zentralbl.* **1938** I, 4585.
43. Bernal, J. D., *Trans. Faraday Soc.* **33**, 27, 279 (1937).
44. Bernal, J. D., and Fowler, R. H., *J. Chem. Phys.* **1**, 515 (1933).
45. Bevilacqua, E. M., Bevilacqua, E. B., Bender, M. M., and Williams, J. W., *Ann. New York Ac. Sci.* **46**, 329 (1945).
46. Biltz, W., and Klemm, W., *Z. anorg. allgem. Chem.* **152**, 267 (1926).
47. Blake, G. G., *J. Sci. Instruments* **24**, 77 (1947).
48. Bloom, H., and Harrap, B. S., and Heymann, E., *Proc. Roy. Soc. (London)* A **194**, 237 (1948).
49. Bloom H., and Heymann, E., *Proc. Roy. Soc. (London)* A **188**, 392 (1947).
50. Boeder, P. *Z. Physik* **75**, 258 (1932).
51. Boltzmann, L., *Wied. Ann.* **53**, 959 (1894).
52. Bondi, A., *J. Chem. Phys.* **14**, 591 (1946).
53. Born, M. *Nature* **159**, 251 (1947).
54. Born, M., and Green, H. S., *Proc. Roy. Soc. (London)* A **188**, 10 (1946).
55. Born, M., and Green, H. S., *Proc. Roy. Soc. (London)* A **190**, 455 (1947).
56. Brady, A. P., *J. Am. Chem. Soc.* **70**, 914 (1948).
57. Bradley, R. S., *J. Chem. Soc.* **1934**, 1910.
58. Bradley, R. S., *Trans. Faraday Sol.* **33**, 1185 (1937).
59. Bridgman, W. B., and Williams, J. W., *Ann. New York Acad. Sci.* **43**, 195 (1942).
60. Bruins, H. R., *Rec. trav. chim.* **50**, 121 (1931).
61. Bruins, H. R., *Kolloid Z.* **54**, 265 (1931).
62. Burrage, L. J., *J. Phys. Chem.* **36**, 2166 (1932).
63. Burrage, L. J., and Allmand, A. J., *J. Phys. Chem.* **41**, 887 (1937).
64. Calvet, E., *J. chim. phys.* **44**, 245 (1947).
65. Calvet, E., and Chevalerias, R., *J. chim. phys.* **43**, 37 (1946).
65 a. Chandler, R. C., and McBain, J. W., *J. Phys. & Colloid Chem.* **53**, 930 (1949).
66. Clack, B. W., *Proc. Phys. Soc. (London)* **36**, 313 (1924) and earlier publications.
67. Claesson, S., *Nature* **158**, 834 (1946).
68. Cohen, E., and Bruins, H. R., *Z. physik. Chem.* **109**, 397 (1924).
69. Cohen, E., and Bruins, H. R., *Z. physik. Chem.* **103**, 404 (1923).
70. Cohen, E., and Bruins, H. R., *Z. physik. Chem.* **109**, 422 (1924).
71. Cohen, E., and Bruins, H. R., *Z. physik. Chem.* **113**, 157 (1924).
72. Cohen, E., and Bruins, H. R., *Z. physik. Chem.* **114**, 441 (1925).
72 a. Cole, A. F. W., and Gordon, A. R., *J. Phys. Chem.* **40**, 733 (1936). (Diffusion in aqueous solutions, diaphragm method)
72 b. Crank, J., *J. Soc. Dyers Colourists* **66**, 366 (1950). (Diffusion of dyes)
73. Coulson, C. A., Cox, J. T., Ogston, A., and Philpot, J. S. L., *Proc. Roy. Soc. (London)* A **192**, 382 (1948).
74. Cremer, E., *Z. physik. Chem.* B **42**, 281 (1939).
74 a. Cremer, E., *Z. physik. Chem.* **193**, 287 (1944).
75. Davies, R. J., *Phil. Mag.* (7) **15**, 489 (1933).

75a. Davies, J. T., *J. Phys. & Colloid Chem.* **54,** 185 (1950). (Diffusion of ions across a phase boundary)
76. Davtyan, O. K., *J. Phys. Chem. USSR* **20,** 575, 645 (1946).
77. Dean, R. B., *J. Am. Chem. Soc.* **67,** 31 (1945).
78. Dean, R. B., *Chem. Rev.* **41,** 503 (1947)
79. Dean, R. B., *J. Am. Chem. Soc.* **71,** 3127 (1949).
80. Dean, R. B., and Vinograd, J. R., *J. Phys. Chem.* **46,** 1091 (1942).
81. Debye, P., *Z. Elektrochem.* **45,** 174 (1939).
82. Debye, P., and Bueche, A. M., *J. Chem. Phys.* **16,** 573 (1948).
83. Debye, P., and Menke, H., *Physik. Z.* **31,** 797 (1930).
84. Debye, P., and Menke, H., Ergebnisse techn. Röntgenkunde II, p. l. Leipzig 1931.
85. Dummer, E., *Z. anorg. allgem. Chem.* **109,** 31 (1949).
86. Einstein, A., *Ann. Physik* (4) **17,** 549 (1905).
87. Einstein, A., *Ann. Physik* (4) **19,** 371 (1906).
88. Einstein, A., *Z. Elektrochem.* **14,** 235 (1908).
89. Eirich, F., and Simha, R., *J. Chem. Phys.* **7,** 116 (1939).
89a. Erdey-Gruz, T., Hunyar, A., Pogany, E., and Vali. A., *Hung. Acta Chim.* **1,** Nr. 3, 7 (1948).
90. Eversole, W. G., and Doughty, E. W., *J. Phys. Chem.* **40,** 55 (1936); **41,** 663 (1937).
91. Eversole, W. G., Kindsvater, H. M., and Peterson, J. D., *J. Phys. Chem.* **46,** 370 (1942).
92. Evstopiev, *Bull. Acad. Sci. USSR Sér. phys.* **3,** 319 (1937).
93. Eyring, H., *J. Chem. Phys.* **4,** 283 (1936).
94. Eyring, H., and Hirschfelder, J. O., *J. Phys. Chem.* **41,** 249 (1937).
94a. Ewell, R. H., *J. Applied Phys.* **9,** 252 (1938).
94b. Ewell, R. H., and Eyring, H., *J. Chem. Phys.* **5,** 726 (1937).
95. Falinski, M., *Compt. rend.* **218,** 754, 938 (1944).
95a. Felicetta, V. F., Markham, A. E., Peniston, Q. P., and J. L. McCarthy, *J. Am. Chem. Soc.* **71,** 2879 (1949).
96. Fick, A.: *Pogg. Ann.* **94,** 59 (1855).
97. Fowler, R. H., and Slater, N. B., *Trans. Faraday Soc.* **34,** 81 (1938).
98. Franke, G., *Ann. Physik* **14,** 675 (1932).
99. Frenkel, I., *Z. Physik* **35,** 652 (1926).
100. Frenkel, I., *Acta physicochim. USSR* **6,** 339 (1937).
101. Freundlich, H., and Krueger, D., *Trans. Faraday Soc.* **31,** 906 (1935).
102. Friedman, L., *J. Am. Chem. Soc.* **52,** 1305, 1311 (1930).
103. Friedman, L., and Carpenter, P. G., *J. Am. Chem. Soc.* **61,** 1745 (1939).
104. Friedman, L., and Kraemer, E. O., *J. Am. Chem. Soc.* **52,** 1295 (1930).
105. Fürth, R., *Physik. Z.* **26,** 719 (1925).
106. Fürth, R., *Kolloid-Z.* **41,** 300 (1927).
107. Fürth, R., *Proc. Phys. Soc. (London)* **52,** 768 (1940).
108. Fürth, R., *Proc. Cambridge Phil. Soc.* **37,** 252, 276 (1941).
109. Fürth, R., *Proc. Cambridge Phil. Soc.* **37,** 281 (1941).
110. Fürth, R., *J. Sci. Instruments* **22,** 61 (1945).
111. Fürth, R., Ornstein, L. S., and Milatz, J. M. W., *Proc. Kon. Akad.Wetensch. Amsterdam* **42.** 107 (1939).
112. Fürth, R., and Ullmann, E., *Kolloid-Z.* **41,** 304 (1927).
113. Fürth, R., and Zuber, R., *Z. Physik* **91,** 609 (1934).
114. Gage, J. C., *Trans. Faraday Soc.* **44,** 253 (1948).

115. Gatovskaya, T. V., and Pasynskii, A. G., *J. Phys. Chem. USSR* **20,** 707, 715 (1946).
116. Gemant, A., *J. Applied Phys.* **19,** 1160 (1948).
117. Gerlach, B., *Ann. Physik* **10,** 437 (1931).
118. Gibert, R., *J. chim. phys.* **44,** 37 (1947).
119. Gingrich, N. S., *J. Chem. Phys.* **11,** 351 (1943).
119a. Gokhshtein, Y. P., *Zhur. Anal. Khim.* **2,** 147 (1947).
120. Gordon, A. R., *J. Chem. Phys.* **5,** 522 (1937).
121. Gordon, A. R., *J. Chem. Phys.* **7,** 89 (1939).
122. Gordon, A. R., *Ann. New York Acad. Sci.* **46,** 285 (1945).
122a. Gostings L. J., Hanson, E. M., Kegeles, G., and Morris, M. S., *Rev. Sci. Instruments* **20,** 209 (1949), (Interference method)
123. Gosting, L. J., and Morris, M. S., *J. Am. Chem. Soc.* **71,** 1998 (1949).
124. Gouy, G. L., *Compt. rend.* **90,** 307 (1880).
125. Graham, Th., *Phil. Trans. Roy. Soc.* **1850,** 1, 905; **1851,** 483.
126. Gralén, N., *Kolloid-Z.* **95,** 188 (1941).
127. Gralén, N., Dissertation Uppsala 1944, "Sedimentation and Diffusion Measurements of Cellulose and Cellulose Derivatives."
128. Groh, J., and Hevesy, G., von, *Ann. Physik* (4) **63,** 85 (1920).
129. Groh, J., and Kelp, J., *Z. anorg. allgem. Chem.* **147,** 321 (1925).
129a. Guggenheim, E. A., *J. Am. Chem. Soc.* **52,** 1315 (1930).
130. de Guzman, J., *Anales soc. españ. fis. quim.* **11,** 353 (1913).
131. Haellstroem, af M., *Ann. Acad. Sci. Fenn.* A 1)42 II, Nr. 2.
132. Harned, H. S., and French, D. M., *Ann. New York Acad. Sci.* **46,** 267 (1945).
132a. Harned, H. S., and Levy, A. L., *J. Am. Chem. Soc.* **71,** 2781 (1949).
133. Harned, H. S., and Nuttall, R. L., *J. Am. Chem. Soc.* **69,** 736 (1947); **71,** 1460 (1949).
133a. Harned, H. S., and Nuttall, R. L., *Ann. N. Y. Acad. Sci.* **51,** 781 (1949).
134. Harrison, L. H., Thesis Munich 1911.
135. Hartley, G. S., *Phil. Mag.* **12,** 473 (1931).
136. Hartley, G. S., *Trans. Faraday Soc.* **42 B,** 6 (1946); **45,** 820 (1949).
136a. Hartley, G. S., and Crank, J., *Trans. Faraday Soc.* **45,** 801 (1949).
137. Hartley, G. S., and Runnicles, D. F., *Proc. Roy. Soc. (London)* A **168,** 401, 420 (1938).
138. Haskell, R., *Phys. Rev.* **27,** 145 (1908).
139. Heimbrodt, F., *Ann. Physik* (4) **13,** 1028 (1904).
140. Hermans, J. J., *Rec. trav. chim. Pays-Bas* **56,** 635 (1937).
141. Hermans, J. J., *Rec. trav. chim. Pays-Bas* **58,** 917 (1939).
142. Hermans, J. J., *Naturwissenschaften* **31,** 257 (1943).
143. Hermans, J. J., *J. Colloid Sci.* **2,** 387 (1947).
144. Hildebrand, J. H., *Proc. Phys. Soc. (London)* **56,** 221 (1944).
145. Hill, T. L., *J. Phys. Chem.* **51,** 1219 (1947).
146. Hirschfelder, J., Stevenson, D., and Eyring, H., *J. Chem. Phys.* **5,** 896 (1937).
147. Hoechberg, A., Thesis. Frankfurt 1915.
148. Holmes, F. H., and Standing, H. A., *Trans. Faraday Soc.* **41,** 542 (1945).
148a. Hollingshead, E. A., and Gordon, A. R., *J. Chem. Phys.* **8,** 423 (1940).
148b. Hollingshead, E. A., and Gordon, A. R., *J. Chem. Phys.* **9,** 152 (1941).
148c. Hutchinson, E., *J. Phys. & Colloid Chem.* **52,** 897 (1948). (Diffusion across oil-water interface)
148d. James, W. A., Hollingshead, E. A., and Gordon, A. R., *J. Chem. Phys.* **7,** 89 (1939).

149. Hook, A., van, and Russell, H. D., *J. Am. Chem. Soc.* **67**, 370 (1945).
150. Hüfner, G., *Wied. Ann.* **60**, 134 (1897).
151. Hüfner, G., *Z. physik. Chem.* **27**, 227 (1898).
151a. Jaffé, G., *Phys. Rev.* **75**, 184 (1949). (Statistical theory of liquids)
152. James, W. A., and Gordon, A. R., *J. Chem. Phys.* **7**, 963 (1939).
153. Jost, W., *Z. physik. Chem.* **A 169**, 129 (1934).
154. Jullander, I., *Arkiv Kemi, Mineral, Geol.* **A 21**, Nr. 8 (1945).
155. Kahler, H., *J. Phys. and Colloid Chem.* **52**, 676 (1948).
156. Kahn, D. S., and Polson, A., *J. Phys. Chem.* **51**, 816 (1947).
157. Kannuna, M., *Helv. Phys. Acta* **21**, 93 (1948).
158. Kawalki, W., *Wied. Ann.* **52**, 185 (1894).
159. Kegeles, G., *J. Am. Chem. Soc.* **69**, 1302 (1947).
160. Kegeles, G., and Gosting, L. J., *J. Am. Chem. Soc.* **69**, 2516 (1947).
161. Kincaid, J. F., and Eyring, H., *J. Chem. Phys.* **6**, 620 (1938).
162. Kincaid, J. F., and Eyring, H., *J. Phys. Chem.* **43**, 37 (1939).
163. Kincaid, J. F., Eyring, H., and Stearn, E. A., *Chem. Rev.* **28**, 301 (1941).
164. Kirkwood, J. G., *J. Chem. Phys.* **14**, 180, 347 (1946).
164a. Kirkwood, J. G., Buff, F. P., and Green, M. S., *J. Chem. Phys.* **17**, 988 (1949).
164b. Kirkwood, J. G., *J. Chem. Phys.* **18**, 901 (1950).
165. Kirkwood, J. G., and Riseman, J., *J. Chem. Phys.* **16**, 565 (1948).
165a. Kirkwood, J. G., *J. Chem. Phys.* **18**, 380 (1950).
166. Kittel, Ch., *J. Chem. Phys.* **14**, 614 (1946).
166a. Kittelberger, W. W., *J. Phys. a. Colloid Chem.* **53**, 392 (1949).
167. Kroepelin, H., *Ber. phys.-medizin. Soz. Erlangen* **59**, 237 (1927); **62**, 285 (1930).
168. Kuhn, W., and Kuhn, H., *Helv. Chim. Acta* **26**, 1394 (1943).
169. Kuhn, W., and Kuhn, H., *Helv. Chim. Acta* **30**, 1233 (1947).
170. Laidler, K. J., and Shuler, K. E., *J. Chem. Phys.* **17**, 851 (1949).
171. Laidler, K. J., and Shuler, K. E., *J. Chem. Phys.* **17**, 856 (1949).
172. Lamm, O., *Nova Acta Reg. Soc. Scient. Upsaliensis Ser.* IV **10**, Nr. 6 (1937).
173. Lamm, O., *Svensk Kem. Tid.* **51**, 139 (1939).
174. Lamm, O., *Kolloid-Z.* **98**, 45 (1942).
175. Lamm, O., *Z. anorg. allgem. Chem.* **250**, 236 (1943).
176. Lamm, O., *Svensk Kem. Tidskr.* **55**, 263 (1943).
177. Lamm, O., *Arkiv Kemi, Mineral, Geol.* **17 A**, Nr. 9 (1943).
178. Lamm, O., *Arkiv Kemi, Mineral, Geol.* **16 B**, Nr. 17 (1943).
179. Lamm, O., *Svensk Kem. Tidskr.* **56**, 37 (1944).
180. Lamm, O., *Arkiv Kemi, Mineral, Geol.* **18 A**, Nr. 2 (1944).
181. Lamm, O., *Arkiv Kemi, Mineral, Geol.* **18 A**, Nr. 8 (1944).
182. Lamm, O., *Arkiv Kemi, Mineral, Geol.* **18 A**, Nr. 9 (1944).
183. Lamm, O., *Arkiv Kemi, Mineral, Geol.* **18 A**, Nr. 10 (1944).
184. Lamm, O., *Arkiv Kemi, Mineral, Geol.* **18 B**, Nr. 5 (1944).
185. Lamm, O., Paper published in honor of T. Svedberg Upsala, 1944, 182.
186. Lamm, O., *Arkiv Kemi, Mineral, Geol.* **17 B**, Nr. 13 (1944).
187. Lamm, O., *J. Phys. Chem.* **51**, 1063 (1947).
188. Lamm, O., and Högberg, H., *Kolloid-Z.* **91**, 10 (1940).
189. Lamm, O., and Sjoestedt, G., *Trans. Faraday Soc.* **34**, 1158 (1938).
190. Laitinen, H. A., and Kolthoff, I. M., *J. Am. Chem. Soc.* **61**, 3344 (1939), and further publications in this journal.
191. Lauffer, M. A., *J. Am. Chem. Soc.* **66**, 1188 (1944).
192. Lemonde, H., *Ann. chim. phys.* (11) **9**, 539 (1938).

193. Lennard-Jones, J. E., *Proc. Phys. Soc. (London)* **52**, 729 (1940).
194. Lennard-Jones, J. E., and Devonshire, A. F., *Proc. Roy. Soc. (London)* **A 163**, 53 (1937).
195. Lennard-Jones, J. E., and Devonshire, A. F., *Proc. Roy. Soc. (London)* **A 165**, 1 (1938).
196. Linhart, Th., *Z. Physik* **105**, 45 (1937).
197. Littlewood, T. H., *Proc. Phys. Soc. (London)* **34**, 71 (1922).
198. Longsworth, L. G., *Ann. New York Acad. Sci.* **39**, 187 (1939).
199. Longsworth, L. G., *J. Am. Chem. Soc.* **61**, 529 (1939).
200. Longsworth, L. G., *Ann. New York Acad. Sci.* **41**, 267 (1941).
201. Longsworth, L. G., *Ann. New York Acad. Sci.* **46**, 211 (1945).
202. Longsworth, L. G., *Ind. Engng. Chem. Anal. Ed.* **18**, 219 (1946).
203. Longsworth, L. G., *J. Am. Chem. Soc.* **69**, 2510 (1947).
204. Longsworth, L. G., and MacInnes, D. A., *J. Am. Chem. Soc.* **62**, 705 (1940).
205. Mc Bain, E. L., *Proc. Roy. Soc. (London)* **A 170**, 415 (1939).
206. McBain, J. W., and Dawson, C. R., *Proc. Roy. Soc. (London)* **A 148**, 32 (1935).
207. McBain, J.W., and Liu, T. H., *J. Amer. Chem. Soc.* **53**, 59 (1931).
208. Malmgren, H., and Lamm, O., *Z. anorg. allgem. Chem.* **252**, 255 (1944).
209. Mark, H., and Simha, R., *Naturwissenschaften* **25**, 833 (1937).
210. Meyer, G., *Ann. Phys. Chem.* **61**, 225 (1897).
211. Miller, C. C., *Proc. Roy. Soc. (London)* **A 106**, 724 (1924).
212. Moore, D. H., and White, J. U., *Rev. Sci. Instr.* **19**, 700 (1948).
213. Mouquin, H., and Cathcart, W. H., *J. Am. Chem. Soc.* **57**, 1791 (1935).
214. Muchin, G. E., and Faermann, G. P., *Z. physik. Chem.* **121**, 180 (1926).
215. Muenter, E., *Ann. Physik* **11**, 558 (1931).
216. Mulcahy, M. F. R., and Heymann, E., *J. Phys. Chem.* **47**, 485 (1943).
217. Nernst, W., *Z. physik. Chem.* **2**, 613 (1888).
218. Neurath, H., *Science New York N. S.* **93**, 431 (1941).
219. Nicolas, L., and Calvet, E., *Compt. rend.* **228**, 559 (1949).
220. Northrup, J. H., and Anson, M. L., *J. Gen. Physiol.* **12**, 543 (1929).
221. Obreimov, I. V., *J. Phys. USSR* **8**, 142 (1944).
222. Oeholm, L. W., *Meddel. Vetenskapsakad. Nobelinst.* **2**, 16 (1912).
223. Oeholm, L. W., *Meddel. Vetenskapsakad. Nobelinst.* **2**, Nr. 23, 24, 26 (1913).
224. Oeholm, L. W., *Suomen Kemistiseuran Tiedonantoja* **43**, 55, 121, 163 (1934).
225. Oeholm, L. W., *Suomen Kemistiseuran Tiedonantoja* **44**, 35, 71 (1935).
226. Oeholm, L. W., *Suomen Kemistiseuran Tiedonantoja* **45**, 18, 25, 35, 71, 122, 133, 142 (1936).
227. Oeholm, L. W., *Soc. Sci. Fennica Comment. physico-math.* **9**, Nr. 2 (1936).
228. Oeholm, L. W., *Suomen Kemistiseuran Tiedonantoja* **46**, 18, 71, 118, 124, 176 (1937).
229. Oeholm, L. W., *Suomen Kemistiseuran Tiedonantoja* **47**, 19, 59, 115 (1938).
230. Oeholm, L. W., *Suomen Kemistiseuran Tiedonantoja* **48**, 23 (1939).
231. Oeholm, L. W., *Suomen Kemistiseuran Tiedonantoja* **49**, 9, 14 (1940).
232. Oeholm, L. W., *Soc. Sci. Fennica Comment. physico-math.* **12**, Nr. 2 and 3 (1943).
233. Oeholm, L. W., *Finska Kemistsamfundets festskrift* **1944**, 177, 302.
234. Oeholm, L. W., *Soc. Sci. Fenn. Comment. physico-math.* **12**, Nr. 9 (1944).
235. Ogston, A. G., *Proc. Roy. Soc. (London)* **A 196**, 272 (1949). (The Gouy diffusiometer)
236. Onsager, L., *Ann. New York Ac. Sci.* **46**, 241 (1945).

237. Onsager, L., and Fuoss, R. M., *J. Phys. Chem.* **36**, 2689 (1932).
238. Orr, W. J. C., and Butler, J. A. V., *J. Chem. Soc. (London)* **1935**, 1273.
239. Paschke, M., and Hauttmann, A., *Arch. Eisenhüttenw.* **9**, 305 (1935).
240. Penner, S. S., *J. Chem. Phys.* **16**, 745 (1948).
240a. Penner, S. S., *J. Phys. & Colloid Chem.* **52**, 949, 1262 (1948).
241. Perrin, J., *Ann. chim. phys.* (8) **18**, 5 (1909).
242. Perrin, F.: *J. Phys. Radium* (7) **7**, 1 (1936).
243. Philpot, J. S. L., *Nature* **141**, 282 (1938).
244. Plesniewicz, S., *Roczniki Chem. (Poland)* **14**, 764 (1934).
245. Plesniewicz, S., *Roczniki Chem. (Poland)* **16**, 223, 241 (1936).
246. Plesniewicz, S., *Roczniki Chem. (Poland)* **18**, 740 (1938).
247. Polissar, M. J., *J. Chem. Phys.* **6**, 833 (1938).
248. Polson, A., *Kolloid-Z.* **87**, 149 (1939).
249. Polson, A., *Kolloid-Z.* **88**, 51 (1939).
250. Polson, A., *Nature* **157**, 406 (1947).
251. Pospekhov, D. A., *J. phys. Chem. USSR* **22**, 59 (1948) .
252. Powell, R. E., Rosevaere, W. E., and Eyring, H., *Ind. Eng. Chem.* **33**, 430 (1941).
253. Prins, J. A., *Physica* **1**, 1171 (1934).
254. Prins, J. A., *Physica* **2**, 1016 (1935).
255. Quensel, O., Paper published in honor of The Svedberg. Upsala **1944**, 193.
256. Rabinowitsch, E., *Trans. Faraday Soc.* **33**, 1225 (1937).
257. Randall, M., Longtin, B., and Weber, H., *J. Phys. Chem.* **45**, 343 (1940).
258. Riecke, E., *Z. physik. Chem.* **6**, 564 (1890).
259. Riehl, N., and Wirths, G., *Z. physik. Chem.* **A 194**, 97 (1944).
260. Riseman, J., and Kirkwood, J. G., *J. Chem. Phys.* **17**, 442 (1949).
260a. Riseman, J., and Kirkwood, J. G., *J. Chem. Phys.* **18**, 512 (1950).
261. Roberts-Austen, W. C., *Phil. Trans. Roy. Soc.* **187**, 383 (1897).
262. Robinson, L. B., and Drew, J. B., *J. Chem. Phys.* **15**, 417 (1947).
263. Roegener, H., *Z. Elektrochem.* **47**, 164 (1941).
264. Roegener, H., *Kolloid-Z.* **105**, 110 (1943).
265. Roegener, H., *Kolloid Z.* **118**, 10 (1950).
265a. Rosenberg, J. L., and Beckmann, C. O., *J. Colloid Sci.* **3**, 483 (1948).
266. Rosevaere, W. E., Powell, R. E., and Eyring, H., *J. Applied Phys.* **12**, 669 (1941).
267. van Rysselberghe, P., *J. Am. Chem. Soc.* **60**, 2326 (1938).
268. Saito, D., and Uemura, K., *Tetsu-to-Hagane, Japan* **23**, 986 (1937).
269. Salvinien, J., *J. chim. phys.* **43**, 340 (1946).
270. Samoilov, O. Y., *J. phys. Chem. USSR* **20**, 1411 (1946).
271. Schaefer, K., *Kolloid-Z.* **100**, 313 (1942).
272. Scheffer, J. D. R., *Z. physik. Chem.* **2**, 390 (1888).
273. Scheffer, J. D. R., and Scheffer, F. E. C., *Proc. Acad. Sci. Amsterdam* **19**, 148 (1916).
273a. Scheibling, G., *J. Chem. Phys.* **47**, 688 (1950). (Interference method)
274. Schuhmeister, J., *Wiener Ber.* (II) **79**, 603 (1879).
275. Schwarz, K. E., *Z. Elektrochem.* **45**, 740 (1939).
276. Schwarz, K., and Stockert, R., *Monatsh. Chem.* **68**, 338 (1936).
276a. Sheinker, N. S., *Zavodskaja Lab.* **13**, 1145 (1947).
277. Shuler, K. E., Dames, C. A., and Laidler, K. J., *J. Chem. Phys.* **17**, 860 (1949).
278. Simha, R., *J. Chem. Phys.* **7**, 202, 857 (1939).
279. Simha, R., *J. Chem. Phys.* **13**, 188 (1945).

280. Simha, R., *J. Applied Phys.* **17,** 406 (1946).
281. Singer, S., *Polymer Bull.* **1,** 79 (1945).
282. Singer, S., *J. Polymer Sci.* **1,** 445 (1946).
283. Singer, S., *J. Chem. Phys.* **15,** 341 (1947).
284. Sitte, K., *Z. Physik* **79,** 320 (1932).
285. Sitte, K., *Z. Physik* **91,** 642 (1934).
286. Sitte, K., *Z. Physik* **91,** 617 (1934).
287. Sitte, K., and Daniel, V., *Z. physik. Chem.* **A 182,** 295 (1938).
288. Souchay, P., *Bull. Soc. Chim. France* **1947,** 914.
289. Stearn, A. E., Irish, E. M., and Eyring, H., *J. Phys. Chem.* **44,** 981 (1940).
290. Stefan, J., *Wiener Ber.* (II) **78,** 957 (1878).
291. Stefan, J., *Wiener Ber.* (II) **79,** 161 (1879).
292. Stern, H. G., *Ber. Deutsch. Chem. Ges.* **66,** 547 (1933).
293. Stern, K. G., *Polymer Bull.* **1,** 31 (1945).
294. Stern, K. G., Singer, S., and Davis, S., *J. Biol. Chem.* **167,** 321 (1947).
295. Stokes, G., *Proc. Cambridge Phil. Soc.* **9,** 5 (1856).
296. Stokes, R. H., *J. Amer. Chem. Soc.* **72,** 763, 2243 (1950).
297. Stuart, H. A., *Kolloid-Z.* **96,** 149 (1941).
298. Stumpf, K. E., *Z. Elektrochem.* **51,** 1 (1945).
299. Sutherland, W., *Phil. Mag.* **9,** 784 (1905).
300. Svedberg, The, *Kolloid-Z., Zsigmondy-Festschrift* **1925,** Erg. Bd. **36,** 53 (1925).
301. Svedberg, The, and Andreen-Svedberg, A., *Z. physik. Chem.* **76,** 145 (1911).
302. Svensson, H., *Kolloid-Z.* **87,** 181 (1939).
303. Svensson, H., *Arkiv Kemi, Mineral, Geol.* **22 A,** Nr. 10 (1946).
304. Svensson, H., *Nature* **161,** 234 (1948).
305. Tammann, G., and Jessen, V., *Z. anorg. allgem. Chem.* **179,** 125 (1929).
306. Taylor, H. S., *J. Chem. Phys.* **6,** 331 (1938).
307. Taylor, P. B., *J. Phys. Chem.* **31,** 1478 (1927).
308. Temkin, M., *Nature* **136,** 552 (1935).
309. Thovert, J., *Ann. chim. phys.* (7) **26,** 366 (1902).
310. Thovert, J., *Compt. rend.* **138,** 481 (1904).
311. Thovert, J., *Ann. chim. phys.* (9) **2,** 369 (1914).
312. Tiselius, A., *Trans. Faraday Soc.* **33,** 524 (1937).
313. Tiselius, A., and Gross, D., *Kolloid-Z.* **66,** 11 (1934).
314. Trevoy, D. J., and Drickamer, H. G., *J. Chem. Phys.* **17,** 1117 (1949).
315. Tuomikoski, P., *Suomen Kemistilehti* **B 16,** 21 (1943).
315a. Uemura, K., *Tetsu-to-Hagane Japan* **25,** 24 (1939); **26,** 813 (1940).
316. Ullmann, E., *Z. Physik* **41,** 301 (1927).
317. Veil, S., *Compt. rend.* **226,** 1603 (1948) and earlier publications.
318. Verschaffelt, J. E., *Bull. classe sci. Acad. roy. Belg.* **35,** 311 (1949); **34,** 146 (1948).
319. Vetter, R. J., *J. Phys. Chem.* **51,** 262 (1947).
320. Vinograd, J. R., and McBain, J. W., *J. Am. Chem. Soc.* **63,** 2008 (1941).
320a. Volkmann, H., *Fiat Rev. German Sci.* 1939—1946, *Phys. Chem.* **1948,** 151—182.
321. Walden, P., *Z. Elektrochem.* **12,** 77 (1906).
322. Waring, C. E., and Becher, P., *J. Chem. Phys.* **15,** 488 (1947).
323. Weber, H. F., *Wied. Ann.* **7,** 469, 536 (1879).
324. Weischedel, F., *Z. Physik* **85,** 29 (1933).
325. Weyssenhoff, J., *Ann. Physik* **62,** 1 (1920).
326. Wheeler, T. S., *Proc. Indian Acad. Sci. Sect.* **A 4,** 298 (1936).

327. Wheeler, T. S., *Trans. Nat. Inst. Sci. India* **1,** 333 (1938).
328. Whiteway, S. G., MacLennan, D. F., and Coffin, C. C., *J. Chem. Phys.* **18,** 229 (1950).
329. Wiener, O., *Ann. Phys. Chem.* N. F. **49,** 105 (1893).
329a. Wilke, C. R., *Chem. Eng. Progress* **45,** 218 (1949).
330. Wirtz, K., *Z. Naturforschg.* **3a,** 672 (1948).
331. Wogau, M. von, *Ann. Physik* (4) **23,** 345 (1907).
332. Wyllie, G., *Proc. Phys. Soc. (London)* **59,** 129 (1947).
333. Yang, L. M., *Proc. Roy. Soc. (London)* A **198,** 94, 471 (1949).
333a. Zeldovich, Y. B., and Todes, O. M., *J. Phys. Chem. USSR* **23,** 156, 180 (1949).
334. Zuber, R., *Physik. Z.* **30,** 882 (1929).
335. Zuber, R., *Z. Physik* **79,** 280 (1932).
336. Zuber, R., *Z. Physik* **79,** 291 (1932).
337. Zuber, R., and Sitte, K., *Z. Physik* **79,** 306 (1932).
337a. Zwolinski, B. J., Eyring, H., and Reese, C. E., *J. Phys. & Colloid Chem.* **53,** 1426 (1949).

CHAPTER XII

THERMAL DIFFUSION

I. Thermal Diffusion, Soret effect and Diffusion Thermoeffect, General remarks

Ludwig (112), 1856, and Soret (141), 1879, found experimentally that liquid solutions of non-uniform temperature undergo partial demixing. Solids exhibit an analogous effect (Ballay (11), Reinhold (135)). The analogous phenomenon with gases, called thermal diffusion, allows of an exact theoretical treatment. Contrary to the development with liquids and solids, however, its theoretical derivation (Enskog (57), 1911, Chapman (25, 26, 27, 28), 1916/17) preceded its first experimental verification by Chapman and Dootson (29), 1917. The existence of thermal diffusion was first suggested by Feddersen (58).

In the present chapter we shall not deal with the kinetic theory of these phenomena but restrict ourselves to a phenomenological treatment, valid independently of the state of aggregation of the substances under consideration. As mentioned elsewhere (cf. Chap. I p. 6) Onsager's reciprocity relations are of fundamental importance for all irreversible processes. For instance, if we consider diffusion in a multicomponent mixture, we might in the most simple case expect the set of equations (where for the sake of simplicity we formulate the problem for a ternary mixture)

$$J_1 = -D_1 \, \partial c_1 / \partial x$$
$$J_2 = -D_2 \, \partial c_2 / \partial x \qquad \qquad [12.1]$$
$$J_3 = -D_3 \, \partial c_3 / \partial x \, .$$

Here the individual diffusion coefficients D_1, D_2, D_3 are not independent of each other, because diffusion currents must be defined in such a way that no resulting convection occurs. Eq. [12.1], however, is not the most general linear relation between the "currents" J_i and the "driving forces" grad c_i*. As in other fields of physics, one might tentatively replace [12.1] by the most general set of linear relations between currents and driving forces

$$J_1 = -D_{11} \, \mathrm{grad} \, c_1 - D_{12} \, \mathrm{grad} \, c_2 - D_{13} \, \mathrm{grad} \, c_3$$
$$J_2 = -D_{21} \, \mathrm{grad} \, c_1 - D_{22} \, \mathrm{grad} \, c_2 - D_{23} \, \mathrm{grad} \, c_3 \qquad [12.2]$$
$$J_3 = -D_{31} \, \mathrm{grad} \, c_1 - D_{32} \, \mathrm{grad} \, c_2 - D_{33} \, \mathrm{grad} \, c_3$$

* Valid for ideal gas mixtures only.

Here, again, the nine coefficients $D_{11} \cdots D_{33}$, are not independent of each other, for the same reasons as above. When the diffusion currents are defined in such a way that

$$\sum_i J_i = 0 \qquad [12.3]$$

one has for instance the additional relations

$$\sum_i D_{ik} = 0 \qquad k = 1, 2, 3, \qquad [12.4]$$

which reduce the number of independent coefficients from 9 to 6.

Now Onsager's reciprocity relations permit a further reduction of the number of independent coefficients, stating that (cf. p. 534)

$$D'_{ik} = D'_{ki}. \qquad [12.5]$$

From the standpoint of the phenomenological theory we cannot predict the magnitude of the coupling terms, entering into the set of eqs. [12.2]; the D_{ik} ($i \neq k$) might even vanish. But we may state, that if there exist non-vanishing coefficients D_{ik} (for $i \neq k$), then these coefficients must be interrelated according to the eq. [12.5].

The reciprocity relations are of far greater importance in cases where not only is diffusion involved, but irreversible processes of different types occur simultaneousley, for instance, electric conduction and heat conduction in the case of thermo-electricity, or diffusion and heat conduction, as in the case of thermal diffusion. Even then reciprocity relations of the form [12.5] are still valid. In all cases, however, it becomes necessary to reconsider the definition of the driving forces. The definition, of course, must be chosen in such a way that coefficients, symmetrical with respect to the main diagonal of the matrix scheme, are of equal dimensions, otherwise reciprocity relations would be impossible. It is to be noted that the dimensions of the different currents are generally not the same, and also the dimensions of the coefficients entering the equations are not all the same. We shall not deal with the theoretical derivation of the reciprocity relations. Their proof is based on the principle of microscopic reversibility and on the general theory of fluctuations, Onsager (127, 128), Casimir (24), cf. also de Groot (4, 74, 75), Harned (5), Meixner (118—121).

We shall write the formal equations for a binary mixture of non-uniform concentration and of non-uniform temperature. Then we have diffusion flow of the components 1 and 2, J_1 and J_2, and flow of heat, J_3*. Excluding the action of external forces, we can define

---

* There remains a certain arbitrariness in defining the flow components. The "forces", however, which need not be of the form [12.6] or [12.7], follow in every case from the "energy dissipation" [12.10], cf. Meixner (120), Prigogine (132), Haase (83a, 83b).

driving forces X_1, X_2, and X_3 which cause the above currents. The driving forces for diffusion are, in accordance with former definitions, cf. p. 156,

$$X_i = -T \operatorname{grad} \frac{\mu_i}{T}, \quad i = 1, 2, \qquad [12.6]$$

while the driving force for the flux of heat must be defined by

$$X_3 = -\frac{1}{T} \operatorname{grad} T. \qquad [12.7]$$

Now we can write the set of phenomenological equations

$$J_i = \sum_k \alpha_{ik} X_k \qquad \begin{array}{l} i = 1, 2, 3 \\ k = 1, 2, 3 \end{array} \qquad [12.8]$$

with the reciprocity relations

$$\alpha_{ik} = \alpha_{ki}. \qquad [12.9]$$

The α_{ik} are generally not identical with the ordinary coefficients of diffusion, heat conduction etc., but may be expressed by these, cf. de Groot (4) and Meixner (119, 120). The eqs. [12.8] are valid not only for the special case, treated above, but for any system of irreversible processes, provided the driving forces are properly defined. It is easily seen that in [12.8] not all the α_{ik} are of the same dimensions, but that every symmetrical pair of coefficients α_{ik} and α_{ki} are of equal dimensions. The X_i must be chosen in such a way that the products $J_i X_i$ have the dimensions [energy]/[length]^3 × [time]. Therefore the sum

$$\sum_i J_i X_i = T\theta \qquad [12.10]$$

is of the same dimension, and the function θ, thus defined, plays an important physical role as rate of production of entropy per cm.^{3} per sec.

In the special case, J_1 and J_2 diffusion flow of components 1 and 2, and J_3 heat flow, eqs. [12.8] lead to the prediction, that if there exist non-vanishing terms in diffusion, due to the presence of a temperature gradient, then there also must exist corresponding terms in the expression for the flow of heat, causing a transport of heat due to a concentration gradient. Therefore, if thermal diffusion does exist, as actually is the case, then a diffusion thermo-effect must exist, too, and the magnitude of this effect can be predicted quantitatively from that of the effect of thermal diffusion. The diffusion thermo-effect for free diffusion was first observed by Clusius and Waldmann (44)*. A thorough theoretical and experimental investigation is due to Waldmann (154, 156, 159, 161, 162). A discussion from the point of

* The prior observation of Dufour (51) had been overlooked.

view of the general theory of irreversible processes has been given by Meixner (120), (cf. also the discussion of this effect by de Groot (4)). In the section on thermal diffusion in gases we shall give a short review of the observations. They are of importance in so far as they permit an independent and comparativey simple determination of the thermal diffusion constant, and, at the same time, of the ordinary diffusion coefficient.

II. Thermal Diffusion in Gases

As we have seen in the preceding section it cannot, generally, be assumed that a binary gas mixture of uniform relative concentration remains in equilibrium when brought into a temperature gradient. In a phenomenological theory of diffusion in a temperature gradient, therefore one would have to consider a coupling between flow of heat and flow of matter, according to the most simple linear scheme

$$
\begin{aligned}
J_1 &= \alpha_{11} X_1 + \alpha_{12} X_2 + \alpha_{13} X_3 \\
J_2 &= \alpha_{21} X_1 + \alpha_{22} X_2 + \alpha_{23} X_3 \\
J_3 &= \alpha_{31} X_1 + \alpha_{32} X_2 + \alpha_{33} X_3
\end{aligned}
\qquad [12.11]
$$

where $J_1 = -J_2$ are the diffusion currents, J_3 is the heat current. X_1, X_2, X_3 are the driving forces, as defined above, p. 491. Because $J_1 = -J_2$ we have

$$
\alpha_{11} = -\alpha_{21}, \qquad \alpha_{12} = -\alpha_{22}, \qquad \alpha_{13} = -\alpha_{23}.
$$

Onsager's reciprocity relations give the additional equations

$$
\alpha_{12} = \alpha_{21}, \qquad \alpha_{13} = \alpha_{31}, \qquad \alpha_{23} = \alpha_{32}. \qquad [12.12]
$$

We, therefore, have only three independent coefficients and can write instead of [12.11]

$$
\begin{aligned}
J_1 &= -J_2 = \alpha_{11}(X_1 - X_2) + \alpha_{13} X_3 \\
J_3 &= \alpha_{13}(X_1 - X_2) + \alpha_{33} X_3.
\end{aligned}
$$

For the relation between these phenomenological coefficients with the coefficients of ordinary diffusion, heat conduction, thermal diffusion and diffusion thermo-effect cf., for instance, R. Haase (83, 83a, 83b). Thermal diffusion and diffusion thermo-effect give rise to only one additional coefficient*.

* The relations between phenomenological coefficients and conventional coefficients for ordinary diffusion, D_{12}, thermal diffusion, D_T, thermal conductivity, λ, and coefficient of diffusion thermo-effect, α', depend on the original definitions of the flow components (cf. p. 490). Independent of this is the relation between D_T and α', for any fluid mixture (Haase (83, 83a)). Pressure diffusion and heat flow induced by a pressure gradient may be described by the coefficients D_{12} and D_T (Haase (83a)).

The kinetic theory of gases in its rigorous form, due to Enskog (2, 57) and Chapman (25, 28), allows of a theoretical calculation of this coefficient.

So far, we have written the diffusion equation for a binary mixture of constituents 1 and 2

$$J_1 = -D_{12} \frac{\partial c_1}{\partial x} \qquad J_2 = -D_{12} \frac{\partial c_2}{\partial x} \qquad [12.13]$$

or

$$\boldsymbol{J}_1 = -D_{12} \operatorname{grad} c_1, \quad \boldsymbol{J}_2 = -D_{12} \operatorname{grad} c_2 \qquad [12.14]$$

where D_{12} is the coefficient of interdiffusion, and c_1 and c_2 are the concentrations of the components 1 and 2 respectively. It is readily seen that it would not be rational to retain [12.13] and [12.14] if the temperature is not uniform. We, therefore, replace the molar concentrations by the mol fractions

$$N_1 = \frac{c_1}{c_1 + c_2} \quad N_2 = \frac{c_2}{c_1 + c_2} \qquad [12.15]$$

and define the diffusion currents independently of an arbitrary surface of reference by

$$J_1 = c_1 (v_1 - v) \qquad \boldsymbol{J}_1 = c_1 (\boldsymbol{v}_1 - \boldsymbol{v}) \qquad [12.16]$$

where v_1 (in the one-dimensional case) or $\boldsymbol{v}_1$ (as vector in three dimensions) is the average velocity of species 1, $v_2 (\boldsymbol{v}_2)$ accordingly that of 2, and $v(\boldsymbol{v})$ is the convection velocity of the gas as a whole

$$v = N_1 v_1 + N_2 v_2, \quad \text{or} \quad \boldsymbol{v} = N_1 \boldsymbol{v}_1 + N_2 \boldsymbol{v}_2 . \qquad [12.17]$$

From [12.13] with [12.15] and [12.16] we have

$$c_1 (v_1 - v) = -D_{12} (c_1 + c_2) \frac{\partial N_1}{\partial x} \qquad [12.18]$$

considering that for T const., $c_1 + c_2$ is constant*. Or, for the one-dimensional case, with [12.17]

$$v_1 - v_2 = \frac{v_1 - v}{N_2} = -\frac{D_{12}}{N_1 N_2} \frac{\partial N_1}{\partial x} \qquad [12.19]$$

and for the general case, in vector notation

$$\boldsymbol{v}_1 - \boldsymbol{v}_2 = -\frac{D_{12}}{N_1 N_2} \operatorname{grad} N_1 . \qquad [12.20]$$

For the isothermal case [12.19] and [12.20] are identical with [12.13] and [12.14], respectively*. By starting from [12.19] and [12.20] for the non-isothermal case we define the ordinary diffusion current in such a way as to vanish with vanishing gradient of relative concentrations. We write, in accordance with Chapman and Cowling (1)**,

* This holds for ideal gases only. We may also define D_{12} by eq. [12.18] instead of [12.13].

** Changing, however, the sign of the last term in the following equations.

for the non-isothermal case

$$v_1 - v_2 = \frac{v_1 - v}{N_2} = -\frac{1}{N_1 N_2}\left\{D_{12}\frac{\partial N_1}{\partial x} - \frac{D_T}{T}\frac{\partial T}{\partial x}\right\} \qquad [12.21]$$

or

$$v_1 - v_2 = -\frac{1}{N_1 N_2}\left\{D_{12}\,\mathrm{grad}\,N_1 - \frac{D_T}{T}\,\mathrm{grad}\,T\right\} \qquad [12.22]$$

where D_T is the coefficient of thermal diffusion. Instead of [12.21] we also may write

$$v_1 - v_2 = -\frac{1}{N_1 N_2}\,D_{12}\left\{\frac{\partial N_1}{\partial x} - \frac{k_T}{T}\frac{\partial T}{\partial x}\right\} \qquad [12.23]$$

or

$$v_1 - v_2 = -\frac{1}{N_1 N_2}\,D_{12}\left\{\frac{\partial N_1}{\partial x} - \frac{\alpha N_1 N_2}{T}\frac{\partial T}{\partial x}\right\} \qquad [12.24]$$

where k_T is the thermal-diffusion ratio

$$k_T = D_T/D_{12} \qquad [12.25]$$

and

$$\alpha = k_T/N_1 N_2 . \qquad [12.26]$$

α is called the thermal-diffusion constant. α is not actually a constant, but in the case of isotopes the deviations from constancy may be neglected to a first approximation, while k_T and D_T generally vanish for $N_1 = 0$ and $N_2 = 0$.

In case of non-vanishing thermal diffusion coefficient, for a binary gas mixture in a temperature gradient a steady state of non-uniform relative concentrations is obtained.

In the steady state convection current and transport must vanish, therefore

$$\mathrm{grad}\,N_1 = \alpha N_1 N_2\,\mathrm{grad}\,\log T . \qquad [12.27]$$

If the temperature dependence of α can be neglected, this gives upon integration

$$\log N_1 - \log(1 - N_1) = \alpha \log T + \mathrm{const.}, \quad \text{or} \quad N_1/N_2 = \mathrm{const}\,T^\alpha$$

since

$$N_1 + N_2 = 1 . \qquad [12.28]$$

Considering two points I and II at temperatures T_I and T_II we may define a separation factor q by

$$q = \frac{(N_1/N_2)_\mathrm{II}}{(N_1/N_2)_\mathrm{I}} \qquad [12.29]$$

in analogy to the corresponding factors in other separation processes. From [12.28] we obtain for q

$$q = (T_\mathrm{II}/T_\mathrm{I})^\alpha = \exp[\alpha \log(T_\mathrm{II}/T_\mathrm{I})] \qquad [12.30]$$

or to a sufficient approximation, if $\Delta T = T_\mathrm{II} - T_\mathrm{I}$ is sufficiently small compared with T_I

$$q \approx 1 + \alpha \log(T_\mathrm{II}/T_\mathrm{I}) \approx 1 + \alpha\,\Delta T/T . \qquad [12.31]$$

From the values for α, listed below (p. 497ff.), it is seen that for a single stage separation factors thus obtained are very small.

Elementary arguments, based upon the concept of free path, are inadequate for a calculation of the thermal diffusion coefficient. The exact theory shows that the effect is highly dependent on the law of force acting between the molecules of the gas, vanishing for a Maxwellian gas, i.e., molecules repelling each other by a force proportional to the inverse fifth power of the distance. It is obvious that an elementary theory cannot take into account such influences though attempts have been made to explain certain features of thermal diffusion on an elementary basis (Gillespie (65), Fürth (62)). Recently Whalley and Winter (169a) made considerable progress in an elementary treatment of thermal diffusion, especially in multicomponent mixtures. It seems remarkable, however, that a dimensional argument leads to correct conclusions for molecules repelling one another by a force proportional to an inverse power of the mutual distance, Frankel (60). Thermal diffusion causes a gradient in relative concentrations in the direction of the temperature-gradient or opposite to it. If we consider the molecules of the lighter constituent, referred to as 1, there must be a force acting upon these molecules which prevents them from diffusing back in the direction of normal diffusion. This force must result from collisions between the lighter molecules, 1, and the heavier ones, 2. The transfer of momentum, corresponding to this force, should be proportional to

$$\overline{(\boldsymbol{p}_2 - \boldsymbol{p}_1)\, v\, \sigma^2} \qquad [12.32]$$

where $\boldsymbol{p}_1$ and $\boldsymbol{p}_2$ are the momenta of molecules 1 and 2 before collision, v is the relative velocity of the colliding molecules, σ^2 is an effective collision cross section, and the bar indicates averaging over all values of the relative velocity, by means of the actual distribution function of velocities. We assume an inverse power law for the force of interaction

$$\varkappa_{12}\, r^{-\nu} \qquad [12.33]$$

where r is the mutual distance, ν the exponent for the repulsive force, and $\varkappa_{12}$ has the dimensions $[\text{mass}] \times [\text{length}]^{\nu+1} \times [\text{time}]^{-2}$. The effective cross section should be determined by the values of v, $\varkappa_{12}$ and the reduced mass μ. An expression of the dimension of a cross section is obtained from the above magnitudes of the form

$$\sigma^2 \sim [\varkappa_{12}/v^2\, \mu]^{2/(\nu-1)}. \qquad [12.34]$$

With this expression for the cross section, we obtain from [12.32] for the transfer of momentum

$$\overline{(\boldsymbol{p}_2 - \boldsymbol{p}_1)\, v^{(\nu-5)/(\nu-1)}}. \qquad [12.35]$$

Consequently; for $\nu = 5$, the transfer of momentum is proportional to the difference of the average momenta of molecules. 1 and 2. Since we are considering a state of equilibrium, these average momenta, proportional to the average velocities, are zero. Therefore, for $\nu = 5$, transfer of momentum and thermal diffusion must vanish. This is in accordance with the result of the exact theory, which, for Maxwellian molecules, i.e., molecules repelling each other by a force proportional to the inverse fifth power of the distance, leads to vanishing thermal diffusion.

It follows that for $\nu = 5$ the coefficient of thermal diffusion must change its sign. It is seen from [12.35] that for $\nu > 5$ the contribution of collisions with high relative velocity is most important while for $\nu < 5$ the opposite is true. On the average the molecules coming from higher temperatures have higher velocities than those coming from lower temperatures, and this difference is more pronounced for the lighter molecules. Thus the collisions with the highest relative velocity are chiefly those in which the lighter molecules are coming from higher temperatures, and vice versa. Consequently, for $\nu > 5$, the average transfer of momentum from molecules 2 to molecules 1 is directed towards the warmer part of the gas, while for $\nu < 5$ the opposite is true. This means that for $\nu > 5$ the thermal diffusion constant α is positive*, the relative concentration of heavier molecules 2 increasing towards lower temperatures, while for $\nu < 5$ the thermal diffusion constant is negative, the relative concentration of the lighter molecules increasing towards the region of lower temperatures.

Due to Onsager's reciprocity relations (127, 128) this dimensional argument also leads to the correct prediction of the sign of the diffusion thermo-effect (155).

Thermal diffusion constants are rather small. Thus Nier (124, 125) found for the neon isotopes Ne^{20} and Ne^{22} α-values of 0.0165, 0.0188 and 0.0302 respectively, for the temperature intervals $-183°$ to $-78°$, $-183°$ to $+21°$ and $+10°$ to $+344°C$. respectively. For $H_2 - D_2$ mixtures Ibbs and co-workers (98) and Grew (67) found $\alpha = 0.1728$. Consequently, separations, to be expected by thermal diffusion in a single stage, are rather small, and with the exception of a few instances where in non-isothermal systems disturbances due to thermal diffusion had been observed, this effect was considered as of theoretical interest only. In 1938, however, Clusius and Dickel (36) reported experiments, in which thermal diffusion had been used for an efficient separation of gas mixtures, which amounted to a multistage operation

---

* If we adopt the convention of labelling the lighter molecules as 1. Cf. eq. [12.27]

TABLE I

Thermal Diffusion in Gases*

1. Mixtures of Isotopes

a) Measurements of Stier (144)

Mixture (C Sutherland's constant)	T_1 °K.	T_2 °K.	T_r °K	$\alpha \pm 5\%$	$R_T \pm 5\%$	$R_T(n)$	$R_T(c)$	R_T(L.—J.)	R_T(H.)
Ne²⁰-Ne²² C = 60°	195	90	129	0.0162	0.39		0.38	0.36	
	490	195	298	0.0254	0.60		0.76	0.66	0.62
	819	621	712	0.0346	0.82		0.85	0.73	
A³⁶-A⁴⁰ C = 142°	195	90	129	0.00315	0.07			−0.44	
	495	195	300	0.0146	0.31	0.34	0.38	0.17	
	685	455	555	0.0218	0.47	0.47	0.60	0.47	0.55

* α and R_T are measured values, T_1 and T_2 the temperatures of the two bulbs, T_r the reduced temperature after the formula of Brown (19)

$$T_r = \frac{T_1 - T_2}{T_1 T_2} \log \frac{T_1}{T_2}$$

R_T (n) was calculated from viscosity data ($\eta \sim T^n$) according to the formula (101, 102),

$$R_T \cong 1.7 \, (1 - n),$$

and R_T (c) according to Sutherland's relation (101, 102)

$$R_T \cong \frac{1 - 0.98 \, C/T}{1 + 0.92 \, C/T}$$

R_T (L.—J.) was calculated by Jones (101, 102), using the 9 : 5-Lennard-Jones model, R_T (H.) by Hirschfelder, Bird and Spotz (94), using the 12 : 6-Lennard-Jones model, and R_T (W.) by Winter (171) using the same model.

TABLE I continued

b) Measurements of other authors

	Per cent of Lighter Constituent	T_r °K.	R_T	R_T(W.)	Observer
H_2-D_2	80.4	313	0.502	0.587	Murphy (123)
. . . .	80.4	118	0.445	0.463	Murphy (123)
$^{12}CH_4$-$^{13}CH_4$	98.9	450	0.297	—	Nier (125)
$^{12}CH_4$-$^{13}CH_4$	98.9	430	—	0.445	„ Nier (125)
$^{12}CH_4$-$^{13}CH_4$	98.9	405	0.274	—	Nier (125)
$^{32}O_2$-$^{34}O_2$	97.5	284	0.367	0.375	Whalley and Winter (168)
$^{32}O_2$-$^{34}O_2$	97.5	386	0.475	0.475	Whalley and Winter (168)
$^{32}O_2$-$^{34}O_2$	97.5	443	0.538	0.504	Whalley and Winter (168)

2. R_T for Mixtures of Rare Gases after Atkins, Bastick and Ibbs (10)

	$T_1 = 373°K.,$ Ne	$T_2 = 273°K.,$ A	$T_r = 314°K.$ Kr	Xe
He	0.80	0.65	0.63	0.59
Ne		0.54	0.51	0.43
A			0.19	0.17
Kr				0.08

TABLE I continued

3. Other Gas Mixtures

a) Dependence on Concentration after van Itterbeek, van Paemel and van Lierde (99)

Mixture	T_1 °K.	T_2 °K.	Molar Fraction of Hydrogen	α	Observer
Hydrogen-Oxygen . .	293.6	90.2	0.338	0.15	T. L. Ibbs, K. E. Grew
			0.482	0.19	and A. A. Hirst (98)
			0.846	0.24	
Hydrogen-Helium . .	291.7	90.2	0.323	0.13	
			0.505	0.16	
			0.818	0.14	

b) Dependence on Temperature

Mixture	Concentration	T_1 °K	T_2 °K	T °K.	α	Observer
Nitrogen-Argon	30.0% A	290.5	273		0.070	T. L. Ibbs, K. E. Grew
			173		0.0360	and A. A. Hirst (98)
			93		0.0076	
Oxygen-Argon				89	— 0.037	L. Waldmann (163)*
				194	0.026	,,
				293	0.050	,,
Argon-Carbondioxide . . .				194	0.026	,,
				293	0.019	,,
				372	0.014	,,
Ethylene-Oxygen				194	— 0.013	,,
				293	— 0.005	,,
				372	0.001	,,

* The values given by Waldmann are derived from measurements of the diffusion-thermoeffect, α being related to a definite temperature T without difficulty and being regarded as independent of concentration.

32*

TABLE I continued

Mixture			T, °K.			Drickamer, Downey and Pierce (50)
Hydrogen-Methane	equimolecular	537	372	445	0.292	(0.30)
"	"	474	299	353	0.261	0.40
"	"	299	189	236	0.212	0.44
Hydrogen-Ethylene	"	532	372	443	0.299	(0,31)
"	"	364	194	262	0.250	0.58
"	"	301	191	239	0.239	0.81
Hydrogen-Propylene	"	530	372	442	0.321	0.60
"	"	417	295	349	0.279	0.59
"	"	376	232	293	0.284	0.59
Hydrogen-Propane	"	531	372	442	0.323	0.62
"	"	524	294	387	0.318	
"	"	375	231	292	0.291	

c) Dependence on Pressure after Becker and Schulzeff und Haase*

$$T_1 = 435°K., \quad T_2 = 293°K.$$

Mixture	Molar Fraction of 1st Gas	Pressure (atm)	α (exp.)	α (theor.)
Hydrogen-Nitrogen	0.5	0 (extrap.)	0.35	(0.30)
		50	0.39	0.40
		80	0.44	0.44
Hydrogen-Carbondioxide.......	0.48	0 (extrap.)	0.31	(0,31)
		50	0.67	0.58
		80	0.98	0.81
	0.25	50	0.68	0.60
	0.40	50	0.61	0.59
	0.65	50	0.56	0.59
	0.75	50	0.57	0.62

* The experimental values were measured by Becker and Schulzeff (16), the theoretical values were calculated by Haase (83, 83 b) by means of the thermodynamical theory of irreversible processes, using the equation of state of Beattie and Bridgeman, and taking account of the thermodynamical corrections only.

of thermal diffusion, analogous to the operation of a fractionating column in distillation.

The experimental determination of the thermal-diffusion ratio is comparatively easy. Chapman and Dootson (29), in their earliest experiments which led to the experimental confirmation of the theoretically predicted effect, used two glass bulbs of 100 c.c. each, connected by a stopcock of wide bore. One bulb could be heated up to 230°C. while the temperature of the other one was kept constant at 10°C. The content of the bulbs was analyzed after an experiment. Concentration differences could be detected within a few hours, the heavier component of the systems H_2–CO_2 and H_2–SO_2 migrating toward he cooler end. Elliot and Masson (56) and Lugg (113) used a similar method. Ibbs (97) considerably improved the sensitivity of the measurements by employing the determination of thermal conductivity for analysis.

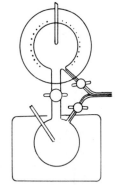

O. and G. Blüh (17) carried out measurements of thermal diffusion using a gas interferometer. For results at elevated pressures and their interpretation, cf. E. W. Becker (15, 16a), R. Haase (83, 83 b), Waldmann (163). In Fig. 12-1 we show the experimental arrangement used by Drickamer (50).

Fig. 12-1. Experimental arrangement for measuring thermal diffusion ratios, after Drickamer, 1949.

III. The Clusius separation tube

The interest in thermal diffusion greatly increased when Clusius and Dickel (36, 38) discovered that by an appropriate combination of convection and thermal diffusion a tremendous improvement in separation is possible.

The apparatus used by Clusius and Dickel consisted of a vertical glass tube with an electrically heated wire along its axis, Fig. 12-2. The temperature gradient between heated wire and cooled wall causes the light molecules to diffuse toward the wire. Near the wire there is an upward flow of the heated gas while near the wall the gas flows downward. Thus, due to the combined effect of diffusion flow and convection flow the lighter molecules are carried inward and upward, the heavier ones, conversely, outward and downward. The influence of convection in this case, therefore, is not to cause mixing, but on the opposite, to help in the establishment of a vertical concentration gradient. Clusius and Dickel were able to achieve separations equivalent to the operation of between 10^2 and 10^3 single stages with a separation factor due to thermal diffusion.

Before going into detail we mention some instructive experiments, reported by Clusius and Dickel, which demonstrate the effectiveness of the separation tube.

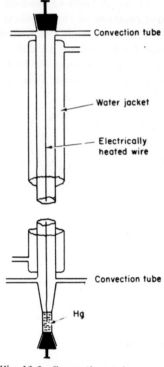

Fig. 12-2. Separation tube, as used by Clusius and Dickel for the separation of the chlorine isotopes.

1. A mixture of equal parts of xenon and hydrogen at a total pressure of 400 mm. Hg was kept in a vertical tube of 65 cm. length and 1.4 cm. inner diameter. Along the axis of the tube a nichrome wire of 0.2 mm. diameter was extended which was heated to a weak red glow by an electric current of ∼1.6 amp. Demixing was accomplished within about two minutes, made visible by the brighter glow of the wire in the lower part of the tube, due to the poor heat conduction of the xenon. The upper end of the wire, in the hydrogen gas of high thermal conductivity, became completely dark. Between both regions there was a transition zone of only 3 to 4 cm. length.

2. A mixture consisting of 3 parts of helium and 1 part of gaseous bromine was filled into a tube of 70 cm. length and 1.5 cm. diameter, with a platinum wire of 0.4 mm. diameter along its axis. The wire was heated by a current of 1.5 amp. to approximately 300°C. A few seconds of heating were sufficient to cause a visible difference in color at the top and bottom ends of the tube. After about one minute bromine began condensing at the lower end, after 10 minutes demixing was completed, bromine being no longer visible at the top end of the tube.

The Clusius tube proved most successful in the separation of isotopes, as will be discussed below. In special experiments the authors investigated the conditions on which the efficiency of the tube depends. Using dried air as test mixture, Clusius and Dickel found the rate of transport of oxygen toward the lower end of the tube to be proportional to $p^2 r^4$, where p is the gas pressure, and r the radius of the tube. The sharpness of separation, on the other hand, was found to be inversely proportional to the fourth power of the radius, at least within a certain range of variation, and inversely proportional to the square of the pressure.

In Fig. 12-2 details of one separation unit are given, as used by
Clusius and Dickel in the separation of the chlorine isotopes. The
tube was of an inner diameter of 8.4 mm., the central heating wire
of platinum was of 0.4 mm. diameter. Platinum discs of 0.2 mm.
thickness were soldered with gold to the platinum wire, at distances
of 60 cm., in order to keep the wire centred. Clusius and Dickel used
a number of such tubes, of lengths from 6 to 8 m., and in addition

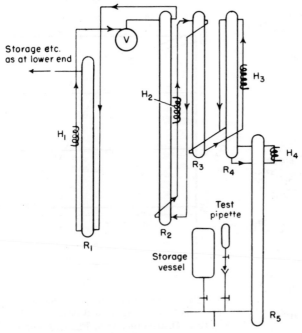

Fig. 12-3. Scheme of group of 5 separation tubes, used for the isolation of HCl³⁷
(Clusius and Dickel).

a tube of 12.8 mm. diameter and 9 m. length. A complete set up,
making use of altogether 5 separating tubes, is shown in Fig. 12-3.
This set up was used for the isolation of HCl³⁷. An 18 l. storage vessel was connected on the one hand to the lower end of the 7 m.
tube R_1, on the other hand to the upper end of the 9 m. tube R_2.
This tube worked in series with the two 6 m. tubes R_3 und R_4 and
with the 8 m. tube R_5. As in all experiments, connections were effected
by circulating systems, one link being heated (H_1, H_2, H_3, H_4).
Samples for analysis could be withdrawn at the lower end of R_5, by
means of an evacuated pipette, and enriched HCl³⁷ was collected in
an evacuated container. Fig. 12-4 shows the apparatus of Fig. 12-3

schematically, giving at the same time the percentage composition of the gas in various parts of the tubes. At the lower end the composition reaches 99.4 per cent of HCl^{37}.

In this experiment the lower part of the apparatus was filled with HCl^{37} which had been concentrated in a former run. After running the apparatus for 17 days, in order to establish a steady state HCl^{37}

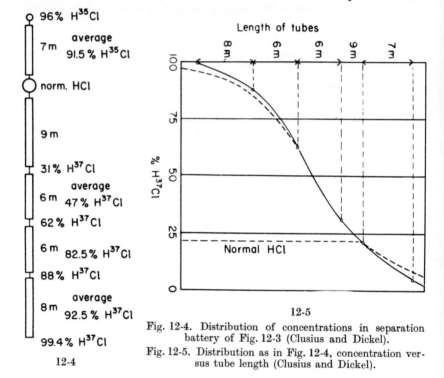

Fig. 12-4. Distribution of concentrations in separation battery of Fig. 12-3 (Clusius and Dickel).

Fig. 12-5. Distribution as in Fig. 12-4, concentration versus tube length (Clusius and Dickel).

was withdrawn at the rate of 8 c.c. per day. Chemical analysis gave 99.4 per cent of the heavy component.

The distribution of concentrations along the tube is shown in Fig. 12-5 and corresponds closely to theoretical expectations for the stationary state.

Clusius and Dickel define as an ideal separation unit the length Δl of the tube, over which, in the cold gas at the wall, the concentration change $N_h - N_c$ is equal to that for ideal separation by thermal diffusion between wall and wire, Fig. 12-6. In their experiments the length of an ideal separation unit was of the order of magnitude of 3 cm. This length is the equivalent to the HETP, height equivalent to a theoretical plate, in distillation. Thus in the separation of the chlorine isotopes, with an effective tube length of up to 36 m., up to 1200 ideal separating units have been used.

The approach to equilibrium with time is shown in Fig. 12-7, again with air as test mixture. The full curves and dashed extensions have been calculated theoretically for a parabolic law, t proportional to $(N - N_0)^2$.

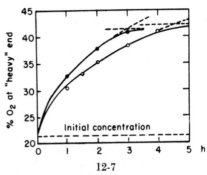

12-7

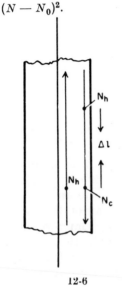

12-6

Fig. 12-6. Definition of ideal separation unit, after Clusius and Dickel. Δl height corresponding to concentration change from N_c to N_h.

Fig. 12-7. Rate of establishment of separation in tube, dry air as test mixture. Oxygen concentration at "heavy" end of the tube (length 93 cm.) as function of time. Wire temperature 670°C.; ● 0,42. ○ 0.34 cm. radius of tube. Square of concentration changes proportional with time (Clusius, Dickel).

Jensen and Waldmann (100) define another characteristic length l of the tube, at the ends of which the relative ratio of the concentrations has been changed by a factor e.

Clusius and Dickel determined this length l in the separation of krypton isotopes Kr^{84} and Kr^{86} (42). A theoretical calculation of l is possible only if α is known. For the krypton isotopes Kr^{84} and Kr^{86} Clusius and Dickel found l equal to 288 cm., giving $\alpha = 3.4 \times 10^{-3}$. Taking into account deviations from the ideal efficiency of the separating tube, the authors consider a value of 4.7×10^{-3} as most probable.

If equilibrium is obtained during separation, the characteristic length l must be found to be constant over the whole length of the tube. If, however, in parts of the tube equilibrium has not yet been established, l for these parts will be found to be longer than the equilibrium value, the longer the greater the distance to equilibrium in the part under consideration. Thus in the concentration of the krypton isotopes the following values were observed

Tube...............	6 m. tube	6 m. tube	7 m. tube	
concentration of Kr^{86}	0.965	0.775	0.365	0.100
l	288 cm.	310 cm.	468 cm.	

It is seen that the distance to equilibrium is the greater the closer one comes to the light-isotope end of the tube. Thus a curious discrepancy is removed which had been encountered in the discussion of the separation of the chlorine isotopes. It had been found that the efficiency of separation for small concentrations of an isotope (<0.1) was considerably higher than for medium concentrations (~ 0.5). Due to the special arrangement chosen, the process of demixing had been proceding from the ends towards the middle. Thus just one of the intermediate tubes, chosen as standard, had not yet reached equilibrium, suggesting a too low efficiency of this tube. The data corresponding to the above are

Tube..........	8 m.	6 m.	6 m.	9 m.	7 m.
concentration of HCl^{37}	0.994 0.88	0.62	0.31	0.243	0.04
l	256 cm. 398 cm.	462 cm.		343 cm.	

Thus a discrepancy between theory and experiment, as originally assumed, does not exist. The influence of the discs is not related at all to this effect. They chiefly serve to centre the wire and thus to stabilize laminar flow in the sections between each pair of discs.

The lay out of a separation tube was improved in later work by Clusius and Dickel (43). They built separating tubes, each of 13.7 m. length, without a cooling jacket, cooling being effected by four water jets surrounding the upper end of the tube. The separation tube permits a concentration of the heavy molecule $O^{18}O^{18}$ though in normal oxygen there are practically only molecules $O^{16}O^{18}$. But since the heated wire helps to establish the equilibrium of the reaction

$$2\,O^{16}O^{18} = O_2^{16} + O_2^{18},$$

a concentration of O_2^{18} occurs. There is, however, a disturbing influence of the intermediate isotope O^{17}, though this is present in only about 20 per cent of the amount of O^{18}. Since, due to the smaller mass difference, the transport of $O^{16}O^{17}$ is only one half that of $O^{16}O^{18}$, the heavy isotope separated in the beginning was almost pure O_2^{18}, while in the steady state afterwards O_2^{18} contained about 5 to 10 per cent of $O^{17}O^{18}$. This could be concentrated in a further system to about 99.5 per cent of O_2^{18}. It took about 4 months to establish optimum concentration of O_2^{18} at the "heavy" end of the main separating system. The complete run took about 18 months.

IV. The theory of the separation tube

We shall treat the elementary theory of the separation tube, because it is interesting and valuable in itself, and because it is an example of a successful attack of a more complicated diffusion problem. In this section we shall follow the report of Jones and Furry (6), see also Fleischmann and Jensen (3) and de Groot (4).

We shall start from eqs. [12.19] and [12.24] of p. 493/4

$$N_1 (v_1 - v) = - D \left\{ \frac{\partial N_1}{\partial z} - \frac{\alpha N_1 N_2}{T} \frac{\partial T}{\partial z} \right\} \qquad [12.36]$$

and aim first at an estimate of the time necessary for establishment of equilibrium in a separation tube. With such approximations as are usual and justified in chemical kinetics, we may proceed as follows, in order to obtain the rate of establishment of equilibrium*. We consider a tube of length L, in the direction of the z-coordinate, the ends of which are connected with two reservoirs at T_{II} and T_I. We assume the temperature gradient to be uniform over the length of the tube: $\frac{\partial T}{\partial z} = \frac{\Delta T}{L}$. Since we have no convection current, $v = 0$, and since concentration changes in a single stage operation are small, we may replace $N_1 N_2$ by its average, thus obtaining from [12.36]

$$N_1 v_1 = D \frac{\Delta T}{L} \left\{ \frac{\alpha \overline{N_1 N_2}}{T} - \frac{d N_1}{d T} \right\}. \qquad [12.37]$$

In writing this equation we have made use of the relation $\frac{dN}{dz} = \frac{dN}{dT} \times$

$\times \frac{dT}{dz} = \frac{dN}{dT} \frac{\Delta T}{L}$. We must assume, in analogy to problems of reaction kinetics, that we have a quasi-stationary state. This means that we consider the upward flow of component 1, $(\rho N_1 v_1)$, as independent of z, where $\rho = $ density. We, therefore, neglect the flow, necessary to bring about concentration changes within the tube, in comparison with the flow required to change the concentration in the reservoirs. From [12.37], on multiplication by ρ we obtain

$$\rho N_1 v_1 = \frac{\rho D}{T} \frac{\Delta T}{L} \left\{ \alpha \overline{N_1 N_2} - T \frac{d N_1}{d T} \right\}. \qquad [12.38]$$

Now, since $\rho N_1 v_1$ is approximately constant, and since D varies approximately as T^2, and ρ as $1/T$, the expression $\frac{\rho D}{T}$ is constant to a sufficient degree of accuracy. Integrating [12.38] with these assumptions we have

$$\rho N_1 v_1 \approx \frac{\rho D}{T} \frac{\Delta T}{L} \left[\alpha \overline{N_1 N_2} - \frac{\Delta N_1}{\log (T_{II}/T_I)} \right] \qquad [12.39]$$

where $\Delta N_1 = (N_1)_{II} - (N_1)_I$, the subscript II referring to the upper, hotter reservoir, I correspondingly to the lower, colder reservoir.

* Actually the time necessary for the establishment of complete equilibrium would be infinite. We shall have to introduce, therefore, a time of relaxation, τ, required for the concentration difference to rise to $(1 - 1/e)$ of its equilibrium value.

If Q is the cross section of the tube, then the total current, carrying the lighter component 1 from the colder to the hotter reservoir, will be $Q \rho N_1 v_1^*$, and a corresponding expression is obtained for the flow of component 2 in the opposite direction. Let the masses of gas in the reservoirs at T_{II} and T_I be s_{II} and s_I, respectively, then we have for the change of concentration in the reservoirs

$$s_{II} \left(\frac{d N_1}{dt} \right)_{II} = \rho N_1 v_1 Q \quad s_I \left(\frac{d N_2}{dt} \right)_I = -s_I \left(\frac{d N_1}{dt} \right) = \rho N_1 v_1 Q, \quad [12.40]$$

and consequently

$$\frac{d \varDelta N_1}{dt} = \rho N_1 v_1 Q \left[\frac{1}{s_{II}} + \frac{1}{s_I} \right]. \tag{12.41}$$

On substituting [12.39] into [12.41], we obtain an equation of the form

$$\frac{d \varDelta N_1}{dt} = A - B \varDelta N_1 \tag{12.42}$$

which may be integrated to give

$$\varDelta N_1 = (\varDelta N_1)_\infty \left[1 - \exp \left(t/\tau \right) \right] \tag{12.43}$$

where the subscript ∞ refers to the equilibrium value attained for $t = \infty$, and where it has been assumed that $\varDelta N_1 = 0$ for $t = 0$. Thus we obtain a time of relaxation, τ, given by

$$\tau = \frac{L}{\rho D Q} \frac{s_{II} s_I}{s_{II} + s_I} \frac{T}{\varDelta T} \log \frac{T_{II}}{T_I}. \tag{12.44}$$

[12.44] is obtained by introducing the expressions for A and B in [12.42]. This time of relaxation is independent of the thermal diffusion constant, α, because it refers to the time for a certain relative separation.

As has been mentioned before, there is a certain analogy between the mode of operation of a separation tube and that of an ordinary fractionating column (and that of any counter-current separation process). The operation of a fractionating column may be described as follows. For the sake of simple comparison we choose a column without plates, either a packed column, or, for small dimensions, an empty tube or the annular space between two concentric tubes. In order to increase the separation above the value obtained in straight distillation, part (or in the limiting case, all), of the vapor, rising inside the column, must be condensed at the top end of the column and must be returned into the column as reflux. This reflux is streaming in a direction opposite to that of the rising vapor, and there is an exchange of matter between vapor and liquid, due to diffusion and turbulent mixing. This results in an enrichment of the more volatile component in the gas and vice versa. On a single plate of a plate-

* Provided that mass differences are sufficiently small.

column of ideal efficiency, the enrichment is such that the concentration ratios for the more and less volatile components 1 and 2, in vapor, v, and liquid, l, obey the equation

$$\frac{(N_1/N_2)_v}{(N_1/N_2)_l} = q \qquad [12.46]$$

where the separation factor q is that calculated for the vapor-liquid equilibrium. In the case of the above-described column with separation proceeding continuously in space, there exists (approximately) a certain height equivalent, l_0, over which the content of the vapor in the more volatile component increases by the same ratio q as it would over the height of one plate in a plate column of ideal efficiency and with complete reflux. The operation of a column is that of a scrubber, the reflux depriving the rising vapor of the less volatile component, in exchange for the more volatile one. In a column, operated with complete reflux, of length $L = n l_0$ an enrichment by a factor q^n is possible.

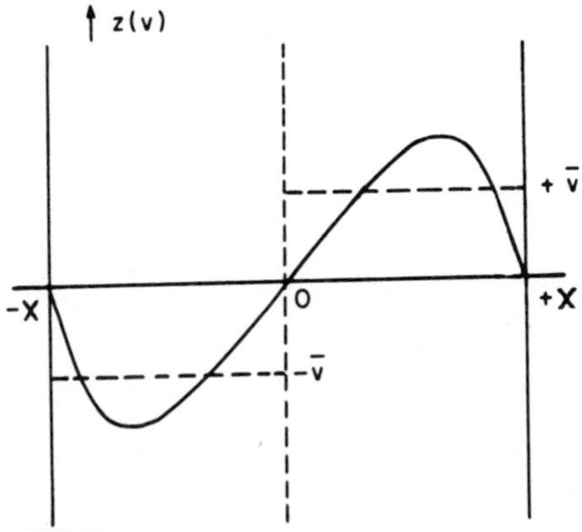

In the separating tube the hot gas, rising near the wire or the inner one of two concentric tubes, corresponds to the vapor in a fractionating column, while the gas, cooled near the wall and flowing downward, corresponds to the condensed reflux. The concentration ratio, valid for equilibrium in analogy to [12.46], is now determined by the separation factor for thermal diffusion.

Fig. 12-8. Separation between parallel plates (warmer one at the right, colder one at the left) of distance $2X$. True distribution of gas velocity (solid curve) and idealized distribution (dashed horizontal lines) after Jones and Furry.

For a quantitative formulation of these ideas it is natural to make use of the following simplifications. Instead of a circular space we consider a gas between parallel plates, the hot plate at temperature T_{II} at $x = X$, the cold one at temperature T_I at $x = -X$, if we choose the x-axis perpendicular to the plates, with origin in the middle between the plates, Fig. 12-8. Due to thermal convection there will arise a gas flow with velocities which are functions of x given by the solid line in Fig. 12-8. In accordance with our preceding considerations we shall replace this flow pattern by that of a discontinuous flow, corresponding to the dashed lines in Fig. 12—8. The gas in the cooler half is supposed to fall with a constant speed $-\bar{v}$, while in the hotter half it is rising with speed $+\bar{v}$. $\bar{v}$ has been so chosen that the total flow is that obtained with the correct velocity distribution, i.e., the area between the solid curve and the x axis is the same as that between the dashed line and x-axis, both for $x < 0$ and for $x > 0$.

In order to obtain a reasonable value for $\bar{v}$, we first must treat the hydrodynamic problem of the gas flow between parallel vertical plates, differing in temperature, thus obtaining the solid curve of Fig. 12-8. The force acting upon unit volume due to viscosity is

$$\eta \frac{d^2 v}{d x^2} \qquad [12.47]$$

where η is the viscosity of the gas, v its velocity, positive for upward flow in the direction of positive z. The gravitational force acting upon unit volume, is

$$(\rho - \bar{\rho}) g \qquad [12.48]$$

if ρ is the local density of the gas, $\bar{\rho}$ its average value, and g the gravitational acceleration. This force is directed toward negative values of z. In the steady state both forces must be equal in magnitude, therefore

$$\eta \frac{d^2 v}{d x^2} = (\rho - \bar{\rho}) g . \qquad [12.49]$$

Jones and Furry (64,6) use the following simplified expression for ρ as a function of x

$$\rho = \bar{\rho} \{1 - [T - \bar{T}]/T\} \qquad [12.50]$$

where $\bar{T}$ is the average temperature, and where, with sufficient accuracy (if the heat conductivity may be considered as constant),

$$T = \bar{T} + x \, \Delta T / 2 \, X . \qquad [12.51]$$

Substituting [12.50] and [12.51] into [12.49] we obtain as the final equation for the gas flow

$$\eta \frac{d^2 v}{d x^2} = -\bar{\rho} g \frac{x \Delta T}{2 X T}. \qquad [12.52]$$

which gives upon integration

$$v = \frac{\bar{\rho} g \Delta T}{12 \eta X T} \times (X^2 - x^2) . \qquad [12.53]$$

Here the boundary condition, $\bar{v} = 0$ for $x = \pm X$, has been assumed. From this equation the value of $\bar{v}$ for $0 < x < +X$ is obtained

$$\bar{v} = \frac{{}_0\!\int^X v \, d x}{X} = -\frac{-x\!\int^0 v \, d x}{X} = \frac{\bar{\rho} g X^2}{48 \eta} \frac{\Delta T}{\bar{T}} . \qquad [12.54]$$

The flow of the lighter component in the upward direction consists of three contributions. A first, positive contribution due to convection upward in the hotter part of the tube, a second, negative one due to the corresponding downward flow in the cooler part of the tube, and a third one due to ordinary diffusion. Hence we have, if by J we denote the net rate of flow

$$J = \rho (N_1^{II} - N_1^I) \, \bar{v} \, X \, Y - 2 \, X \, Y \, \rho \, D \frac{\partial N_1}{\partial z} . \qquad [12.55]$$

In this equation Y is the breadth of the column, $X Y$ the cross section of one half of it, N_1^{II} and N_1^I are the average concentrations of the lighter component 1 in the hot and in the cool part of the column, respectively, N_1 in the last term being the mean of these two values.

Again we must introduce the assumption of a quasi-stationary state. This means that we may treat $N_1^{II} - N_1^I$ as stationary, i.e., the sum of the terms (of different sign) responsible for a change in $N_1^{II} - N_1^I$ must be almost equal to zero. This concentration difference is changed first by convection in the direction of z and opposite to it. This causes a decrease of N_1^{II} by $\bar{v} \frac{\partial N_1}{\partial z}$ and an increase of N_1^I by $\bar{v} \frac{\partial N_1}{\partial z}$, hence the total change due to convection, is

$$[\partial (N_1^{II} - N_1^I) / \partial t]_{convect} = - 2 \, \bar{v} \, \frac{\partial N_1}{\partial z} . \qquad [12.56]$$

The change due to diffusion and thermal diffusion gives a transverse flow of the lighter component of $\rho \, N_1 \, v_{1x}$, where v_{1x} is the resulting velocity of the molecules 1 in the x-direction. This magnitude, on account of eq. [12.21], p. 494 is given by

$$\rho \, N_1 \, v_{1x} = \rho \, D \, \{\alpha \, N_1 \, N_2 \, \text{grad log} \, T - \text{grad} \, N_1\} . \qquad [12.57]$$

For the further treatment we must replace the x-components of grad log T and of grad N_1 by simple approximate expressions. Since the average distance between the hot and the cold gas streams is X, it is assumed that $\frac{\partial N_1}{\partial z} \approx \frac{N_1^{II} - N_1^I}{X}$, while for $\partial \log T / \partial x$ we must put $\Delta T / (2 \, X \, \bar{T})$, because the distance between the hot and the cold plates is $2X$. Substituting these values into [12.57] we obtain for the resulting current in the x-direction

$$\rho \, N_1 \, v_{1x} \approx \rho \, D \left\{ \alpha \, N_1 \, N_2 \, \frac{\Delta T}{2 \, X \, \bar{T}} - \frac{N_1^{II} - N_1^I}{X} \right\} . \qquad [12.58]$$

This is the flux of the lighter component in grams per unit area per second. Since the thickness of either half of the column is X, the rate of increase of $N_1^{II} \rho$ is $\rho \, N_1 \, v_{1x} / X$, the rate of decrease of $N_1^I \rho$ being the same*. The total rate of change of $N_1^{II} - N_1^I$ thus becomes

$$0 \approx \partial [N_1^{II} - N_1^I] / \partial t = \frac{2 \, N_1 \, v_{1x}}{X} - 2 \, \bar{v} \, \frac{\partial N_1}{\partial z} \qquad [12.59]$$

* Because the masses are almost equal.

and for the quasi-stationary state this must be zero to a sufficient degree of approximation. Substituting [12.58] into [12.59] we obtain

$$\frac{D}{X^2}\left\{\alpha\,N_1\,N_2\,\frac{\Delta T}{2\,T}-(N_1^{\mathrm{II}}-N_1^{\mathrm{I}})\right\}-\bar{v}\,\frac{\partial N_1}{\partial z}=0\,. \qquad [12.60]$$

From this equation the value for $N_1^{\mathrm{II}}-N_1^{\mathrm{I}}$ is obtained

$$N_1^{\mathrm{II}}-N_1^{\mathrm{I}}=\alpha\,N_1\,N_2\,\frac{\Delta T}{2\,T}-\frac{\bar{v}\,X^2}{D}\,\frac{\partial N_1}{\partial z} \qquad [12.61]$$

and by substituting this into eq. [12.55]

$$J_1=X\,Y\,\rho\,\bar{v}\,\frac{\alpha\,\Delta T}{2\,T}\,N_1\,N_2-\left\{X\,Y\,\rho\,\bar{v}\,\frac{\bar{v}\,X^2}{D}+2\,X\,Y\,\rho\,D\right\}(\partial N_1/\partial z). \quad [12.62]$$

With the value [12.54] for $\bar{v}$ we finally have

$$J_1=H\,N_1\,(1-N_1)-(K_c+K_d)\,\frac{\partial N_1}{\partial z} \qquad [12.63]$$

with the abbreviations introduced by Jones and Furry

$$H=\frac{\alpha\,\rho^2\,g\,X^3\,Y}{96\,\eta}\left(\frac{\Delta T}{T}\right)^2 \qquad [12.64]$$

$$K_c=\frac{\rho^3\,g^2\,X^7\,Y}{2304\,\eta^2\,D}\left(\frac{\Delta T}{T}\right)^2 \qquad [12.65]$$

$$K_d=2\,X\,Y\,\rho\,D\,. \qquad [12.66]$$

The first term in the transport eq. [12.63] is the contribution due to thermal diffusion, the second represents remixing due to convection, and the last remixing due to ordinary diffusion along the tube.

The quantities H, K_c and K_d, as derived here differ only by factors of order unity from the expressions obtained by a more accurate treatment of the plane case*. For this rigorous treatment and for that of the cylindrical case we refer to the original papers (63, 103).

With slight simplification [12.63] may be written

$$J_1=H\,N_1\,N_2-K\,\frac{dN_1}{dz} \qquad K=K_c+K_d\,. \qquad [12.67]$$

J_1 is the transport of molecules 1 up the tube, measured in grams per second. A completely analogous equation could be written for the transport of component 2 down the column, both quantities being practically equal in the case of isotopes. We, therefore, write, dropping the subscripts

$$J=H\,N\,(1-N)-K\,\frac{dN}{dz}\,. \qquad [12.68]$$

We shall derive the separation factor for a discontinuously operated tube. Discontinuous operation may be defined, following Jones and Furry, as an operation in which the total transport of gas through

---

* These values are: $H^0=16/15\,H$, $K_c^0=256/315\,K_c$, and $K_d^0=K_d$.

the tube is zero. We, therefore, obtain the equilibrium separation factor by equating [12.68] to zero

$$\frac{dN}{N(1-N)} = d\log\left[\frac{N}{1-N}\right] = \left[\frac{H}{K}\right]dz \qquad [12.69]$$

and on integration

$$\frac{N}{1-N} = \exp\left[\frac{H}{K}(z-z_0)\right]. \qquad [12.70]$$

This equation gives the separation factor q_e for the tube in equilibrium

$$q_e = \frac{[N/(1-N)]_{\mathrm{II}}}{[N/(1-N)]_{\mathrm{I}}} = \exp\left(\frac{H}{K}L\right) \qquad [12.71]$$

where L is the length of the tube, and the subscripts II and I refer to the upper and lower end of the tube, respectively, with temperatures T_{II} and T_{I}.

We shall now consider the rate of establishment of equilibrium for a tube closed at both ends (i.e., no reservoirs connected to the tube). Therefore N is a function of both z and t. The conservation of mass for either component is expressed by an equation

$$s\frac{\partial N}{\partial t} = -\frac{\partial J}{\partial z} \qquad [12.72]$$

where s is the mass of gas per unit length of the tube, and J the rate of flow, (eq. [12.67]). Eq. [12.72] states that an increase in mass of one component is due to the fact that more molecules of the species under consideration have entered a volume element than have left it. On substitution of [12.68] this becomes

$$s\frac{\partial N}{\partial t} = -H\,\partial[N(1-N)]/\partial z + K\,\partial^2 N/\partial z^2 . \qquad [12.73]$$

So far only the limiting case, $N \ll 1$, $1-N \approx 1$ has been treated. Eq. [12.73] must be solved for the boundary conditions

$$J = 0 \quad \text{at} \quad z = 0 \quad \text{and} \quad z = L \qquad [12.74]$$

and the initial conditions

$$J = H N_0 \quad \text{at} \quad t = 0 , \qquad [12.75]$$

N_0 being the initial concentration. The solution given by Bardeen (12, 13) is

$$N(z,t) = k\exp\left(\frac{H}{K}z\right) + \exp\left(\frac{H}{2K}z\right) \times$$

$$\times \sum_n b_n\left[\cos\left(\frac{n\pi z}{L}\right) + \left(\frac{HL}{2Kn\pi}\right)\sin\left(\frac{n\pi z}{L}\right)\right]\exp\left(-t/t_n\right)$$

$$n = 1, 2, \ldots\ldots \qquad [12.76]$$

The constants entering this equation are defined as follows

$$k = H L N_0 / (K [\exp (H L / K) - 1])$$

$$b_n = 4 N_0 (n^2 \pi^2 / [H L / 2 K]^3) \times$$

$$\times \left[1 - (- 1)^n \exp \left(- \frac{H L}{2 K} \right) \right] \Big/ [1 + n^2 \pi^2 / (H L / 2 K)^2]^2 \qquad [12.77]$$

$$t_n = 2 (2 s K / H^2) / (1 + 4 n^2 \pi^2 K^2 / H^2 L^2) .$$

From [12.76] an effective separation factor q at time t may be calculated $(q = N_{II} / N_I$, since $1 - N \approx 1)$

$$q = N_{II} / N_I = \exp \left(\frac{H L}{K} \right) \frac{1 + k^{-1} \sum_n b_n (-1)^n \exp \left(- \frac{H L}{2 K} - \frac{t}{t_n} \right)}{1 + k^{-1} \sum_n b_n \exp (- t / t_n)} . \qquad [12.78]$$

For $\frac{H L}{2 K}$ sufficiently small $(\leq \sim 2)$, t_1 is much greater than the remaining t_n's. Within this range the approach to equilibrium is approximately characterized by a time of relaxation

$$\tau \approx t_1 = \left(\frac{4 s K}{H^2} \right) \Big/ \left[1 + \frac{4 \pi^2}{H^2 L^2} \right] . \qquad [12.79]$$

The case $\frac{H L}{2 K} \ll 1$ has received a more detailed treatment for which we refer to original papers of Debye (45) and of Jones and Furry (6).

V. Review of theoretical relations

A theoretical treatment of the process of thermal diffusion would be beyond the scope of this book. For this we must refer to the original papers (Enskog (2, 57), Chapman (28)) and especially to the monograph of Chapman and Cowling (1), to a later paper of Chapman (30), and, for isotopes, to the report of Jones and Furry (6). Here we shall give a qualitative description, only, and reproduce some formulae for practical application.

For the same degree of approximation in calculations, the coefficient of thermal diffusion turns out to be less accurate than the coefficients for the other transport processes in gases, viz. viscosity, thermal conductivity and diffusion. The theory shows quite generally that for small concentrations of either component the thermal diffusion ratio k_T becomes proportional to the concentration of the minor component, therefore vanishing for zero concentration. The experimental curves for k_T, reproduced in Fig. 12-9, therefore are typical for the concentration dependence of this magnitude. Thus also the definition [12.26], p. 494, of the thermal diffusion constant is justified.

The thermal diffusion ratio depends strongly on the law of interaction of the colliding molecules, being largest for rigid elastic spheres and vanishing for Maxwellian molecules, i.e., point centres, repelling each other by a force proportional to the inverse fifth power of the distance.

It is possible, however, that the thermal diffusion ratio will change its sign for some intermediate value of the concentrations, cf. the discussion in Chapman's paper (30).

For rigid elastic spheres some general statements are possible for limiting cases.

1. For molecules of equal diameter, especially for isotopes, the heavier molecules will diffuse toward the cooler end of the system.

2. For molecules of equal mass, but different diameter, the molecules of larger diameter will diffuse toward the cooler end of the system.

These relations will still hold, if either the diameters or the masses are only approximately equal, provided the ratio of the masses or of the diameters, respectively, differs sufficiently from 1.

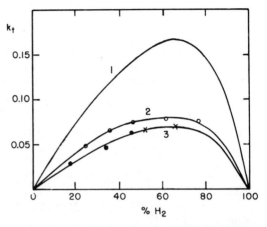

Fig. 12-9. Thermal diffusion ratio, k_T, for H_2—CO_2. 1. Theoretical curve for rigid elastic spheres, after Chapman and Cowling. 2. ○ experimental values, Becker and Schulzeff, $p = 2$ atm., $t_1 = 20°C.$ $t_2 = 160°C.$ 3. Experimental values for atmospheric pressure. Ibbs and co-workers (● Ibbs, Grew and Hirst 1928, $t_1 = 11$—$13°C.$, t_2 between —38 and —76°C.; × Ibbs and Wakeman, 1932).

Since the thermal diffusion ratio is largest for rigid elastic spheres, the ratio R_T, of observed values of k_T (or of values calculated for other models) to the values calculated for rigid elastic spheres will always be smaller than 1. For point centres of force R_T will be higher the higher the exponent of mutual repulsion, an exponent ∞ corresponding to rigid spheres. Therefore it is possible to calculate the exponent for mutual repulsion from observed values of R_T, cf. Chapman and Cowling (1).

The thermal diffusion constant α, with $k_T = N_1 N_2 \alpha$, may be written (Chapman (30))

$$[\alpha]_1 = 5 (C - 1) g . \qquad [12.80]$$

N_1, N_2 are the mole fractions of 1 and 2. Subscript 1 denotes first approximation, the factor g will be defined below. C depends on the law of interaction of the colliding molecules, being given by

$$C = 6/5 \text{ for rigid elastic spheres, and}$$

$$C = \frac{2\,(3\,\nu_{12}-5)}{5\,(\nu_{12}-1)}, \qquad 5\,(C-1) = \frac{\nu_{12}-5}{\nu_{12}-1}$$

for molecules, repelling one another by a force inversely proportional to the distance

$$\varkappa\, r^{-\nu_{12}}.$$

The value for rigid elastic spheres is obtained as limiting value for $\nu_{12} \to \infty$. Consequently the thermal diffusion constant and the other coefficients vanish for $\nu_{12} = 5$, Maxwellian molecules.

The factor g is given, in Chapman's notation, by

$$g = \frac{N_1 S_1 - N_2 S_2}{N_1^2 Q_1 + N_1 N_2 Q_{12} + N_2^2 Q_2}. \qquad [12.81]$$

The other magnitudes, entering [12.81], are defined as follows

$$S_1 = (1/2\,x_{12})\,(1 + M)^{3/2}\,[1 - x_{12}\,S(M)] \qquad [12.82]$$

$$S_2 = (1/2\,x_{12})\,(1 - M)^{3/2}\,[1 - x_{21}\,S(-M)] \qquad [12.83]$$

with

$$S(M) = (1 - M)^{3/2}\,(1 - G\,M)/(1 + M) \qquad [12.84]$$

and

$$G = 3/2A - 1 > 0. \qquad [12.85]$$

Here M, and the magnitudes M_1 and M_2, to be used below, are defined by

$$M = \frac{m_1 - m_2}{m_1 + m_2} \qquad M_1 = \frac{m_1}{m_1 + m_2} \qquad M_2 = \frac{m_2}{m_1 + m_2} \qquad [12.86]$$

where m_1 and m_2 are the molecular masses of components 1 and 2. A and the constants x_{12} etc. depend on certain integrals, involving the laws of interaction, which will not be discussed here. We have

$$A = 2/5 \text{ for rigid elastic spheres, and} \qquad [12.87]$$

$$A = \frac{3\,\nu_{12}-5}{5\,(\nu_{12}-1)}\,\frac{A_2\,(\nu_{12})}{A_1\,(\nu_{12})} \qquad [12.88]$$

for the inverse power law. Values for A_1 and A_2 will be found below, Table II. For rigid elastic spheres we have

$$x_{12} = s_0^2/s_1^2, \qquad x_{21} = s_0^2/s_2^2 \qquad [12.89]$$

where s_1 and s_2 are the diameters of the molecules 1 and 2, and

$$s_0 = s_{12} = 1/2\,(s_1 + s_2). \qquad [12.90]$$

The general expressions for x_{12} and x_{21} are

$$x_{12} = \frac{5A}{2}\,\frac{s_{12}^2}{s_1^2} \qquad x_{21} = \frac{5A}{2}\,\frac{s_{12}^2}{s_2^2} \qquad [12.91]$$

TABLE II

Auxiliary functions for the evaluation of thermal diffusion constants, after Chapman (30) and Jones (101)

	$v = 3$	5	7	9	11	15	∞
$A_1(v)$	0.796	0.422	0.386	0.381	0.384	0.393	0.5
$A_2(v)$	1.056	0.436	0.357	0.330	0.319	0.309	$1/3$
$f(v)$	1.327	1.292	1.234	1.193	1.163	1.25	1.000
$6f(v)/5$	1.592	1.550	1.480	1.432	1.396	1.350	1.200
$C(v)$	0.807	0.816	0.843	0.865	0.882	0.906	1.000
A	0.531	0.517	0.493	0.477	0.465	0.450	$2/5$
B	0.8	0.75	0.711	0.687	0.672	0.653	$3/5$
$5 - 4B$	1.8	2	2.156	2.25	2.312	2.388	2.6
H	3.012	3.033	3.026	3.017	3.008	2.997	2.950
$1/G$	0.532	0.526	0.489	0.466	0.449	0.429	0.364
J	1.30	1.45	1.61	1.71	1.79	1.90	2.27

where s_1, s_2 and s_{12} are appropriately defined "viscosity" and "diffusion" diameters, given in the case of the inverse power law by

$$s_i^2 = \frac{1}{2}\, \Gamma\left(4 - \frac{2}{\nu_i - 1}\right) A_2\left(\nu_i\right)\left(\frac{\varkappa_i}{2kT}\right)^{2/(\nu_i - 1)} \quad i = 1, 2\,, \qquad [12.92]$$

and

$$s_{12}^2 = \Gamma\left(3 - \frac{2}{\nu_{12} - 1}\right) A_1\left(\nu_{12}\right)\left(\frac{\varkappa_{12}}{2kT}\right)^{2/(\nu_{12} - 1)} \qquad [12.93]$$

where Γ is the Gamma-function, and $\varkappa_1$, $\varkappa_2$, ν_1, ν_2 and $\varkappa_{12}$, ν_{12} are the constants entering the equation of the power law for molecules 1, 2 respectively, and for the interaction between molecules 1 and 2. Values of A_1 and A_2 are found in Table II.

The Q's are defined by

$$Q_1 = (1 + M)^{1/2}\, q_1 / \varkappa_{12}, \quad Q_2 = (1 - M)^{1/2}\, q_2 / \varkappa_{21} \qquad [12.94]$$

and

$$Q_{12} = 4\, A / \varkappa_{12} \varkappa_{21} + q_{12} \qquad [12.95]$$

with

$$q_1 = 6\, M_2^2 + (5 - 4\, B)\, M_1^2 + 8\, A\, M_1 M_2 = H - (1/2 + 2\, B)\, M$$
$$+ (H - 4A)\, M^2 \qquad [12.96]$$

$$q_2 = 6\, M_1^2 + (5 - 4\, B)\, M_2^2 + 8\, A\, M_1 M_2 = H + (1/2 + 2\, B)\, M$$
$$+ (H - 4\, A)\, M^2 \qquad [12.97]$$

$$q_{12} = 1/2\, (11 - 4\, B)\, [J\, M^2 (1 - M^2)^{1/2} + (1 - M^2)^{3/2}] \qquad [12.98]$$

$$H = 11/4 - B + 2A \qquad J = 3\, (5 - 4\, B)/A\, (11 - 4\, B)\,. \qquad [12.99]$$

B has the values

$$B = 3/5 \text{ for rigid elastic spheres, and} \qquad [12.100]$$

$$B = \frac{(3\,\nu_{12} - 5)\,(\nu_{12} + 1)}{5\,(\nu_{12} - 1)^2} \qquad [12.101]$$

for the inverse power law.

Values of the functions appearing above are listed in Table II.

The magnitudes x_{12} and x_{21} are connected with the coefficients of viscosity of the pure components and with the coefficient of interdiffusion D_{12} by

$$x_{12} = \frac{6\, A\, [\eta_1]_1}{(1 - M)^{1/2}\,(1 + M)\,(n_1 + n_2)\,(m_1 + m_2)\,[D_{12}]_1} \qquad [12.102]$$

and

$$x_{21} = \frac{6\, A\, [\eta_2]_1}{(1 + M)^{1/2}\,(1 - M)\,(n_1 + n_2)\,(m_1 + m_2)\, M_1 M_2\, [D_{12}]_1}\,. \qquad [12.103]$$

Here $[\eta_1]_1$, $[\eta_2]_1$, and $[D_{12}]_1$ are the values obtained as first approximation to the coefficients of viscosity and to the diffusion coefficient (cf. Chapman and Cowling (1)); n_1 and n_2 are the number of molecules/c.c. of 1 and 2. The other magnitudes have been defined above. In the special case of rigid elastic spheres we have

$$[\eta_i]_1 = \frac{5}{16\, s_i^2} \left(\frac{k\, m_i\, T}{\pi} \right)^{1/2} \qquad i = 1, 2 \qquad [12.104]$$

and

$$[D_{12}]_1 = \frac{3}{8\,(n_1 + n_2)\, s_{12}^2} \left(k\, T\, \frac{m_1 + m_2}{2\,\pi\, m_1\, m_2} \right)^{1/2} \qquad [12.105]$$

and for the exact values of η and D

$$\eta_i = f_i\, [\eta_i]_1 \qquad [12.106]$$

and

$$D_{12} = f_{12}\, [D_{12}]_1 \qquad [12.107]$$

where $f_1 = 1.016$, and f_{12} differs from unity by a few per cent only.

VI. Thermal diffusion constants for mixtures of isotopes

In the case of isotopes the equations for α can be much simplified. Following Jones and Furry (6) we list a number of expressions.

Rigid elastic spheres (101, 102)

$$\alpha = \frac{105}{118}\, \frac{m_2 - m_1}{m_2 + m_1} \qquad [12.108]$$

Force centres, repelling each other by a force $\varkappa\, r^{-\nu}$ (101, 102)

$$\alpha = \frac{105}{118}\, \frac{m_2 - m_1}{m_2 + m_1}\, \frac{\nu - 5}{\nu - 1}\, C(\nu) \qquad [12.109]$$

with

$$C(\nu) = \frac{59}{21}\, \frac{(15/f) + 6}{43 + 16\,[f - 1/\,(\nu - 1) + 1/(\nu - 1)^2]} \qquad [12.110]$$

and

$$f(\nu) = 3/2\, [1 - 2/3\,(\nu - 1)]\, A_2(\nu)/A_1(\nu)^* \qquad [12.111]$$

$A_1(\nu)$ and $A_2(\nu)$ are the integrals defined by Chapman and listed in Table II with Jones and Furry's values for $f(\nu)$, $6f(\nu)/5$ and for $C(\nu)$.

Sutherland model, for the special case where the field of attractive force falls off as the inverse 7th power of the distance (101, 102)

$$\alpha = \frac{105}{118}\, \frac{m_2 - m_1}{m_2 + m_1}\, \frac{1 - 0.9679\, C/T}{1 + C/T}\, \frac{1 + 0.9771\, C/T}{1 + 0.9110\, C/T} \qquad [12.112]$$

$$\approx \frac{105}{118}\, \frac{m_2 - m_1}{m_2 + m_1}\, \frac{1 - 0.98\, C/T}{1 + 0.92\, C/T}.$$

Sutherland's constant C must be taken from the empirical formula for the dependence of the viscosity on temperature

$$\eta \text{ proportional to } T^{1/2}/(1 + C/T). \qquad [12.113]$$

---

* This expression differs from that of Jones and Furry by a factor $\frac{3}{2}$, occasioned by the fact that we have tabulated Chapman's $A_2(\nu)$ which is only $\frac{2}{3}$ of the magnitude of that used by Jones and Furry.

Jones and Furry (6) further show that it is possible to obtain an estimate of R_T and of α by using a relation, first derived by Lord Rayleigh (134), between the exponent of the force law ν, and the exponent n, if the dependence of the viscosity on temperature is represented by T^n. Thus α may be estimated from viscosity data.

VII. Diffusion thermoeffect

From the kinetic theory of gases or from Onsager's reciprocity relations one may conclude that a diffusion thermo-effect must exist as the inverse effect of thermal diffusion. This effect was first observed by Clusius and Waldmann (44)*. Interdiffusion of gases causes temperature differences which may be of the order of magnitude of several degrees centigrade. In Fig. 12-10 we reproduce observations of Waldmann (162). Here temperature changes were registered by means of a resistance thermometer and galvanometer. Diffusion of N_2 versus $80 N_2 + 20 H_2$ was observed in a Loschmidt type of apparatus (cf. p. 407). The resistance thermometer consisted of an horizontal platinum wire of 0.015 mm. diameter which could be placed at different heights z above the middle of a diffusion cell of height l cm.

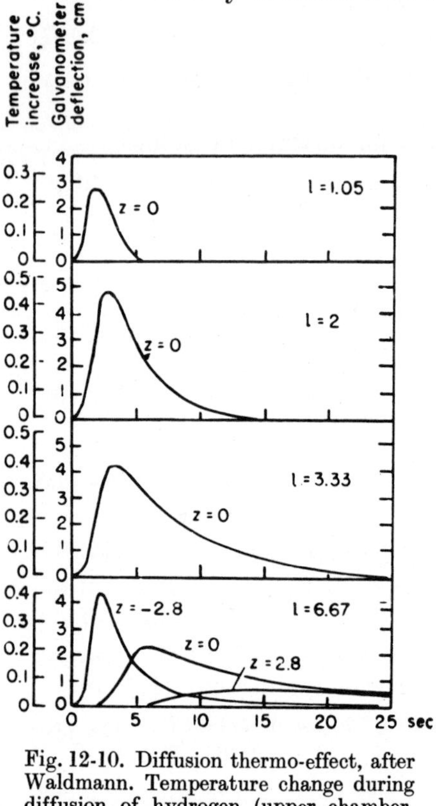

In a binary mixture with a diffusion flow of the first component (present in mole fraction N')

$$J_1 = - n D \operatorname{grad} N' \qquad [12.114]$$

there exists a heat flow

$$J_3 = - \alpha' k T n \operatorname{grad} N' \qquad [12.115]$$

where n is the total concentration of particles 1 and 2 (number of

Fig. 12-10. Diffusion thermo-effect, after Waldmann. Temperature change during diffusion of hydrogen (upper chamber, original composition $80 N_2 + 20 H_2$) and nitrogen (lower chamber, originally pure nitrogen). Ordinate: Temperature change and galvanometer deflection for various heights z (cm.) above middle of upper diffusion chamber of height l; abscissa time (seconds).

* Additional effects may occur in non-ideal gas mixtures (cf. Becker (16, 16a), Haase (83, 83b), Waldmann (163)).

molecules per c.c.). The coefficient α', characteristic for the heat flow, is related to the thermal diffusion constant α, as may be derived either from Onsager's reciprocity relations (127, 128), Meixner (120), or may be proved by a kinetic theory of the effect, Waldmann (154—156)*. Therefore on the one hand a quantitative prediction of diffusion thermo-effects is possible from measured thermal-diffusion constants, while on the other hand measurements of diffusion thermo-effects provide us with a new method of determining thermal diffusion constants. Furthermore, it is possible to calculate from the change of temperature with time ordinary diffusion coefficients, D, and consequently thermal diffusion coefficients, D_T, also (Waldmann (159)). This is somewhat analogous with de Groot's (4) method of determining these coefficients in liquids from the rate of change of concentration in a temperature field.

VIII. Thermal diffusion in condensed phases. Soret effect

Thermal diffusion in liquids was discovered experimentally by Ludwig (112), 1856, who used an inverted U-tube, cooled by ice on one side while heated by boiling water on the other. If filled with a solution of sodium sulfate, crystallization of the salt started several hours after the beginning of an experiment, at the cool end, indicating a migration of the dissolved salt toward the cooler part of the tube.

In 1879, Soret (141) independently rediscovered the effect. He used a vertical tube of 30 cm. length, heated to 80°C. at its upper end, and kept at room temperature, 20°C., at its lower end. He worked with aqueous solutions of KCl, NaCl, LiCl, KNO_3, and $CuSO_4$. In all cases the concentration increased at the cooler end of the tube. De Groot (4) has pointed out that the times employed by Soret (about 50 days) were not long enough for the establishment of complete equilibrium (cf. p. 523ff.).

The technique of measuring Soret coefficients (defined below, p. 523) was much improved by later observers, especially by a reduction of the dimensions of the apparatus employed, Wereide (167), Eilert (55), Bruins (20), Chipman (31). The distance between hot and cold reservoirs was 1.5 cm. in Wereide's experiments, Tanner (145) went still farther, placing the solution between silver-plated copper surfaces,

* The general relation between α and α' for any binary fluid mixture is cf. Haase (83, 83a, 83b)

$$\alpha' = -\frac{D\,\alpha}{R\,T}\,N_1\left(\frac{\partial\mu_1}{\partial N_1}\right)_{P,\,T},$$

and for ideal mixtures $\alpha' = -D\,\alpha$, provided that J_3 has been defined properly.

maintained at constant temperature 10 mm. apart. The concentration gradient, established in the temperature field, was measured by means of Wiener's (170) optical method (cf. Chap. XI, p. 448) which amounts to a measurement of the gradient of the index of refraction. Since a temperature change, without a change in concentration, also gives rise to a change of the index of refraction, this change is determined during the first few minutes of an experiment, before concentration changes become measurable. In Fig. 12-11 the apparatus used by Wereide is shown.

A rapid method for the determination of Soret coefficients has been

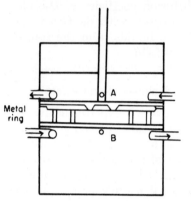

Metal ring

described by Riehl (136). An upper, cooler volume and a lower, hotter one are separated by a thin membrane of cellophane. Strong convection currents, arising in either part of this arrangement, help to establish uniform concentrations and uniform temperatures within either container, the temperature change and concentration change being restricted to the vicinity of the membrane. Against this method the objection may be raised that the equilibrium obtained depends on the presence of the membrane. Actually a transport of water towards the cooler reservoir occurs

Fig. 12-11. Apparatus for measuring Soret coefficients, after Wereide.

simultaneously with thermal diffusion. A kinetic theory of this effect has been attempted by Wirtz (178), cf. also (45a, 96).

Ballay (11) investigated concentration changes of molten alloys in a temperature gradient. With a lead-tin alloy and temperatures varying from 360°C. at the cooler end to 600°C. at the hot end of the tube used, he obtained the following results, the lead concentration increasing toward lower temperatures.

Per cent lead in alloy	Excess lead content at cooler end
10	+ 1.07
36	+ 5.28
64	+ 3.74
90	+ 0.66

In copper-tin and in zinc-tin alloys the tin migrated towards higher temperatures.

If we write for the resulting flux of one component*, cf. [12.24]:

$$J_1 = -D\,(c_1 + c_2)\,\frac{\partial N_1}{\partial z} - D'\,\frac{c_1 c_2}{c_1 + c_2}\,\frac{\partial T}{\partial z} \qquad [12.116]$$

where the first term refers to ordinary diffusion, and the second term is the flow of matter, caused by the temperature gradient, we have for the stationary state

$$0 = -D\,(c_1 + c_2)\,\frac{\partial N_1}{\partial z} - D'\,\frac{c_1 c_2}{c_1 + c_2}\,\frac{\partial T}{\partial z} \qquad [12.117]$$

and

$$\frac{D'}{D} = -\frac{1}{N_1 N_2}\,\frac{d N_1}{d T} \equiv s \qquad [12.118]$$

where N_1, N_2 are mole fractions.

The coefficient s, which is a measure of the relative concentration change in a temperature gradient, is called the Soret coefficient.

For small concentrations, $N_1 \ll N_2$, we may write instead of [12.118]

$$s = -\frac{1}{N_1}\,\frac{d N_1}{d T}. \qquad [12.119]$$

Obviously if s, the Soret coefficient, is defined for the concentration change of the second component instead of that for the first one one has

$$s' = -s. \qquad [12.120]$$

Wirtz (172, 173) defines s with the opposite sign.*

In Table III and Fig. 12-12 we reproduce Soret coefficients as measured by Wereide, Tanner and Trevoy and Drickamer.

De Groot (4) has shown that the rate of establishment of equilibrium depends upon the expression

$$\theta = \frac{a^2}{\pi^2 D} \qquad [12.121]$$

where a is the distance between hot and cold ends of the apparatus, D is the ordinary diffusion coefficient. After a time $t = 5\theta$ the final state has been reached to within about $\exp(-5) = 0.0067$. For Soret's experiments, de Groot estimates θ as being of the order of

* For concentrated solutions we write according to [12.24]:

$$\frac{J_1}{c_1 + c_2} = N_1\,(v_1 - v) = -D\,\text{grad}\,N_1 + D\,\alpha\,N_1 N_2\,\frac{\text{grad}\,T}{T}$$

c_1, c_2 are volume concentrations and N_1, N_2 are mole fractions.

In the stationary state $\text{grad}\,N_1 = \alpha\,N_1 N_2\,\dfrac{\text{grad}\,T}{T}$, and from [12.116] and [12.118]

$$\frac{D'}{D} = s = -\frac{\alpha}{T}.$$

It is inadvisable to define s using $\dfrac{\partial c_1}{\partial z}$ instead of $\dfrac{\partial N_1}{\partial z}$ in [12.116], cf. de Groot (4).

TABLE III

Soret Effect

1. Soret coefficients s for aqueous solutions according to measurements o
Wereide (167)

Solute	Initial concentration of solute (weight per cent)	s (calculated by de Groot (4)) grad^{-1}
Acetic acid.	5	$2,87 \times 10^{-3}$
Antipyrine	1	
	3	
	6	9.5×10^{-3}
	9	

$T_H/T_C = 1.102,$ $\Delta T = 30°$ in all experiments.

$T_H =$ Temperature of the hot wall (°K.)
$T_C =$ Temperature of the cold wall (°K.)

2. Thermal diffusion constants α obtained with a concentric tube column fo
50 mole per cent liquid mixtures, after Trevoy and Drickamer (148)

Mixture	T_H	T_C	α
Benzene-	298.8	293.4	-1.19
n-Heptane	324.0	318.7	-1.06
	314.7	298.4	-1.28
n-Heptane-	308.8	303.5	0.61
n-Dodecane.	353.9	348.6	0.44
n-Heptane-	308.5	303.6	0.90
n-Tetradecane	340.2	333.3	1.05

A positive α indicates that the first named component concentrated at the ho
wall. Mean values are given at each temperature.

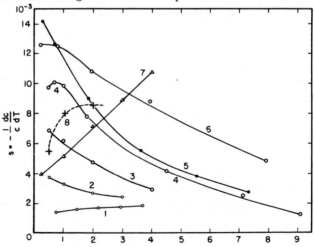

Fig. 12-12. Soret coefficients, measured by Tanner. 1 KCl, 2 BaCl$_2$, 3 MgSO$_4$, 4 H$_2$SO
5 KOH, 6 NaOH, 7 AgNO$_3$, 8 Na$_2$SO$_4$.

magnitude of 80 days, therefore $5\,\theta = 400$ days, and consequently in Soret's experiments equilibrium could not have been reached. Where variation of the concentration with time has been recorded, it is possible to utilize de Groot's theory for an evaluation of the ordinary diffusion coefficient D, and therefore of the thermal diffusion coefficient also, because the ratio D'/D is known according to eq. [12.118], p. 523.

For the case of small concentrations ($N' \ll 1$), an exact solution of the equation, determining the approach to equilibrium, is possible (de Groot (4)). An approximate solution of sufficient accuracy, thus obtained, is

$$\frac{N'}{N_0'} = 1 + [1 - \exp(-t/\theta)] \left[\frac{p}{1 - \exp(-p)} \exp(-p\,\xi) - 1\right] \quad [12.122]$$

where

$N' = $ mol fraction of diffusing component, N_0' referring to $t = 0$,
$t = $ time
θ is defined by equation [12.121]
$a = $ distance between cold and hot plate
$p = (D'/D)\varDelta T$
D, D' are coefficients of ordinary diffusion and of thermal diffusion, respectively
$\varDelta T = $ temperature difference between cold and hot plate
$x = $ coordinate in the direction of the temperature gradient
$\xi = x/a$.

From [12.122] we find for the ratio of the concentrations at the upper (hot) and lower (cold) plates, respectively ($x = a$ and $x = 0$)

$$\frac{N_u'}{N_L'} = \frac{1 + [1 - \exp(-t/\theta)] [p/\{\exp(p) - 1\} - 1]}{1 + [1 - \exp(-t/\theta)] [p/\{1 - \exp(-p)\} - 1]} \quad [12.123]$$

with the limiting values

$$\left(\frac{N_L'}{N_u'}\right)_{t \to 0} = 1 + \frac{pt}{\theta} = 1 + \frac{\pi^2 D' \varDelta T\, t}{a^2} \quad [12.124]$$

and

$$\left(\frac{N_L'}{N_u'}\right)_{t \to \infty} = \exp(p) = \exp\left(\frac{D' \varDelta T}{D}\right). \quad [12.125]$$

Therefore it is possible to calculate from the slope at $t = 0$ of a measured curve of N_L'/N_u' versus t the value D', using [12.124]. The Soret coefficient $s = D'/D$, obtained for sufficiently large t, gives the ratio of the two coefficients, and consequently either magnitude can be obtained separately.

In Fig. 12-13 we reproduce measurements of Wereide (167), as evaluated by de Groot (4).

Thermal diffusion in solid ionic crystals has been investigated by Reinhold (135). He observed considerable effects with mixed crystals of the halides and sulfides of copper and silver. Most of the observed concentration changes, however, cannot be considered as caused by thermal diffusion, as pointed out by de Groot (4). For large concentration differences in mixed crystals which have been kept in a temperature gradient are observed only if the hot and the cold parts of the system belong to different phases. But different phases in equilibrium exhibit. concentration differences even when kept at uniform temperature.

Wirtz (177) has attempted to explain the Soret effect in solids on a kinetic basis. He considers particles moving on interstices of

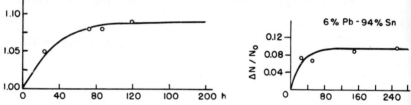

Fig. 12-13. Measurements of Wereide, evaluated by de Groot. a) 5% Acetic acid. $D = 2.05 \times 10^{-6}$ cm.^{2} sec.$^{-1}$, $D' = 5.90 \times 10^{-9} \dfrac{\text{cm}^2}{\text{sec.}^\circ\text{C.}}$. Diagram shows relative concentration change versus time (hours). b) Lead-tin alloy, investigated by Ballay, 6% Pb–94% Sn and 9.2% Pb–90.8% Sn.

a crystal lattice. If , in the motion of these particles, an energy of activation is involved (cf. Chap. III, p. 140) the number of transitions of particles on neighboring sites in a temperature gradient will not be the same, and, therefore, a concentration gradient will be established as a consequence of the temperature gradient.

In order to account for the observations, Wirtz must introduce a somewhat detailed picture of the process of activation. He considers that the energy of activation consists of three contributions:

1. ε_i, an energy of inhibition, to be supplied at the original position of the ion, ·

2. ε_h, an energy necessary to increase a "hole" sufficiently, in the final position of the migrating ion, and

3. ε_v, an energy of vibration of neighboring particles between initial and final positions of the moving particle. These neighboring particles should recede sufficiently from the path of the migrating particle, in order to let it pass.

Thus the probability for migration of an interstitial particle is assumed to be proportional to

$$\exp\left(-[\varepsilon_i + \varepsilon_h + \varepsilon_v]/kT\right). \qquad [12.126]$$

n a temperature gradient $\partial T/\partial x$, the temperatures for two adjacent
nterstitial positions, at distance a, are

$$T \text{ and } T + (\partial T/\partial x)a = T + \varDelta T \qquad [12.127]$$

nd consequently the probabilities for migration from T to $T + \varDelta T$
nd in the opposite direction will become different. In the picture
hosen by Wirtz, the energy ε_i is to be supplied at the initial position
f a migrating particle, the energy ε_h at the final position, and the
nergy ε_v at a position between initial and final site. Consequently,
or a particle moving from a site at temperature T to a new one at
$T + \varDelta T$, the probability of migration will be proportional to

$$\exp\left(\frac{-\varepsilon_i}{kT}\right) \exp\left(\frac{-\varepsilon_h}{k(T+\varDelta T)}\right) \exp\left(\frac{-\varepsilon_v}{k(T+\frac{1}{2}\varDelta T)}\right) \qquad [12.128]$$

nd accordingly for particles moving in the opposite direction from
$T + \varDelta T$ to T

$$\exp\left(\frac{-\varepsilon_i}{k(T+\varDelta T)}\right) \exp\left(\frac{-\varepsilon_h}{kT}\right) \exp\left(\frac{-\varepsilon_v}{k(T+\frac{1}{2}\varDelta T)}\right). \qquad [12.129]$$

Since for the stationary state the ratio of the concentrations at T
and at $T + \varDelta T$ must be inversely proportional to the ratio of the
transition probabilities, we find for this ratio

$$\frac{n_T}{n_{T+\varDelta T}} = \frac{\exp\left(\frac{-\varepsilon_i}{k(T+\varDelta T)}\right) \exp\left(-\frac{\varepsilon_h}{kT}\right)}{\exp\left(\frac{-\varepsilon_i}{kT}\right) \exp\left(\frac{-\varepsilon_h}{k(T+\varDelta T)}\right)} \qquad [12.130]$$

the terms referring to the intermediate temperature cancelling. Now
for small temperature differences we have

$$\exp\left(\frac{-\varepsilon}{k(T+\varDelta T)}\right) \approx \exp\left(\frac{-\varepsilon}{kT}\right) \exp\left(\frac{\varepsilon \varDelta T}{kT^2}\right) \approx \exp\left(\frac{-\varepsilon}{kT}\right)\left(1 + \frac{\varepsilon}{kT^2}\varDelta T\right) [12.131]$$

and instead of [12.130] we may write

$$\frac{n_T}{n_{T+\varDelta T}} \approx \frac{1 + (\varepsilon_i/kT^2)(\partial T/\partial x)a}{1 + (\varepsilon_h/kT^2)(\partial T/\partial x)a}. \qquad [12.132]$$

From [12.132]

$$1 + \frac{1}{n}\frac{\partial n}{\partial T}\frac{\partial T}{\partial x}a \approx 1 + \left[\frac{\varepsilon_h - \varepsilon_i}{kT^2}\right]\frac{\partial T}{\partial x}a \qquad [12.133]$$

and

$$-s = \frac{1}{n}\frac{\partial n}{\partial T} = \frac{\varepsilon_h - \varepsilon_i}{kT^2}. \qquad [12.134]$$

A quasi-thermodynamical argument (Eastman (52, 53), Wagner (151,
152)) led to an expression

$$s = \frac{q^*}{kT^2}. \qquad [12.135]$$

Comparison of [12.134] with [12.135] shows that Wirtz' theory gives a kinetic interpretation of the heat of transport

$$q^* = \varepsilon_i - \varepsilon_h .$$ [12.136

Eqs. [12.134] and [12.135] hold for dilute solutions only, cf. eq [12.119].

Wirtz (181) applied his theory also to liquid phases. For the above see also de Groot (4).

After the success of the Clusius-Dickel separation tube for gases it was obvious to attempt a separation by an analogous method for liquid mixtures (Clusius and Dickel (37), Korsching and Wirtz (108 109)). It was possible to work with liquid systems, but for an efficient separation layers as thin as a fraction of a millimeter had to be used A theoretical treatment of the separation tube for liquids has been given by Debye (45), de Groot (4) and by Hiby and Wirtz (86).

REFERENCES

Monographs and Review Articles

1. Chapman, S., and Cowling, T. G., The Mathematical Theory of Non-uniform Gases. Cambridge 1939.
2. Enskog, D., The Kinetic Theory of Phenomena in fairly Rare Gases, Dissertation. Upsala 1917.
3. Fleischmann, R., and Jensen, H., Das Trennrohr, *Erg. exakt. Naturwiss.* **20**, 121 (1942).
4. de Groot, S. R., L'effet Soret, Thesis. Amsterdam 1945.
4a. de Groot, S. R., Thermodynamics of Irreversible Processes, Amsterdam 1951.
5. Harned, H. S., *Chem. Rev.* **40**, 461 (1947).
6. Jones, R. C., and Furry, W. H., *Rev. Mod. Phys.* **18**, 151 (1946).
7. Prigogine, J., Etude thermodynamique des phénomènes irréversibles. Paris and Liège 1947.
8. Waldmann, L., Article "Diffusion and Thermal Diffusion in Gases"; in: Kappler, E., Physics of Liquids and Gases, FIAT-*Review of German Science* (1939—1946). Wiesbaden 1948.

General Bibliography

9. Arrhenius, S., *Oefversigt Kongl. Vetensk. Akad. Förhandl.* **1894**, Nr. 2, 61, see *Z. physik. Chem.* **26**, 187 (1898).
10. Atkins, B. E., Bastick, R. E., and Ibbs, T. L., *Proc. Roy. Soc. (London)* A **172**, 142 (1939).
11. Ballay, M., *Rev. métal.* **25**, 427, 509 (1928).
12. Bardeen, J., *Phys. Rev.* **57**, 35 (1940).
13. Bardeen, J., *Phys. Rev.* **58**, 94 (1940).
14. Bastick, R. E., Heath, H. R., and Ibbs, T. L., *Proc. Roy. Soc. (London)* A **173**, 543 (1939).
15. Becker, E. W., *Z. Naturforschg.* **2a**, 441, 447 (1947).

16. Becker, E. W., and Schulzeff, A., *Naturwissenschaften* **35**, 219 (1948).

16a. Becker, E. W., *Z. Naturforschung* **5a**, 457 (1950).

17. Blueh, G., and Blueh, O., *Z. Physik* **90**, 12 (1934).

18. Blueh, G., Blueh, O., and Puschner, M., *Phil. Mag.* (7) **24**, 1103 (1937).

19. Brown, H., *Phys. Rev.* **58**, 661 (1940).

20. Bruins, H. R., *Z. physik. Chem.* **130**, 601 (1927).

21. Callen, H. B., *Phys. Rev.* **73**, 1349 (1948).

22. Carr, H. E., *Phys. Rev.* **61**, 726 (1942).

23. Carr, H. E., *J. Chem. Phys.* **12**, 349 (1944).

24. Casimir, M. B. G., *Rev. Mod. Phys.* **17**, 343 (1945).

25. Chapman, S., *Phil. Trans. Roy. Soc.* **A 211**, 433 (1911).

26. Chapman, S., *Phil. Trans. Roy. Soc.* **A 216**, 279 (1916).

27. Chapman, S., *Phil. Trans. Roy. Soc.* **A 217**, 115 (1917).

28. Chapman, S., *Proc. Roy. Soc. (London)* **A 93**, 11 (1917).

29. Chapman, S., and Dootson, F. W., *Phil. Mag.* **33**, 248 (1917).

30. Chapman, S., *Proc. Roy. Soc. (London)* **A 177**, 38 (1940).

31. Chipman, J., *J. Am. Chem. Soc.* **48**, 2577 (1926).

32. Chipman, J., and Dastur, M. N., *J. Chem. Phys.* **16**, 636 (1948).

33. Clusius, K., *Helv. Phys. Acta* **22**, 135 (1949).

34. Clusius, K., *Helv. Phys. Acta* **22**, 473 (1949).

35. Clusius, K., and Becker, E. W., *Z. Naturforschg.* **2a**, 154 (1947).

36. Clusius, K., and Dickel, G., *Naturwissenschaften* **26**, 546 (1938).

37. Clusius, K., and Dickel, G., *Naturwissenschaften* **27**, 148, 149, 487 (1939).

38. Clusius, K., and Dickel, G., *Z. physik. Chem.* **B 44**, 397, 451 (1939).

39. Clusius, K., and Dickel, G., *Naturwissenschaften* **28**, 711 (1940).

40. Clusius, K., and Dickel, G., *Helv. Phys. Acta* **23**, 103 (1950).

41. Clusius, K., and Dickel, G., *Naturwissenschaften* **29**, 560 (1941).

42. Clusius, K., and Dickel, G., *Z. physik. Chem.* **B 52**, 348 (1942).

43. Clusius, K., and Dickel, G., *Z. physik. Chem.* **A 193**, 274 (1944).

44. Clusius, K., and Waldmann, L., *Naturwissenschaften* **30**, 711 (1942).

44a. Dastur, M. N., and Chipman, J., *Discussion Faraday Soc.* 1948, Nr. 4, 100.

45. Debye, P., *Ann. Physik* (5) **36**, 284 (1939).

45a. Denbigh, K. G., *Nature* **163**, 60 (1949).

46. Dickel, G., and Clusius, K., *Naturwissenschaften* **28**, 461 (1940).

47. Dickel, G., and Clusius, K., *Z. physik. Chem.* **B 48**, 50 (1940).

47a. Docherty, A. C., and Ritchie, H., *Proc. Roy. Soc. Edinburgh* **62 A**, 297 (1948).

48. van Dranen, J., and Bergsma, F., *Physica* **13**, 558 (1947).

49. Drickamer, H. G., O'Brien, K. J., Bresee, J. C., and Ockert, C. E., *J. Chem. Phys.* **16**, 122 (1948).

50. Drickamer, H. G., Downey, S. L., and Pierce, N. C., *J. Chem. Phys.* **17**, 408 (1949).

50a. Drickamer, H. G., Mellow, E. W., and Tung, L. H.. *J. Chem. Phys.* **18**, 945 (1950). (Theory of thermal diffusion column)

51. Dufour, L., *Archives de sciences physiques et naturelles, Genève,* **45**, 9 (1872). Cf. *Pogg. Ann.* **148**, 490 (1873).

52. Eastman, E. D., *J. Am. Chem. Soc.* **48**, 1482 (1926).

53. Eastman, E. D., *J. Am. Chem. Soc.* **50**, 283, 292 (1928).

54. Eckart, C., *Phys. Rev.* **58**, 267, 269 (1940).

55. Eilert, A., *Z. anorg. allgem. Chem.* **88**, 1 (1914).

56. Elliot, G. A., and Masson, I., *Proc. Roy. Soc. (London)* **A 108**, 378 (1925).

57. Enskog, D., *Physik. Z.* **12**, 56, 533 (1911).

58. Feddersen, W., *Pogg. Ann.* **148**, 308 (1873) (dated December 26th 1872).
59. Fourhier, A., *J. Phys. Radium* (8) **5**, 45 (1944).
60. Frankel, S. P., *Phys. Rev.* **57**, 661 (1940).
61. Fritzemeier, H., and Hermans, J. J., *Bull. soc. chim. Belg.* **57**, 136 (1948).
62. Fuerth, R., *Proc. Roy. Soc. (London)* **A 179**, 461 (1942).
63. Furry, W. H., and Jones, R. C., *Phys. Rev.* **69**, 459 (1946).
64. Furry, W. H., Jones, R. C., and Onsager, L., *Phys. Rev.* **55**, 1083 (1939).
65. Gillespie, L. J., *J. Chem. Phys.* **7**, 530 (1939).
66. Gillespie, L. J., and Breck, S., *J. Chem. Phys.* **9**, 370 (1941).
66a. Giller, E. B., Duffield, R. B., and Drickamer, H. G., *J. Chem. Phys.* **18**. 1027 (1950). (Thermal diffusion in the critical region)
66b. Giller, E. B., Duffield, R. B., and Drickamer. H. G., *J. Chem. Phys.* **18**. 1683 (1950).
67. Grew, K. E., *Proc. Roy. Soc. (London)* **A 178**, 390 (1941).
68. Grew, K. E., *Nature* **150**, 320 (1942).
69. Grew, K. E., *Phil. Mag.* **35**, 30 (1944).
70. Grew, K. E., *Proc. Roy. Soc. (London)* **A 189**, 403 (1947).
71. Grew, K. E., *Proc. Phys. Soc. (London)* **62 A**, 655 (1949).
72. Grew, K. E., *J. Chem. Phys.* **18**, 149 (1950).
73. van der Grinten, W., *Naturwissenschaften* **27**, 230 (1939).
74. de Groot, S. R., *Physica* **9**, 699, 801 (1942).
75. de Groot, S. R., *J. Phys. Radium* (7) **8**, 129, 188, 193 (1947).
76. de Groot, S. R., *Physica* **13**, 555 (1947).
77. de Groot, S. R., *Compt. rend.* **225**, 173 (1947).
78. de Groot, S. R., *Compt. rend.* **225**, 377 (1947).
79. de Groot, S. R., Hoogenstraaten, W., and Gorter, C. J., *Physica* **9**, 923 (1942).
80. de Groot, S. R., Gorter, C. J., and Hoogenstraaten, W., *Physica* **10**, 81 (1943).
81. Groth, W., and Harteck, P., *Naturwissenschaften* **27**, 584 (1939).
82. Groth, W., and Harteck, P., *Z. Elektrochem.* **47**, 167 (1941).
82a Guthrie, jr., G., Wilson, J. N., and Schomaker, V., *J. Chem. Phys.* **17**, 310 (1949).
83. Haase, R., *Z. Physik* **127**, 1 (1950).
83a. Haase, R., *Z. Elektrochem.* **54**, 450 (1950).
83b. Haase, R., *Z. physik. Chem.* **196**, 4 (1950).
84. Heath, H. R., Ibbs, T. L., and Wild, N.E., *Proc. Roy. Soc. (London)* **A 178**, 380 (1941).
85. Hellund, E. J., *Phys. Rev.* **57**, 328 (1940).
86. Hiby, J. W., and Wirtz, K., *Physik. Z.* **41**, 77 (1940).
87. Hirota, K., *Bull. Chem. Soc. Japan* **16**, 232 (1941).
88. Hirota, K., *J. Soc. Chem. Ind. Japan* **44**, 1049 (1941).
89. Hirota, K., *J. Chem. Soc. Japan* **62**, 480 (1941).
89a. Hirota, K., *J. Chem. Phys.* **18**, 396 (1950).
90. Hirota, K., and Kimura, C., *Bull. Chem. Soc. Japan* **18**, 111 (1943).
91. Hirota, K., and Koguro, K., *J. Soc. Chem. Ind. Japan* **47**, 9 (1944).
92. Hirota, K., and co-workers, *J. Chem. Soc. Japan* **64**, 756, 1097 (1943).
92a. Hirota, K., and Miyashita, I., *J. Chem. Phys.* **18**, 581 (1950).
93. Hirschfelder, J. O., Bird, R. B., and Spotz, E. S., *J. Chem. Phys.* **16**, 968 (1948).
94. Hirschfelder, J. O., Bird, R. B., and Spotz, E. S., *Chem. Rev.* **44**, 205 (1949).
95. van't Hoff, J. H., *Z. physik. Chem.* **1**, 481 (1887).
95a. Huse, E. S., Trevoy, D. J., and Drickamer, H. G., *Rev. Sci. Instr.* **21**, 60 (1950).
96. Hutchison, H. P., Nixon, I. S., and Denbigh, K. G., *Trans. Faraday Soc.* 1948, Discussion: Interaction of water and porous Materials, p. 86.

97. Ibbs, T. L., *Physica* **4**, 1133 (1927).
98. Ibbs, T. L., Grew, K. E., and Hirst, A. A., *Proc. Phys. Soc. London* **41**, 456 (1929).
99. van Itterbeek, A., van Paemel, O., and van Lierde, J., *Physica* **13**, 231 (1947).
100. Jensen, H., and Waldmann, L., *Naturwissenschaften* **29**, 467 (1941).
101. Jones, R. C., *Phys. Rev.* **58**, 111 (1940).
102. Jones, R. C., *Phys. Rev.* **59**, 1019 (1941).
103. Jones, R. C., and Furry, W. H., *Phys. Rev.* **57**, 547 (1940).
104. Kimura, O., *Bull. chem. Soc. Japan* **18**, 45 (1943).
105. Klemm, A., *Z. Naturforschg.* **3a**, 211 (1948).
105a. Klemm, A., *Z. Physik*, **123**, 10 (1947). (Separation process)
106. Korsching, H., *Naturwissenschaften* **31**, 348 (1943).
107. Korsching, H., *Naturwissenschaften* **32**, 220 (1944).
108. Korsching, H., and Wirtz, K., *Naturwissenschaften* **27**, 110, 367 (1939).
109. Korsching, H., and Wirtz, K., *Ber. dtsch. Chem. Ges.* **73**, 249 (1940).
109a. Kramers, H., and Broeder, J. J., *Anal. Chim. Acta* **2**, 687 (1948).
110. Leaf, B., *Phys. Rev.* **70**, 748 (1946).
111. van Lierde, J., *Verhandel. Koninkl. Vlaam. Akad. Wetensch. Belg. Klasse Wetensch.* **9**, Nr. 24, 7 (1947).
111a. van Lierde, J., Thesis Antwerpen 1947.
112. Ludwig, C., *Sitzungsber. Akad. Wiss. Wien, Math.-Naturw. Kl.* **20**, 539 (1856).
113. Lugg, J. W. H., *Phil. Mag.* (7) **8**, 1019 (1929).
114. MacInteer, B. B., Aldrich, L. T., and Nier, A. O., *Phys. Rev.* **72**, 510 (1947).
115. Mann, A. K., *Phys. Rev.* **73**, 412 (1948).
116. Meixner, J., *Ann. Physik* **35**, 701 (1939).
117. Meixner, J., *Ann. Physik* **39**, 333 (1941).
118. Meixner, J., *Ann. Physik* **40**, 165 (1941).
119. Meixner, J., *Ann. Physik* **41**, 409 (1942).
120. Meixner, J., *Ann. Physik* **43**, 244 (1943).
121. Meixner, J., *Z. physik. Chem.* B **53**, 235 (1943).
121a. Miller, L., *Z. Naturforschg.* **4a**, 262 (1949).
122. Murin, A. N., *Compt. Rend. USSR* **41**, 291 (1943).
123. Murphy, B. F., *Phys. Rev.* **72**, 834 (1947).
124. Nier, A. O., *Phys. Rev.* **56**, 1009 (1939).
125. Nier, A. O., *Phys. Rev.* **57**, 338 (1940).
126. Niini, R., *Suomen Kemistilehti* **20 B**, 49 (1947).
127. Onsager, L., *Phys. Rev.* **37**, 405 (1931).
128. Onsager, L., *Phys. Rev.* **38**, 2265 (1931).
129. Onsager, L., *Ann. New York Acad. Sci.* **46**, 241 (1945).
130. Onsager, L., and Fuoss, R. M., *J. Phys. Chem.* **36**, 2689 (1932).
130a. Pierce, N. C., Duffield, R. B., and Drickamer, H. G., *J. Chem. Phys.* **18**, 950 (1950). (Thermal diffusion in the critical region)
131. Prigogine, I., *Physica* **13**, 319 (1947).
132. Prigogine, I., *Bull. Classe Sci. Acad. Roy. Belg.* (5) **34**, 930 (1948).
133. Prigogine, I., *Physica* **15**, 272 (1949).
133a. Prigogine, J., De Brouckère, L., and Amand, R., *Physica* **16**, 577 (1950). (Thermal diffusion in liquids)
133b. Ratte, H., *Z. Physik* **126**, 141 (1949).
134. Rayleigh, Lord, *Proc. Roy. Soc. (London)* **66**, 68 (1900).
135. Reinhold, H., and Schulz, R., *Z. physik. Chem.* A **164**, 241 (1933).
136. Riehl, N., *Z. Elektrochem.* **49**, 306 (1943).

136a. Ritchie, M., *Proc. Roy. Soc. Edinburgh* **62 A**, 305 (1946/48).
136b. Robb, W. L., and Drickamer, H. G., *J. Chem. Phys.* **18**, 1380 (1950).
(Thermal diffusion in isotopic mixtures)
137. Schaefer, K., *Angew. Chem.* **59**, 83 (1947).
138. Schaefer, K., and Corte, H., *Naturwissenschaften* **33**, 92 (1946).
139. Simon, R., *Phys. Rev.* **60**, 172 (1941).
140. Simon, R., *Phys. Rev.* **69**, 596 (1946).
141. Soret, Ch., *Arch. de Genève* **3**, 48 (1879).
142. Soret, Ch., *Arch. de Genève* **4**, 209 (1880).
143. Soret, Ch., *Ann. chim. phys.* (5) **22**, 293 (1881).
144. Stier, L. G., *Phys. Rev.* **62**, 548 (1942).
145. Tanner, C. C., *Trans. Faraday Soc.* **23**, 75 (1927).
146. Taylor, D., and Ritchie, M., *Nature* **145**, 670 (1940).
147. Tilvis, E., *Soc. Sci. Fennica Commentationes Phys. Math.* **13,** Nr. 15, 1 (1947).
148. Trevoy, D. J., and Drickamer, H. G., *J. Chem. Phys.* **17**, 1120 (1949).
149. van Velden, P. F., van der Voort, H. G. P., and Gorter, C. J., *Physica* **12**, 151 (1946).
150. Verschaffelt, J. E., *Bull. Acad. Belg.* **31**, 372 (1946).
151. Wagner, C., *Ann. Physik* (5) **3**, 629 (1929).
152. Wagner, C., *Ann. Physik* (5) **6**, 370 (1930).
153. Waldmann, L., *Z. Physik* **114**, 53 (1939).
154. Waldmann, L., *Naturwissenschaften* **31**, 204 (1943).
155. Waldmann, L., *Z. Physik* **121**, 501 (1943).
156. Waldmann, L., *Naturwissenschaften* **32**, 222, 223 (1944).
157. Waldmann, L., *Z. Physik* **123**, 28 (1944).
158. Waldmann, L., *Z. Naturforschg.* **1**, 10, 12 (1946).
159. Waldmann, L., *Z. Naturforschg.* **1**, 59 (1946).
160. Waldmann, L., *Z. Naturforschg.* **1**, 483 (1946).
161. Waldmann, L., *Z. Naturforschg.* **2a**, 358 (1947).
162. Waldmann, L., *Z. Physik* **124**, 2, 30, 175 (1948).
163. Waldmann, L., *Z. Naturforschg.* **4a**, 105 (1949).
164. Waldmann, L., and Becker, E. W., *Z. Naturforschg.* **3a**, 180 (1947).
165. Watson, W. W., Buchanan, J. O., and Elder, F. K., *Phys. Rev.* **71,** 887 (1947).
166. Watson, W. W., and Woernley, D., *Phys. Rev.* **72**, 78 (1947).
167. Wereide, Th., *Ann. Physik* (9) **2**, 55 (1914).
168. Whalley, E., Winter, E. R. S., and Briscoe, H. V. A., *Trans. Faraday Soc.* **45,** 1085 (1949).
169. Whalley, E., and Winter, E. R. S., *Trans. Faraday Soc.* **45**, 1091 (1949).
169a. Whalley, E., and Winter, E. R. S., *Trans. Faraday Soc.* **46**, 517 (1950).
170. Wiener, O., *Wied. Ann.* **49**, 105 (1893).
171. Winter, E. R. S., *Trans. Faraday Soc.* **46**, 81 (1950).
172. Wirtz, K., *Naturwissenschaften* **27**, 369 (1939).
173. Wirtz, K., *Ann. Physik* (5) **36**, 295 (1939).
174. Wirtz, K., *Z. Physik* **118**, 510 (1941).
175. Wirtz, K., *Naturwissenschaften* **31**, 349 (1943).
176. Wirtz, K., *Naturwissenschaften* **31**, 416 (1943).
177. Wirtz, K., *Physik. Z.* **44**, 221 (1943).
178. Wirtz, K., *Z. Naturforschg.* **3a**, 380 (1948).
179. Wirtz, K., *Z. Naturforschg.* **3a**, 672 (1948).
180. Wirtz, K., *Z. Physik* **124**, 482 (1948).
181. Wirtz, K., and Hiby, J. W., *Physik. Z.* **44**, 369 (1943).

ADDENDUM

CHAPTER I

Crank and Park*), Crank and Henry**) and Park†) treat non-stationary diffusion of gases in polystyrene with concentration dependent diffusion coefficient, cf. Hartley and Crank††). Wall reactions and diffusion in static and flow systems (Gomer, R., *J. Chem. Phys.* **19**, 284 (1951)). Periodic precipitation' (Wagner, C., *J. Coll. Sci.* **5**, 85 (1950)).

*) Crank, J., and Park, G. S., *Trans. Faraday Soc.* **45**, 240 (1949).
) Crank, J., and Henry, M. E., *Trans. Faraday Soc.* **45, 636, 1119 (1949).
†) Park, G. S., *Trans. Faraday Soc.* **46**, 684 (1950).
††) Hartley, G. S., and Crank, J., *Trans. Faraday Soc.* **45**, 801 (1949).

CHAPTER III

Theory of diffusion in metals. Zener, C., *J. applied Physics* **22**, 372 (1951), cf. Wert, C., and Zener, C., *Phys. Rev.* **76**, 1169 (1949), Wert, C., ibid. **79**, 601 (1950), *J. Applied Physics* **21**, 1196 (1950), Dienes, G. J., *J. Applied Physics* **21**, 1189 (1950).

Breckenridge ((31a), quoted p. 176) (Low frequency dispersion in ionic crystals containing foreign ions, cf. Grimley ((46a), quoted p. 177).

Theory of diffusion in metals, cf. Seitz ((96a), quoted p. 178) and Zener ((117), quoted p. 178).

System AgCl - CdCl$_2$, cf. Wagner and Hantelmann ((112a), quoted p. 178).

Disorder and photochemistry of AgBr, cf. Stasiw and Teltow ((99a), quoted p. 178).

CHAPTER IV

For diffusion measurements by means of radioactive tracers cf. Zimen, K. E., Johannsen, G., and Hillert, M., *J. Chem. Soc. (London)*, **1949**, 392 (Self diffusion of silver and mercury in Ag$_2$HgI$_4$); Lindner, R., ibid. **1949**, 395; Lindner, R., and Johannsen, G., *Acta Chem. Scand.* **9**, 307 (1951); Lindner, R., *Elektrochem.* **54**, 430 (1951); Zimen, K. E., Fundamental Mechanisms of Photographic Sensitivity 1951, p. 53.

Schöne, E., Stasiw, O., and Teltow, J., *Z. physik. Chem.* **197**, 145 (1951), (Diffusion of Cd, Pb, and Cu$^+$-Ions in AgBr).

Etzel and Maurer ((41a), quoted p. 207): Concentration and mobility of vacancies in NaCl.

Mapother, Crooks, and Maurer ((85d), quoted p. 208): Self diffusion of Na in NaCl and NaBr.

Ronge and Wagner ((103a), quoted p. 208), transport numbers in solid KCl with SrCl$_2$, K$_2$O and Na$_2$S.

Wagner and Hantelmann ((149a), quoted p. 210), system AgCl - CdCl$_2$, ((149b), quoted p. 210) vacancies in solid KCl.

Wagner ((149c), quoted p. 210), diffusion in AgCl - PbCl$_2$.

CHAPTER V

Kuczynski, G. C., J. Applied Physics 21, 632 (1950), (Self diffusion of silver).

CHAPTER VII

Simril, V. L., and Hershberger, A., Modern Plastics 27, Nr. 11, p. 95 (1950) (Permeability of polymeric films to gases).

Newitt, D. N., and Weale, K. E., J. Chem. Soc. (London) 1948, 154, (Solution and diffusion of gases in polystyrene at high pressures).

Eichholtz, G. G., and Flack, F. C., J. Chem. Phys. 19, 363 (1951), (Diffusion of thoron atoms through photographic gelatine).

CHAPTER IX

Stanley, J. K., v. Hoene, J., and Huntoon, R. T., Trans. Am. Soc. Metals Prepint Nr. 5 (1950), (Oxidation of pure Iron).

Hauffe, K., Z. Metallkunde 42, 34 (1951), (Development of oxidation resistant alloys by applying Wagner's theory of oxidation).

Hauffe, K., Disorder and conduction (ionic and electronic) in solids, forthcoming article in: Ergebnisse d. exakt. Naturwiss. 1951.

Cabrera and Mott, ((46a), quoted on p. 399). (Theory of oxidation of metals).

CHAPTER X

Winter, E. R. S., Trans. Faraday Soc. 46, 81 (1950), 47, 342 (1951). Diffusion of $^{14}N\ ^{15}N$, $^{16}O\ ^{18}O$, $^{12}C^{16}O^{18}O$ into normal N_2, O_2 and CO_2 has been measured and found in agreement with the result of the Chapman-Enskog theory, using the Lennard-Jones 12:6 model.

Fairbanks, D. F., and Wilke, C. R., Ind. Eng. Chem. 42, 471 (1950) (Diffusion coefficients in multi-component mixtures).

Waldmann, L., Z. Naturf. 59, 327 (1950) (Stationary method for measuring diffusion coefficients).

CHAPTER XI

Hartley and Crank ((136a), quoted p. 483) discuss the several definitions of diffusion coefficients in binary liquid mixtures. They give a generalization of Eyring's equation [11.75] for $D\eta$ in non-ideal binary mixtures

$$D\eta = (D_{o1}\,\eta_1\,N_1 + D_{o2}\,\eta_2\,N_2)\left(1 + \frac{\partial \log \gamma_1}{\partial \log N_1}\right)$$

where D_{oi} diffusion coefficient for $N_i \to 1$, η_i viscosity of pure fluid component i. Under certain conditions this passes into Gordon's relation for dilute electrolytes (cf. Table VII, p. 476).

Antweiler, H. J., Kolloid Ztschr. 115, 130 (1949), Microchimica Acta 36/37, 561 (1951) (Limits of sensitivity of Interferometric diffusion methods.).

CHAPTER XII

Eq. [12.5] for the re-defined magnitude $D_{ik}{}'$. The diffusion flow in an isothermal ternary system (cf. eq. [12.11]) is given in accordance with Onsager's reciprocity relations by

$$J_1 = \alpha_{11}\,(X_1 - X_3) + \alpha_{12}\,(X_2 - X_3)$$
$$J_2 = \alpha_{12}\,(X_1 - X_3) + \alpha_{22}\,(X_2 - X_3)$$
$$J_3 = -\,J_1 - J_2\,.$$

For constant pressure we have (cf. [12.6])

$$X_i = -(\text{grad } \mu_i)_{T,\,P} = -\left(\frac{\partial \mu_i}{\partial c_1} \text{grad } c_1 + \frac{\partial \mu_i}{\partial c_2} \text{grad } c_2\right), \qquad i = 1, 2, 3.$$

Comparison, with eq. [11.2] gives the relations for the original D_{ik}.

Winter ((171), quoted p. 532) compars experimental values of thermal-diffusion coefficients with values calculated by Hirschfelder, Bird and Spotz ((93), quoted p. 530). Whalley and Winter ((169a), quoted p. 532) give an elementary theory of thermaldiffusion.

Drickamer and co-workers ((130a, 66a, 136b), quoted p. 530, 531 and 532) measured thermal-diffusion constants in the critical region for ethane-xenon and treated the results by a modification of Haase's ((83, 83b), p. 530) equations.

Prigogine and co-workers ((133a), quoted p. 531) measured Soret coefficients of binary organic liquid mixtures by means of de Groot's (4) method.

Eq. [2.12] p. 95 has been given in the meantime by R. W. Christie and A.W. Lawson (J. Chem. phys. **19**, 517 (1951)) and tested for AgBr. There is excellent agreement between this expression and measured specific heats. The absolute values, however, are still higher than estimated on p. 95 (almost 20 cal/mol degree at the melting point). The authors obtain 3.7 percent Frenkel disorder at 420^0 C.

Berry, C. R., *Phys. Rev.* **82**, 422 (1951), Lattice defects in silver bromide. Frenkel defects assumed. — Peschanski, D., *Journ. chim. phys.* **47**, 933 (1950), Self diffusion of sulfur in Ag_2S. — Haissinski, M., and Peschanski, D., *Journ. chim. phys.* **47**, 191 (1950), Self diffusion of solid sulfur. — Frenkel, I., *Journ. exp. theor. Phys. USSR* **19**, 814 (1949), Theory of self diffusion in solid sulfur. — Cuddeback, R. B., and Drickamer, H. G., *Journ. Chem. Phys.* **19**, 790 (1951), Diffusion in solid sulfur. — Hoffmann, R. E., and Turnbull, D., *Journ. Applied Physics* **22**, 634 (1951), Lattice and grain boundary self diffusion in silver. — Birchenall, C. F., and Mehl, R. F., *Am. Inst. Mining Met. Engrs.* **188**, 144, (1950), New data for self diffusion in iron. — Dienes, G. J., *J. Applied Physics* **22**, 848 (1951), On the volume diffusion of metals. Criticism of Zener's theory. — Rhodin jr., T. N., *Journ. Am. Chem. Soc.* **72**, 5102 (1950), Low temperature oxidation of copper. Test of Cabrera and Mott's theory. — Tichenor, R. L., *Journ. Chem. Phys.* **19**, 796 (1951), Role of oxide composition in oxidation of nickel and cobalt. — Cubicciotti, D., *Journ. Am. Chem. Soc.* **72**, 4138 (1950), Oxidation of zirconium at high temperatures. ibid. **72**, 2094 (1950), Oxidation of beryllium at high temperatures. — Furry, W. H., and Pitkanen, P. H., *Journ. Chem. Phys.* **19**, 729 (1951), Gaseous diffusion as random process. — Boyd, Ch. A., Stein, N., Steingrimsson, V., and Rumpel, W. F., *ibid.* **19**, 548 (1951), Interferometric method for measuring diffusion of gases. — Schwertz, F. A., and Brow, J. E., *ibid.* **19**, 640 (1951), Diffusion of water vapor in some common gases. — Philpot, J. St. L., and Cook, G. H., *Res.* **1**, 234 (1948), Self plotting interferometric plotting system. — Longsworth, L. G., *Rev. Sci. Instr.* **21**, 524 (1950), Test of flowing junction cells with interference methods. — Svensson, H., *Acta Chem. Scand.* **3**, 1170 (1949), *ibid.* **4**, 399 (1950), *ibid.* **5**, 72 (1951), Interferometric method. Measurement of diffusion of sugar in water. — Lyons, M. S., and Thomas, J. V., *J. Am. Chem. Soc.* **72**, 4506 (1950), Diffusion in solution. Gouy method. — English, A. C., and Dole, M., *ibid.* **72**, 3261 (1950), Diffusion in supersaturated solutions. — Harned, H. S., and co-workers, *ibid.* **72**, 2265 (1950), **73**, 159, 650, 652 (1951), Diffusion of electrolytes. — Gosting, L. J. *ibid.* **72**, 4418 (1950), Diffusion of KCl in Water. — Wang, J. H., *ibid.* **73**, 510 (1951), Self diffusion and structure of liquid water. — Whalley. E., *J. Chem. Phys.* **19**, 509 (1951), Thermal diffusion in $H_2 - H_2O$.

AUTHOR INDEX

A

Adams, E. Q. 333, 335
Adler, F. T. 451
Ageew, N. W. 223
Aharoni, J. 328
Aiken, W. H. 297
Albert, M. 305
Amand, R. 535
Amdur, I. 429
Anderson, J. S. 202, 203
Andrade, E. N. da C. 460
Andreen-Svedberg, A. 447
Anson, M. L. 11, 439, 442
Antweiler, H. J. 534
Archibald, W. J. 47
van Arkel, A. E. 106
Armistead, F. C. 430
Arzybyschew, S. A. 202
Atkins, B. E. 498
Aurivillius, B. 86
Avrami, M. 46

B

Badum, E. 298
Baedeker, K. 345, 348
Bain, E. C. 119
Baker, H. D. 46
Bakhmeteff, B. A. 78
Ballay, M. 489, 522, 526
Banks, F. R. 229, 237, 239, 258, 259
Bannister, C. O. 223, 349
Bardeen, J. 255, 352, 354, 356, 357,
  360, 361, 394, 395, 513
Bardenheuer, P. 223
Barnes, C. 11, 443
Barrer, R. M. 4, 10, 12—16, 43, 44,
  117, 136, 171, 175, 245, 273—277,
  287—295, 296—310, 350
Barrett, C. S. 248
Bartschat, F. 246, 249
Bastick, R. E. 498

Batschinski, A. J. 465
Baukloh, W. 222
v. Baumbach, H. H. 366
Beattie, J. A. 500
Becker, A. 413
Becker, E. W. 500, 501, 515, 520
Becker, R. 118, 171, 260
Beckmann, C. O. 477
Bedworth, R. E. 340, 341, 352, 361,
  366, 369
Beerwald, A. 216, 217, 234
Beilstein, F. 446
Belosevsky, N. A. 479
Bénard, J. 364, 367
Bender, M. M. 477
Benrath, A. 186
Bethe, H. A. 121, 126, 127, 129
Bevilacqua, E. B. 477
Bevilacqua, E. M. 477
Beyer, J. 93, 105, 110, 371
Biggs, H. F. 328
Bijvoet, J. M. 119
Biltz, W. 458
Birchenall, C. E. 235, 239, 244, 245
Bircumshaw, L. L. 367
Bird, R. B. 429, 430, 497, 535
Blake, J. 293
Blanchard, C. H. 451
Bloom, H. 458
Blüh, G. 501
Blüh, O. 501
Boardman, L. E. 407, 409, 427
de Boer, J. H. 106, 329
Boggs, C. 293
Bogomolowa, M. J. 202
Bollenrath, F. 216, 230, 234
Boltzmann, L. 31, 32, 75—77, 98, 123,
  127, 139, 198, 214, 215, 221, 223, 240,
  249, 301, 409, 420
Borelius, C. 305, 307
Borelius, G. 120
Borissow, N. B. 202

SUBJECT INDEX

A

Addition compounds, formation of, 392 ff.

Additives, influence on electrolytic conduction, 191 ff.

—, influence on rate of oxidation of metals, 370 ff.

Alloys, oxidation of, 368 ff.

Anisotropic substances, diffusion in, 4 ff., 229, 235, 248, 259

Amalgams, diffusion in, 458, 478

Anomalous, concentration distribution in diffusion, 249 ff.

— mixed crystals, 93 ff.

— — —, conductivity of, 191 ff.

— — — in oxidation of alloys, 368

— — —, solubility in, 278 ff.

— permeation, 297 ff.

— solubility of gases in metals, 282

Association of centers of disorder, 110 ff., 390

Axial symmetry, diffusion equation for, 3, 4, 12 ff., 15, 18, 29 ff., 51 ff.

B

Boltzmann's method, 31, 215

Bragg-Williams' theory, 121 ff.

Brownian movement, 25, 27 ff.

C

Centers of disorder, association of, 110 ff., 390

Centrifuge, 48

Chemical reaction, cf. diffusion and chemical reaction

Clusius separation tube, 501 ff., 506 ff., 528

Color centers, cf. diffusion of color centers

Concentration dependence of diffusion in gases, 408 ff., 422 ff.

— — — —, in liquids, 437 ff., 472 ff., 476 ff.

Concentration dependence of diffusion, in metals, 238 ff.

— — — —, in solids, 156 ff., 198 ff.

Condensed phases, thermal diffusion in, 521 ff.

Conductivity, electrolytic, of anomalous mixed crystals, 191 ff.

— —, of solids, 186 ff.

—, electronic, 167, cf. electronic disorder and electronic semiconductor

— —, of AgCl and AgBr, 350

— —, of pure CuBr, 380

Cooperative phenomena, 118 ff.

Convection, 46 ff., 77

Crystals, disorder in, 82 ff.

Current, cf. diffusion current

D

Debye-Hückel theory for centers of disorder, 389 ff.

Defect electrons, 387

Diaphragm, diffusion through a, 10, 11

Diaphragm cell, for diffusion in liquids, 11, 442 ff.

Diffusion in amalgams, cf. amalgams

— in anisotropic substances, 4 ff., 229, 235, 248, 259

— and chemical reaction, 57 ff.

— coefficient, definition of, 2

— —, dependence on concentration, 4, 12, 31, 75 ff.

— —, dependence on position coordinate, 12

— —, evaluation by means of nomograph, 21

— — of gases, 406 ff.

— — — —, dependence on concentration, pressure, temperature, cf. concentration, pressure, temperature

— — — —, evaporation method for measuring, 411 ff.

FORMULA INDEX

A

A, 277, 287, 290—93, 302, 413, 423, 429, 430, 497—99
Acetone, 412, 433, 477
Acetone-H_2, 412
Acetic acid, 475, 524, 526
Acetylene, 475
A-CO_2, 499
Ag, 142—44, 199, 201, 206, 211, 216, 224, 226, 227, 233—39, 256—59, 273, 282, 342—50, 367, 370, 371—80, 395, 401, 402, 470, 478
Ag-Al, 334
Ag-Bi, 334
AgBr, 93—95, 110, 138, 144, 145, 148, 152—54, 166, 167, 181—83, 186, 188, 192, 193, 197, 199, 201, 348, 349, 350, 367, 378—80, 401, 466, 478, 526, 533, 535
AgBr-CuBr, 145, 186
AgBr-KBr, 487
Ag-Cd, 334
AgCl, 93—95, 138, 142, 145, 148, 152—55, 166, 181—83, 186, 188, 192, 193, 195, 196, 199, 201, 278—80, 348—50, 368, 371—73, 378, 379, 380, 382, 458, 466, 526, 533
AgCl-$CdCl_2$, 533
AgCl-NaCl, 145—186
AgCl-$PbCl_2$, 533
Ag-Cu, 334
Ag-Cu-Sn, 334
Ag_2HgI_4, 121, 183, 186, 342, 373, 374—76, 533
α-Ag_2HgI_4, 88, 118, 168, 169, 188
β-Ag_2HgI_4, 88, 118, 168, 169
AgI, 76, 145, 158, 160—62, 166—68, 182, 183, 186, 198—201, 342, 346, 348, 349, 373—76, 382, 478, 526
α-AgI, 87, 93, 182, 188
β-AgI, 188
AgI-CuI, 145, 186
AgI-KI, 478

$AgNO_3$, 478, 524
$AgNO_3$-KNO_3, 478
$AgNO_3$-$NaNO_3$, 478
Ag_2O, 282
Ag-Pb, 334, 371
Ag_2S, 76, 145, 148, 160—62, 166—68, 183, 198, 200, 344—47
α-Ag_2S, 87, 88, 93, 148, 183, 343—45
Ag_2S-Cu_2S, 145
Ag-Sb, 334
Ag_2Se, 166—68, 183
α-Ag_2Se, 87, 88
Ag-Sn, 334, 479
Ag_2Te, 167, 168, 183, 347, 348
α-Ag_2Te, 88
Ag-Zn, 334
Al, 85, 86, 216, 218, 223, 224, 230, 234, 235, 240, 242, 334, 341, 351, 368, 397, 399, 402, 479
Al-Au, 334
Al-Cu, 334
Al-Fe-Sn, 334
Al-Mg, 216, 334
Al_2O_3, 85, 342, 376, 377
γ-Al_2O_3, 85, 86
Al-Sb, 334
Al-Sn, 334
Al-Zn, 334
sec-Amyl alcohol, 412, 475
Analcite, 175, 301, 304
Aniline, 412
Antipyrine, 524
Au, 144, 145, 158, 165, 202, 211, 218, 220, 221, 224, 226, 234—39, 256—59, 330—32, 334, 335, 369, 370, 478, 479, 503
Au-Bi, 334, 479
Au-Ni, 221, 238, 369, 370
Au-Pb, 330—32, 334, 479, 326
Au-Pd, 221, 331
Au-Pt, 158, 221
Au-Sb, 334
Au-Sn, 479
Austenite, 70, 244, 245, 251

Appendix

Supplement Summarizing Developments in the Field to 1959

SOME GENERAL REMARKS

(Supplementary to Chapter I, pages 1-82 in this volume)

To make Fourier's theory of heat conduction applicable to diffusion processes we usually introduce some restrictions without which many formulations would become unnecessarily complicated. One should, however, be conscious of the simplifications involved.

Even the normal laws of heat conduction are strictly valid for solids only, and even there only if either thermal expansion is negligible, or the temperature differences occurring are kept sufficiently small. Actually, with diffusion in solids relations are formally simpler than with liquids and gases* where normally convection plays a role. Under conditions chosen for diffusion experiments convection is either systematically prevented, or kept well defined in order to make use of it for the measurement.

In diffusion experiments we almost always meet with the problem of a proper system of reference, except with solids at constant volume. One has considerable freedom in the choice of this system, provided it is unambiguously defined, and one is conscious of the fact that with change in the frame of reference the meaning of the diffusion coefficients may be changed**. With gases, usually, the solid container is a natural frame of reference. This choice is identical with that of the center of number density (not mass!) as origin, if the gas under consideration is sufficiently ideal. For fundamental considerations the system connected with the center of gravity may be advantageous.

The processes of equalization of temperature, due to thermal conduction, and of equalization of concentration, due to diffusion, though formally analogous, exhibit some fundamental differences. Even in inhomogeneous systems (where we think especially of those with continuously varying physical properties) heat always flows in the direction of falling temperature (though, in case of anisotropic sub-

---

* With gases, even if convection is suppressed, nonstationary heat conduction is *always* connected with flow phenomena, due to the fact that density varies like $1/T$.

** Cf. de Groot (36).

stances, the direction of the flow vector and that of the temperature gradient normally do not coincide). The equilibrium condition is $T = $ constant, inside a single phase, and at interfaces. If we plot the temperature distribution in a complicated system, and if we know that heat is flowing in the $+ x$ direction, then the temperature decreases monotonically in the same direction. There will be no discontinuities in the T-x-plot at phase boundaries (neglecting, of course, the usually very small temperature drop solid/gas due to gas kinetic effects), although usually there will be kinks at phase boundaries. Continuity of heat flow $(= - \lambda \partial T/\partial x)$ requires that at phase boundaries

$$\lambda' (\partial T'/\partial x) = \lambda'' (\partial T''/\partial x) \qquad [\text{A } 1.1]$$

with single prime and double prime referring to the phase, and λ to the thermal conductivity. Since, however, thermal conductivity normally differs for different phases, $\lambda' \neq \lambda''$, the same must hold for $\partial T/\partial x$.

For diffusion within a single phase* constancy of concentration will be an equilibrium condition only if we introduce certain assumptions with respect to ideal behavior. For the transition from one phase into another one equality of concentrations at the interface will occur in exceptional cases only. Contrary to the problem of heat conduction, in the case of diffusion in multicomponent systems we shall have to expect at interfaces not only kinks in the concentration curve (discontinuities of the gradient) but in addition discontinuities of concentration itself (cf. p. 26).

The concentration jump in the direction of diffusion flow may be both downward and upward (formally there can be "uphill diffusion"** which never occurs in heat conduction). This apparently anomalous

---

* With respect to the concept of phase, as used here, cf. p. 24. It is convenient, as in metallurgy, to generalize Gibbs' phase definition (as a homogeneous region of matter) to a region of compositions which can be reached by continuous changes.

** By "uphill" diffusion, of course, we mean diffusion in the direction of increasing concentration, apparently counteracting an equalization of concentration. This paradox formulation actually is familiar to everybody: if, for instance, we extract an aqueous solution of an organic substance with ether, then we know that the substance preferentially enters the solvent favored by the partition coefficient. In heat conduction we could arrive at the same, apparently paradox formulations if, instead by $- \lambda (\partial T/\partial x)$ we would define the heat flux by $- k (\partial H/\partial x)$, where H is the enthalpy per unit volume. Thus the difference between heat conduction and diffusion is only due to the fact that, contrary to chemical potential or activity, temperature can be measured easily. Practically the diffusion flux is best set equal to $- D (\partial c/\partial x)$. The formulation for the heat flux $- k (\partial H/\partial x)$ has actually proved useful in aerothermochemistry (aerothermodynamics).

fact* disappears if instead of concentrations "absolute activities"** are plotted. This does not mean that by introducing activities instead of concentrations we should obtain the correct generalized equations. Uphill diffusion is possible even within a single phase (in the generalized definition, cf. p. 24), if, for instance, a third component, not participating in diffusion***, causes a decrease in activity combined with an increase of concentration.

We consider heat conduction in a homogeneous body or diffusion in a sufficiently ideal mixture, and we assume, for the sake of simplicity, that there is a temperature (concentration) gradient**** $\partial \varphi / \partial x < 0$ in the $+ x$ direction. There will be a net decrease of heat content per unit volume, or of concentration, in a volume element between x and $x + dx$, if

$$\left| (\partial \varphi / \partial x)_{x + dx} \right| > \left| (\partial \varphi / \partial x)_x \right|.$$

It was assumed that $\partial \varphi / \partial x$ was negative, consequently $(\partial \varphi / \partial x)_{x + dx} < (\partial \varphi / \partial x)_x$, concentration (temperature) decreases for $\partial^2 \varphi / \partial x^2 < 0$, and vice versa (Fig. A 1-1). This means that a region which is concave toward the x-axis, is emptied on account of the equalization processes, while a region convex toward the abscissa is filled up. The transition where concentration does not change is characterized by an inflection point of the φ-x-curve. There are numerous experimental setups where two regions of different concentrations (φ_1 and φ_2) are brought into contact at $t = 0$ and $x = 0$, and where for $t > 0$ and $x = 0$ we

* The same holds for uphill diffusion within a single phase, cf. p. A 10.
** Activities in thermodynamics are defined by relations of the type

$$d\mu_i = RT \, d \ln a_i \qquad \text{[A 1.2]}$$

where μ_i is chemical potential and a_i is activity of component i. Here the zero of the logarithmic activity scale (the value $a_i = 1$) still can be chosen arbitrarily as actually is being done. Then for equilibrium of several phases $'$, $''$, $'''$, etc., we have

$$\mu_i' = \mu_i'' = \mu_i''' = \ldots \qquad \text{[A 1.3]}$$

while the analogous equations

$$a_i' = a_i'' = \ldots \qquad \text{[A 1.4]}$$

would not hold. If, however, instead of by [A 1.2] we define

$$\mu_i = RT \ln a_i \qquad \text{[A 1.5]}$$

without additive constant, then [A 1.4] follows from [A 1.3], and activities, thus defined, are called "absolute" activities [cf. Fowler and Guggenheim (5 on p. 129 in this volume); Guggenheim (7 on page 129 in this volume)] which sometimes are useful].

*** Cf. first footnote on page A 2.
**** In equations referring both to temperature and to concentration we use φ instead of T and c.

have $\varphi = (\varphi_1 + \varphi_2)/2$, independent of time*. As long as $\varphi(0, t)$ remains constant, $= (\varphi_1 + \varphi_2)/2$ there must remain an inflection point at $x = 0$. In addition all the substance which left the region $x < 0$ must be found in the region $x > 0$, and this is

$$A \int_0^t J_x dt \,|_{x=0} = - AD \int_0^t (\partial c/\partial x)_{x=0} dt \,. \qquad [A\ 1.6]$$

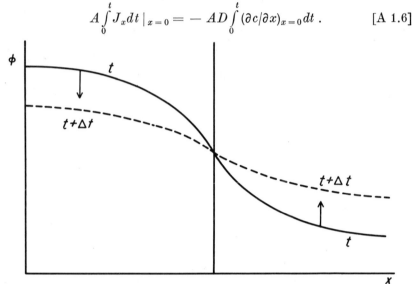

Fig. A 1-1. $\Phi(t)$ and $\Phi(t + \varDelta t)$, one-dimensional case, $D = $ const.

J_x is the flux and A the cross-sectional area. If $\partial c/\partial x$ is known as a function of t for $x = 0$, the above integral can be evaluated (cf. p. 22). We may express this in the form

$$A \int_{-\infty}^0 \frac{\partial J_x}{\partial x}\, dx = - A \int_0^\infty \frac{\partial J_x}{\partial x}\, dx = A\,(J_x)_{x=0} \qquad [A\ 1.7]$$

as a special case of Gauss' law

$$\iiint_V \mathrm{div}\ \boldsymbol{J} d\tau = \iint_S J_n ds \qquad [A\ 1.8]$$

* This case is treated on p. 20. We see without calculation that for an arrangement symmetrical with respect to $x = 0$ (often a sufficiently long cylinder) where for $t = 0$ we had $\varphi = \varphi_1$ for $x < 0$, and $\varphi = \varphi_2$ for $x > 0$, the final state for $t \to \infty$ will be given by $\varphi = (\varphi_1 + \varphi_2)/2$. For $D = $ constant we have the general solution $\varphi = [(\varphi_1 + \varphi_2)/2] + \Phi\,(x, t)$, where $\Phi\,(x, t) = 0$ for $x = 0$, $t > 0$ and for all x and $t = \infty$, and where $\Phi\,(x, t) = -\ \Phi\,(-\ x, t)$, and, of course, $\Phi\,(x, t)$ obeys the differential equation ([1.4] p. 3); Φ being an odd function of x, the distribution is antisymmetric with respect to $x = 0$.

where the integral on the left is extended over the volume V ($d\tau$ is the volume element) of the system integral on the right over its boundary surface S, J_n being the normal component of J on the boundary*.

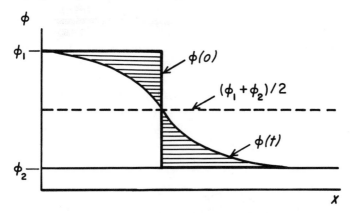

Fig. A 1-2. $\Phi(0)$ for $t = 0$ (step distribution) and $\Phi(t)$, for $t > 0$, one-dimensional case, $D = $ const.

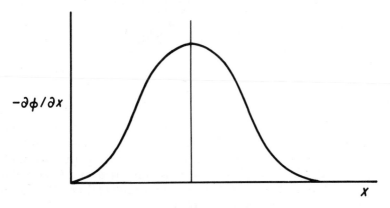

Fig. A 1-3. $- \partial\Phi/\partial x$ of Fig. A 1-2.

Equation [A 1.7] is independent of the assumption that in the equation

$$J = - D \operatorname{grad} c \qquad\qquad [\text{A } 1.9]$$

* Equation [A 1.7] is illustrated by Fig. A 1–2, Fig. A 1–3 shows the corresponding values of $\partial\varphi/\partial x$, Fig. A 1–4 shows the corresponding values of $\partial^2\varphi/\partial x^2$. Equation [A 1.7] expresses the fact that the two shaded areas in Fig. A 1–4 are equal.

the diffusion coefficient D be a constant. Consequently, if we observe in diffusion experiments that the plane defined by

$$\int_{-\infty}^{x_1} [\varphi(t) - \varphi(0)] dx = -\int_{x_1}^{\infty} [\varphi(t) - \varphi(0)] dx \qquad [\text{A } 1.10]$$

where $\varphi(0)$ refers to $t = 0$, does not coincide with the plane $x = 0$, then, obviously, an additional process must have occurred (Kirkendall effect in metals!).

In the case of (non-negligible) volume changes of the system we always have a flow process. Since it is not difficult to formulate diffusion equations with simultaneous flow (cf. p. 46ff.), one could

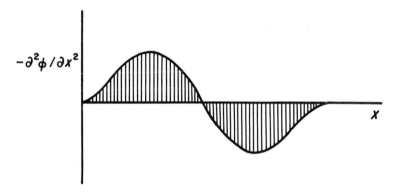

Fig. A 1-4. — $\partial^2 \Phi / \partial x^2$ of Fig. A 1-2.

treat this problem if the flow properties were given. Actually, volume changes are caused by the diffusion process. If we keep the diffusion medium in a cylindrical container, closed by an impermeable wall at $x = 0$, then the movement at $x = x_1$ is composed of all the volume changes between 0 and x_1 (cf. Hartley and Crank (44) and Wagner (88, 89) and Cohen, Wagner, and Reynolds (12)

If the diffusion coefficient depends on concentration (or on the space coordinate x) we have

$$\frac{\partial c}{\partial t} = \frac{\partial}{\partial x}\left(D\frac{\partial c}{\partial x}\right) \qquad [\text{A } 1.11]$$

(always for diffusion in the x-direction only, the necessary generalizations being obvious). Concentration is increasing with time where [for $D = f(c)$]

$$\frac{\partial}{\partial x}\left(D\frac{\partial c}{\partial x}\right) = D\frac{\partial^2 c}{\partial x^2} + \frac{dD}{dc}\left(\frac{\partial c}{\partial x}\right)^2 > 0, \qquad [\text{A } 1.12]$$

and vice versa. If $dD/dc > 0$ concentration still increases for $\partial^2 c/\partial x^2 = 0$, and even beyond the inflection point in the region where

$$\frac{dD}{dc}\left(\frac{\partial c}{\partial x}\right)^2 > \left| D\,\frac{\partial^2 c}{\partial x^2} \right|, \qquad\qquad \text{[A 1.13]}$$

if the latter expression is negative. The region of concentration increase with time is no longer divided from that of concentration

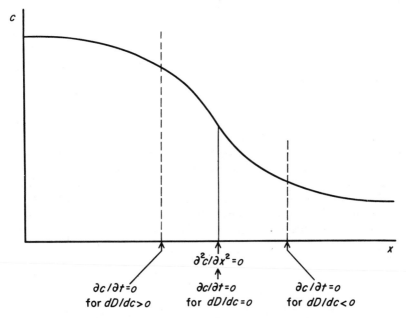

Fig. A 1-5. One-dimensional diffusion, $D = D(c)$, concentration-dependent.

decrease by an inflection point, but by the condition

$$D\,\partial^2 c/\partial x^2 + (dD/dc)\,(\partial c/\partial x)^2 = 0 \qquad\qquad \text{[A 1.14]}$$

Depending on whether $dD/dc \lessgtr 0$, this boundary is to the left or to the right of the inflection point in Fig. A 1-5. A simple estimate of the concentration change with time from the plot of c versus x will now be possible only if either it is known that $D = $ constant, or if one knows the concentration dependence of D (with metals one easily may have a change in D by a power of ten over the whole concentration range).

If, in a system, volume or temperature or both are not constant, then obviously the equilibrium state cannot be that of equal concentrations.

In a system with varying T a state of equilibrium is impossible without equalization of temperature. If, however, a stationary temperature drop is being maintained from outside, a stationary state will be established in the system, too, without flow of matter. This stationary state cannot be given by the constancy of the individual concentrations of the components, because the total concentration varies with T. Consequently, as a maximum, one might expect constancy of the mole fractions. If, in the stationary state, we observe deviations from the constancy of the mole fractions, then we call this phenomenon "thermal diffusion" (the stationary deviations from constancy of molar fractions being due to the counteraction of thermal diffusion and of ordinary diffusion). Now the normal diffusion flux may be set equal to

$$J_1 = - D_{12} c \frac{\partial N_1}{\partial x} \qquad [\text{A } 1.15]$$

where D_{12} is the coefficient of interdiffusion of components 1 and 2, $N_1 = c_1/(c_1 + c_2)$, $c = c_1 + c_2$ with c_1, c_2 molar concentrations (for a binary mixture). For $V =$ constant or $T =$ constant, equation [A 1.15] passes into the normal diffusion equation. Otherwise equation [A 1.15] is the appropriate form for consideration of thermal diffusion. We define diffusion as the mutual interdiffusion of at least two components, for instance by requiring*

$$J_1 + J_2 = 0 \qquad [\text{A } 1.16]$$

where we still are free to choose different frames of reference (such that there is no resulting flow of mass [center of gravity system], or no resulting flow of particles [convenient definition for gases])**.

For multicomponent mixtures we must introduce more than one diffusion coefficient, e.g. $n(n-1)/2$ independent coefficients for a system of n components as may be justified by means of thermodynamics of irreversible processes (Onsager's reciprocity relations***, cf. p. 6).

---

* Not the form of this additional condition is essential, but the fact that there is always an additional condition, reducing the number of independent diffusion coefficients correspondingly.

** We mentioned already our relative freedom in the choice of the frame of reference. cf. footnote on preceding page.

*** Onsager's reciprocity relations are easily formulated: if J_i are any fluxes, (especially the three diffusion fluxes in a three-component system, $i = 1, 2, 3$), X_i are corresponding "forces", then we may formulate the "phenomenological" relations with 9 (in general n^2) components of the diffusion tensor α_{ik}

$$J_i = \sum_k \alpha_{ik} X_k, \quad i, k = 1, 2, 3 . \qquad [\text{A } 1.17]$$

Diffusion in an n-component system may be described in many ways. For instance, one may simply generalize Fick's law to yield

$$J_i = - \sum_k D_{ik} \partial c_k / \partial x \qquad i = 1, 2 \ldots n \qquad \text{[A 1.19]}$$

with altogether n^2 (dependent) coefficients D_{ik} (Onsager (129) on p. 531 of this volume). But the D_{ik}'s, thus defined, have a meaning different from that of normal diffusion coefficients. Then one first may show that, due to additional conditions* there remain only $(n - 1)^2$ independent coefficients. This number, because of the reciprocity relations, is further reduced to $n(n - 1)/2$. The reciprocity relations, however, do not give $D_{ik} = D_{ki}$, but more complicated conditions**.

---

or in general i, $k = 1, 2 \ldots n$. For the definition of X_k see below. In case of diffusion additional conditions and Onsager's reciprocity relations

$$\alpha_{ik} \approx \alpha_{ki} \qquad \text{[A 1.18]}$$

reduce the original number of 9 coefficients to 3 independent coefficients (in general $n(n - 1)/2$). We had given the explicit equations, corresponding to [A 1.17], for the special case of diffusion in an anisotropic body, p. 4ff. But now we can no longer identify the X_i with the concentration gradients. For a detailed treatment we refer the reader to the original papers Onsager (109 and 110 on p. 81 of this volume); Meixner (104 and 105 on p. 81); de Groot (25 on p. 79, and 78 and 79 on p. 81)

When formulating [A 1.19] one first has freedom in the definition of the fluxes J_i, but then the driving forces are fixed, for there exists a dissipation function (called after the corresponding function, introduced into hydrodynamics by Rayleigh)

$$\Phi = \sum_i J_i X_i = \sum_i \sum_k \alpha_{ik} X_i X_k \equiv T\theta \qquad \text{[A. 1.20]}$$

where θ is the rate of entropy production per unit volume. Therefore $\Phi \geqq 0$, which permits conclusions with respect to the coefficients of the quadratic form $\sum_i \sum_k \alpha_{ik} X_i X_k$. The coefficients α_{ik} may be expressed by the normal diffusion coefficients. In a binary system, referred to the center of gravity, we have (with one single remaining coefficient α [Haase (39)]

$$D = \alpha \overline{V} \frac{(M_1 N_1 + M_2 N_2)^2}{M_1{}^2 M_2{}^2 N_2{}^2} \frac{\partial \mu_1}{\partial N_1}. \qquad \text{[A 1.21]}$$

Here N_1, N_2 are mole fractions, $\overline{V}$ the molar volume, M_1, M_2 the molar masses, and μ_1 the chemical potential of component 1.

* For instance by requiring that there is no resultant flow v of the whole system

$$v = \sum_i \overline{V}_i J_i = 0 \qquad \text{[A 1.22]}$$

with $\overline{V}_1$ partial molar volume of component i

$$\sum_i \overline{V}_i D_{ik} = 0. \qquad \text{[A 1.23]}$$

** Cf. also de Groot (36).

We have $R_{ik} = R_{ki}$ where the R_{ik} are related to the D_{ik} through

$$\sum_j R_{ij} D_{jk} = \overline{V} \frac{\partial \mu_i}{\partial N_k} \qquad \text{[A 1.24]}$$

[cf. Onsager (129 on p. 531 of this volume)].

For gases it is advantageous to define a system of diffusion coefficients D_{ik} (Hirschfelder *et al.**) such that $D_{ii} \equiv 0$. Then there must be $n(n-1)/2$ additional relations between the remaining $n(n-1)$ coefficients $D_{ik} (i \neq k)$, and $n(n-1)/2$ independent coefficients are left. But $n(n-1)/2$ is just the number of independent diffusion coefficients $\mathfrak{D}_{ik}$ for the $n(n-1)/2$ possible binary mixtures. Actually, the D_{ik} may be expressed by means of the $\mathfrak{D}_{ik}$ binary coefficients (Hirschfelder)*. It is easily seen that for a ternary mixture the simple equations

$$J_i = - D_i \frac{\partial c_i}{\partial x}, \qquad i = 1, 2, 3 \qquad \text{[A 1.25]}$$

are insufficient. We consider three components 1, 2, 3 in a solvent the role of which we shall neglect. If we use the expression introduced for binary mixtures

$$J_1 = - \frac{c_1 u_1}{N} \frac{\partial \mu_1}{\partial x} \qquad \text{[A 1.26]}$$

where u_1 is the mobility of particle 1, N is Avogadro's number, and if we further assume c_1 and c_2 as independent of x, then the simplest law according to [A 1.25] would give

$$J_1 = - D_1 \frac{\partial c_1}{\partial x} = 0 \qquad \text{[A 1.27]}$$

and J_1 would vanish. However, if we have a nonideal mixture, then μ_1 depends not only on c_1, but on c_2 and c_3 as well, and in our special case there remains

$$J_1 = - \frac{c_1 u_1}{N} \frac{\partial \mu_1}{\partial c_3} \frac{\partial c_3}{\partial x}. \qquad \text{[A 1.28]}$$

Thus we see that the diffusion flux for component 1 must contain a term proportional to $\partial c_3 / \partial x$

$$J_1 = \ldots - D_{13} \frac{\partial c_3}{\partial x} \qquad \text{[A 1.29]}$$

and we may expect as most general relations

$$J_i = - \sum_k D_{ik} \frac{\partial c_k}{\partial x}, \qquad i, k = 1, 2, 3. \qquad \text{[A 1.30]}$$

* For complete reference see Monographs in list of References at the end of this chapter.

This would give $9 = n^2$ coefficients in a ternary system, the number of which would be reduced because of the above mentioned reasons.

From Hirschfelder's* treatment we know that even in mixtures of three (or more) ideal gases coupling terms are to be expected. For the experimental verification of such (not at all small) effects (cf. Hellund, p. 431 of this volume).

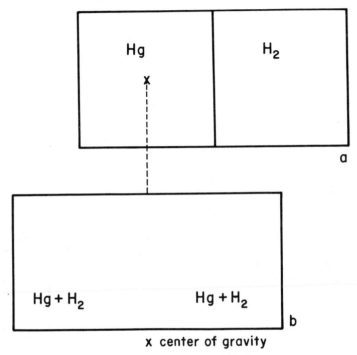

x center of gravity

Fig. A 1-6. Diffusion of mercury vapor and hydrogen in mass-less, free box.
a) before opening of shutter; b) after diffusion has been completed;
x = center of gravity.

The above mentioned diffusion process in metals with unilateral flow of matter needs special considerations. Let us consider an idealized case of gas phase diffusion. We assume a box of negligible mass, divided in the middle by a sliding shutter, Fig. A 1-6. We assume this box filled with mercury vapor to the left, with hydrogen to the right, both of equal pressure. We further assume that convection has been excluded (if necessary by an appropriate honeycomb system of negligible mass). If we start diffusion by removing the shutter, then the

* For complete reference see Monographs in list of References at the end of this chapter.

center of mass moves from slightly to the right of the center of the mercury compartment to the center of the box. If this mass-less box is suspended without friction, then it will move by almost one-quarter of its length to the left*. Normally one will not denote this shift of the box by "diffusion". One will say that normal diffusion occurred, coupled with a shift of the container due to conservation of center of gravity.

The relation [1.36] derived on p. 10 of this volume can be obtained in a more straightforward way as has been pointed out to the author by G. Hertz, Hamburg.

If we start from the equation, corresponding to equation [12.19] on p. 493 of this volume

$$\bar{v}_1 - \bar{v}_2 = -\frac{D_{12}}{N_1 N_2}\frac{dN_1}{dx} = -\frac{C_0}{cC}D_{12}\frac{dc}{dx} \qquad [A\ 1.31]$$

where c, C are defined on p. [12.19], N_1 and N_2 being mol fractions

$$N_1 = \frac{c}{c+C}, \quad N_2 = \frac{C}{c+C}, \quad c + C = C_0 = \text{constant}. \quad [A\ 1.32]$$

Here $\bar{v}_1$ and $\bar{v}_2$ are the average speeds of vapor and air molecules. Taking the air molecules as a frame of reference, $\bar{v}_2 = 0$, then the flux of vapor molecules, $J_1 = \bar{v}_1 c$ becomes

$$J_1 = -\frac{C_0}{C}D_{12}\frac{dc}{dx} = -\frac{C_0}{C_0-c}D_{12}\frac{dc}{dx}. \qquad [A\ 1.33]$$

In the quasi-stationary state where $\dot{J}_1 = $ constant we have by integrating [A 1.33] between $x = 0$ and $x = -h$:

$$J_1 h = C_0 D_{12}\ln\frac{C_0}{C_0-c_e} \qquad [A\ 1.34]$$

identical with [1.36].

REFERENCES

Monographs

Carslaw, H. S., and J. C. Jaeger, Conduction of heat in solids. 2nd ed. Oxford, Clarendon Press, 1959.

Crank, J., The mathematics of diffusion. Oxford, University Press, London and New York, 1956.

Frank-Kamenetskij, D. A., Diffusion and heat exchange in chemical kinetics. Translated by N. Thon, Princeton University Press, New Jersey, 1955.

Hirschfelder, J. O., Curtiss, C. F., and Bird, R. B., Molecular theory of gases and liquids. Wiley, New York, 1954.

Jost, W., Diffusion, Darmstadt, Steinkopff 1957.

* From this it follows that diffusion must be accompanied by pressure effects, though very small ones.

General Bibliography

1. Aris, R., On the dispersion of a solute by diffusion, convection and exchange between phases. *Proc. Roy. Soc. London* A **252**, 538 (1959).
1a. Auer, P. I., and Murbach, E. W., Diffusion across an interface, *J. Chem. Phys.* **22**, 1054 (1954).
2. Baldwin, R. L., Dunlop, P. J., and Gosting, L. J., Interacting flows in liquid diffusion: equations for evaluation of the diffusion coefficients from moments of the refractive index gradient curves, *J. Am. Chem. Soc.* **77**, 5235 (1955).
3. Batchelor, G. K., Diffusion in a fluid in turbulent motion, *Appl. Mechanics Revs.* **9**, 81−91 (1956).
4. Bearman, R. J., On the linear phenomenological equations, *J. Chem. Phys.* **28**, 662−664 (1958). (The transport processes of diffusion and heat flow in nonreacting, nonelectrolyte fluid system are discussed in terms of the linear phenomenological equations without benefit of the Onsager reciprocal relations.)
5. Bennett, C. O., Diffusion in binary mixtures, *Chem. Eng. Sci.* **9**, 45 (1958).
6. Beyers-Brown, W., The thermodynamics of steady conduction-diffusion reaction states of multicomponent fluid system, *Trans. Faraday Soc.* **54**, 772−784 (1958).
7. Brown, R. A., Davies, M. C., and Englert, M. E., The calculation of reduced moments of refractive index gradient curves obtained in diffusion experiments by means of Rayleigh Fringes, *J. Am. Chem. Soc.* **79**, 1787 (1957).
8. Carmann, P. C., and Stein, L. H., Self-diffusion in mixtures, *Trans. Faraday Soc.* **52**, 619 (1956).
9. Chambre, P. L., and Young, J. D., On the diffusion of a chemically reactive species in a laminar boundary layer flow, *Phys. Fluids* **1**, 48 (1958).
10. Christiansen, J. A., Form and content of diffusion equations, *Z. Elektrochem.* **59**, 338 (1955).
11. Clarke, D. M., Free diffusion: diffusion coefficient varying exponentially with concentration, *J. Chem. Phys.* **27**, 29 (1957).
12. Cohen, M., Wagner, C., and Reynolds, J. E., Calculation of interdiffusion coefficients when volume changes occur, *J. Metals* **5**, Trans. AIME 1534 (1953). (If the total volume of a diffusion couple changes during the diffusion, the measurement of distance becomes ambiguous. Use of distance parameters as suggested by Hartley and Crank is discussed. For small concentration differences, the standard form of Fick's second law is retained with conventional length units and the interdiffusion coefficient D. It is shown how D can be calculated from experiments involving large concentration differences and analyzed in terms of distance parameters. The merits of incremental diffusion couples involving small concentration differences are emphasized.)
13. Crank, J., and Henry, M. E., Diffusion in media with variable properties, *Trans. Faraday Soc.* **45**, 1119 (1949).
14. Crank, J., Diffusion in media with variable properties, *Trans. Faraday Soc.* **47**, 450 (1951).
15. Crank, J., Simultaneous diffusion and reversible chemical reaction, *Phil. Mag.* **7**, 811 (1952). (Problem of diffusion in which some of the diffusing substance is immobilized by reversible chemical reaction of first order. Mathematical solutions are derived for the diffusion of a limited amount of solute into a plane sheet, a cylinder, and a sphere, respectively.)

16. Crank, J., The mathematics of diffusion, *Nature* **178**, 609 (1956).
17. Crank, J., Diffusion with rapid irreversible immobilization, *Trans. Faraday Soc.* **53**, 1083 (1957).
18. Creeth, J. M., Studies of free diffusion in liquids with the Rayleigh method. I. The determination of differential diffusion coefficients in concentration-dependent systems of two components, *J. Am. Chem. Soc.* **77**, 6428—6440 (1955).
19. Delahay, P., and Fike, C. T., Adsorption kinetics with diffusion control. The plane and the expanding sphere, *J. Am. Chem. Soc.* **80**, 2628 (1958). (Computer solutions of the corresponding boundary value problems.)
20. Dole, M., Relation between the Onsager and measurable diffusion coefficients in three component systems, *J. Chem. Phys.* **25**, 1082 (1956).
21. Dunlop, P. J., and Gosting, L. J., Interacting flows in liquid diffusion: expressions for the solute concentration curves in free diffusion, and their use in interpreting Gouy diffusimeter data for aqueous three-component systems, *J. Am. Chem. Soc.* **77**, 5238 (1955).
22. Elworthy, P. H., Diffusion measurements by a sampling technique, *J. Sci. Instr.* **35**, 102—103 (1958).
23. Fara, H., and Balluffi, R. W., Analysis of diffusion in media undergoing deformation, *J. Appl. Phy.* **29**, 1133 (1958).
24. Flanders, D. A., and Fricke, H., Applications of a high-speed electronic computer in diffusion kinetics, *J. Chem. Phys.* **28**, 1126 (1958).
25. Frisch, H. L., and Collins, F. C., Diffusional processes in the growth of aerosol particles, *J. Chem. Phys.* **20**, 1797 (1952).
26. Frisch, H. L., Diffusion controlled phase growth, *Z. Elektrochem.* **56**, 324 (1952). (Perturbation theory for unidimensional diffusion problems for semi-infinite space with mobile phase boundary.)
27. Frisch, H. L., The time lag in diffusion, *J. Phys. Chem.* **61**, 93 (1957).
28. Frisch, H. L., The time lag in diffusion II, *J. Phys. Chem.* **62**, 401—404 (1958). (With functional form of the concentration dependence of the diffusion coefficient known, measurements of the time lag in permeation experiments through a membrane at several pressures (or concentrations) allows us to determine both the diffusion coefficient and the solubility of the diffusant in the membrane.)
28a. Frisch, H. L., The time lag in diffusion IV, *J. Phys. Chem.* **63**, 1249 (1959).
29. Fujita, H., and Kishimoto, A., A method for determining the concentration dependence of the diffusion coefficient, *J. Phys. Soc. Japan* **6**, 408—409 (1951).
30. Fujita, H., A numerical solution of the differential equation for adsorption-controlled diffusion in a solid, *Textile Research J.* **22**, 281 (1952); *Bull. Japan. Soc. Sci. Fisheries* **17**, 393 (1952).
31. Fujita, H., and Gosting, L. J., An exact solution of the equations for free diffusion in three-component systems with interacting flows, and its use in evaluation of the diffusion coefficients, *J. Am. Chem. Soc.* **78**, 1099 (1956).
32. Garner, F. H., and Grafton, R. W., Mass transfer in fluid flow from a solid sphere, *Proc. Roy. Soc. (London)* **A224**, 64—82 (1954).
33. Glueckauf, E., Formulae for diffusion into spheres and their application to chromatography, *Trans. Faraday Soc.* **51**, 1540 (1955).
34. Gosting, L. J., and Onsager, L., A general theory for the Gouy diffusion method, *J. Am. Chem. Soc.* **74**, 6066 (1952).

35. de Groot, S. R., Mazur, P., and Overbeek, J. T. G., Nonequilibrium thermodynamics of the sedimentation potential and electrophoresis, *J. Chem. Phys.* **20**, 1825 (1952).

36. de Groot, S. R., Thermodynamic theory of diffusion, *J. chim. phys.* **54**, 851 (1957).

37. de Groot, S. R., Thermodynamics of irreversible processes in physical chemistry, *Svensk Kem. Tidskr.* **65**, 157 (1953).

38. Grün, F., and Blatter, C., A generalization of the frit method for the measurement of diffusion coefficients, *J. Am. Chem. Soc.* **80**, 3838—3839 (1958). (The frit method for determining diffusion coefficients, orginally developed for cylindrical frits, applies for frits of any shape.)

39. Haase, R., Thermodynamic phenomenological theory of irreversible processes, *Ergeb. exakt. Naturw.* **26**, 56, Berlin-Göttingen-Heidelberg (1952).

40. Hall, L. D., An analytical method of calculating variable diffusion coefficients, *J. Chem. Phys.* **21**, 87 (1953). (Matano-Boltzmann method of graphical calculation of diffusion coefficients in solutions is replaced by an analytical method in certain systems.)

41. Hammond, B. R., and Stokes, R. H., Diffusion in binary liquid mixtures, *Trans. Faraday Soc.* **49**, 890 (1953).

42. Hammond, B. R., and Stokes, R. H., Diffusion in binary liquid mixtures, *Trans. Faraday Soc.* **51**, 1641 (1955).

43. Hammond, B. R., and Stokes, R. H., Diffusion in binary liquid mixtures, *Trans. Faraday Soc.* **52**, 781 (1956).

44. Hartley, G. S., and Crank, J., Some fundamental definitions and concepts in diffusion processes, *Trans. Faraday Soc.* **45**, 801 (1949).

45. Hartree, D. R., A method for the numerical integration of the linear diffusion equation, *Proc. Cambridge Phil. Soc.* **54**, 207—213 (1958).

46. Hooyman, G. J., and de Groot, S. R., Phenomenological equations and Onsager relations. The case of dependent fluxes or forces, *Physica* **21**, 73—76 (1954).

47. Hooyman, G. J., de Groot, S. R., and Mazur, P., Transformation properties of the Onsager relations, *Physica* **21**, 360—366 (1955).

48. Hooyman, G. J., Holtan, H. jr., Mazur, P., and de Groot, S. R., Thermodynamics of irreversible processes in rotating systems, *Physica* **19**, 1095—1108 (1953).

49. Hooyman, G. J., Thermodynamics of sedimentation in paucidisperse systems, *Physica* **22**, 761—769 (1956).

50. Hooyman, G. J., Thermodynamics of diffusion in multicomponent systems, *Physica* **22**, 751—759 (1956).

51. Ilschner, B., Calculation of diffusion processes with varying temperature, *Arch. Eisenhüttenwes.* **27**, 337—342 (1956).

52. Jain, S. C., Simple solutions of the partial differential equation for diffusion (or heat conduction), *Proc. Roy. Soc. (London)* **A 243**, 359—374 (1958). (Simple approximate solutions of the partial differential equation for diffusion in finite solids of various shapes and under various conditions can be derived from the simple solutions which are rigorously applicable to linear diffusion in a semi-finite slab.)

53. Jost, W., On a problem of diffusion and simultaneous gas flow, *Chem. Eng. Sci.* **2**, 199—202 (1953); A diffusion problem of spherical symmetry, involving gas flow, cf. W. Morawietz (69).

54. Jost, W., and Oel, H. J., Diffusion in multiphase unidimensional systems, *Z. physik. Chem. (Frankfurt)* [N.S.] **13**, 265 (1957).

55. Karger, W., A method for continuous observation of diffusion processes in solids, *Z. physik. Chem. (Frankfurt)* [N.S.] **14**, 88 (1958).

56. Kaye, J., A table of the first eleven repeated integrals of the error function, *J. Math. and Phys.* **34**, 119—125 (1955).

57. King, G. W., Monte-Carlo method for solving diffusion problems, *Ind. Eng. Chem.* **43**, 2475 (1951).

58. Klinkenberg, A., Krajenbrink, H. J., and Lauwerier, H. A., Diffusion in a fluid moving at uniform velocity in a tube, *Ind. Eng. Chem.* **45**, 1202—1208 (1953).

59. Kraus, G., On the calculation of integral diffusion coefficients from free diffusion experiments, *J. Chem. Phys.* **20**, 200 (1952).

60. Lamm, O., The dynamics of the diffusion of fluids in relation to the choice of components, *J. Phys. Chem.* **59**, 1149 (1955).

61. Lamm, O., An analysis of the dynamical equations of three-component diffusion for the determination of friction coefficients, *J. Phys. Chem.* **61**, 948 (1957).

61a. Lamm, O., Dynamical principles applied to the sedimentation diffusion processes at finite concentrations, *Trans. Roy. Inst. Technology, Stockholm, Sweden* **134** (1959).

62. Lauwerier, H. A., Diffusion from a source in a skew velocity field, *Appl. Sci. Research* **4**, 153—156 (1954). (A fluid flows with nonuniform velocity $v_0 (1 + ay)$ in the x-direction of an x, y plane. The origin is a source of constant strength. For the boundary condition $c = 0$ at $y = -1/a$ the diffusion equation can be solved in an explicit form. A slightly skewed normal distribution function is obtained.)

63. Liu, V. W., Note on diffusive separation of gas mixtures in flow fields, *J. Appl. Phys.* **29**, 1188 (1958). (Effect of pressure-diffusion flux upon the concentration distribution of gas mixtures in flow fields.)

64. Ljunggren, S., and Lamm, O., Diffusion from a bottom layer; diffusion with moving boundaries, *Acta Chem. Scand.* **11**, 340—359 (1957).

65. McMillan, J. A., A countercurrent gaseous diffusion process; theory of the separation at equilibrium, *Z. Naturforsch.* **11a**, 284 (1956).

66. Memelink, O. W., The distribution of impurity in a semi-infinite solidified melt, *Philips Research Repts.* **11**, 183—189 (1956).

67. Miller, D. G., The Validity of Onsager's reciprocal relations in ternary diffusion, *J. Phys. Chem.* **62**, 767 (1958).

68. Monchick, L., Notes on the theory of diffusion controlled reactions: application to photodissociation in solution, *J. Chem. Phys.* **24**, 381 (1956).

69. Morawietz, W., Thermal oxidation of iron sulfide with SO_2 to give elementary sulfur, *Z. Elektrochem.* **57**, 539—548 (1953). (A problem of diffusion and gas flow of spherical symmetry.)

70. Nishijima, Y., and Oster, G., Concentration dependence of diffusion coefficient: analysis of skewed diffusion curve, *J. Chem. Phys.* **27**, 269 (1957).

71. Oel, H. J., Diffusion through membranes, *Z. physik. Chem. (Frankfurt)* [N.S.] **15**, 280 (1958).

72. Ogston, A. G., Methods of describing unidimensional diffusion in binary liquid systems, *Trans. Faraday Soc.* **50**, 1303 (1954).

73. Parsons, D. H., One-dimensional diffusion with the diffusion coefficient a linear function of concentration: reduction to an equation of the first order, *Quart. appl. math.* **15**, 298—303 (1957).

74. Philip, J. R., Numerical solution of equations of the diffusion type with diffusivity concentration-dependent, *Trans. Faraday Soc.* **51**, 885 (1955).

(Iterative procedure for numerical solution of the equation $\partial c/\partial t = \partial/\partial x$ $[D\ \partial c/\partial x]$.)

74a. Philip, J. R., A very general class of exact solutions in concentration-dependent diffusion, *Nature (London)* **185**, 233 (1960).

75. Plesset, M. S., Helfferich, F., and Franklin, J. N., Ion exchange kinetics. A non-linear diffusion problem. II. Particle diffusion controlled exchange of univalent and bivalent ions, *J. Chem. Phys.* **29**, 1064 (1958).

73. Prager, S., Diffusion in binary systems, *J. Chem. Phys.* **21**, 1344 (1953). (Onsager-Fuoss equation for the concentration dependence of the diffusion coefficient is derived from a kinetic picture.)

77. Prigogine, I., and Mazur, P., The thermodynamics of irreversible phenomena associated with internal degrees of freedom, *Physica* **19**, 242—254 (1953).

78. Riehl, N., and Wirths, G., Separation of solutes by countercurrent diffusion, *Z. physik. Chem. (Frankfurt)* [N.S.] **6**, 265 (1956).

79. Roe, G. M., and Stark, R. H., Numerical solution of diffusion in cylindrical coordinates, *Phys. Rev.* **96**, 820 (1954).

80. Rosen, P., On variational principles for irreversible processes, *J. Chem. Phys.* **21**, 1220 (1953).

81. Schulz, G. V., Relations between diffusion coefficient and rate constant of bimolecular reactions in solution, *Z. physik. Chem. (Frankfurt)* [N.S.] **8**, 284 (1956).

82. Simmons, J., and Dorn, J. E., Analyses for diffusion during plastic deformation, *J. Appl. Phys.* **29**, 1308 (1958).

83. O'Sullivan, D. G., Treatment of the equations of classical diffusion in homogeneous isotropic media, *J. Chem. Phys.* **25**, 270 (1956).

84. Stokes, R. H., One-dimensional diffusion with the diffusion coefficient a linear function of concentration, *Trans. Faraday Soc.* **48**, 887 (1952).

85. Tannhauser, D. S., Concerning a systematic error in measuring diffusion constants, *J. Appl. Phy.* **27**, 662 (1956).

85a. Tykodi, R. J., Thermodynamics, stationary states, and steady-rate processes, I, II, III, IV, *J. Chem. Phys.* **31**, 1506, 1510, 1517, 1521 (1959); II and IV with Erikson, T. A.

86. Vielstich, W., Nernst's diffusion layer and Prandtl's boundary layer, *Z. Elektrochem.* **57**, 646 (1953). (Thickness of diffusion layer derived by means of dimensional analysis from Prandtl's boundary layer. Results are compared with experiment.)

87. Wagner, C., Flow, diffusion, and chemical reaction in heterogeneous catalysis, *Z. physik. Chem. (Leipzig)* **193 A**, 1 (1944).

88. Wagner, C., The solution of diffusion problems involving concentration-dependent diffusion coefficients, *J. Metals* **4**, *AIME Trans.* 91—96 (1952). (Solutions of the equation of diffusion in binary alloys if the diffusion coefficient is an exponential function of the concentration.)

89. Wagner, C., Theoretical analysis of diffusion of solutes during the solidification of alloys, *J. Metyls* **6**, *AIME Trans.* **200**, 154—160 (1954). (Theoretical calculations have been made for a liquid, involving natural convection, and for solidification of a liquid alloy at the surface of a rotating disk.)

90. Waite, T. R., Theoretical treatment of kinetics of diffusion-limited reactions, *Phys. Rev.* **107**, 463 (1957).

91. Wall, F. T., and Wendt, R. G., Determination of differential diffusion coefficients, *J. Phys. Chem.* **62**, 1581 (1958). (Numerical solutions of the diffusion equation were obtained for determining concentration-dependent diffusion coefficients by means of the "buoyant frit" method.)

92. Ward, A. F. H., and Brooks, L. H., Diffusion across interfaces, *Trans. Faraday Soc.* **48**, 1124 (1952).

93. Weller, A., A generalized theory of diffusion controlled reactions, and its application to fluorescence quenching, *Z. physik. Chem. (Frankfurt)* [N.S.] **13**, 335 (1957).

94. White, J. R., Diffusion coefficient measurement with glass diaphragm cells, *J. Chem. Phys.* **24**, 470 (1956).

95. Wild, W., Non-stationary diffusion in striated media, *Z. angew. Phys.* **9**, 38 (1957).

96. Wilke, C. R., and Prausnitz, J. M., Mass transfer: molecular diffusion in gases, liquids, and solids; turbulent diffusion; interfacial phenomena; mass transfer by diffusion and convection, *Ind. Eng. Chem.* **50**, 557 (1958).

97. Wise, H., and Ablow, C. M., Diffusion and heterogeneous reaction. I. The dynamics of radical reactions, *J. Chem. Phys.* **29**, 634 (1958). (Theoretical treatment of diffusion and heterogeneous reaction in a cylinder of finite length.)

DIFFUSION IN SOLIDS

(Supplementary to Chapters II-IX, pages 83-405 in this volume)

The field of diffusion in solids has grown so tremendously since the first edition of this book was published, that it is impossible to attempt to present a complete survey of the field. Only a brief treatment will be attempted here.

Theory gives for the mobility of a particle in a crystal an expression which is essentially proportional to $M^{-1/2}$, M being the molecular mass*. To a certain approximation this had been found for the rate of diffusion of H and D in palladium (cf. pp. 311—312 of this volume). For the diffusion of sodium ions in NaCl this has been verified by Chemla (B, 4)** for the ions Na^{22} and Na^{24}. For the migration of interstitial particles a mechanism, first suggested by Koch and Wagner (73 on p. 177 of this volume), has been further treated by Seitz (96a on p. 178 of this volume), McCombie (B, 27); cf. also Lidiard (A, 18)., This assumes a process combined of a jump of the interstitial to a normal lattice site,

---

* See, however, Thor A. Bak (B 2a), p. 80ff.

** In this chapter of the supplement the references at the end of the chapter are divided into five sections as follows: A. Monographs and Review Articles Concerned with Fundamental Questions in this Field; B. Diffusion in Solids, General; C. Diffusion, Chiefly in Inorganic Compounds, Especially Ionic Crystals; D. Diffusion in Metals; E. Permeation. In the text citations of reference in this chapter the letter preceding the reference number indicates the section of the reference list in which the particular reference can be found; thus (B, 4) refers to reference 4 in section B.

and of the normal lattice particle to another interstitial site. This process may involve lower activation energy than the motion from one interstitial site to another, and be responsible for apparently very low energy barriers observed in diffusion and conductivity at low temperatures.

For a properly defined self-diffusion coefficient the Nernst-Einstein relation connecting diffusion and ionic conduction (cf. p. 139 of this volume) should always be valid. This is, however, no longer true if tracer diffusion is considered, even if we correct for effects due to the remaining small differences in mass. As first pointed out and discussed by Bardeen and Herring (A, 28) in the case of a vacancy mechanism there is a correlation between successive jumps of a tracer ion. This gives rise to a correlation factor decreasing the tracer diffusion coefficient by a factor between one-half and one, as compared with the Nernst-Einstein value (the factor for face centered cubic lattice is 0.78) cf. Haven and Compaan (B, 5, 6, 7). For Frenkel disorder and normal interstitial migration no correlation is to be expected. This becomes different, however, if the process suggested by Koch and Wagner and called interstitialcy mechanism by Seitz plays a role. If an interstitial ion pushes a particle from its normal site to another interstitial site, occupying itself the emptied lattice site, there exists a correlation. This has been treated by McCombie and Lidiard (B, 27).

It should be emphasized that all equations referring to disorder and migration of disordered particles or vacancies originally contain free energies while for practical applications these magnitudes often must be replaced by total energies (or enthalpies). This fact must always be kept in mind, especially if a dependence on temperature or pressure is under consideration.

The importance of the entropy of activation was first stressed by Zener (A, 28) especially the fact that ΔS usually should be positive. Haven (B, 13a) pointed out that for a system where the energy of activation decreases with temperature, due to a difference in specific heats, the entropy of activation is negative.

We treat as an example, a simplified one-dimensional model, Fig. A 2-1. We assume an oscillator which may represent a particle in its equilibrium position in a lattice, 0, Fig. 1, the levels 0, 1, 2, . . . referring to the different vibrational levels of the oscillator (assumed to be harmonic). In an irregular position 1 (for instance as interstitial particle) we have a higher energy, E_0 per N particles (including zero point energy, $h(\nu' - \nu)/2)^*$ with vibrational levels $0', 1', 2', \ldots$ If we

---

* In the "Einstein" approximation. For the sake of simplicity we also assume constant volume.

consider $n = n_0 + n_1$ particles, the fraction of irregular particles $\alpha = n_1/n$ or the ratio of irregular to regular particles, $\alpha' = n_1/n_0$, would be, neglecting the contribution of vibrations

(a) $$\alpha = \exp \frac{-E_0/RT}{[1 + \exp(-E_0/RT)]}$$

(b) $$\alpha' = \exp(-E_0/RT) \approx \alpha \qquad \text{if } E_0 \gg RT .$$

[A 2.1]

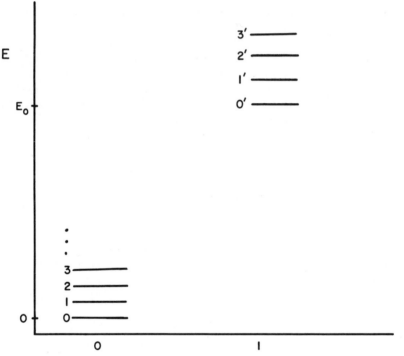

Fig. A 2-1. Simplified one-dimensional model.

Considering now the influence of vibrations we have, if we denote the vibrational frequency in the normal state by ν and that in the irregular state by ν'

$$\alpha = \frac{\exp(-E_0/RT) \sum\limits_{0}^{\infty} \exp(-nh\nu'/kT)}{\sum\limits_{0}^{\infty} \exp(-nh\nu/kT) + \exp(-E_0/RT) \sum\limits_{0}^{\infty} \exp(-nh\nu'/kT)} .$$

[A 2.2]

To obtain a feeling for the content of this formula, we calculate the simpler ratio α' which for E_0 sufficiently large is identical with [A 2.2] and treat some limiting cases*

$$\frac{n_1}{n_0} = \alpha' = \exp\left(- E_0/RT\right) \frac{\overset{\infty}{\underset{0}{\Sigma}} \exp\left(- nh\nu'/kT\right)}{\overset{\infty}{\underset{0}{\Sigma}} \exp\left(- nh\nu/kT\right)} .$$ [A 2.3]

1. $$\nu = \nu'$$

$$\frac{n_1}{n_0} = \alpha' = \exp\left(-E_0/RT\right),$$ [A 2.4]

a trivial result which, however, is useful for comparison.

2. $$\nu' \gg \nu$$

$$\frac{n_1}{n_0} = \alpha' \approx \exp\left(- E_0/RT\right) \frac{1}{\overset{\infty}{\underset{0}{\Sigma}} \exp\left(- nh\nu/kT\right)}$$ [A 2.5]

$$< \exp\left(- E_0/RT\right)$$

and vice versa for

(3) $$\nu' \ll \nu$$

$$\frac{n_1}{n_0} = \alpha' \approx \exp\left(- E_0/RT\right) \overset{\infty}{\underset{0}{\Sigma}} \exp\left(- nh\nu'/kT\right) > \exp\left(- E_0/RT\right).$$
[A 2.6]

Qualitatively cases (2) and (3) mean the following. In (2) we have only the lowest upper state 0, while in the lower state the particles are spread over several vibrational levels. Consequently, the average energy difference $\Delta\bar{E}$ of irregular particles with respect to normal particles is smaller than E_0, because the average lower level has been raised

$$\Delta\bar{E} = E_0 - \beta T < E_0 \, (\beta > 0)$$ [A 2.7]

β being the average specific heat of the lower state which might be calculated by standard methods.

If we would have started with equation [A 2.4] and just inserted $\Delta\bar{E}$ of [A 2.7] we should have obtained

$$\frac{n_1}{n_0} = \exp\left(- E_0/RT\right) \exp\left(\beta/R\right) > \exp\left(- E_0/RT\right),$$ [A 2.8]

which obviously is wrong. Since $\exp\left(\beta/R\right) > 1$, equation [A 2.8] states qualitatively the opposite of what equation [A 2.5] says:

* Though not all of these are of practical importance.

actually, by spreading the normal particles over a number of vibrational levels we provide more possibilities for having normal particles, thus increasing their relative number though the average energy gap to the irregular level has been decreased. Conversely, the same argument holds with respect to [A 2.6], and for the general case. Thus it is not permitted, as is generally known, to insert a temperature-dependent energy into the final formula for equilibrium. This error would not have occurred when employing free energy.

The above example refers to a temperature dependence of a reaction energy if this dependence is due to a difference in specific heats (here caused by a difference in vibrational frequencies) of the different modifications.

In the classic limiting case, $kT \gg h\nu, h\nu'$ there remains to a first approximation:

$$\frac{n_1}{n_0} = \exp\left(-E_0/RT\right)\frac{\nu}{\nu'}, \qquad [A\ 2.9]$$

with an obvious generalization for more than one degree of freedom.

But now we can imagine a different type of temperature dependence. Suppose that due to a mechanism independent of the thermodynamics of the above equilibria the magnitude E_0 itself depends on temperature (and pressure), $E_0 = E(T, P)$*. This might be valid, for instance, if 0 refers to an interstitial ion and 1 to its activated state on top of an energy barrier. Then the ratio n_1/n_0 becomes

$$\frac{n_1}{n_0} = \alpha' = \exp\left(-E(T,P)/RT\right)\frac{\sum\limits_{0}^{\infty}\exp\left(-h\nu'/kT\right)}{\sum\limits_{0}^{\infty}\exp\left(-h\nu/kT\right)} \qquad [A\ 2.10]$$

where we refrain from discussing whether ν and ν' might or might not depend on T and P**. Thus, here, it is permitted both, to insert a temperature-dependent energy into the exponential and to connect temperature and pressure dependence. For, if both are interconnected by the change of a lattice parameter, E is primarily determined as a function of the lattice parameter, and its change with temperature is given by applying the known relation for thermal expansion, and of compressibility in case of pressure. This is the effect as originally suggested by Jost (62 on p. 177 of this volume) and first observed by Jost and Nehlep (68 on p. 177 of this volume).

---

* Of course we no longer may assume constancy of volume.
** Here, in addition, anharmonicity of vibrations must be considered because otherwise there would be no thermal expansion.

A purely thermodynamic treatment would be as follows. We have an energy of activation U, which depends explicitly on the volume V, and on T and P only through V, thus

$$\left(\frac{\partial U}{\partial T}\right)_V = 0 \qquad \text{[A 2.11]}$$

$$\left(\frac{\partial U}{\partial T}\right)_P = \left(\frac{\partial U}{\partial V}\right)_T \left(\frac{\partial V}{\partial T}\right)_P \qquad \text{[A 2.12]}$$

$$\left(\frac{\partial U}{\partial P}\right)_T = \left(\frac{\partial U}{\partial V}\right)_T \left(\frac{\partial V}{\partial P}\right)_T . \qquad \text{[A 2.13]}$$

Putting

$$\left(\frac{\partial U}{\partial V}\right)_T = a \qquad \text{[A 2.14]}$$

where a generally will be negative, and introducing the usual coefficients

$$\alpha = \frac{1}{V}\left(\frac{\partial V}{\partial T}\right)_P \qquad \text{[A 2.15]}$$

$$\varkappa = -\frac{1}{V}\left(\frac{\partial V}{\partial P}\right)_T \qquad \text{[A 2.16]}$$

we have

$$\left(\frac{\partial U}{\partial T}\right)_P = a\,\overline{V}\,\alpha \qquad \text{[A 2.17]}$$

where $\overline{V}$ is the molal volume, and

$$\left(\frac{\partial U}{\partial P}\right)_T = -a\,\overline{V}\varkappa . \qquad \text{[A 2.18]}$$

In the approximation: $a, \alpha, \varkappa$ are independent of T (which precludes a consideration of very low temperatures and implies certain other simplifications) we have

$$U = U_0 + a\,\overline{V}\alpha T \qquad P = \text{constant} \approx 0^* \qquad \text{[A 2.19]}$$

$$U = U_0 - a\,\overline{V}\varkappa P \qquad T = \text{constant} \qquad \text{[A 2.20]}$$

The standard free energy of activation G_{12}^o for the transition $1 \to 2$ would be

$$\overline{G_{12}^o} = \overline{U_{12,0}^o} + a\,\overline{V}\alpha T + P\,\overline{V_{12}^o} - T\,\overline{S_{12}^o} . \qquad \text{[A 2.21]}$$

The activation volume $\overline{V_{12}^o}$ will be such that the reversible work done for activation, $-P\,\overline{V_{12}^o}$ must be compensated by the heat supplied $\overline{Q_{12}^o}$

* With sufficient accuracy valid for $P = 1$ atm.

to keep T = constant thus

$$P\,\overline{V^o_{12}} = \overline{Q^o_{12}} \qquad\qquad \text{[A 2.22]}$$

and consequently for the entropy $\overline{S^o_{12}}$

$$\overline{S^o_{12}} = \frac{P\,\overline{V^o_{12}}}{T} \qquad\qquad \text{[A 2.23]}$$

It follows that in [A 2.21] the last two terms cancel each other. On the other hand

$$\overline{S^o_{12}} = -\,\frac{\partial \overline{G^o_{12}}}{\partial T} \qquad\qquad \text{[A 2.24]}$$

and consequently

$$\overline{S^o_{12}} = -\,a\,\overline{V}\alpha\ . \qquad\qquad \text{[A 2.25]}$$

In addition it follows from [A 2.21] and [A 2.22]:

$$\overline{V^o_{12}} = \frac{\partial \overline{G^o_{12}}}{\partial P} = a\alpha\,T\,\frac{\partial \overline{V}}{\partial P}\ . \qquad\qquad \text{[A 2.26]}$$

Now there is the general thermodynamic relation

$$\left(\frac{\partial S}{\partial V}\right) = \left(\frac{\partial P}{\partial T}\right) = \frac{\alpha}{\varkappa}\ . \qquad\qquad \text{[A 2.27]}$$

Since we have assumed that with sufficient accuracy linear relations are valid, this is equivalent to

$$\frac{\overline{S^o_{12}}}{\overline{V^o_{12}}} = \frac{P}{T} = \frac{\alpha}{\varkappa} \qquad\qquad \text{[A 2.28]}$$

and with [A 2.25]

$$\overline{V^o_{12}} = \frac{\varkappa}{\alpha} \qquad \overline{S^o_{12}} = -\,a\,\overline{V}\varkappa\ . \qquad\qquad \text{[A 2.30]}$$

Thus we have a thermodynamically consistent description of the pressure and temperature dependence of the activation equilibrium.

REFERENCES FOR DIFFUSION IN SOLIDS*

A. Monographs and Review Articles Concerned with Fundamental Questions in this Field

1. Chalmers, B., Structure of crystal boundaries, *Progr. in Metal Phys.* **3**, 293—318 (1952).
2. Cupp, C. R., Gases in metals, *Progr. in Metal Phys.* **4**, 105—166 (1953).

* These references are divided into five sections as follows: A. Monographs and Review Articles Concerned with Fundamental Questions in the Field; B. Diffusion in Solids, General; C. Diffusion, Chiefly in Inorganic Compounds, Especially Ionic Crystals; D. Diffusion in Metals; E. Permeation.

3. Darken, L. S., and Gurry, R. W., Physical chemistry of Metals. McGraw-Hill, New York, 1953.
4. Dekker, A. J., Solid State Physics. Prentice-Hall, Eaglewood Cliffs, New Jersey, 1958.
5. Dienes, G. J., and Vineyard, G. H., Vol. I: The Fundamental Constants of Physics; Vol. II: Radiation Effects in Solids. Interscience, New York, 1957.
6. Fast, J. D., van Bueren, H. G., and Philibert, J., La Diffusion dans les Metaux. Comt. rend. colloque tenu a Eindhoven les 10 et 11 September, 1956. Bibliotheque Technique Philips, Eindhoven, Netherlands, 1956.
7. Garner, W. E., Chemistry of the Solid State. Academic Press, New York, 1955.
8. Geach, G. A., The theory of sintering, Progr. in Metal Phys. 4, 174—201 (1953).
9. Hauffe, K., The mechanism of oxidation of metals and alloys at high temperatures. Progr. in Metals Phys. 4, 71—102 (1953).
10. Hauffe, K., Reaktionen in und an festen Stoffen. Springer, Berlin, 1955.
11. Hauffe, K., Oxydation von Metallen und Metallegierungen. Springer, Berlin, 1957.
12. Hobstetter, J. N., Equilibrium, diffusion and imperfections in semiconductors, Progr. in Metal Phys. 7, 1—63 (1958).
13. Jost, W., Fortschritte der physikalischen Chemie 1. Bd. Diffusion. D. Steinkopff, Darmstadt, 1957.
14. Kleppa, O. J., The solid state: diffusion in metals and alloys, Ann. Rev. Phys. Chem. 6, 119 (1955).
15. Kittel, C., Introduction to Solid State Physics. Wiley, New York, 1953.
15a. Lazarus, D., Diffusion in Metals, Solid State Physics Vol. 10 (1960).
16. Le Claire, A. D., Diffusion of metals in metals, Progr. in Metal Phys. 1, 306—375 (1949).
17. Le Claire, A. D., Diffusion in metals, Progr. in Metal Phys. 4, 265—329 (1953).
18. Lidiard, A. B., Ionic conductivity, in Encyclopedia of Physics (Handbuch der Physik), edited by S. Flügge, Vol. XX: Electrical Conductivity II, pp. 246—349. Springer, Berlin, 1957.
19. Lipson, H., Order-disorder changes in alloys, Progr. in Metal Phys. 2, 1—50 (1950).
20. A. S. Nowick, Internal friction in metals, Progr. in Metal Phys. 4, 1—67 (1953).
21. Prigogine, I., ed., Proceedings of the International. Symposium on Transport Processes in Statistical Mechanics. Interscience, New York, 1958.
22. Schottky, W., Halbleiterprobleme: Bd. 1 (1954); Bd. 2 (1955); Bd. 3 (1956); Bd. 4 (1958). Friedrich Vieweg & Sohn, Braunschweig.
23. Seeger, A., Theory of lattice defects, in Encyclopedia of Physics (Handbuch der Physik), edited by S. Flügge, Vol. VII, 1 Crystal Physics I, pp. 383—663. Springer, Berlin, 1955.
24. Seeger, A., Crystal plasticity, in Encyclopedia of Physics (Handbuch der Physik), edited by S. Flügge Vol. VII, 2 Crystal Physics II, pp. 1—193. Springer, Berlin, 1958.
25. Seith, W., Diffusion in Metallen. Springer, Berlin, 1955.
26. Seitz, F., The Physics of Metals. McGraw-Hill, New York, 1943.
27. Seitz, F., and Turnbull, D., Solid State Physics: Advances in Research and Applications. Vol. 1 (1955); Vol. 2 (1956); Vol. 3 (1956); Vol. 4 (1957); Vol. 5 (1957). Academic Press, New York.

28. Shokley, W., Hollomon, J. H., Maurer, R., and Seitz, F., eds. Imperfections in Nearly Perfect Crystals (Symposium held at Pocono Manor, October 12—14, 1950). Wiley, New York, 1952; Chapman and Hall, London, 1952.
29. Smiths, F. M., Diffusion in homöopolaren Halbleitern *Ergeb. exakt. Naturw.* **31**, Bd. (1959).
30. Smoluchowski, R., Meyer, J. E., and Weyl, W. A., Phase Transformations in Solids (Symposium, 1948, Cornell University). Wiley, New York, 1951.
31. Stasiw, O., Elektronen- und Ionenprozesse in Ionenkristallen. Springer, Berlin, 1959.
32. Stevels, J. M., The electrical properties of glass, *in* Encyclopedia of Physics (Handbuch der Physik), edited by S. Flügge, Vol. XX, Electrical Conductivity II, pp. 350—91, Springer, Berlin, 1957.
33. Colloque sur la diffusion a l'état solide [Symposium on Solid State Diffusion North-Holland Publ., Amsterdam, Holland, 1959.] organisé à Saclay les 3, 4, et 5 juillet 1958 sous la présidence de Monsieur le Professeur Chaudron, Membre de l'Institut with contributions by: 1. A. D. G. Claire; 2. A. G. Mortlock; 3. R. Graf and A. Guinier; 4. H. Bückle; 5. Cl. Leymonie and P. Lacombe; 5. P. Michel; 7. A. Accary; 8. R. S. Barnes; 9. J. Blin; 10. J. A. Stohr and J. L. Bernard; 11. G. Sainfort; 12. A. Vinogradzki and M. Azam; 13. M. Gauthron; 14. Y. Adda and J. Philibert; 15. R. Boucher; 16. G. Chauvin, H. Coriou, and J. Hure; 17. A. Herold; 18. R. Sifferlen; 19. S. Besnard and M. J. Talbot; 20. J. Plusquellec, P. Azou and P. Bastien; 21. J. Philibert and Y. Adda.

B. Diffusion in Solids, General

1. Anderson, P. W., Absence of diffusion in certain random lattices, *Phys. Rev.* **109**, 1492 (1958).
2. Babbitt, J. D., Diffusion of adsorbed molecules, *Nature* **182**, 201 (1958). Reply by Carman, P. C., *Nature* **182**, 201 (1958); Carman. P. C., Flow of gases through porous media, *Nature* **178**, 824 (1956).
2a. Bak, T. A., Contributions to the theory of chemical kinetics, Munksgaard, København, 1959.
3. Brinkman, J. A., The effect of temperature gradients on diffusion, *Phys. Rev.* **93**, 345 (1954). (On the basis of a treatment by Shockley it is shown, that vacancies should move toward warm regions if their energy of formation E_f exceeds the activation energy for migration E_m, and vice versa.)
4. Chemla, M., Diffusion of radioactive ions in crystals, (with 94 references) *Ann. phys.* [13] **1**, 159 (1956).
5. Compaan, K., and Haven, Y., Some fundamental aspects of the mechanism of diffusion in crystals, *Discussions Faraday Soc.* **23**, 105 (1957).
6. Compaan, K., and Haven, Y., Correlation factors for diffusion in solids. II. Indirect interstitial mechanism, *Trans. Faraday Soc.* **54**, 1498 (1958).
7. Compaan, K., and Haven, Y., Diffusion of tracers through solids, *in* Transport Processes in Statistical Mechanics (I. Proigogine, ed.), pp. 414—418. Interscience, New York, 1958.
8. Compton, W. D., Self-diffusion and conductivity in silver chloride, *Phys. Rev.* **101**, 1209 (1956).
9. Crank, J., Diffusion coefficients in solids, their measurement and significance *Discussions Faraday Soc.* **23**, 99 (1957).
10. Freund, T., Diffusion and gas sorption rates obeying the Elovich equation, *J. Chem. Phys.* **26**, 713 (1957).

11. Haul, R. A. W., Surface diffusion, *Angew. Chem.* **68**, 444 (1956). (Review.)
12. Haul, R. A. W., Surface diffusion in porous adsorbents, *Angew. Chem.* **69**, 393 (1957). (Review.)
13. Haven. Y., and van Santen, J. H., Dielectric relaxation of lattice defects in crystals, *Nuovo Cimento* [10] **7**, Suppl. 2, 605—611 (1958).
13a. Haven, Y., and van Santen, J. H., On preexponential factors in formulae for ionic conductivity in solids, *Philips Research Repts* **7**, 474 (1952).
14. Hoffmann, R. E., Turnbull, D., and Hart, E. W., Self-diffusion in dilute binary solid solutions, *Acta. Met.* **3**, 417 (1955).
15. Honig, J. M., Application of order-disorder concepts to kinetics of diffusionless transitions in solids, *J. Chem. Phys.* **28**, 723 (1958).
16. Ilschner, B., Determination of the electronic conductivity in silver halides by means of polarisation measurements, *J. Chem. Phys.* **28**, 1109—1112 (1958).
17. Ilschner-Gensch, C., and Wagner, C., Local cell action during the scaling of metals. I., *J. Electrochem. Soc.* **105**, 198 (1958).
18. Ilschner-Gensch, C., Local cell action during the scaling of metals. II., *J. Electrochem. Soc.* **105**, 635 (1958).
19. Jordan, P., and Pochon, M., Determination of diffusion coefficients of silver and iodine in the three modifications of Ag I, *Helv. Phys. Acta.* **30**, 33—48 (1957).
20. Keyes, R. W., Diffusion of lattice defects in a temperature gradient, *Phys. Rev.* **94**, 1389 (1954).
21. Keyes, R. W., Volumes of activation for diffusion solids, *J. Chem. Phys.* **29**, 467 (1958).
22. Kröger, F. A., and Vink, H. J., Relation between the concentrations of imperfections in solids, *Phys. and Chem. Solids* **5**, 208 (1958).
23. Kuper, A., Letaw, H. jr., Slifkin, L., Sonder, E., and Tomizuka, C. T., Self-diffusion in copper $[D = 0.468 \exp (- 47140/RT)$ between 685 and 1062° C], *Phys. Rev.* **96**, 1224 (1954).
24. Le Claire, A. D., and Lidiard, A. B., Correlation effects in diffusion in crystals, *Phil. Mag.* [8] **1**, 518 (1956).
25. Lieser, K. H., Disorder and phase transformations in silver iodide, *Fortschr. Mineral.* **36**, 96—118 (1958).
26. Lidiard, A. B., Impurity diffusion in crystals (mainly ionic crystals with sodium chloride structure), *Phil. Mag.* **46**, 1218—1237 (1955).
27. McCombie, C. W., Ratio of ionic conductivity to tracer diffusion in intersticialcy migration, *Phys. Rev.* **101**, 1210 (1956).
27a. Manning, J. R., Correlation effects in impurity diffusion, *Phys. Rev.* **116**, 819 (1960).
28. Pimental, G. C., Reactions kinetics by the Matrix isolation method: diffusion in argon; *cis-trans* isomerization of nitrous acid, *J. Am. Chem. Soc.* **80**, 62 (1958).
29. Pochon, M., Study of the self-diffusion in silver iodide by means of the heterogeneous isotope exchange technique, Thesis, Swiss Polytechnic Institute, Zürich, 1956.
29a. Prigogine, I., and Bak, Th. A., Diffusion and chemical reaction in a one-dimensional condensed system, *J. Chem. Phys.* **31**, 1368 (1959).
30. Rubin, R. J., Random motion of a heavy particle substituted in a one-dimensional crystal lattice, *in* Transport Processes in Statistical Mechanics (I. Prigogine, ed.), pp. 155—160. Interscience, New York, 1958.
31. Schoen, A. H., Correlation and the isotope effect for diffusion in crystalline solids, *Phys. Rev. Letters* **1**, 138 (1958).

32. Shuchowitzki, A. A., and Geodakjan, W. A., On the measurement of small diffusion coefficients, *J. Phys. Chem. (U.S.S.R.)* **29**, 1334—1337 (1955).

32a. Simmons, R. O., and Baluffi, R. W., Measurements of equilibrium vacancy concentrations in aluminum, *Phys. Rev.* **117**, 52 (1960).

32b. Simmons, R. O., and Baluffi, R. W., Measurement of the high-temperature electrical resistance of aluminum: resistivity of lattice vacancies, *Phys. Rev.* **117**, 62 (1960).

33. Smith, R. L., Jaumot, F. E., and Arné, L. A. jr., Comparison of diffusion techniques using radioactive tracers, *Phys. Rev.* **94**, 1407 (1954).

34. ter Haar, D., On the theory of transport phenomena in solids, *in* Transport Processes in Statistical Mechanics (I. Prigogine, ed.), pp. 192—197. Interscience, New York, 1958.

35. Tomizuka, C. T., and Slifkin, L., Diffusion of cadmium, indium and tin in single crystals of silver, *Phys. Rev.* **96**, 610 (1954).

36. Verkerk, B., Winkel, P., and de Groot, D. G., On the mechanism of oxidation of tantalum, *Philips Research Repts.* **13**, 506—508 (1958).

37. Wagner, C., Passivity during the oxidation of silicon at elevated temperatures, *J. Appl. Phys.* **29**, 1295 (1958).

38. Weisz, P. B., Diffusivity of porous particles: I. Measurements and significance for internal reaction velocities. *Z. physik. Chem. (Frankfurt)* [N.S.] **11**, 1 (1957).

39. Zimen, K. E., Isotope exchange with solids as method for self-diffusion measurements, *Proc. Intern. Symposium on Reactivity of Solids. Gothenburg*, **1952**, 85—92 (1954).

C. Diffusion, Chiefly in Inorganic Compounds, Especially Ionic Crystals

1. Aronson, S., Roof, R. B., Jr., and Belle, J., Kinetic study of the oxidation of uranium dioxide, *J. Chem. Phys.* **27**, 137 (1957).

2. Auskern, A. B., and Belle, J., Self-diffusion of oxygen in uranium dioxide *J. Chem. Phys.* **28**, 171 (1958).

3. Auth, J., Diffusion of charge carriers in photoconductors, *Ann. Physik* **20**, 210 (1957).

4. Auth, J., and Ridder, R., Diffusion of charge carriers in CdS, *Z. Naturforsch.* **13a**, 426 (1958).

5. Bass, R., The theory of the mechanical relaxation in pure ice crystals (diffusion of lattice defects), *Z. Physik* **153**, 16 (1958).

6. Beattie, I. R., and Dyer, A., The diffusion of sodium ions in analcite as a function of water content, *Trans. Faraday Soc.* **53**, 61 (1957).

7. Belle, J., and Auskern, A. E., Oxygen ion self-diffusion in uranium oxide, *Angew. Chem.* **70**, 603 (1958).

8. von Bogdandy, L., and Janke, W., On the importance of diffusion in pores during reduction of iron ore, *Z. Elektrochem.* **61**, 1146 (1957).

9. Brebick, R. F., and Scanlon, W. W., Chemical etches and etch pit patterns on PbS crystals, *J. Chem. Phys.* **27**, 607 (1957).

10. Burstein, E., Davisson, J. W., and Sclar, N., Low-frequency dielectric loss peaks in KCl containing bivalent-cation impurities, *Phys. Rev.* **96**, 819 (1954).

11. Chemla, M., Self-diffusion coefficients of chloride ion in single crystals of sodium chloride, *Compt. rend.* **234**, 2601—2602 (1952).

12. Chemla, M., Diffusion of radioactive ions in crystals, *Ann. Phys.* [13] **1**, 959 (1956).

13. Compton, W. D., Self-diffusion and conductivity in silver-chloride, *Phys. Rev.* **101**, 1209 (1956).
14. Compton, W. D., and Maurer, R. J., Self-diffusion and electrical conductivity in silver-chloride, *Phys. and Chem. Solids* **1**, 191—199 (1956).
15. Doremus, R. H., Diffusion of calcium to dislocations in potassium chloride, *J. Phys. Chem.* **61**, 1677—1678 (1957).
16. Dux, J. P., and Steigman, J., The self-diffusion coefficient of strontium as counter-ion to polystyrenesulfonic acid, *J. Phys. Chem.* **62**, 288 (1958).
17. Ebert, I., and Teltow, J., Ionic conductivity and disorder of AgCl with additives, *Ann. Physik* **15**, 268 (1955).
18. Eyring, L., Diffusion of oxygen in rare earth oxides, *Angew. Chem.* **70**, 603 (1958). (Review.)
19. Ewles, J., and Jain, S. C., Diffusion of negative ion vacancies in potassium chloride, *Proc. Roy. Soc. (London)* **A 243**, 353 (1957).
20. Fischer, W. A., and Hoffmann, A., Volume changes in diffusion zone of oxide systems, *Naturwissenschaften* **41**, 162 (1954).
21. Fischer, W. A., and Hoffmann, A., Measurement of electromotive forces at 1500°C and x-ray investigations in the system ferrous oxide-alumina, *Arch. Eisenhüttenw.* **26**, 43—50 (1955).
22. Fischer, W. A., and Hoffmann, A., Measurement of the electromotive forces at 1500°C and x-ray investigations in the system magnesia-alumina, *Arch. Eisenhüttenw.* **26**, 63—70 (1955).
23. Friauf, R. J., Polarization effects in the ionic conductivity of silver bromide, *J. Chem. Phys.* **22**, 1329 (1954).
24. Friauf, R. J., Diffusion of Ag in AgBr and evidence for interstitialcy migration, *Phys. Rev.* **105**, 843 (1957).
25. Gilman, J. J., and Johnston, W. G., Dislocations, point-defect clusters, and cavities in neutron irradiated LiF crystals, *J. Appl. Phys.* **29**, 877 (1958).
26. Glasner, A., and Reinsfeld, R., New experimental method for the evaluation of diffusion constants in alkali halides, *J. Chem. Phys.* **25**, 381 (1956).
27. Goddard, P. E., and Urbach, F., Ionic mobility at grain boundaries, *J. Chem. Phys.* **20**, 1975 (1952).
28. Harpur, W. W., Moss, R. L., and Ubbelohde, A. R., Electrical conductance mechanisms in solid caesium halides, *Proc. Roy. Soc. (London)* **A 232**, 196 (1955).
29. Harpur, W. W., and Ubbelohde, A. R., Conductance mechanisms and the thermal transition in caesium chloride, *Proc. Roy. Soc. (London)* **A 232**, 310 (1955).
30. Harrison, A. G., Morrison, J. A., and Rudham, R., Chloride ion Diffusion in sodium chloride. Interactions between point imperfections at low temperature, *Trans. Faraday Soc.* **54**, 106 (1958).
31. Herring, C., Diffusional viscosity in polycrystals, *J. Appl. Phys.* **21**, 437—445 (1950).
32. Hill, R. A. W., A diffusion chain theory of the decomposition of inorganic solids, *Trans. Faraday Soc.* **54**, 685 (1958).
33. Jacobs, G., Dielectric relaxation in sodium chloride crystals, *Naturwissenschaften* **42**, 575 (1955).
34. Jacobs, P. W. M., and Tompkins, F. C., Ionic conductance of some solid metallic azides, *J. Chem. Phys.* **23**, 1445 (1955).
35. Johnston, W. G., Effect of plastic deformation on the electrical conductivity of silver bromide, *Phys. Rev.* **98**, 1777 (1955).

36. Jost, W., and Nölting, J., Disorder in α-silver iodide, *Z. physik. Chem. (Frankfurt)* [N.S.] **7**, 383—385 (1956). (Self-diffusion of I^- ions: $D = D_0 e^{-Q/RT}$ $Q = 16.2$ kcal/mol, $D_0 = 4.41 \cdot 10^{-4}$ cm$^2 \cdot$ sec^{-1}. From excess specific heat $k[E_f^2/2 RT^2]e^{-E_f/2 RT} : E_f$ $14-20$ kcal/mol if $20-100$ is used for the constant k.)

37. Jost, W., and Oel, H. J., Diffusion in ionic crystals and the process of sintering, *Discussions Faraday Soc.* **23**, 137 (1957).

38. Junghauss, H., and Staude, H., Densities and sidorder of AgBr single crystals with additives, *Z. Elektrochem.* **57**, 391 (1953).

39. Kinumaki, J., and Ito, T., The diffusion of Silver into glass, *Sci. Repts. Research insts., Tohoku Univ., Ser. A* **8**, 60—69 (1956). (Diffusion coefficient of Ag into glass, between 500 and 600° $= 1.91$ $10^{-2} \exp [-27000/RT]$ cm.^{2} sec.$^{-1}$.)

40. Kobayashi, K., Heat capacity and lattice defects of silver chloride, *Phys. Rev.* **85**, 150 (1952).

41. Kurnick, S. W., The effects of hydrostatic pressure on the ionic conductivity of AgBr, *J. Chem. Phys.* **20**, 218 (1952).

42. Laurent, J. F., and Bénard, J., Determination of self-diffusion in mono- and polycrystalline sodium chloride, *Compt. rend.* **241**, 1204—1207 (1955). (Activation energies 37000 cal/mol for Na$^+$ and 51400 for Cl$^-$.)

43. Lidiard, A. B., Vacancy pairs in ionic crystals, *Phys. Rev.* **112**, 54 (1958).

44. Lindner, R., and Akerström, A., Self-diffusion and reaction in oxide and spinel systems, *Z. physik. Chem., (Frankfurt)* [N.S.] **6**, 129, 162 (1956). (Reaction of PbO $+$ SiO$_2$ and CaO $+$ SiO$_2$ investigated by means of radioactive tracers. Measurements in NiCr$_2$O$_4$, ZnCr$_2$O$_4$, NiAl$_2$O$_4$, ZnAl$_2$O$_4$ by means of radioactive tracers.)

45. Lindner, R., and Parfitt, G. O., Diffusion of radioactive magnesium in magnesium oxide crystals, *J. Chem. Phys.* **26**, 182 (1957).

46. Lindner, R., and Akerström, A., Diffusion of Nickel-63 in nickel oxide (NiO), *Discussions Faraday Soc.* **23**, 133 (1957).

47. Lindner, R., and Matzke, H. J., On the diffusion of Xe-133 out of uranium oxides, *Z. Naturforsch.* **13a**, 794 (1958).

48. McAfee, K. B., Stress-enhanced diffusion in glass. I. Glass under tension and compression, *J. Chem. Phys.* **28**, 218 (1958).

49. McAfee, K. B., Stress-enhanced diffusion in glass. II. Glass under shear, *J. Chem. Phys.* **28**, 226 (1958).

50. Mapother, D., Effect of x-ray irradiation on the self-diffusion coefficient of sodium chloride, *Phys. Rev.* **89**, 1231 (1953).

51. Matejec, R., The kinetics of the formation and recombination of Frenkel defects in silver halide crystals, *Z. Physik* **151**, 595 (1958).

52. Moore, W. J., A parabolic law for metal oxidation which is not controlled by diffusion, *Phil. Mag.* **7**, 688 (1952).

53. Moore, W. J., Ebisuzaki, Y., and Sluss, J. A., Exchange and diffusion of oxygen in crystalline cuprous oxide, *J. Phys. Chem.* **62**, 1438 (1958).

54. Münnich, F., Diffusion of zinc in zinc oxide, *Naturwissenschaften* **42**, 340 to 341 (1955).

55. Murin, A. N., and Lure, B. G., Diffusion in the mixed crystals AgBr $+$ CdBr$_2$, *J. Phys. Chem. (U.S S.R.)* **32**, 2575 (1958). (Ag^{110} diffusion in the concentration range from 0 to 6 mol percent CdBr$_2$ at 225°C. Minimum at 0.05% CdBr$_2$. Ratio of observed diffusion coefficient to that derived by means of Nernst-Einstein relation is 0.67.)

56. Noddack, W., and Zeitler, G., Diffusion of argon in potassium feldspars, *Z. Elektrochem.* **60,** 1192 (1956).
57. Noyer, F., and Laurent, J. F., Measurement of self-diffusion in monocrystalline and polycrystalline potassium iodide, *Compt. Rend.* **242,** 3068—3071 (1956).
58. Patrick, L., and Lawson, A. W., Thermoelectric power of pure and doped AgBr, *J. Chem. Phys.* **22,** 1492 (1954).
59. Patterson, D., Rose, G. S., and Morrison, J. A., Diffusion of the chloride ion in NaCl, *Phil. Mag.* **1,** 393 (1956). ($D = D_0 \exp [- E/kT]$, E 1.67 e.v.)
60. Peterson, R. W., Anderson, D. E., and Shepherd, W. G., Influence of the cathode base on the chemical activation of oxide cathodes, *J. Appl. Phys.* **28,** 22 (1957).
61. Peterson, R. W., Donor diffusion in oxide cathodes, *J. Appl. Phys.* **28,** 1176 (1957).
62. Pochapsky, T. E., Heat capacity and thermal diffusivity of silver bromide, *J. Chem. Phys.* **21,** 1539 (1953). (Disorder equilibrium is established in less than about 10^{-4} second above 350°C.)
63. Reif, F., Nuclear magnetic resonance studies of imperfect ionic crystals, *Phys. Rev.* **100,** 1597 (1955).
64. Schamp, H. W., Jr., and Katz, E., Self-diffusion and ionic conductivity in sodium bromide, *Phys. Rev.* **94,** 828 (1954).
65. Price, P. J., Ambipolar thermal diffusion of electrons and holes in semiconductors, *Phil. Mag.* **46,** 1252—1260 (1955).
66. Schöne, E., Statsiw, O., and Teltow, J., Diffusion of cadmium, lead, and copper (I) ions in AgBr crystals, *Z. physik. Chem. (Leipzig)* **197,** 145 (1957).
67. Secco, E. A., and Moore, W. J., Diffusion and exchange of Zn in ZnO, *J. Chem. Phys.* **26,** 942 (1957).
68. Secco, E. A., Diffusion and exchange of zinc in crystalline zinc sulfide, *J. Chem. Phys.* **29,** 406 (1958).
69. Seitz, F., Color centers in alkali halide crystals II, *Rev. Mod. Phys.* **26,** 7—94 (1954).
70. Seitz, F., On the generation of vacancies by moving dislocations, *Advances in Physics* **1,** 43 (1952).
71. Shapiro, I., and Kolthoff, I. M., Low temperature conductivity of silver bromide, *J. Chem. Phys.* **15,** 41 (1947).
72. Shim, M. T., and Moore, W. J., Diffusion of nickel in nickel oxide, *J. Chem. Phys.* **26,** 802 (1957).
73. Sinclair, W. R., and Loomis, T. C., Measurements of diffusion in the system TiO₂/SnO₂, *Angew. Chem.* **70,** 603 (1958). (Review.)
74. Strelkow, P. G., The coefficient of expansion of silver chloride and bromide IV., *Physik. Z. Sowjetunion* **12,** 73—82 (1937)
75. Sun, R., Diffusion of cobalt and chromium in chromite spinel, *J. Chem. Phys.* **28,** 290 (1958).
76. Teltow, J., and Wilke, G., Dipole resonance of associated lattice defects in AgBr, *Naturwissenschaften* **41,** 423 (1954).
77. Theimer, O., Equilibrium concentration of vacancy pairs in ionic crystals, *Phys. Rev.* **109,** 1095 (1958).
78. Verduch, A. G., and Lindner, R., Self-diffusion of Ba and of Ti in barium-metatitanate, *Proc. intern. Symposium on Reactivity of Solids, Gothenberg,* 1952, 207—208 (1954). $D_{Ba} \approx 10^{-14}$ cm.² sec.⁻¹ at 1150°C; $D_{Ti} \approx 10^{-15}$ cm². sec.⁻¹ at 920°C; $D_{Ti} \approx 10^{-13}$ cm.² sec.⁻¹ at 1230°C.

79. Wagner, C., Theoretical analysis of diffusion processes in oxidation of alloys, *J. Electrochem. Soc.* **99**, 369—380 (1952).
80. Walker, G. F., Diffusion of interlayer water in vermiculite, *Nature* **177**, 239 (1956).
81. Waring, W., Pitman, D. T., and Steele, S. R., Germanium arsenide as diffusion surface compound, *J. Appl. Phys.* **29**, 1002 (1958).
82. Yamashita, J., and Kurosawa, T., Formation energy of lattice defects in single oxide crystals, *J. Phys. Soc. Japan* **9**, 944 (1954).
83. Zimen, K. E., Schmeling, P., and Svensson, F. S., Measurement of self-diffusion in AgBr and in mixed crystals of AgBr and Ag_2S, *Proc. intern. Symposium on Reactivity of Solids, Gothenburg,* **1952**, 93—96 (1954).

D. Diffusion in Metals

1a. Achter, M. R., Birks, L. S., and Brooks, E. J., Grain boundary diffusion of zinc in copper measured by the electron probe microanalyzer. *J. Appl. Phys.* **30**, 1825 (1959).
1. Adda, Y., Philibert, J., and Mairy, C., Diffusion and Kirkendall effect in the system U-Zr (at 1075°C, γ-phase), *Compt. rend.* **243**, 1115—1118 (1956).
2. Adda, Y., Philibert, J., and Faraggi, H., Investigation of diffusion in the system U-Zr between 950 and 1075°C, *Rev. mét.* **54**, 597—610 (1957).
3. Allison, H. W., and Moore, G. E., Diffusion of tungsten in nickel and reaction at interface with SrO, *J. Appl. Phys.* **29**, 842 (1958).
4. Ang, C. Y., Activation energies and diffusion coefficients of oxygen and nitrogen in niobium and tantalum, *Acta Met.* **1**, 123 (1953).
5. Ang, C., and Wert, C., Internal friction of alloys of gold and nickel, *Phys. Rev.* **93**, 922 (1954).
6. Balluffi, R. W., Supersaturation and precipitation of vacancies during diffusion, *Acta Met.* **2**, 194—202 (1954).
7. Balluffi, R. W., and Alexander, B. H., Development of porosity during diffusion in substitutional solid solutions, *J. Appl. Phys.* **23**, 1237 (1952).
8. Balluffi, R. W., and Seigle, L. L., Diffusion in bimetal vapor-solid couples, *J. Appl. Phys.* **25**, 607 (1954).
9. Balluffi, R. W., and Seigle, L. L., Conditions for porosity formation during diffusion, *J. Appl. Phys.* **25**, 1380 (1954).
10. Barnes, R. S., Effects associated with the flow of vacancies in intermetallic diffusion, *Proc. Phys. Soc. (London)* **65**B, 512 (1952).
11. Bartlett, J. H., and Dienes, G. J., Combined pairs of vacancies in copper, *Phys. Rev.* **89**, 848 (1953).
12. Batz, W., Mead, H. W., and Birchenall, C. E., Diffusion of silicon in iron, *J. Metals* **4**, *AIME Trans.* 1070 (1952).
13. Berkowitz, A. E., Jaumot, F. E. Jr., and Nix, F. C., Diffusion of Co^{60} in some Ni-Al alloys containing excess vacancies, *Phys. Rev.* **95**, 1185 (1954).
14. Birchenall, C. E., Diffusion and oxidation of solid metals, *Ind. Eng. Chem.* **47**, 604—613 (1955).
15. Blewitt, T. H., and Coltman, R. R., Radiation ordering in Cu_3Au, *Acta Met.* **2**, 549 (1954).
16. Bokstein, S., Kischkin, T., and Moros, M., Volume and surface self-diffusion of iron, volume diffusion: $D = 10^6 \exp (64\,000/RT)$, grain boundary: $D = 2.3 \exp (-30\,600/RT)$, *Metallkunde u. Metallverarbeitung (russ.)* **2**, 2—10 (1957).
17. Boling, J. L., and Dolan, W. W., Blunting of tungsten needles by surface diffusion, *J. Appl. Phys.* **29**, 556 (1958).

18. Bösenberg, W., Diffusion of antimony, arsenium and indium in solid germanium, Z. Naturforsch. 10a, 285 (1955).

$D = D_0 \exp (-Q/RT)$ for diffusion of

	D_0 (cm.^{2}/sec.)	Q (kcal/mol)	Q (eV)	
Sb	1.2	53.0	2.3	
As	2.1	55.3	2.4	in germanium
In	20	69.2	3.0	

19. Brinkman, J. A., Effect of temperature gradients on diffusion in crystals, Phys. Rev. 93, 345 (1954).
20. Brinkman, J. A., Dixon, C. E., and Meechan, J. C., Interstitial and vacancy migration in Cu$_3$Au and copper, Acta Met. 2, 38 (1954).
21. Broom, T., Lattice defects and the electrical resistivity of metals, Advances in Phys. 3, 26 (1954).
22. Buffington, F. S., and Cohen, M., Self-diffusion in α-iron under uniaxial compressive stress, J. Metals 4, 859 (1952).
23. Buffington, F., and Cohen, M., Self-diffusion in cubic metals, Acta Met. 2, 660 (1954). (Frequency factors and activation energies of self-diffusion in cubic metals are correlated.)
24. Bugakov, V. Z., Diffusion in metals and alloys (russ.) Moskau, 1949, Metals Rev. 25, 45 (1952).
25. Busby, P. E., Warga, M. E., and Wells, C., Diffusion and solubility of boron in iron and steel, J. Metals 5, 1463 (1953).
26. Busby, P. E., and Wells, C., Diffusion of boron in alpha iron, J. Metals 6, AIME Trans. 200, 972 (1954).
27. Canter, M. A., Self-diffusion in natural graphite crystals, Phys. Rev. 98, 1563 (1955).
28. Carpenter, L. G., Some properties of sodium and potassium near their melting points, J. Chem. Phys. 21, 2244 (1953).
29. Chatterjee, G. P., Hardness of metals and alloys, Indian. J. Phys. 28, 9—20 (1954); J. Metals 8, AIME Trans. 206, 454 (1956).
30. Chatterjee, G. P., The oxidation of phosphorus in Indian pig iron with enriched air, Trans. Indian Inst. Metals 8, 117 (1954—1955).
31. Chatterjee, G. P., Interfaces between metallic crystal grains, Trans. Indian Inst. Metals 9, 275—284 (1955—1956).
32. Chatterjee, G. P., Effects of aluminum and manganese on the resistance against atmospheric corrosion of some copper alloys, Trans. Indian Inst. Metals 7, 211—222 (1955).
33. Chatterjee, G. P., Diffusion in solid metals and alloys, Trans. Indian Inst. Metals 7, 223 (1955).
34. Chatterjee, G. P., Rate of formation of films on metals and alloys, J. Appl. Phys. 26, 363 (1955).
35. Childs, B. G., and Le Claire, A. D., Relaxation effects in solid solutions arising from changes in local order. I. Experimental, Acta Met. 2, 718 (1954).
36. Cohen, M., Wagner, C., and Reynolds, J. E., Calculation of interdiffusion coefficients when volume changes occur, J. Metals 5, 1534 (1953).
37. Compaan, K., and Haven, Y., Correlation factors for diffusion in solids, Trans. Faraday Soc. 52, 786 (1956).

38. Compaan, K., and Haven, Y., Correlation factors for diffusion in solids, *Trans. Faraday Soc.* **54**, 1498 (1958).
39. Correa da Silva, L. C., and Mehl, R. F., Interface and marker movements in diffusion in solutions of metals, *J. Metals* **191**, *AIME Trans.* 155—173 (1951). (Marker movements in the systems Cu/α-brass, Cu/Sn α-solid solution, Cu/Al α-solid solution, Cu/Ni, Cu/Au, Ag/Au.)
40. Couling, S. R. L., and Smoluchowski, R. S., Anisotropy of diffusion in grain boundaries, *J. Appl. Phys.* **25**, 1538—1542 (1954). (Grain boundary penetration of radioactive silver into copper bicrystals [autoradiographic technique].)
41. Couling, L., and Smoluchowsky, R., Anisotropy of grain boundary diffusion, *Phys. Rev.* **91**, 245 (1953).
42. Coupland, M. J., Control of surface concentration in the diffusion of phosphorus in silicon, *Nature* **181**, 1331 (1958).
43. Crussard, C., Mechanism of diffusion in solid solutions, *Acta Met.* **2**, 296 (1954).
44. Damask, A. C., and Nowick, A. S., Internal friction associated with precipitation in an Al-Ag alloy, *Phys. Rev.* **94**, 1421 (1954).
45. Darken, L. S., and Oriani, R. A., Thermal diffusion in solid alloys, *Acta Met.* **2**, 841 (1954).
46. Das, D. K., Differential expansion diffusion couple welding device, *Rev. Sci. Instr.* **29**, 70 (1958).
47. Demarez, A., Hock, A. G., and Meunier, F. A., Diffusion of hydrogen in mild steel, *Acta Met.* **2**, 214 (1954).
48. Dienes, G. J., Entropies of activation in metallic diffusion, *Phys. Rev.* **89**, 185 (1953).
49. Drechsler, M., Calculation of adsorption energies and place change energies at single crystal faces of metals, *Z. Elektrochem.* **58**, 327 (1954).
50. Dugdale, R. A., and Green, A., Some ordering effects in Cu_3Au at about 100°C, *Phil. Mag.* **45**, 163 (1954).
51. Dunlap, W. C., and Brown, D. E., p-n junction method for measuring diffusion in germanium, *Phys. Rev.* **86**, 417 (1952).
52. Dunlap, W. C., Measurement of diffusion in germanium by means of p-n junctions, *Phys. Rev.* **86**, 615 (1952). (Diffusion coefficients of six elements between 600° and 900°C. 900°C antimony $2 \cdot 10^{-10}$ cm.^{2}/sec. arsenic $2 \cdot 10^{-10}$, phosphorus $8 \cdot 10^{-11}$, zinc $1 \cdot 10^{-11}$, gallium $3 \cdot 10^{-12}$, indium $2 \cdot 10^{-13}$ cm.^{2}/sec. Activation energy for antimony ~ 2.5 ev.)
53. Eager, R. L., and Langmuir, D. B., Self-diffusion of tantalum, *Phys. Rev.* **89**, 911 (1953).
54. Eckert, R. E., and Drickamer, H. G., Diffusion in indium near the melting point, *J. Chem. Phys.* **20**, 13 (1952).
55. Eichenauer, W., Determination of diffusivity and solubility of hydrogen in Al, Cu, Fe, *Angew. Chem.* **70**, 60 (1958). (VB Deutsche Gesellschaft für Metallkunde 20.—23. Sept. 1957 in Münster.)
56. Elcock, E. W., and McCombie, C. W., Vacancy diffusion in binary ordered alloys, *Phys. Rev.* **109**, 605 (1958).
57. Fara, H., and Balluffi, R. W., Application of the Boltzmann-Matano analysis to vapor-solid diffusion couples, *J. Appl. Phys.* **27**, 964 (1956).
58. Fast, J. D., and Verrijp, M. B., Diffusion of nitrogen in iron, *J. Iron Steel Inst. (London)* **176**, 24—27 (1954). (Diffusion in γ-Fe much slower than in α-Fe. Analogous phenomena were found for interstitial diffusion of C and H in Fe.)

59. Feder, R., and Nowick, A. S., Use of thermal expansion measurements to detect latt ce vacancies near the melting point of pure lead and aluminum, *Phys. Rev.* **109**, 1959 (1958). (Dilatometric and x-ray measurements of the thermal expansion of pure lead and aluminum. Vacancy concentration in lead at the melting point (mole fraction) less than or equal to $1.5 \cdot 10^{-4}$. For aluminum vacancy concentration at the melting point $\sim 3 \cdot 10^{-4}$. Estimate for formation energy of a vacancy: lead 0.53 ev. aluminum 0.77 ev.)

60. Ferro, A., Theory of diffusion constants in interstitial solid solutions of b.c.c. metals, *J. Appl. Phys.* **28**, 895 (1957).

61. Fitzer, E., Exchange reactions in the system iron-silicon, *Z. Metall.* **44**, 462 (1953).

62. Flanagan, R., and Smoluchowsky, R., Grain boundary diffusion of zinc in copper, *J. Appl. Phys.* **23**, 785 (1952).

63. Frank, R. C., Some observations regarding the present status of measurements of the diffusion coefficients of hydrogen in iron and mild steel, *J. Appl. Phys.* **29**, 1262 (1956).

64. Frank, R. C., and Swets, D. E., Hydrogen permeation through steel during abrasion, *J. Appl. Phys.* **28**, 380 (1957).

65. Frank, R. C., Swets, D. E., and Fry, D. L., Mass spectrometer measurements of the diffusion coefficient of hydrogen in steel in the temperature range of $25° - 90°$ C, *J. Appl. Phys.* **29**, 892 (1958).

66. Frank, R. C., Lee, R. W., and Williams, R. L., Ratio of the diffusion coefficients for the diffusion of hydrogen and deuterium in steel, *J. Appl. Phys.* **29**, 898 (1958). (Ratio of diffusion coefficients for hydrogen and deuterium in steel in the temperature range of 26°C to 86°C, constant within the limits of experimental error $\sim 1.37 \pm 0.02$.)

67. Freise, V., and Sauer, F., Concentration dependence of the diffusion coefficients in the system Cu-Ni, *Z. physik. Chem. (Frankfurt)* [N.S.] **8**, 387 (1956).

68. Friedel, J., Electronic structure of primary solid solutions in metals, *Advances in Phys.* **3**, 446 (1954).

69. Fuller, C. S., Diffusion of donor and acceptor elements into germanium, *Phys. Rev.* **86**, 136 − 137 (1952).

70. Fuller, C. S., and Struthers, J. D., Copper as an acceptor element in germanium, *Phys. Rev.* **87**, 526 − 527 (1952). (Diffusion constants of Cu in Ge at $654 - 919°$C. At 1100°C Cu diffuses into Si at a rate comparable to that found for Ge.)

71. Fuller, C. S., and Ditzenberger, J. A., Diffusion of donor and acceptor elements in silicon, *J. Appl. Phys.* **27**, 544 (1956).

72. Fuller, C. S., and Morin, F. J., Diffusion and electrical behavior of Zn in Si, *Phys. Rev.* **105**, 379 (1957).

73. Fuller, C. S., and Ditzenberger, J. A., Effect of structural defects in germanium on the diffusion acceptor behavior of copper, *J. Appl. Phys.* **28**, 40 (1957).

74. Gatos, H. C., and Kurtz, A. D., Determination of the self-diffusion coefficients of gold by autoradiography, *J. Metals* **6**, *AIME Trans.* **200**, 616 (1954). (Autoradiography with β-rays of sufficiently low energy [range: order of magnitude less than the diffusion distance].)

75. Gomer, R., Surface diffusion of Co on W, *J. Chem. Phys.* **28**, 168 (1958).

76. Gomer, R., Adsorption and diffusion of inert gases on tungsten, *J. Chem. Phys.* **29**, 441 (1958).

77. Gomer, R., and Hulm, J. K., A method for studying the mobility of chemisorbed films: oxygen and tungsten, *J. Am. Chem. Soc.* **75**, 4114 (1953).

78. Gordon, B. M., and Wahl, A. C., Kinetics of the silver(I)-silver(II) exchange reaction, *J. Am. Chem. Soc.* **80**, 273 (1958).

79. Gruzin, P. L., Use of artificially radioactive indicators in the study of diffusion and self-diffusion in alloys. Self-diffusion of cobalt, *Doklady Akad. Nauk S.S.S.R.* **86**, 289—292 (1952). (Diffusion of radioactive Co^{60} (5.3 years). Measurement after 25—200 hours. Heating in vacuo gave at 1000, 1050, 1100, 1200, 1300°: $10^{11} D = 0.82$; 1.2; 3.8; 18; 61 cm.^{2}/sec. $\sim D = 0.2 \exp[-62000/RT]$ cm.^{2} sec.$^{-1}$.)

80. Granato, A., Hikata, A., and Lücke, K., Determination of activation energy of vacancy migration in Cu by ultrasonic methods, *Phys. Rev.* **108**, 1344 (1957).

81. Gruzin, P. L., and Litvin, D. F., Determination of diffusion coefficients in solids by the method of radioactive isotopes, *Doklady Akad. Nauk. S.S.S.R.* **94**, 41—44 (1954). (Method based on the fact that β-particles are more strongly absorbed than γ-rays, and therefore the relative intensities of the two radiations change during diffusion.)

82. Haynes, C. W., and Smoluchowsky, R., Grain boundary self-diffusion in body-centered lattice, *Phys. Rev.* **91**, 245 (1953).

83. Hendrickson, A. A., and Machlin, E. S., Self-diffusivity along edge-dislocation singular lines in silver, *J. Metals* **6**, 1035 (1954).

84. Heumann, T., Diffusion in multiphase alloys, *Z. physik. Chem. (Leipzig)* **201**, 168 (1952).

85. Heumann, T., and Lohmann, P., Diffusion in the β-phase of silver-zinc, *Z. Elektrochem.* **59**, 849 (1955).

86. Heumann, T., and Dittrich, S., Diffusion in Ag-Al alloys, *Z. Elektrochem.* **61**, 1138 (1957).

87. Heumann, T., and Heinemann, F., Multiphase diffusion in the system Cu-Sb, *Z. Elektrochem.* **60**, 1160 (1956).

88. Heumann, T., and Kottmann, A., Diffusion processes in substitution solid solutions, *Z. Metallk.* **44**, 139 (1953).

89. Heumann, T., and Wicke, W., Macroscopic and x-ray density measurements of Ag-Zn alloy, with respect to diffusion behavior, *Z. Elektrochem.* **60**, 1154 (1956).

90. Hoffmann, R. E., and Turnbull, D., Lattice and grain boundary self-diffusion in silver, *J. Appl. Phys.* **22**, 634 (1951). (Lattice diffusion coefficients: $D_L \approx 0.895 \exp(-49500/RT)$ cm.^{2} sec.$^{-1}$ grain boundary: $D_B \approx 0.03 \exp(-202000/RT)$ cm.^{2} sec.$^{-1}$.)

91. Hoffmann, R. E., and Turnbull, D., Effect of impurities on the self-diffusion of silver, *J. Appl. Phys.* **23**, 1409—1410 (1952). (In Ag-Pb alloys self-diffusion of Ag: $D = D^0 + xD'$, where D^0 self-diffusion coefficient in pure Ag, x mole fraction of Pb, and $D' = 7.6 \exp[-40500/RT]$ cm.^{2} sec.$^{-1}$.)

92. Holomon, J. H., and Turnbull, D., *U.S. Atomic Energy Comm. Publ.* 50—2030 (1953).

93. Hopkin, L. M. T., Effect of stress on hole formation during the diffusion of zinc from brass in vacuo, *Nature* **180**, 808 (1957).

94. Horne, G. T., and Mehl, R. F., Mobilities in diffusion in alpha brass, *J. Metals* **7**, *AIME Trans.* **203**, 88 (1955).

95. Huntington, H. B., Mobility of interstitial atoms in a face-centered metal, *Phys. Rev.* **91**, 1092 (1953).

96. Huntington, H. B., Shirn, G. A., and Wajda, E. S., Activation entropies for diffusion mechanisms, *Phys. Rev.* **91**, 246 (1953).

97. Inman, M. C., Johnston, D., Mercer, W. L., and Shuttleworth, R., The measurement of self-diffusion coefficients in binary alloys, *Radioisotope Conf. Oxford, Eng.*, **1954**, pp. 85—97 (1954).

98. Jaumot, F. E., Jr., and Sawatzky, A., Diffusion of gold in single crystals of silver, *J. Appl. Phys.* **27**, 1186 (1956).

99. Johnson, R. D., and Mangio, C. A., The possibility of time dependence of the silver self-diffusion coefficient, *U.S. Atomic Energy Comm.* **BMI-851**, 16 (1953). (Measurements at 902, 699, and 543°C. At the lowest temperature grain-boundary diffusion is appreciable and measured diffusion coefficients decrease with increased annealing time. This might be expected when grain-boundary and volume diffusion take place simultaneously.)

100. Johnson, R. D., and Martin, A. B., The effect of cyclotron bombardment on self-diffusion in silver, *J. Appl. Phys.* **23**, 1245 (1952).

101. Jongenburger, P., The extra-resistivity owing to vacancies in copper, *Phys. Rev.* **90**, 710 (1953).

102. Kanter, M. A., Self-diffusion in natural graphite crystals, *Phys. Rev.* **98**, 1563 (1955). (Measurements between 1600 and 2150°C. Activation energy for diffusion $\sim$ 170 kcal/mol.)

103. Kanter, M. A., Diffusion of C atoms in natural graphite crystals, *Phys. Rev.* **107**, 655 (1957).

104. Karger, W., Method for continous observation of diffusion processes in solids, *Z. physik. Chem. (Frankfurt)* [N.S.] **14**, 88 (1958).

105. Kauffmann, J. W., and Koehler, J. S., Formation energy of lattice vacancies in gold, *Phys. Rev.* **98**, 245 (1955). (99.999% or better gold wires were rapidly quenched from high temperatures to liquid nitrogen temperature. The quench produces an increase in the electrical resistance up to 0.8% which is completely annealed out at higher temperatures. This is interpreted as due to lattice vacancies. The slope of the log of the resistance increase versus reciprocal of the temperature at quench gives 1.28 — 0.03 ev. for the energy of formation of a vacancy.)

106. Keyes, R. W., Diffusion of lattice defects in a temperature gradient, *Phys. Rev.* **94**, 1389 (1954).

107. Keywell, F., Improved diffusion boundary junction in silicon due to scratch-free polishing, *J. Appl. Phys.* **29**, 871 (1958).

108. Klein, R., The surface migration of carbon on tungsten, *Phys. Rev.* **94**, 1407 (1954).

109. Kinger, W. D., and Berg, M., Study of the initial stages of sintering solids by viscous flow, evaporation-condensation and self-diffusion, *J. Appl. Phys.* **26**, 1205 (1955).

110. Kirkaldy, J. S., Diffusion in multicomponent metallic systems, *Can. J. Phys.* **35**, 435 (1957).

111. Kitchener, J. A., Bockris, J. O'M., Gleiser, M., and Evans, J. W., Note on the solubility of oxygen in gamma iron, *Trans. Faraday Soc.* **48**, 995 (1952).

112. Kitchener, J. A., Bockris, J. O'M., Gleiser, M., and Evans, L. W., Solubility of oxygen in gamma-iron, *Acta Met.* **1**, 93 (1953).

113. Knappwost, A., Magnetic investigations of diffusion in the system Cu-Fe, *Z. Elektrochem.* **56**, 840 (1952).

114. Kochendörfer, A., Relations between vacancy energy, surface energy and elastic constants of crystals, *Naturwissenschaften* **41**, 36 (1954).

115. Krivoglaz, M. A., and Smirnov, A. A., Influence of interstitials on self-diffusion of metals, *Doklady Akad. Nauk. S.S.S.R.* **96**, 495 (1954).

116. Kunitomi, N., Anelastic study on the diffusion coefficients of α-brass, *Sci. Repts. Research Insts. Tohoku, Univ. Ser. A* **5**, 335 (1953).

117. Kuper, A. B., and Tomizuka, C. T., Diffusion of copper and zinc in ordered and disordered CuZn, *Phys. Rev.* **98**, 244 (1955).

118. Kurtz, A. D., and Gravel, C. L., Diffusion of gallium in silicon, *J. Appl. Phys.* **29**, 1456 (1958).

118a. Kurtz, A. D., and Vee, R., Diffusion of boron into silicon, *J. Appl. Phys.* **31**, 303 (1960).

119. Lacombe, P., Intergrain diffusion and relations with the structure of the grain joints. Extrait de "La Diffusion Dans Les Metaux", Bibliotheque Technique Philips, pp. 23—52.

120. Lander, J. J., Kern, H. E., and Beach, A. L., Solubility and diffusion coefficient of carbon in nickel: reaction rates of nickel-carbon alloys with barium oxide, *J. Appl. Phys.* **23**, 1305 (1952). [Diffusion coefficients from 700 to 1300°C: $\ln D = 0.909 - 20200/T$ (cm.^{2} sec.$^{-1}$).]

121. Landergren, U. S., and Mehl, R. F., Rates of diffusion and marker movements in beta brass, *J. Metals* **5**, 153 (1953).

122. Lawson, A. W., Effect of compressive stress on self-diffusion in zinc, *J. Chem. Phys.* **22**, 1948 (1954).

123. Lazarus, D., Effect of screening on solute diffusion in metals, *Phys. Rev.* **93**, 973 (1954).

124. Lazarus, D., and Okkerse, B., Anomalous isotope effect in metallic diffusion, *Phys. Rev.* **105**, 1677 (1957).

125. Le Claire, A. D., Diffusion in metals, *Progr. in Metal Phys.* **1**, 306 (1949).

126. Le Claire, A. D., Diffusion in metals, *Progr. in Metal Phys.* **4**, 265 (1953).

127. Le Claire, A. D., Diffusion in metals, *J. Iron Steel Inst. (London)* **174**, 229 (1953).

128. Le Claire, A. D., Some predicted effects of temperature gradients on diffusion in crystals, *Phys. Rev.* **93**, 344 (1954). (It is shown that interstitial atoms always move toward cooler regions, but that the direction of motion of vacancies is a function of their activation energy and of the energy of formation of a vacancy.)

129. Le Claire, A. D., The theory of D_0 in the Arrhenius equation for self-diffusion in cubic metals, *Acta Met.* **1**, 438 (1953).

130. Lehovec, K., and Levitas, A., Fabrication of multiple junctions in semiconductors by surface melt and diffusion in the solid state, *J. Appl. Phys.* **28**, 106 (1957).

131. Letaw, H., Slifkin, L. M., and Portnoy, W. M., Self-diffusion in germanium, *Phys. Rev.* **93**, 892 (1954). (D[1060—1200°K] = 87 · exp [−73500/RT] cm.^{2} sec.$^{-1}$. Diffusion coefficient for vacancies: $D_v = 3.9 \cdot \exp$ [−23500/RT] cm.^{2} sec.$^{-1}$. Grain boundary diffusion coefficient about 10^4.)

132. Leymonie, C., and Lacombe, P., Preferential self-diffusion in the grain joints of cubic centred iron, *Acta Met.* **5**, 115 (1957).

133. Leymonie, C., and Lacombe, P., Preferential diffusion of radioactive iron in the grain joints of α-iron, *Rev. met. Liv.* **9**, 654 (1957).

134. Leymonie, C., Lacombe, P., and Libanati, C., Measurement of volume self-diffusion in α-iron by means of radioactive tracers, *Compt. rend.* **245**, 1922—1925 (1957).

135. Leymonie, C., and Lacombe, P., Intergranular self-diffusion in α-iron. Extrait de "La Diffusion Dans Les Metaux", *Bibliothèque Technique Philips*, pp. 53—57.

136. Lidiard, A. B., Vacancy diffusion mechanism in ordered alloys, *Phys. Rev.* **106**, 823 (1957).

137. Linnenborn, V., Tetenbaum, M., and Cheek, C., J. *Appl. Phys.* **26**, 932 (1955). (Tracer diffusion of iron in 18—8 stainless steel. Lattice diffusion coefficients described by $D = 0.58 \exp [-67100/RT]$ cm.² sec.⁻¹.)

138. Liu, T., and Drickamer, H. G., The effect of compression and of hydrostatic pressure on the diffusion anisotropy in zinc, *J. Chem. Phys.* **22**, 312 (1954). (Self-diffusion is always greater in the direction of the c-axis. Diffusion rate is decreased by pressures up to 10000 atmospheres, the influence in the c-direction being higher.)

139. Logan, R. A., and Peters, A. J., Diffusion of oxygen in silicon, *J. Appl. Phys.* **28**, 819 (1957).

140. Lomer, W. M., and Cottrell, A. H., Annealing of point defects in metals and alloys, *Phil. Mag.* **46**, 711 (1955).

141. Machlup, S., Relaxation of a monatomic crystal lattice around a vacancy, *Phys. Rev.* **98**, 1558 (1955).

142. Mackliet, C. A., Diffusion of iron, cobalt, and nickel in single crystals of pure copper, *Phys. Rev.* **109**, 1964 (1958). (Diffusion of radioactive tracers of Fe, Co, and Ni in single crystals of pure copper, between 700 and 1075°C. $D_{\text{Fe, Cu}} = 1.4 \cdot \exp [-51800/RT]$; $D_{\text{Co, Cu}} = 1.93 \cdot \exp [54100/RT]$; $D_{\text{Ni, Cu}} = 2.7 \cdot \exp [-56500/RT]$ cm.² sec.⁻¹.)

143. Mallett, M. W., Baroody, E. M., Nelson, H. R., and Papp, C. A., The diffusion and solubility of nitrogen in beta zirconium, *J. Electrochem. Soc.* **100**, 103 (1953).

144. Manning, J. R., Correlation correction to the activation energy for diffusion in crystalline solids, *Phys. Rev. Letters* **1**, 363 (1958).

145. Martin, A. B., Johnson, R. D., and Asaro, F., Diffusion of gold into copper, *J. Appl. Phys.* **25**, 364 (1954).

146. Marx, J. W., Baker, G. S., and Sivertsen, J. M., The internal friction of tantalum and niobium foils at ultrasonic frequencies, *Acta Met.* **1**, 193 (1953).

147. McDonald, D. K. C., Self-diffusion in the alkali metals, *J. Chem. Phys.* **21**, 177 (1953).

148. McDonell, W. R., and Kierstead, H. A., Expansion of copper bombarded by 21-mev deuterons, *Phys. Rev.* **93**, 247 (1954).

149. McKelvey, J. P., Diffusion effects in drift mobility measurements in semiconductors, *J. Appl. Phys.* **27**, 341 (1956).

150. McAfee, K. B., Shockley, W., and Sparks, M., Measurements of diffusion in semiconductors by a capacitance method, *Phys. Rev.* **86**, 137 (1952). (Diffusion coefficient for As in Ge at 800°: $1 \cdot 50 \cdot 10^{-13}$ cm.² sec.⁻¹, activation energy 3.0 e.v.)

151. Meechan, C. J., and Eggleston, R. R., Formation energies of vacancies in copper and gold, *Acta Met.* **2**, 680 (1954). (Additional electric resistance attributed to the presence of vacancies in thermodynamic equilibrium.)

152. Menzel, E., Self-diffusion on a copper surface, *Z. Physik* **132**, 508 (1952).

153. Meyer, R. E., and Nachtrieb, N. H., Self-diffusion in sodium near the melting point, *J. Chem. Phys.* **23**, 405 (1955).

154. Miller, R. C., and Savage, A., Diffusion of aluminum in single crystal silicon, *J. Appl. Phys.* **27**, 1430 (1956).

155. Miller, R. C., and Smits, F. M., Diffusion of Sb out of Ge and some properties of the Sb-Ge system, *Phys. Rev.* **107**, 65 (1957).
156. Mizuno, H., Influence of doping on diffusion rate of impurities in cathode nickel, *J. Appl. Phys.* **29**, 1265 (1956).
157. Nachtrieb, N. H., Catalano, E., and Weil, J. A., Self-diffusion in solid sodium. I, *J. Chem. Phys.* **20**, 1185 (1952). (D $\approx$ 242 exp $[-10450/RT]$ cm.^{2} sec.$^{-1}$ $[0-35°C]$.)
158. Nachtrieb, N. H., Weil, J. A., Catalano, E., and Lawson, A. W., Self-diffusion solid sodium. II. The effect of pressure, *J. Chem. Phys.* **20**, 1189 (1952).
159. Nachtrieb, N. H., and Handler, G. S., A relaxed vacancy model for diffusion in crystalline metals, *Acta Met.* **2**, 797 (1954).
160. Nachtrieb, N. H., and Handler, G. S., Self-diffusion in lead, *J. Chem. Phys.* **23**, 1569 (1955). (D $\approx$ 0.281 · exp $[-24210/RT]$ cm.^{2} sec.$^{-1}$.)
161. Nachtrieb, N. H., Petit, J., and Wehrenberg, J., Self-diffusion of silver in silver-palladium alloys, *J. Chem. Phys.* **26**, 106 (1957).
162. Navon, D., and Chernishov, V., Retrograde solubility of aluminum in silicon, *J. Appl. Phys.* **28**, 823 (1957).
163. Neiman, M. B., and Schinjajew, A. J., Diffusion of iron in iron-nickel alloys, *Doklady Akad. Nauk. S.S.S.R.* **102**, 969 (1955).
164. Norton, F. J., Nondiffusibility of oxygen through platinum, *J. Appl. Phys.* **29**, 1122 (1958).
165. Nowick, A. S., Anelastic measurements of atomic mobility in substitutional solid solution, *Phys. Rev.* **88**, 925 (1952). (Values for heat of activation in Ag-Zn alloys as function of Zn concentration from 36.1 kcal/mole at 15.8 at.% Zn to 32.5 kcal/mole at 30.2 at.% Zn. Entropy of activation positive, in reasonable agreement with Zener's "strain theory".)
166. Nowick, A. S., Internal friction in metals, *Progr. in Metal. Phys.* **4**, 1—70 (1953).
167. Nowick, A. S., and Sladek, R. J., Anelastic measurement of atomic mobility under nonequilibrium conditions, *Acta Met.* **1**, 131 (1953).
168. Okkerse, B., Self-diffusion in lead, *Acta Met.* **2**, 551 (1954).
169. Overhauser, A. W., The influence of impurities on diffusion in solids, *Phys. Rev.* **91**, 246 (1953).
170. Overhauser, A. W., Isothermal annealing effects in irradiated copper, *Phys. Rev.* **90**, 393 (1953).
171. Overhauser, A. W., Stored energy measurements in irradiated copper, *Phys. Rev.* **94**, 1551 (1954).
172. Pankove, J. I., Effect of edge dislocations on the alloying of indium to germanium, *J. Appl. Phys.* **28**, 1054 (1957).
173. Penning, P., Coefficient for self-diffusion determined from the rate of precipitation of Cu in Ge, *Phys. Rev.* [2] **110**, 586 (1958).
174. Prager, S., Diffusion in binary systems, *J. Chem. Phys.* **21**, 1344 (1953).
175. Posch, W., Measurement of self-diffusion in compressed silver powder by means of an auto-radiographic method, *Z. Elektrochem.* **62**, 882 (1958).
176. Reiss, H., A note on the cooperative diffusion of vacancies and impurity atoms, *Z. Elektrochem.* **61**, 79 (1957).
177. Resnick, R., and Seigle, L. L., Void formation in silver-gold diffusion couples, *J. Appl. Phys.* **28**, 513 (1957).
178. Roswell, A. E., and Nowick, A. S., Decay of lattice defects frozen into an alloy by quenching, *J. Metals* **5**, *AIME Trans.* **197**, 1259 (1953).
179. Sawatzky, A., Diffusion of indium in tin single crystals, *J. Appl. Phys.* **29**, 1303 (1958).

180. Schillmann, E., Diffusion of impurities in indium arsenide, *Z. Naturforsch.* **11 a,** 472 (1956).

181. Schopper, H., Optical investigation of diffusion of metals, *Z. Physik* **143,** 93 (1955). (Determination of small diffusion coefficients ($D \leqq 10^{-13}$ cm.^{2}/sec.$^{-1}$] [Au-Pb between 10 and 100°C].)

182. Seith, W., and Ludwig, R., Diffusion processes in the system copper-nickel, *Z. Metallk.* **45,** 401 (1954).

183. Seith, W., and Ludwig, R., Changes in dimension of diffusion samples, *Z. Metallk.* **45,** 550 (1954).

184. Seith, W., Heumann, T., and Walther, G., Investigation of marker migration during diffusion of Au and Ag, *Naturwissenschaften* **42,** 532 (1955).

185. Seitz, F., On the generation of vacancies by moving dislocations, *Advances in Phys.* **1,** 43 (1952).

186. Severiens, J. C., and Fuller, C. S., Mobility of impurity ions in germanium and silicon, *Phys. Rev.* **92,** 1322 (1953). (Diffusion of Li [150−851°] in Ge: $D = 0.0025 \cdot \exp [-11800/RT]$; in Si: $D = 0.0019 \cdot \exp [-14700/RT]$.)

187. Seymour, E. F. W., Nuclear magnetic resonance line width transition in aluminum, *Proc. Phys. Soc. (London)* **66 A,** 85 (1953). (Line narrowing at 330° almost certainly attributed to self-diffusion.)

188. Shewmon, P., Diffusion in metals, *Ind. Eng. Chem.* **50,** 492 (1958).

189. Shewmon, P. G., and Rhines, F. N., Rate of self-diffusion in polycrystalline magnesium, *J. Metals* **6,** 1021 (1954).

190. Shirn, G. A., Wajda, E. S., and Huntington, B., Self-diffusion in zinc, *Acta Met.* **1,** 513 (1953). (Self-diffusion of single crystal high purity Zn, between 240° and melting point [Zn^{65}]. For diffusion parallel to the hexagonal axis: activation energy $Q = 21.8$ kcal/mol, $D_0 = 0.13$ cm.^{2} sec.$^{-1}$; for diffusion perpendicular to the hexagonal axis: $Q = 24.3$ kcal/mol, $D_0 = 0.58$ cm.^{2} sec.$^{-1}$.)

191. Shirn, G. A., Self-diffusion in thallium, *Acta Met.* **3,** 87 (1954). (Self-diffusion of single crystal Tl between 150 and 275°C [Tl^{204}]. Diffusion parallel to c axis: $Q = 22.9$ kcal/mol; $D_0 = 0.4$ cm.^{2} sec.$^{-1}$; diffusion perpendicular to c axis: $Q = 22.6$ kcal/mol, $D_0 = 0.4$ cm.^{2} sec.$^{-1}$.)

192. Shockley, W., Effects of temperature gradients on diffusion in crystals, *Phys. Rev.* **91,** 1563 (1953). [Cf. Brinkmann (19), Le Claire (128).]

193. Shockley, W., Some predicted effects of temperature gradients on diffusion in crystals, *Phys. Rev.* **93,** 345 (1954).

194. Simnad, M. T., Diffusion and oxidation of metals, *Ind. Eng. Chem.* **48,** 586 (1956). (Progress report, 130 references.)

195. Simnad, M. T., Diffusion and oxidation of metals, *Ind. Eng. Chem.* **49,** 617 (1957).

196. Slifkin, L. M., Lazarus, D., and Tomizuka, T., The diffusion of antimony in silver single crystals, *J. Appl. Phys.* **23,** 1405 (1952). (Diffusion of Sb^{124} in Ag single crystals: $D = 0.29 \exp [-39400/RT]$.)

197. Slifkin, L. M., and Tomizuka, C. T., Mechanism of intermetallic diffusion, *Phys. Rev.* **97,** 836 (1955).

198. Smeltzer, W. W., and Everett, L. H., Oxidation of metals, *Ind. Eng. Chem.* **50,** 497 (1958).

199. Smith, R. P., The diffusivity of carbon in iron by the steady-state method, *Acta Met.* **1,** 578 (1953).

200. Smith, J. F., and Danielson, G. C., Sodium diffusion in sodium tungsten bronze, *J. Chem. Phys.* **22,** 266 (1956).

201. Smoluchowsky, R., Theory of grain boundary diffusion, *Phys. Rev.* **87**, 482 (1952).

202 Sonder, E., Effect of low concentrations of impurity on diffusion in silver, *Phys. Rev.* **98**, 245 (1955).

203. Sonder, E., Slifkin, L., and Tomizuka, C. T., Diffusion of antimony in silver, *Phys. Rev.* **93**, 970 (1954).

204. Steeb, S., Jürgensen, K. H., and Magun, S., Diffusion of mercury in amorphous selenium, *Z. Elektrochem.* **61**, 763 (1957).

205. Struthers, J. D., Solubility and diffusivity of gold, iron and copper in silicon, *J. Appl. Phys.* **27**, 1560 (1956). ($D_{Au} = 0.0011 \exp [-25800/RT]$ cm.^{2} sec.$^{-1}$; $D_{Fe} = 0.0062 \exp [-20000/RT]$ cm.^{2} sec.$^{-1}$].)

206. Swalin, R. A., Model for solute diffusion in crystals with diamond structure, *J. Appl. Phys.* **29**, 670 (1958.)

207. Swalin, R. A., Martin, A., and Olson, R., Diffusion of magnesium, silicium and molybdenum in nickel, *Angew. Chem.* **70**, 140 (1958). (Review.)

208. Thomas, W. R., and Leak, G. M., The diffusion of nitrogen in alpha iron, *Phil. Mag.* **45**, 656, 986 (1954).

209. Tomizuka, G., and Kuper, A. B., Diffusion of Cu and Zn in ordered and disordered CuZn, *Phys. Rev.* **98**, 244 (1955). (Review.)

210. Tomizuka, C. T., and Slifkin, L., Diffusion of cadmium, indium, and tin in single crystals of silver, *Phys. Rev.* **96**, 610 (1954).

211. Tucker, C. W., and Sampson, J. B., Interstitial content of radiation-damaged metals from precision X-ray lattice parameter measurements. I. Principles of the measurements, *Acta Met.* **2**, 433 (1954).

212. Turnbull, D., and Hoffmann, R. E., The effect of relative crystal and boundary orientations on grain boundary diffusion rates, *Acta Met.* **2**, 419 (1954).

213. Valenta, M. V., and Ramasaatry, C., Effect of heavy-doping on self-diffusion of Ge, *Phys. Rev.* **106**, 73 (1957).

214. van Bueren, H. G., Electrical resistance and plastic deformation of metals, *Z. Metallk.* **46**, 272 (1955).

215. van der Maesen, F., and Brenkman, J. A., The behavior of rapidly diffusing acceptors in germanium, *J. Electrochem. Soc.* **102**, 229 (1955). (Diffusion coefficients of Cu and Ni in Ge $\sim 10^{-5}$ cm.^{2} sec.$^{-1}$.)

216. Vineyard, G. H., and Dienes, G. J., The theory of defect concentration in crystals, *Phys. Rev.* **93**, 265 (1954).

217. Wagner, C., The solution of diffusion problems involving concentration-dependent diffusion coefficients, *J. Metals*, **4**, *AIME Trans.* 91—96 (1952). (Diffusion in binary alloys.)

218. Wagner, C., Theoretical analysis of the diffusion processes determining the oxidation rate of alloys, *J. Electrochem. Soc.* **99**, 369 (1952).

219. Wagner, C., Theoretical analysis of diffusion of solutes during the solidification of alloys, *J. Metals* **6**, *AIME Trans.* **200**, 154 (1954).

220. Waite, T. R., Diffusion-limited annealing of radiation damage in Ge, *Phys. Rev.* **107**, 417 (1957).

221. Wajda, E. S., Grain boundary self-diffusion in zinc, *Acta Met.* **2**, 184 (1954).

222. Wajda, E. S., Shirn, G. A., and Huntington, H. B., Lattice and grain-boundary self-diffusion in cadmium, *Acta Met.* **3**, 39 (1954).

223. Wechsler, M. S., Influence of quenching on structure of Au-Cd, *Phys. Rev.* **98**, 245 (1955).

224. Wegener, H., Surface diffusion of rubidium, *Z. Physik* **143**, 548 (1956).

225. Weisberg, L. R., and Quimby, S. L., Ordering and disordering processes in Cu$_3$Au. I, *Phys. Rev.* [2] **110**, 338 (1958).
226. Weiss, H., *Compt. rend.* **171**, 168 (1920); **173**, 146 (1921); **174**, 292, 1426 (1922); **175**, 1402 (1922). (Pioneer work which the author is sorry to have overlooked in the first edition.)
227. Weller, H., Diffusion of antimony in silver, *Ann. Physik* **20**, 42 (1957).
228. Wert, C., Diffusion and precipitation of carbon in some alloys of iron, *J. Metals* **4**, 602 (1952).
229. Winegard, W. C., Anisotropy of surface self-diffusion of silver, *Acta Met.* **1**, 230 (1953).
230. Winegard, W. C., and Chalmers, B., Self-diffusion at silver surfaces, *Can. J. Phys.* **30**, 422 (1952).
231. Zimen, K. E., and Dahl, L., Diffusion of fission xenon out of uranium metal, *Z. Naturforsch.* **12 a**, 167 (1957).

E. Permeation

1. Aitken, A., and Barrer, R. M., Transport and solubility of isomeric paraffins in rubber, *Trans. Faraday Soc.* **51**, 116 (1955).
1 a. Allen, R. B., Bernstein, H., and Kurtz, A. D., Effect of oxide layers on the diffusion of phosphorous into silicon, *J. Appl. Phys.* **31**, 334 (1960).
2. Barrer, R. M., Some properties of diffusion coefficients in polymers, *J. Phys. Chem.* **61**, 178 (1957).
3. Barrer, R. M., and Fergusson, R. R., Diffusion of benzene in rubber and polythene, *Trans. Faraday Soc.* **54**, 989 (1958).
4. Crowe, C. M., A kinetic model for diffusion of gases in polymer, *Trans. Faraday Soc.* **53**, 692 (1957).
5. Frisch, H. L., Gas permeation through membranes due to simultaneous diffusion and convection, *J. Phys. Chem.* **60**, 1177 (1956).
6. Hayes, M. J., and Park, G. S., The diffusion of benzene in rubber. Part 1. Low concentrations of benzene, *Trans. Faraday Soc.* **51**, 1134—1142 (1955).
7. Hayes, M. J., and Park, G. S., The diffusion of benzene in rubber. Part 2. High concentrations of benzene, *Trans. Faraday Soc.* **52**, 949 (1956).
8. Hill, T. L., Surface diffusion and thermal transpiration in fine tubes and pores, *J. Chem. Phys.* **25**, 730 (1956).
9. Knappe, W., Diffusion of plastisizers in polyvinyl-chloride, *Z. angew. Phys.* **6**, 97 (1954).
9 a. Leiby, jr., C. C., and Chen, C. L., Diffusion coefficients, solubilities and permeabilities for He, Ne, H$_2$ and N$_2$ in γ cor glass, *J. Appl. Phys.* **31**, 268 (1960).
10. Luck, W., Diffusion in polyamide fibers, *Melliand Textilber.* **36**, 927—928, 1028—1033 (1955).
11. McCall, D. W., Diffusion in ethylene polymers, I. Desorption kinetics for a thin slab, *J. Polymer Sci.* **26**, 151 (1957).
12. McCall, D. W., and Slichter, W. P., Molecular motion in polyethylene, *J. Polymer Sci.* **26**, 171 (1957).
13. McCall, D. W., and Slichter, W. P., Diffusion in ethylene polymers. III. Effects of temperature and pressure, *J. Am. Chem. Soc.* **80**, 1861 (1958).
14. Mackie, J. S., and Meares, P., The sorption and diffusion of ethanol in a cation exchange resin membrane, *Discussions Faraday Soc.* **21**, 111 (1956).
15. Meares, P., The diffusion of gases in polyvinyl acetate in relation to the second-order transition, *Trans. Faraday Soc.* **53**, 101 (1957).

16. Medley, J. A., The diffusion of acid ions in keratin. Part 1. The "Chemical" diffusion coefficient for sulfuric acid, *Trans. Faraday Soc.* **53**, 1380 (1957).
17. Norten, F. J., Permeation of gases through solids, *J. Appl. Phys.* **28**, 34 (1957).
18. Park, G. S., Radioactive studies of diffusion in polymer systems. Part 2. The system isopentane + Polyisobutene, *Trans. Faraday Soc.* **53**, 107 (1957).
19. Schulz, G. V., and Gerrens, H., Diffusion and capillary flow of indifferent gases in glassy polystyrol. *Z. physik. Chem. (Frankfurt)* [N.S.] **7**, 182 (1956).
19a. Richman, D., and Long, F. A., Measurement of concentration gradients for diffusion of vapors in polymers, *J. Am. Chem. Soc.* **82**, 509 (1960).
19b. Richman, D., and Long, F. A., Measurement of concentration gradients for diffusion of vapors in polymers and their relation to time dependent diffusion phenomena, *J. Am. Chem. Soc.* **82**, 513 (1960).

DIFFUSION IN GASES

1. TRENDS OF THEORY

(Supplementary to Chapter X, pages 406-435 in this volume)

The solving of the Boltzmann equation by the perturbation method of Chapman and Enskog leads to nearly Maxwellian distribution functions which are used to obtain expressions for the fluxes of transport properties and for the transport coefficients (3). Finally the transport coefficients are formulated in terms of a set of collision integrals Ω. These integrals involve the dynamics of the molecular collisions. The quantities Ω depend on the reduced mass, on the reduced initial relative velocity of the colliding molecules, on the angle by which the molecules are deflected and on the "impact parameter", which is closely related to the distance of nearest approach.

The actual evaluation of the integrals Ω depends upon the force law assumed for the molecular interaction (7). For rigid spheres an analytical expression of the angle of deflection can be derived and Ω evaluated. For realistic potential functions numerical methods must be used. It is convenient to reduce Ω by its corresponding rigid sphere value. Thus Ω^* is used as a symbol for the reduced collision integral in the following passages. Consequently the equation for the first approximation of the coefficient of diffusion of a binary mixture is:

$$[D_{12}]_1 = 0.001858 \frac{T^{3/2}}{p\,\sigma_{12}^2\Omega_{12}^*} \cdot \left(\frac{M_1 + M_2}{M_1 M_2}\right)^{1/2} \text{[cm}^2 \text{ sec}^{-1}] \quad [\text{A } 10.1]$$

p = pressure in atmospheres
$M_{1,2}$ = molecular weights
σ_{12} = collision diameter in Å.

* Sections 1, 2, 4 by E. U. Franck, Göttingen.

For rigid sphere molecules holds $\Omega^* = 1$. Hence equation [A 10.1] becomes identical with equation [10. 24] for this special case.

The applicability of equation [A 10.1] is restricted by several assumptions inherent in the Chapman-Enskog theory. Numerous investigations in recent years traced the consequences of these limiting assumptions.

Since only *binary collisions* are considered in the theory the value of equation [A 10.1] has to be tested at elevated gas densities, where three-body collisions are known to be important. This problem is discussed in Section 4. The restriction to *classical mechanics* excludes quantum phenomena which can be of practical importance at low temperatures. Several papers have been dedicated to this subject.

The use of first order approximations in the Chapman-Enskog perturbation method restricts its results to situations with *small gradients* of physical quantities. This requirement is met by most diffusion experiments. In shock waves, in extreme fields of gravity, or in the range of steep temperature gradients however, expressions of the type of equation [A 10.1] may prove to be invalid.

Complicated conditions are encountered where *chemical reactions* are closely connected with diffusion, especially if temperature gradients are involved. These problems have been discussed in a number of papers.

By means of modern tracer techniques more accurate information on the *concentration dependence* of diffusion coefficients for binary mixtures has been collected. The observed concentration dependence has not yet been explained completely by the theory. It will be mentioned once more in the next Section 2.

Great effort has been dedicated to the attempts to find *realistic molecular models* appropiate to calculate the corresponding integrals Ω. Some of them will be reviewed in the following section. Only recently new techniques permitted the measuring of gaseous diffusion coefficients at high temperatures and comparison of the results with the findings from molecular beam investigations. Since these experiments give important information on that part of the intermolecular potential which is effective in high energy collisions they are discussed separately in Section 3.

2. INTERMOLECULAR POTENTIALS

The various assumptions regarding intermolecular forces and their relations to transport properties have been described most thoroughly by Hirschfelder *et al.* in an extensive monograph (7). The subject is discussed in a condensed manner by Bird (1).

Among the variety of molecular models, which have been proposed, the Lennard-Jones potential as expressed by equation [A 10.2] appears to be the one most generally employed recently:

$$\varphi(r) = 4\varepsilon\left[\left(\frac{\sigma}{r}\right)^{12} - \left(\frac{\sigma}{r}\right)^{6}\right] \qquad \text{[A 10.2]}$$

Here $\varphi(r)$ is the potential energy of interaction between the two molecules; r is the intermolecular distance; ε and σ denote the maximum energy of attraction and the intermolecular distance at zero potential energy. Both constants are explained by Fig. A 10-1 a.

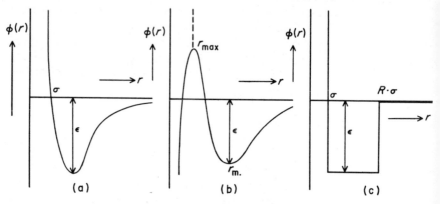

Fig. A 10-1. Three important spherically symmetrical potential functions. (a) Lennard-Jones potential. (b) Buckingham (exp-six)-potential. (c) Squarewell potential.

Hirschfelder et al. have calculated and tabulated numerical values of the collision integral Ω^* as a function of the reduced temperature kT/ε (7)*. A few values from these tables are listed in Table A 10.1.

TABLE A 10.1
Values of the collision integral calculated on the basis of the Lennard-Jones potential by Hirschfelder et al. (7)

kT/ε	0.30	0.40	0.50	0.70	1.00
Ω^*	2.662	2.318	2.066	1.729	1.439

kT/ε	1.50	2.00	5.0	10	100
Ω^*	1.198	1.075	0.8422	0.7424	0.5130

* In the tables of Hirschfelder et al. (7) the notation Ω_{12} (1.1)* is used for the collision integral of diffusion in binary mixtures.

The best way to examine the adequacy of the Lennard-Jones model is to try to reproduce experimental self-diffusion coefficients for several temperatures by equation [A 10.1] with adjusted values of σ_{11} and ε_{11}, making use of the Ω^*-tables. If the experimental data of self-diffusion are insufficient, the force constants σ_{11} and ε_{11} are best obtained from viscosity data. The constants can also be estimated from the PVT-behavior using critical data and the simple empirical relations:

$$\varepsilon_{11}/k = 0.77 \; T_c \text{ and } \sigma_{11} = 0.833 \; V_c^{1/3} \qquad [A\ 10.3]$$

A selection of ε and σ-constants is given in Table A 10.2.

TABLE A 10.2

Selected Lennard-Jones force constants calculated from viscosity data*

Molecule	ε/k ($^{\circ}$K)	σ (Å)
He	10.2	2.576
A	124	3.418
Xe	229	4.055
H_2	33.3	2.968
N_2	91.5	3.681
O_2	113	3.433
CO_2	190	3.996
CH_4	136.5	3.822
C_2H_6	230	4.418

* Cf. Reid and Sherwood (15), Hirschfelder et al. (7).

TABLE A 10.3

Calculated and observed self diffusion coefficients of several gases at 1 atmosphere[a]

Gas	Temperature ($^{\circ}$K)	D_{11} (calc.) (cm.^{2} sec.$^{-1}$)	D_{11} (exp) (cm.^{2} sec.$^{-1}$)
A	273.2	0.154	0.156 $\pm$ 0.002[b]
Xe	300.5	0.0571	0.0576 $\pm$ 0.001[c]
H_2	273	1.243	1.258 $\pm$ 0.002[d]
N_2	273.2	0.174	0.172 $\pm$ 0.002[e]
CO_2	273.2	0.092	0.097[f]

[a] Cf. Hirschfelder et al. (7).

[b] Winn, E. B., Phys. Rev. 80, 1024 (1950).

[c] Visner, S., Rept. K-688 (May 1951) of K-25 Plant, Carbide and Carbon Chemicals Co.

[d] Harteck, P., and Schmidt, H. W., Z. Phys. Chem. 21 B, 447 (1933).

[e] Winter, E. R. S., Trans. Far. Soc. 47, 342 (1952).

[f] Amdur, I., Irvine, I. W., Mason E. A. and Ross, I., J. Chem. Phys. 20, 436 (1952).

In Table A 10.3 several experimental self diffusion coefficients are compared with values calculated by means of equation [A 10.1] with force constants from viscosity measurements. The agreement is quite good for A, Xe, H_2, and N_2 but less satisfactory for CO_2 which could be expected from the nonspherical shape of the CO_2-molecules.

Equation [A 10.1] represents only the first approximation of diffusion coefficients. The second approximation is related to the first by

$$[D_{11}]_2 = [D_{11}]_1 \, f_{D_{11}}^{(2)}$$

and

$$[D_{12}]_2 = [D_{12}]_1 \, f_{D_{12}}^{(2)} \qquad\qquad [A\ 10.4]$$

The factors $f_D^{(2)}$ are complicated functions of the collision integrals and molecular weights. $f_{D_{12}}^{(2)}$ depends also on the composition of the gas mixture. Chapman and Cowling (3) and also Kihara (69) developed different methods to evaluate $f_D^{(2)}$ which have recently been summarized and critically compared by Mason (89, 90). According to both methods the values of $f_D^{(2)}$ vary only between 1.00 and 1.04 or 1.05, even for mixtures with a very small concentration of a very light gas (trace) in a carrier gas of much heavier molecules (Lorentzian gas mixture). For the opposite composition: a small amount of heavy gas in a light carrier (quasi-Lorentzian gas) Mason has shown that $f_D^{(2)} = 1$ for both the Chapman-Cowling and Kihara results. Both second approximations $f_D^{(2)}$ do not differ more than 1% from the exact value $f_D^{(\infty)}$, which has been calculated by Mason (89, 90) for several potential functions. Kihara's second approximation is considered to be somewhat simpler than that of Chapman and Cowling.

Since the first approximation $[D_{12}]_1$, equation [A 10.1], is independent of composition, a concentration dependence of $[D_{12}]_2$ is introduced only by $f_{D_{12}}^{(2)}$. Exact modern measurements of the influence of composition on diffusion are scarce. Walker and Westenberg (132, 133) recently investigated the system He-N_2, Amdur and Schatzki (19) the system A-Xe. The results are listed in Table A 10.4. in the first example the

TABLE A 10.4

Concentration dependence of the diffusion coefficient for the systems He-N_2 [Walker and Westenberg (132, 133)] and A-Xe [Amdur and Schatzki (19)]

System	Temperature (°K)	D_{12}(exp.) (cm.^{2} sec.$^{-1}$)
He (trace)-N_2	298	0.730
N_2 (trace)-He	298	0.688
A (trace)-Xe	329.9	0.1366 ± 0.0008
Xe (trace)-A	329.9	0.1373 ± 0.0022

variation of D_{12} over the whole range of concentrations is 6%, in the second example the variation does not exceed the experimental accuracy, which was about 1%. In both examples the observed variation is in agreement with theory. Schäfer et al. (112), however, with binary mixtures containing H_2, N_2, and CO_2 measured variations of D_{12} with concentration which at $0°$ C and $-21°$ C amounted to more than 10%. Probably the evaluation of $f^{(2)}_{D_{12}}$ on the basis of the Lennard-Jones potential is not sufficient to account for this variation.

To predict binary diffusion coefficients for practical purposes by the first approximation (equation [A 10.1]), the force constants σ_{12} and ε_{12} between unlike pairs of molecules must be known. At the present the best approach to these quantities is to take the arithmetic mean of σ_{11} and σ_{22} and the geometric mean of ε_{11} and ε_{22}:

$$\sigma_{12} = \frac{1}{2}(\sigma_{11} + \sigma_{22})$$

$$\varepsilon_{12} = \sqrt{\varepsilon_{11} \cdot \varepsilon_{22}}$$

$$\frac{kT}{\varepsilon_{12}} = \frac{kT}{\sqrt{\varepsilon_{11} \cdot \varepsilon_{22}}} \,. \qquad \text{[A 10.5]}$$

Somewhat more flexible than the Lennard-Jones (6—12)-potential is the modified Buckingham (exp-six)-potential cf. [(7)].

$$r \geq r_{\max}$$

$$\varphi(r) = \frac{\varepsilon}{1 - (6/\alpha)} \left[\frac{6}{\alpha} \exp\left(\alpha\left[1 - \frac{r}{r_m}\right]\right) - \left(\frac{r_m}{r}\right)^6 \right]$$

$$r \leq r_{\max}$$

$$\varphi(r) = \infty \,. \qquad \text{[A 10.6]}$$

The corresponding curve $\varphi(r)$ is shown in Fig. A 10-1 b; $r_{\max}$ is the value of r for which $\varphi(r)$ has a maximum; ε is the depth of the potential energy minimum at r_m. A third parameter, α, is a measure of the steepness of the repulsion energy. This potential permits the variation of the low velocity collision diameter, σ, as compared to the separation of the minimum r_m. The energy of the maximum is normally large enough to avoid difficulties. Mason (87) has calculated a set of collision integrals Ω^* for the (exp-six) potential (cf. 7). Recently Walker and Westenberg (133) were able to fit the observed energy of interaction for He-N_2 with the (exp-six)-potential covering a very extended range of intermolecular distances. The resulting parameters are:

$$\alpha_{\text{He-N}_2} = 12 \qquad \varepsilon_{\text{He-N}_2}/k = 31.9°\,\text{K} \qquad (r_m)_{\text{He-N}_2} = 3.80\,\text{Å} \,.$$

The square-well model which is shown in Fig. A 10-1 c has also three adjustable parameters:

$$r < \sigma \qquad\qquad \varphi(r) = \infty$$

$$\sigma < r < R \cdot \sigma \qquad \varphi(r) = -\varepsilon \qquad\qquad [A\ 10.7]$$

$$r > R \cdot \sigma \qquad\qquad \varphi(r) = 0 \, .$$

Though less realistic than the (exp-six)-model it is easier to handle for exploratory calculations. The integrals Ω^* for this potential have been calculated by Holleran and Hulburt (62) [cf. also (7)]. Schaefer and Moesta (113) also presented numerical data of the effective collision diameter for this model as a function of reduced temperature, taking $R = 1.8$ and $R = 2.0$ as parameters.

Schäfer and Schuhmann (114) determined D_{11} for Kr and D_{12} for Ne-A and A-Kr experimentally in the region from 90 to 473° K and from 200 to 473° K. They were able to reproduce the D_{11} (Kr)-values over the whole temperature range with not more than 2% deviation by calculations based on the square well model. The values of the three individual constants:

$$R\,(\mathrm{Kr}) = 2.0 \qquad \varepsilon\,(\mathrm{Kr})/k = 75°\mathrm{K} \qquad R \cdot \sigma(Kr) = 6.9 \text{ Å}$$

were derived from the experimental second virial coefficient of Whalley and Schneider (136). The attempt to derive D_{12} (Ne-A) and D_{12} (A-Kr) from the self-diffusion coefficients of the pure components proved to be less successful. The experimental D_{12}-values exceeded the calculated ones by 7 to 11%. Insufficiency of the square well model as well as the simple combining rules for σ, $R \cdot \sigma$ and ε (analogous to equation [A 10.5]) may be responsible for the discrepancy.

For the majority of real molecules the assumption of spherical models is a very severe simplification. Kinetic theory on the basis of angle dependent potentials, however, though intensively studied by several groups, is not yet as advanced as that for simpler models.

The intermolecular potential may be angle dependent because of a dipole moment of the molecules. The Stockmayer potential which is a superposition of a Lennard-Jones (6—12)-potential and of the interaction of two point dipoles is an attempt to represent the situation in such systems:

$$\varphi\,(r,\,\Theta_a,\,\Theta_b,\,\Phi_b - \Phi_a) = 4\,\varepsilon\left[\left(\frac{\sigma}{r}\right)^{12} - \left(\frac{\sigma}{r}\right)^{6}\right]$$

$$-\frac{\mu_a \mu_b}{r^3}\,g\,(\Theta_a,\,\Theta_b,\,\Phi_a - \Phi_b) \qquad\qquad [A\ 10.8]$$

$g(\Theta_a, \Theta_b, \Phi_a - \Phi_b)$ is the angular dependence of the interaction of the dipole moments μ_a and μ_b. At present diffusion coefficients calculated for this potential are not available.

For very high energy collisions, where the attractive forces are less important than the repulsive forces, an approximation may be justified which assumes the g-function in equation [A 10.8] to be equal to unity and retains only the angle independent term μ^2/r^3. Reduced collision integrals for this model have been calculated by Krieger at least for viscosity and thermal conductivity (cf. 7).

The effective potential energy of interaction between a polar and a nonpolar molecule has the same distance dependence as the potential energy of two nonpolar particles. Hence the Lennard-Jones function may be used for this situation too. According to Hirschfelder $et\ al.$ for the polar-nonpolar (n.p.) interaction the following combining laws hold:

$$\sigma_{np} = \frac{1}{2}\left(\sigma_n + \sigma_p\right)\xi^{-1/6}$$

$$\varepsilon_{np} = \sqrt{\varepsilon_n \cdot \varepsilon_p}\,\xi^2$$

in which ξ is a function of the polarizability of the nonpolar molecule, the dipole moment of the polar molecule and the quantities σ_n, σ_p, ε_n, and ε_p.

The coefficients of diffusion for H_2O and several nonpolar gases could be fairly well evaluated by this method (Table A 10.5).

TABLE A 10.5
Coefficients of diffusion for H_2O in several nonpolar gases*.

	H_2O-H_2	H_2O-CO_2	H_2O-He	H_2O-N_2
D_{12} (exp.) (cm.^{2} sec.$^{-1}$)	1.02	0.202	0.90	0.256
D_{12} (calc.) (cm.^{2} sec.$^{-1}$)	0.95	0.183	0.95	0.255

* Experimental data from Schwertz and Brow (117); calculated data from Hirschfelder $et\ al.$ (7). ($T = 34.4°$C).

Nonpolar molecules may have been angle dependent potentials because of their structure. In certain cases their real shape can be represented by rigid impenetrable ellipsoids of revolution of prolate or oblate shape. Another possibility is to idealize real molecules by rigid spherocylindrical bodies. Both kinds of models have been extensively studied by Kihara and co-workers [cf. (7)]. Recently

Kihara (69) and Kihara and Ouchi (70) evaluated average cross sections for collisions between heavy ovaloids and light spherical molecules.

A kinetic theory of rigid spherocylindrical molecules has been developed by Curtiss (44) and Curtiss and Muckenfuss (46). In a third paper (96) the authors extended the theory to multicomponent mixtures. The treatment is based on a set of generalized Boltzmann

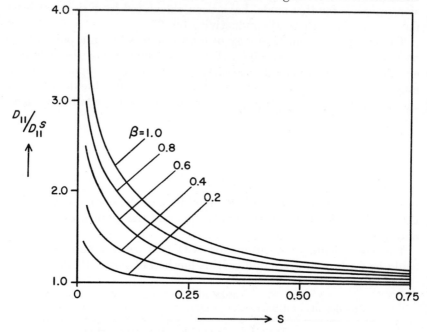

Fig. A 10-2. Self-diffusion for rigid spherocylinders after Muckenfuss and Curtiss (96). D_{11}: spherocylinders, D_{11}^s: spheres of the same volume. β = shape parameter. S = mass distribution parameter.

equations analogous to that used in the treatment of a pure gas, which are solved by a perturbation method similar to that of Chapman and Enskog. Finally the transport coefficients are obtained in terms of four-dimensional integrals. The integrals depend only on the geometry of the molecules, and the integrations are carried out over the surface of the two molecules. Final integrations are carried out for the spherocylindrical model. The coefficients of diffusion as well as the other transport coefficients are obtained in terms of two parameters characteristic of the shape and mass distribution of each molecule.

A spherocylindrical body is a right circular cylinder with hemispherical caps. L and a denote the length of the cylinder and its radius.

Γ is the principal moment of inertia about an axis perpendicular to the symmetry axis. Two parameters are defined by these quantities and by the mass of a molecule m:

$$\beta = \frac{L}{2a} \text{ and } \delta = \frac{\Gamma}{ma^2}.$$

For rigid spheres β would be zero and δ equal to unity. To discuss the self-diffusion only one set of these parameters is necessary. Muckenfuss and Curtiss (96) calculated the ratio D_{11}/D_{11}^s, i.e. the self-diffusion coefficient for rigid spherocylinders reduced by that for rigid spheres of the same volume as the spherocylinders. Fig. A 10-2 gives the result. The diffusion coefficients of the nonspherical molecules always exceed the coefficients of the spheres.

3. DIFFUSION IN GASES AT HIGH TEMPERATURES

As a method applicable under rather extreme conditions of temperature the "point source" technique has been developed by Walker and Westenberg (132, 133). It consists in injecting a trace gas from a fine hypodermic tube into a slow, uniform, laminar stream of a second gas. In order to measure the diffusion coefficient of the trace gas one determines the concentration in gas samples taken down stream.

For a steady state (in a cylindrical tube, the hypodermic tube in the center) the over-all continuity equation holds

$$\Delta(\varrho V) = 0 \qquad \text{[A 10.9]}$$

with density ϱ and V the mass average velocity. In addition for component 1

$$\Delta[c_1(V + V_1)] = 0 \qquad \text{[A 10.10]}$$

with c_1 the concentration of 1 (moles cm^{-3}), and V the diffusion velocity. Specializing for a binary system at constant P and T

$$V_1 = \frac{c^2 M_2 D \nabla (c_2/c_1)}{\varrho\, c_1} \qquad \text{[A 10.11]}$$

with c_2 concentration of 2, $c = c_1 + c_2$, M_2 the molar mass of 2 and D the diffusion coefficient $(= D_{12})$.

With the further specialization $c_1 \ll c$ we have ϱ and $D \sim$ constant, $\varrho \approx cM_2$ and from equation [A 10.9]

$$\nabla V \approx 0.$$

Thus

$$D\Delta^2 c_1 - V\nabla c_1 = 0, \qquad \text{[A 10.12]}$$

or, introducing the mole fraction $N_1 = c_1/c$,

$$D\nabla^2 N_1 - V\nabla N_1 = 0* \qquad [A\ 10.13]$$

with coordinates $x, r\ [r = (x^2 + y^2 + z^2)^{1/2}]$ the direction of flow, of uniform velocity coinciding with the x-axis, the volumetric flow rate of component 1 being Q mole sec^{-1} at $x = 0$ and $r = 0$, we have

$$Q = \lim 4\pi r^2 D(\partial c/\partial r) \qquad r \to 0$$

with the solution*

$$c = \frac{Q}{4\pi D r} \exp\left[-\frac{(r-x)u}{2D}\right] \qquad [A\ 10.14]$$

Walker and Westenberg (132, 133) compare their results and diffusion coefficients derived by Amdur (17) from scattering experiments with theoretical values on the basis of the modified Buckingham (exp-six) potential (cf. Section 2).

TABLE A 10.6

Observed and calculated values of the diffusion coefficient of the system He-N$_2$

$T(°K)$	$D_{obs}*$	D(Amdur)	D(exp-six)
300	0.743	—	0.70
600	2.40	—	2.32
900	4.76	—	4.70
1200	7.74	7.67	7.72
1500		11.41	11.38
1800	—	15.80	15.77
2100	—	20.79	20.48
2400	—	26.39	25.67
2700	—	32.56	31.59
3000	—	39.28	38.02

* D_{obs} for He(trace)-N$_2$ is represented by $D_{\text{Ne-N}_2} = 4.81 \times 10^{-5}\ T^{1.691}$ cm.^{2} sec.$^{-1}$.

4. DIFFUSION IN GASES AT HIGH PRESSURES

In dilute gases at constant density the diffusion coefficient is proportional to the coefficient of viscosity η [10.23]. In liquids, however, according to Stokes' law [11.43] D is proportional to $1/\eta$. At supercritical temperatures continuous increase of density from gas-like to liquid-like ranges is possible. At present there is no rigorous

* The solution of this differential equation is equivalent to the steady state reached for $t \to \infty$ in the case of a moving source, cf. Carslaw and Jaeger (ref. 2, Chapter I), § 106, p. 223, especially equation (2), p. 224.

theory, however, which offers quantitative results of transport properties for the whole range of densities on the basis of realistic intermolecular potential functions. The statistical mechanical approach of Kirkwood and others (72) ultimately may lead to a kinetic theory of sufficient accuracy for diffusion in dense gases. This approach leads to a theory of the friction factor similar to that which Chandrasekhar (32) developed on the basis of the phenomenological theory of Brownian motion. Kirkwood generalized the concept of the friction factor to apply to very small particles or molecules.

With restriction to the simplified rigid sphere model for actual molecules Enskog (3, 7) obtained:

$$(\eta/\eta_0) = \left(\frac{b_0}{\overline{V}}\right)\left(\frac{1}{y} + 0.8 + 0.761\,y\right) \qquad \text{[A 10.15]}$$

$$(D_{11}/D_{11}{}^0) = \left(\frac{b_0}{\overline{V}}\right)\frac{1}{y}. \qquad \text{[A 10.16]}$$

The index "0" denotes limiting values for very low density ϱ; D_{11}^0 is the coefficient of self diffusion calculated from the value of this quantity at $p = 1$ atm and using the relation $D_{11}\varrho = \text{const}$. $\overline{V}$ stands for the molecular volume; $b_0 = (2\pi/3)N_0\sigma_0{}^3$ is four times the volume of the rigid spheres ($N_0 = $ Avogadro's number; $\sigma_0 = $ diameter of the particles): y is related to $\chi_{11}[10.43]$ by

$$y = \chi_{11}\left(\frac{b_0}{\overline{V}}\right). \qquad \text{[A 10.17]}$$

For a gas of rigid spheres the following expression holds:

$$y = \frac{p\,\overline{V}}{RT} - 1. \qquad \text{[A 10.18]}$$

Such a gas would obey the virial expansion:

$$y = \left(\frac{b_0}{\overline{V}}\right) + 0.625\left(\frac{b_0}{\overline{V}}\right)^2 + 0.287\left(\frac{b_0}{\overline{V}}\right)^3 + 0.115\left(\frac{b_0}{\overline{V}}\right)^4 + . \quad \text{[A 10.19]}$$

With [A 10.19] the first two terms of this expansion are equivalent to the relation [10.43].

The full curve of Fig. A 10-3 shows $y = f\,(b_0/\overline{V})$ according to equation [A 10.19]. The dotted curve has been obtained from the radial distribution function with the application of the superposition approximation by Kirkwood et al. (73). The dashed curve has been calculated for a sample of 256 rigid spheres by Rosenbluth and Rosenbluth (106) using Monte Carlo methods. There is good agreement of these last results with formula [A 10.19] at densities up to $(b_0/\overline{V}) = 2$.

Thus equation [A 10.19] seems to be adequate to calculate y for the rigid sphere gas.

Division of equation [A 10.15] by equation [A 10.16] leads to the limiting relation for dilute gases at constant density: $\eta \sim D_{11}$. Forming the product of [A 10.15] and [A 10.16] and using the definition of D_{11} yields the result that at very high densities $\eta \cdot D_{11}$ is proportional to $(b_0/\overline{V})$. Stokes' law demands $\eta \cdot D_{11}$ to be independet of $(b_0/\overline{V})$. The proportionality obtained, however, is a relatively weak density dependence as compared with the strong dependence of y and of η and D_{11} themselves (Fig. [A 10-3]).

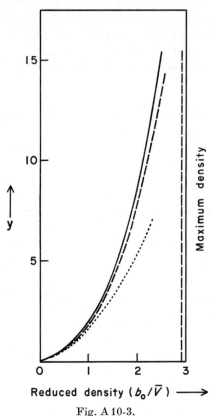

Fig. A 10-3.
The quantity $y = (p\overline{V}/RT)\text{-}1$ for rigid spheres calculated by different methods.

Recent measurements of the density dependence of several diffusion coefficients permit to test the value of the Enskog equation [A 10.16] in the region of medium densities. Drickamer and others investigated the diffusion of TCH_3 in CH_4 (64) as well as the diffusion of $C^{14}O_2$-molecules in CO_2 (105, 128, 129) and in mixtures of CO_2 and CH_4 (65). A pair of small cells with their content at equal pressure have been moved into contact by sliding along carefully ground plain surfaces. The increase of concentration of tagged molecules at the end of one of the cells was determined by a scintillation counter. To prevent convection the cells were filled with porous fritted metal or fritted glass. The average pore size was between 5 and $15\,\mu$. The "effective length" of the diffusion path in the cells was determined by diffusion measurements at pressures below 30 atm, which were carried out in cells filled with fritted material as well as in others containing only parallel glass capillaries. The insertion of the fritted material extended the effective length of the cells by a factor of 1.5 to 2.

Table A 10.7 contains experimental data of coefficients of self-diffusion of CH_4 and CO_2 for different temperatures. In the Figs. A10-4 and A 10-5 the ratios $(D\varrho)/(D/\varrho)_0$ have been plotted as a function of the reduced density $(b_0/\overline{V})$. $(D\varrho)_0$ denotes the limiting value of the product of the coefficient of self-diffusion and the density at very low pressures. The Enskog theory is adequate to describe the self-diffusion in CH_4 as is demonstrated by Fig. A 10-4. For carbon dioxide, however, the measured coefficients at low and moderate densities are much higher than the predicted values. Similar results have been reported

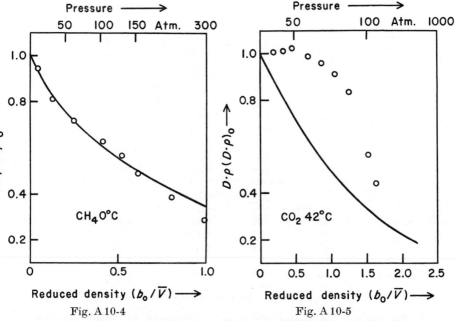

Fig. A 10-4   Fig. A 10-5

Fig. A 10-4. Variation of self-diffusion in CH_4 with density; o = experimental [Jeffries and Drickamer (64)]. — = Enskog theory.

Fig. A 10-5. Variation of self-diffusion in CO_2 with density; o = experimental [Drickamer *et al.* (105, 128, 129)]. — = Enskog theory.

by O'Hern and Martin (98) for CO_2. No sufficient explanation for this behavior has been offered as yet. The rod-like shape of the CO_2 molecules may be responsible for the phenomenon. Perhaps the rotation of dimers of short lifetime is also of some importance.

According to Jeffries and Drickamer (65) the diffusion of CO_2 in a 50% CO_2-CH_4 mixture approximately obeys the Enskog theory while with mixtures richer in CO_2 deviations as in pure carbon dioxide occur. Chou and Martin (33) obtained comparable results from investigation of the diffusion of C^{14}-tagged CO_2 in CO_2-H_2 mixtures and CO_2-C_3H_8 mixtures.

Mifflin and Bennett (92) recently determined the self-diffusion coefficient of argon at $50°C$ up to 300 atm (~ 11 gmole/liter). Satisfactory representation of the data could only be achieved if the Enskog equation was used with the quantity y derived from experimental P-V-T data of argon. The original space model was insufficient in this case.

TABLE A 10.7

Diffusion coefficients of the systems CH_4-TCH_3 (64) and CO_2-$C^{14}O_2$ (105, 128, 129) at elevated pressures

CH_4-TCH_3

$T(°C)$	P(atm)	σ(gm.cm.$^{-3}$)	$D \times 10^3$ (cm^2. sec.$^{-1}$)
0	20	0.0156	5.3
0	60	0.051	1.51
0	100	0.0916	0.75
0	150	0.145	0.40
0	300	0.242	0.150
50	40	0.026	3.65
50	100	0.0686	1.13
50	150	0.103	0.664

CO_2-$C^{14}O_2$

42	27	0.05	4.00
42	37	0.08	2.59
42	53	0.12	1.75
42	64	0.18	1.20
42	83	0.30	0.684
42	103	0.60	0.287

To predict unknown diffusion coefficients at high densities the Enskog theory probably will be satisfactory only at high reduced temperatures and for nonpolar and nearly spherical molecules. Slattery and Bird (119) have used the principle of corresponding states and compilations of the reduced viscosity and compressibility of gases to derive a diagram of the reduced diffusion coefficient $(DP)/(DP)_0$ as a function of reduced temperature, T_r, and reduced pressure, P_r. In the case of binary mixtures the "pseudocritical" values for T_r and P_r are to be used (15, 39).

REFERENCES

Monographs and Review Articles

1. Bird. R. B., Theory of diffusion, *Advances in Chem. Eng.* **1**, 156 (1956).
2. Chapman, S., and Cowling, T. G., The Mathematical Theory of Nonuniform Gases, 2nd ed. Cambridge University Press, London and New York, 1952.

3. Curtiss, C. F., Statistical mechanics, *Ann. Rev. Phys. Chem.* **9**, 379—395 (1958).
4. Flügge, S., ed., Encyclopedia of Physics, Vol. XII, Springer, Berlin, 1958. (Contains contributions by Grad, H., Principles of the Kinetic Theory of Gases, and Waldmann, L., Transport Properties of Gases at Medium Pressures.)
5. Hamann, S. D., Physico-Chemical Effects of Pressure. Academic Press, New York, 1957.
6. Hilsenrath, J., Sources of transport coefficients and correlations of thermodynamic and transport data (1945—1954). *In* Selected Combustion Problems II, pp. 199—244. Butterworths, London.
7. Hirschfelder, J. O., Curtiss, C. F., and Bird, R. B., Molecular Theory of Gases and Liquids. Wiley, New York, 1954.
8. Jost, W., Diffusion, Methoden der Messung und Auswertung. Steinkopff, Darmstadt, 1957.
9. Kirk, R. E., and Othmer, D. F., eds., Diffusion in gases, *in* Encyclopedia of Chemical Technology, Vol. 5. by M. Benedict, Interscience, New York, 1950.
10. Present, R. D., Kinetic Theory of Gases. McGraw-Hill, New York, 1958.
11. Proceedings of the International Symposium on Transport Processes in Statistical Mechanics, Brüssels, 1956 (J. Prigogine, ed.). Interscience, New York, 1958.
12. Proceedings of the Second Gas Dynamics Symposium on Transport Properties in Gases, Evanston, Illinois, 1957 (1958).
13. Proceedings of the Joint Conference on Thermodynamic and Transport Properties of Fluids, London, 1957. Institution of Mechanical Engineers, London, 1958.
14. Proceeding of the Symposium on Thermal Properties of Gases, Liquids, Solids, Purdue University, Lafayette, Indiana, 1959. American Society of Mechanical Engineers, New York, 1959.
15. Reid, R. C., and Sherwood, T. K., The Properties of Gases and Liquids. McGraw-Hill, New York, 1958.
16. Ullmanns Encyclopädie der technischen Chemie, (W. Foerst, ed.), see article on Diffusion, *in* Vol. 5, pp. 845—855. München, Berlin, 1954.

General Bibliography

Papers containing additional information on thermal diffusion in gases are denoted by "TD".

17. Amdur, J., Mason, E. A., and Jordan, J. E., Scattering of high velocity neutral particles. X. He-Ne; A-N_2. The N_2-N_2 interaction, *J. Chem. Phys.* **27**, 527 (1957).
18. Amdur, I., and Schatzki, T. F., Diffusion coefficients of the systems Xe-Xe and A-Xe, *J. Chem. Phys.* **27**, 1049 (1957).
19. Amdur, I., and Schatzki, T. F., Composition dependence of the diffusion coefficient of the system A-Xe, *J. Chem. Phys.* **29**, 1425 (1958).
20. Baulknight, C. W., The calculation of transport properties at elevated temperatures. Transport Properties in Gases, Proceedings of the Second Gas Dynamics Symposium, Evanston, Illinois, 1957, pp. 89—95 (1958).
21. Bearman, R. J., and Kirkwood, J. G., Statistical mechanics of transport processes XI. Equations of transport in multicomponent systems, (TD), *J. Chem. Phys.* **28**, 136—145 (1958).

22. Becker, E. W., and Beyrich, W., Effect of isotopic substitution on the collision properties of the carbon dioxide molecule, (TD), *J. Phys. Chem.* **56**, 911—913 (1952).

23. Bendt, P. J., Measurements of He^3-He^4 and H_2-D_2 gas diffusion coefficients, *Phys. Rev.* **110**, 85 (1958).

24. Bernard, J., Diffusion par "Balayage". Application a la separations des constituants d'un melange gazeux, *J. chim. phys.* **55**, 846 (1958).

25. Boyd, C. A., Stein, N., Steingrimsson, V., and Rumpel, W. F., An interferometric method of determining diffusion coefficients in gaseous systems, *J. Chem. Phys.* **19**, 548 (1951).

26. Brown, B. W., The thermodynamics of steady conduction-diffusion-reaction states of multicomponent fluid systems, (TD), *Trans. Faraday Soc.* **54**, 772—784 (1958).

27. Buckingham, R. A., Davies, A. E., and Davies, A. R., The deduction of intermolecular forces from the transport properties of hydrogen and helium, *Proc. Inst. Mech. Engrs. (London)*, 1958.

28. Butler, J. N., and Brokaw, R. S., Thermal conductivity of gas mixtures in chemical equilibrium, *J. Chem. Phys.* **26**, 1636—1643 (1957).

29. Carmichael, L. T., Reamer, H. H., Sage, B. H., and Lacey, W. N., Diffusion coefficients in hydrocarbon systems. Heptane in gas phase of methane-heptane system, *Ind. Eng. Chem.* **47**, 2205—2210 (1955).

30. Carmichael, L. T., and Sage, B. H., Diffusion coefficients in hydrocarbon systems. Heptane in the gas phase of the ethane-heptane and propane-heptane systems, *A. I. Ch. E. Journal* **2**, 273—276 (1956).

31. Carmichael, L. T., Sage, B. H., and Lacey, W. N., Diffusion coefficients in hydrocarbon systems: hexane in the gas phase of the methane-, ethane- and propane-hexane systems, *A. I. Ch. E. Journal* **1**, 385—390 (1955).

32. Chandrasekhar, S., Stochastic problems in physics and astronomy, *Revs. Modern Phys.* **15**, 1 (1943).

33. Chou, C-H., and Martin, J. J., Diffusion in gases at elevated pressures. Carbon-14-labeled CO_2 in CO_2-H_2 and CO_2-propane, *Ind. Eng. Chem.* **49**, 759 (1957).

34. Cohen, E. G. D., Offerhaus, M. J., and de Boer, J., Transport properties and equation of state of gaseous mixtures of helium isotopes, (TD), *Physica* **20**, 501—515 (1954).

35. Cohen, E. G. D., Offerhaus, M. J., van Leeuwen, J. M. J., Roos, B. W., and de Boer, J., The transport properties and the equation of state of gaseous para- and ortho-hydrogen and their mixtures below 40°K, (TD), *Physica* **21**, 737—739 (1955).

36. Cohen, E. G. D., Theory of the transport properties in dilute gases and in gas mixtures, (TD), *Bull. inst. intern. froid, Annexe* **2**, 159—172 (1956).

37. Cohen, E. G. D., Offerhaus, M. J., van Leeuwen, J. M. J., Roos, W. B., and de Boer, J., The transport properties and the equation of state of gaseous para- and ortho-hydrogen and their mixtures below 40°K, (TD), *Physica* **22**, 791—815 (1956).

38. Cohen, E. G. D., and Offerhaus, M. J., Symmetry effects in the kinetic theory of gaseous para-ortho mixtures, (TD), *Physica* **24**, 742—750 (1958).

39. Comings, E. W., High Pressure Technology. McGraw-Hill, New York, 1956.

40. Crider, W. L., The use of diffusion coefficients in the measurement of vapor pressure, *J. Am. Chem. Soc.* **78**, 924 (1956).

41. Csanady, G. T., Flow lines in atmospheric diffusion, *Ind. Eng. Chem.* **49**, 1453 (1957).

42. Cummings, G. A. McD., and Ubbelohde, A. R., Collision diameters of flexible hydrocarbon molecules in the vapor phase, *J. Chem. Soc.* pp. 2524 to 2525 (1955).

43. Cummings, G. A. McD., and Ubbelohde, A. R., Collision diameters of flexible hydrocarbon molecules in the vapor phase: hydrogen effect, *J. Chem. Soc.* pp. 3751—3755 (1953).

44. Curtiss, C. F., Kinetic theory of nonspherical molecules, *J. Chem. Phys.* **24,** 225—241 (1956).

45. Curtiss, C. F., Hirschfelder, J. O., and Bird, R. B., Theories of gas transport properties. Transport properties in gases, (TD), Proceedings Second Gas Dynamics Symposium, Evanston, Illinois, 1957, pp. 3—11 (1958).

46. Curtiss, C. F., and Muckenfuss, C., Kinetic theory of nonspherical molecules. II, *J. Chem. Phys.* **26,** 1619 (1957).

47. Dahler, J. S., Transport phenomena in a dense gas of rigid spheres, *J. Chem. Phys.* **27,** 1428 (1957).

48. de Groot, S. R., and Mazur, P., Extension of Onsager's theory of reciprocal relations. I, (TD), *Phys. Rev.* **94,** 218—224 (1954).

49. DeLuca, L. B., Self-diffusion coefficient of nitrogen, *Phys. Rev.* **95,** 306 (1954).

50. DeNordwall, H. J., and Flowers, R. H., The diffusion of iodine in air, *Atomic Energy Research Establ. (Gt. Brit.) C/M* **342,** 5 pp., 1958.

51. Dye, R. F., and Dalla Valle, J. M., Diffusion of gases in porous media, *Ind. Eng. Chem.* **50** 1196 (1958).

52. Eisenschitz, R., Molecular theory of the nonequilibrium condition in fluids, *Kolloid-Z.* **139,** 38—42, Discussion 42—43 (1954).

53. Estermann, I., Molecular beam applications to transport properties in gases. Transport Properties in Gases. Proceedings Second Gas Dynamics Symposium, Evanston, Illinois, 1957, (1958).

54. Fair, J. R., and Lerner, B. J., A generalized correlation of diffusion coefficients, *A. I. Ch. E. Journal* **2,** 13—17 (1956).

55. Friedlander, S. K., and Litt, M., Diffusion controlled reaction in a laminar boundary layer, *Chem. Eng. Sci.* **7,** 229 (1958).

56. Green, H. S., Molecular theory of irrevresible processes in fluids, *Proc. Phys. Soc. (London)* **69** B, 269 (1956).

57. Green, M. S., Markoff random processes and the statistical mechanics of time-dependent phenomena. II. Irreversible processes in fluids, *J. Chem. Phys.* **22,** 398 (1954).

58. Heymann, D., and Kistemaker, I., Separation of some isotopes by convection diffusion, *J. Chem. Phys.* **24,** 105 (1956).

59. Hilsenrath, J., Report on sources and compilations of transport properties of gases, (TD), second Biennial Gas Dynamics Symposium, Northwestern University, Evanston, Illinois, 1957.

59 a. Hirschfelder, J. O., Diffusion coefficients in flames and detonations with constant enthalpy, *Phys. Fluids* **3,** 109 (1960).

60. Holleran, E. M., Diffusion and thermal diffusion of isotopic gases, *J. Chem. Phys.* **21,** 2184 (1953).

61. Holleran, E. M., Interrelation of gaseous viscosity, self-diffusion, and isotopic thermal diffusion, (TD), *J. Chem. Phys.* **23,** 847 (1955).

62. Holleran, E. M., and Hulburt, H. M., Transport properties of gases (with a square-well molecular interaction potential), *J. Chem. Phys.* **19,** 232 (1951).

63. van Itterbeck, A., Measurements on thermal diffusion combined with ordinary diffusion in gas mixtures (using velocity of sound measurements). Proceeding International Symposium on Transport Processes in Statistical Mechanics (I. Prigogine, ed.), p. 387. Interscience, New York, 1958.

64. Jeffries, Q. R., and Drickamer, H. G., Diffusion in the system CH_4-TCH_3 to 300 atmospheres pressure, *J. Chem. Phys.* **21**, 1358 (1953).

65. Jeffries, Q. R., and Drickamer, H. G., Diffusion in CO_2-CH_4 mixtures to 225 atmospheres pressure, *J. Chem. Phys.* **22**, 436 (1954).

66. Johnson, E. F., Molecular transport properties of fluids, (TD), *Ind. Eng. Chem.* (Rev.) **50**, 488 (1958).

67. Keyes, J. J. Jr., and Pigford, R. L., Diffusion in a ternary gas system with application to gas separation, *Chem. Eng. Sci.* **6**, 215 (1957).

68. Kihara, T., Virial coefficients and models of molecules in gases, *Revs. Modern Phys.* **25**, 831 (1953).

69. Kihara, T., Geometrical theory of convex molecules in nonuniform gases, *J. Phys. Soc. Japan* **12**, 564 (1957).

70. Kihara, T., and Ouchi, A., *J. Phys. Soc. Japan* **12**, 1052 (1957).

71. Kimpton, D. T., and Wall, F. T., Determination of diffusion coefficients from evaporation of H_2, H_2O, CH_4, C_2H_6, C_2H_4, SO_2, D_2O in air, *J. Phys. Chem.* **56**, 715 (1952).

72. Kirkwood, I. G., Statistical theory of transport processes. I. General theory, *J. Chem. Phys.* **14**, 180 (1946). (Cf. subsequent papers II—IX, *J. Chem. Phys.* 1947—1956.)

73. Kirkwood, I. G., Maun, E. K., and Alder, B. J., Radial distribution functions and the equation of state of a fluid composed of rigid spherical molecules, *J. Chem. Phys.* **18**, 1040 (1950).

74. Klibanova, T. M., Pomerantsev, V. V., and Frank-Kamenetskii, D. A., Diffusion coefficients of gases at high temperatures, *J. Tech. Phys. (U.S.S.R.)* **12**, 14 (1942).

75. Kluitenberg, G. A., de Groot, S. R., and Mazur, P., Relativistic thermodynamics of irreversible processes. I. Heat conduction, diffusion, viscous flow and chemical reaction; formal part, *Physica* **19**, 689 (1953).

76. Kluitenberg, G. A., de Groot, S. R., and Mazur, P., Relativistic thermodynamics of irreversible processes. II. Heat conduction and diffusion, physical part, *Physica* **19**, 1079 (1953).

77. van der Laan, E. T., Notes on the diffusion type model for the longitudinal mixing in flow, *Chem. Eng. Sci.* **7**, 187 (1958).

78. Lapidus, L., Flow distribution and diffusion in fixed-bed two-phase reactors, *Ind. Eng. Chem.* **49**, 1000 (1957).

79. Lin, S. C., Shock-wave studies of transport properties in high-temperature gases. Transport properties in Gases. Proceedings Second Gas Dynamics Symposium, Evanston, Illinois, 1957, pp. 96—102 (1958).

80. Longuet-Higgins, H. C., and Pople, J. A., Transport properties of a dense fluid of hard spheres, (TD), *J. Chem. Phys.* **25**, 884 (1956).

81. Longuet-Higgins, H. C., and Valleau, J. P., Transport of energy and momentum in a dense fluid of hard spheres, (TD), *Discussion Faraday Soc.* **22**, 47 (1956).

82. Madan, M. P., Transport properties of some gas mixtures, (TD), *Proc. Natl. Inst. Sci. India* **19**, 713 (1953).

83. Madan, M. P., Diffusion coefficients and law of molecular interaction, (TD), *Indian J. Phys.* **29**, 11 (1955).

84. Madan, M. P., Potential parameters for krypton, (TD). *J, Chem. Phys.* **27,** 113 (1957).
85. Madan, M. P. Law of molecular interaction with krypton, (TD), *Nuovo cimento* **10,** 1369 (1957).
86. Madan, M. P., Nonequilibrium properties of rare gases, (TD), *J. Phys. Chem.* **62,** 893 (1958).
87. Mason, E. A., Transport properties of gases obeying a modified Buckingham (exp-six)-Potential, (TD), *J. Chem. Phys.* **22,** 169 (1954).
88. Mason, E. A., Forces between unlike molecules and the properties of gaseous mixtures, (TD), *J. Chem. Phys.* **23,** 49 (1955).
89. Mason, E. A., Higher approximations for the transport properties of binary gas mixtures. I. General formulas, *J. Chem. Phys.* **27,** 75 (1957).
90. Mason, E. A., Higher approximations for the transport properties of binary gas mixtures. II. Applications, *J. Chem. Phys.* **27,** 782 (1957).
90a. Mason, E. A., Vanderslice, J. T., and Yos, J. M., Transport properties of high-temperature multicomponent gas mixtures, *Phys. Fluids* **2,** 688 (1959).
91. McCoubrey, J. C., Recent work on the equilibrium and transport properties of polyatomic gases, (TD), *J. Imp. Coll. Chem. Eng. Soc.* **9,** 40 (1955).
92. Mifflin, T. R., and Bennett, C. O., Self-diffusion in argon to 300 atmospheres, *J. Chem. Phys.* **29,** 975 (1958).
92a. Monchick, L., Collision integrals for the exponentail repulsive potential, *Phys. Fluids* **2,** 695 (1959).
93. Montroll, E. W., Statistical mechanics of transport and nonequilibrium processes, (TD), *Ann. Rev. Phys. Chem.* **5,** 449 (1954).
94. Mori, H., Time-correlation functions in the statistical mechanics of transport processes, *Phys. Rev.* **111,** 694 (1958).
95. Mori, H., and Ross, J., Transport equation in quantum gases, *Phys. Rev.* **109,** 1877 (1958).
96. Muckenfuß, C., and Curtiss, C. F., Kinetic theory of nonspherical molecules. III, *J. Chem. Phys.* **29,** 1257 (1958).
97. Muckenfuß, C., and Curtiss, C. F., Thermal conductivity of multicomponent gas mixtures, *J. Chem. Phys.* **29,** 1273 (1958).
98. O'Hern, H. A., and Martin, J. J., Diffusion in carbon dioxide at elevated pressure, *Ind. Eng. Chem.* **47,** 2081 (1955).
99. Pasquill, F., Atmospheric diffusion and air pollution, *Nature* **182,** 1134 (1958).
100. Peters, C., and Krabetz, R., Influence of diffusion on reaction rate in ammonia synthesis, *Z. Elektrochem.* **60,** 859 (1956).
101. Prigogine, I., and Buess, R., Distribution of matter and transport phenomena in the presence of a temperature gradient and chemical reaction, *Bull. classe sci., Acad. roy. Belg.* **38,** 711 (1952).
102. Prigogine, I., and Buess, R., Distribution of matter and transport phenomena in the presence of a temperature gradient and a chemical reaction. II, *Bull. classe sci., Acad. roy. Belg.* **38,** 851 (1952).
103. Prigogine, I., and Henkin, F., The transport equation for dilute gases, (TD), *Physica* **24,** 214 (1958). [Cf. *Physica* **22,** 621 (1956).]
104. Reik, H. G., Viscosity pressure tensor, diffusion and heat flow in strongly inhomogeneous gases, *Z. Naturforsch.* **12 a,** 663 (1957).
105. Robb, W. L., and Drickamer, H. G., Diffusion in CO_2 up to 150 atmospheres pressure, *J. Chem. Phys.* **19,** 1504 (1951).
106. Rosenbluth, M. N., and Rosenbluth, A. W., Further results on Monte Carlo equations of state, *J. Chem. Phys.* **22,** 881 (1954).

107. Saxena, S. C., Thermal conductivity of He-A-Xe ternary mixture, (TD), *J. Chem. Phys.* **25**, 360 (1956).
108. Saxena, S. C., Higher approximation to diffusion coefficient and determination of force constants, *Indian. J. Phys.* **29**, 453 (1955).
109. Saxena, S. C., Evaluation of collision integrals occurring in higher approximations to diffusion coefficients, *J. Chem. Phys.* **24**, 1209 (1956).
110. Saxena, S. C., Generalized relations for the three elementary transport coefficients of inert gases, *Physica* **22**, 1242 (1956).
111. Saxena, S. C., Transport coefficients and force between unlike molecules, *Indian J. Phys.* **31**, 146—155 (1957).
112. Schäfer, K., Corte, H., and Moesta, H., Measurement of the temperature and concentration dependence of diffusion coefficients in gases, *Z. Elektrochem.* **55**, 662 (1951).
113. Schäfer, K., Moesta, H., Intermolecular strengths and collision cross sections determined from transport phenomena, *Z. Elektrochem.* **58**, 743—752 (1954).
114. Schäfer, K., and Schuhmann, K., Intermolecular forces and temperature dependence of diffusion and self-diffusion in noble gases, *Z. Elektrochem.* **61**, 246 (1957).
115. Schmidt, F. H., Diffusion of stack gases in the atmosphere, *Nature* **182**, 1575 (1951).
116. Schottky, W. F., Progress in the treatment of transport phenomena gases, *Z. Elektrochem.* **58**, 442—454 (1954).
117. Schwertz, F. A., and Brow, J. E., Diffusivity of water vapor in some common gases, *J. Chem. Phys.* **19**, 640 (1951).
118. Simmons, R. F., and Wolfhard, H. G., The influence of methyl bromide on flames. Part. 2 Diffusion flames, *Trans. Faraday Soc.* **52**, 53 (1956).
119. Slattery, J. C., and Bird, R. B., *A. I. Ch. E. Journal* **4**, 137 (1958).
120. Smith, S. R., and Gordon, A. S., Studies of diffusion flames. I. The methane diffusion flame, *J. Phys. Chem.* **60**, 759 (1956).
121. Smith, S. R., and Gordon, A. S., Studies of diffusion flames. II. Diffusion flames of some simple alcohols, *J. Phys. Chem.* **60**, 1059 (1956).
122. Smith, S. R., Gordon, A. S., and Hunt, M. H., Studies of diffusion flames. III. The diffusion flames of the butanols, *J. Phys. Chem.* **61**, 553 (1957).
123. Snider, R. F., and Curtiss, C. F., Kinetic theory of moderately dense gases, *Phys. fluids* **1**, 122 (1958).
124. Srivastava, K. P., Unlike molecular interactions and properties of gas mixtures, *J. Chem. Phys.* **28**, 543 (1958).
125. Srivastava, B. N., and Madan, M. P., Intermolecular force constants from thermal diffusion on other properties of gases, (TD), *J. Chem. Phys.* **21**, 807—815 (1953).
126. Srivastava, B. N., and Madan, M. P., Intermolecular force and transport coefficients, (TD), *Nature* **171**, 441—442 (1953).
127. Strehlow, R. A., The temperature dependence of the mutual diffusion coefficient for four gaseous systems, *J. Chem. Phys.* **21**, 2101—2106 (1953).
128. Timmerhaus, K. D., and Drickamer, H. G., Self-diffusion on CO_2 at moderate rpessure (up to 28 at.), *J. Chem. Phys.* **19**, 1242 (1951).
129. Timmerhaus, K. D., and Drickamer, H. G., Diffusion in the system $C^{14}O_2$-CO_2 to 1000 atmospheres pressure, at temperatures from 0 to 50°C *J. Chem. Phys.* **20**, 981 (1952).

130. Tollert, H., Investigation of the flow-diffusion effect, *Z. Elektrochem.* **61,** 1224 (1957).

131. Toor, H. L., Diffusion in three-component gas mixtures, *A. I. Ch. E. Journal* **3,** 198—207 (1957).

132. Walker, E. R., and Westenberg, A. A., Molecular diffusion studies in gases at high temperatures, *J. Chem. Phys.* **29,** 1139 (1958).

133. Walker, R. E., and Westenberg, A. A., Diffusion at high temperatures. Interpretation of results on the He-N_2 and CO_2-N_2 system, *J. Chem. Phys.* **29,** 1147 (1958).

134. Westenberg, A. A., Review on gaseous diffusion, *Combustion and Flame* **1,** 346 (1957).

135. Westenberg, A. A., and Walker, R. E., New method of measuring diffusion coefficients of gases, *J. Chem. Phys.* **26,** 1753 (1957).

136. Whalley, E., and Schneider, W. G., Intermolecular potentials of argon, krypton and xenon, *J. Chem. Phys.* **23,** 1644 (1955).

137. Wilke, C. R., and Lee, C. Y., Estimation of diffusion coefficients for gases and vapors, *Ind. Eng. Chem.* **47,** 1253—1257 (1955).

137a. Wise, H., Diffusion coefficient of atomic hydrogen through multicomponent mixtures, *J. Chem. Phys.* **31,** 1414 (1959).

138. Wu, T.-Y., and Amdur, I., Note on the He-He interaction potential and its determination from Amdur's scattering measurements, *J. Chem. Phys.* **28,** 986 (1958).

LIQUIDS

(Supplementary to Chapter XI, pages 436-488 in this volume)

Dunlop and Gosting carried out admirably thorough calculations for an experimental test of the Onsager reciprocal relations in the systems NaCl-KCl-H_2O at 25° C, for four different concentrations.

If the flow of component i ($i = 1, 2$) relative to the solvent (component 0) is given by the phenomenological expressions

$$(J_1)_0 = - (L_{11})_0 \frac{\partial \mu_1}{\partial x} - (L_{12})_0 \frac{\partial \mu_2}{\partial x} \qquad \text{[A 11.1 a]}$$

$$(J_2)_0 = - (L_{21})_0 \frac{\partial \mu_1}{\partial x} - (L_{22})_0 \frac{\partial \mu_2}{\partial x} \qquad \text{[A 11.1 b]}$$

then there exists one Onsager relation

$$(L_{12})_0 = (L_{21})_0 . \qquad \text{[A 11.1 c]}$$

The task consists in converting observed diffusion coefficients* to the

---

* The diffusion coefficients (Gouy diffusiometer values) were taken from the work of L. J. O'Donnell and L. J. Gosting, paper presented in a symposium at the 1957 meeting of the Electrochemical Society in Washington, D. C. (to be published by John Wiley and Sons, New York, N. Y.).

coefficients $(L_{ik})_0$ and of calculating the gradient of chemical potential from observed activity data*.

For details of the calculation and for further references the reader should consult the original paper. A selection of numerical values is contained in Table A 11.1.

TABLE A 11.1
Data extracted from Dunlop and Gosting (54)
$NaCl$-KCl-H_2O at $25°C$

	1	2	3	4
c_1	0.2500	0.2500	0.5000	0.5000
c_2	0.2500	0.5000	0.2500	0.5000
$(L_{11})_0 RT \times 10^9$	2.60_9	2.78_5	4.76_1	5.15_0
$(L_{22})_0 RT \times 10^9$	3.49_8	6.35_9	3.82_9	7.01_6
$(L_{12})_0 RT \times 10^9$	-0.75_5	-0.98_9	-1.04_0	-1.54_8
$(L_{21})_0 RT \times 10^9$	-0.72_9	-0.94_6	-1.00_6	-1.47_4
$\% \Delta_{exp}$	-3.5	-4.4	-3.3	-4.9

In the table c_1 and c_2 are concentrations of $NaCl$ and of KCl (moles/l). The coefficients $(L_{ik})_0$ refer to flows expressed in moles.

$$\% \Delta_{exp} = 100 \left\{ \frac{(L_{21})_0 - (L_{12})_0}{[(L_{12})_0 + (L_{21})_0]/2} \right\}_{exp}.$$

For the field of diffusion in electrolyte solutions the reader should refer to the presentation offered in the third edition of Harned and Owen (12 on p. 480 of this volume) and Robinson and Stokes (2nd ed. 1959).

The last decade has brought much experimental research on diffusion in liquids, part of it by application of tracer technique. Combining diffusion and viscosity measurements both at constant temperature and at constant pressure, one can test theoretical concepts without using explicit specialized theories. On the whole these experiences seem to support the picture of the hole theory of liquids.

There is generally a marked difference between the apparent energy of activation for diffusion at constant pressure E_p and at constant volume E_v, E_p being higher than E_v. E_p contains the energy necessary for the formation of holes, while E_v contains essentially the energy barrier connected with the movement of particles. McKenzie (111a) has pointed out that the ratio E_v/E_p is smallest for normal liquids, higher for associated liquids where for migration hydrogen bonds must be broken. With highly associated liquids like molten silica and boron trioxide this ratio might approach unity.

* Robinson and Stokes; Robinson; for complete citation of these references see list of Monographs and Review Articles at end of this Chapter.

Claesson and Sundelof (33) have investigated diffusion in the system n-hexane-nitrobenzene between 20 and 35°C. From their results one extrapolates $D \to 0$ for $T \to T_c$; T_c is the critical temperature of mixing. This is to be expected if one considers that the expression for the diffusion coefficient in nonideal mixtures

$$D = D_0 \frac{\partial \ln a}{\partial \ln c}$$

where a = activity, will vanish for $\partial \ln a / \partial \ln c = 0$. As a consequence, the quotient $D_T/D = k_T$, the thermal-diffusion ratio, may be expected to show anomalies near the critical mixing temperature although this need not be the only influence responsible.

REFERENCES

Monographs and Review Articles

Diffusion in Liquids. 7e réunion de la Société de Chimie Physique, Paris, 1957. *J. chim. phys.* **54**, 851—937; **55**, 77—158.

Harned, H. S., and Owen, B. B., The Physical Chemistry of Electrolyte Solutions, 3rd. ed. Reinhold, New York, 1958. (Chapter 4: Theory of irreversible processes in electrolyte solutions. Chapter 6: Experimetal investigation of irreversible processes in solutions of strong electrolytes. Conductance, transference numbers, viscosity, and diffusion.)

Hirschfelder, J. O., Curtiss, C. F., and Bird, R. B., Molecular Theory of Gases and Liquids. Wiley, New York, 1954.

Reid, R. C., and Sherwood, T. K., The Properties of Gases and Liquids, Their Estimation and Correlation. McGraw-Hill, New York, 1958.

Robinson, R. A., Electrochemical Constants. National Bureau of Standard Circular 524, 1953.

Robinson, R. A., and Stokes, R. H., Electrolyte Solutions 2nd ed. Academic Press, New York, 1959.

Transport Processes in Statistical Mechanics. Proceedings of the International Symposium, Brussels, 1956 (I. Prigogine, ed.), Interscience, New York, 1958. (Content, cf. References Chapter X, p. 59Aff.). In addition: H. Falkenhagen, Some results of the theory of strong electrolytes, p. 251; R. M. Mazo and J. de Boer, A kinetic theory of the viscosity of liquid helium II, p. 261; and G. Careri and A. Paoletti, Diffusion in a quasi-crystalline, liquid, p. 309.

References

1. Adamson, A. W., Diffusion and self-diffusion in aqueous saccharose solutions and in H_2O-D_2O mixtures, *Angew. Chem.* **96**, 675 (1957).
2. Adamson, A. W., and Irandi, R., Diffusion and self-diffusion in aqueous solutions of saccharose and in H_2O-D_2O, *J. chim. phys.* **55**, 102 (1958).
3. Akely, D. F., and Gosting, L. J., Studies of the diffusion of mixed solutes with the Gouy diffusiometer, *J. Am. Chem. Soc.* **75**, 5685 (1953). (KCl-Sucrose; Sucrose-KCl-BPA; KCl-Urea; BPA = "Bovine Plasma Albumine".)

4. Amis, E. S., Choppin, A. R., and Padgitt, F. L., Temperature and composition coefficients of the density, refractive index and viscosity of the methyl alcohol-dioxane system, *J. Am. Chem. Soc.* **64**, 1207ff. (1942).

5. Anderson, D. K., Hall, J. R., and Babb, A. L., Mutual diffusion in nonideal binary liquid mixtures. *J. Phys. Chem.* **62**, 404 (1958). (Mixtures: acetone-benzene at 25.15°C; acetone-water at 25.15°; acetone-chloroform at 25.15° and 39.95°; acetone-carbon tetrachloride at 25.15°; ethanol-benzene at 25.15 and 39.98°; methanol-benzene at 39.95°C.)

6. Andrussow, L., Diffusion in liquids, *J. chim. phys.* **54**, 862 (1957).

7. Aris, R., On shape factors for irregular particles. I. The steady state problem. Diffusion and reaction, *Chem. Eng. Sci.* **6**, 262 (1957).

8. Bak, T. G., and Kauman, W. G., Contribution to the theory of electrodiffusion, *J. Chem. Phys.* **28**, 509 (1958).

9. Bacon, R. F., and Fanelli, R., The viscosity of sulfur, *J. Am. Chem. Soc.* **65**, 639–648 (1943).

10. Baldwin, R. L., Dunlop, P. J., and Gosting, L. J., Interacting flows in liquid diffusion: equations for evaluation of the diffusion coefficients from moments of the refractive index gradient curves, *J. Am. Chem.* **77**, 5235 (1955).

11. Bambynek, W., and Freise, V., Self-diffusion of tetramethyl tin, *Z. physik. Chem. (Frankfurt)* [N.S.] **7**, 317 (1956).

12. Barrer, R. M., Viscosity of pure liquids. I. Non-polymerized fluids, *Trans. Faraday Soc.* **39**, 48 (1943).

13. Beckman, C. O., The concentration dependence of sedimentation and diffusion, *Angew. Chem.* **68**, 338 (1956).

14. Bennet, J. A. R., and Lewis, J. B., Diffusion and chemical control in the dissolution of metals by mercury, *J. chim. phys.* **55**, 83 (1958).

15. Berne, E., and Weill, M. J., Measurement of self-diffusion in gels by means of radioactive isotopes, *J. chim. phys.* **56**, 103 (1959).

16. Biancheria, A., and Kegeles, G., Diffusion measurements in aqueous solutions of different viscosities, *J. Am. Chem. Soc.* **79**, 5908 (1957). (Glycolamide-water; glycolamide-polyvinyl alcohol; glycolamide-acetamide; glycolamide-acetate buffer; glycolamide-methanol; glycolamide-raffinose stock; glycolamide-glycerol; acetamide-polyvinyl alcohol; acetamide-methanol.)

17. Beran, M. J., Dispersion of soluble matter in flow through granular media, *J. Chem. Phys.* **27**, 270 (1957).

18. Bastian, W. C., and Lapidus, L., Longitudinal diffusion in ion exchange and chromatographic columns. Finite columns, *J. Phys. Chem.* **60**, 816 (1956).

19. Bondi, A., The pressure coefficient of viscosity, *J. Chem. Phys.* **15**, 527 (1947).

20. Borucka, A. Z., Bockris, J. O'. M., and Kitchener, J. A., Test of the applicability of the Nernst-Einstein equation to self-diffusion and conduction of ions in molten sodium chloride, *J. Chem. Phys.* **24**, 1282 (1956).

21. Borucka, A. Z., Bockris, J. O'M., and Kitcheener, J. A., Self-diffusion in molten sodium chloride: a test of applicability of the Nernst-Einstein equation, *Proc. Roy. Soc. (London)* **A 241**, 554 (1957).

22. Broersma, S., Stokes and Einstein's law for non-uniform viscosity, *J. Chem. Phys.* **28**, 1158 (1958).

23. Brown, R. A., Davies, M. C., and Englert, M. E., The calculation of reduced moments of refractive index gradient curves obtained in diffusion experiments by means of Rayleigh fringes, *J. Am. Chem. Soc.* **79**, 1787

(1957). (Method for calculating reduced second and fourth moments of gradient curves obtained in diffusion experiments by means of Rayleigh fringes.)

24. Caldwell, C. S., and Babb, A. L., Diffusion in the system methanol-benzene, *J. Phys. Chem.* **59,** 1113 (1955).

25. Caldwell, C. S., and Babb, A. L., Diffusion in ideal binary liquid mixtures, *J. Phys. Chem.* **60,** 51 (1956). (Benzene-carbon tetrachloride; chloro-benzene-bromobenzene; toluene-chlorobenzene.)

26. Calvet, E., and Patin, H., Interferometric study of vertical diffusion in liquids, *J. chim. phys.* **54,** 910 (1957).

27. Carassiti, V., Separation of optical antipodes by means of diffusion in optically active solvents, *Angew. Chem.* **69,** 677 (1957).

28. Carassiti, V., Diffusion of optical antipodes in solution, *Angew. Chem.* **70,** 598 (1958).

29. Carman, P. C., and Stein, L. H., Self-diffusion in mixtures, *Trans. Faraday Soc.* **52,** 619 (1956). (Part I. Theory and its application to a nearly ideal binary liquid mixture.) (Ethyl iodide-n-butyl iodide.)

30. Carassiti, V., Separation of optical antipodes by diffusion in asymmetric liquids, *J. chim. phys.* **55,** 120 (1958).

31. Carmichael, L. T., Reamer, H. H., Sage, B. H., and Lacey, W. N., Diffusion coefficients in hydrocarbon-systems, *Ind. Eng. Chem.* **47,** 2205 (1955).

32. Chang, P., and Wilke, C. R., Some measurements of diffusion in liquids, *J. Phys. Chem.* **59,** 592 (1955). (Benzoic acid in carbon tetrachloride, in benzene, in toluene, in acetone, in ethylene glycol. Acetic acid in carbon tetrachloride, in benzene, in toluene, in ethylene glycol, in acetone. Formic acid in carbon tetrachloride, in benzene, in toluene, in acetone, in ethylene glycol. Cinnamic acid in carbon tetrachloride, in benzene, in toluene, in acetone. Iodine in n-tetradecane, in n-octane, in n-hexane, in cyclo-hexane, in methylcyclohexane, in ethyl alcohol, in bromobenzene, in carbon tetrachloride. Toluene in n-hexane, in n-heptane, in n-decane, in n-dodecane, in n-tetradecane, in n-heptane.)

33. Claesson, S., and Sundelof, L. O., Free diffusion in the neighborhood of the critical mixing temperature, *J. chim. phys.* **54,** 914 (1957).

33a. Cohen, M. H., and Turnbull, D., Molecular transport in liquids and glasses, *J. Chem. Phys.* **31,** 1164 (1959).

34. Collins, F. C., and Raffel, H., Statistical mechanical theory of transport processes in liquids, *J. Chem. Phys.* **29,** 699 (1958).

35. Cooper, W. C., and Furman, N. H., The diffusion coefficients of certain metals in mercury, *J. Am. Chem. Soc.* **74,** 6183 (1952). (Diffusion of the following metals through mercury: Zn, Cd, Pb, Cu, Tl, Sn, Bi.)

36. Corbett, J. W., and Wang, J. H., Self-diffusion in liquid argon, *J. Chem. Phys.* **25,** 422 (1956).

37. Cova, D. R., and Drickamer, H. G., The effect of pressure on diffusion in liquid sulfur, *J. Chem. Phys.* **21,** 1364 (1953).

38. Crank, J., Diffusion of dyes, *J. Soc. Dyers Colourists* **66,** 366 (1955).

39. Creeth, J. M., Studies of free diffusion in liquids with the Rayleigh method. I. The determination of differential diffusion coefficients in concentration-dependent systems of two components, *J. Am. Chem. Soc.* **77,** 6428−6440 (1955).

40. Creeth, J. M., and Gosting, L. J., Studies of free diffusion in liquids with the Rayleigh method. II. An analysis for systems containing two solutes, *J. Phys. Chem.* **62,** 58 (1958).

41. Creeth, J. M., Studies of free diffusion in liquids with the Rayleigh method. III. The analysis of known mixtures and some preliminary investigations with proteins, *J. Phys. Chem.* **62**, 66 (1958).
42. Cuddeback, R. B., Koeller, R. C., and Drickamer, H. G., The effect of pressure on diffusion in water and in sulfate solutions, *J. Chem. Phys.* **21**, 589 (1953).
43. Cuddeback, R. B., and Drickamer, H. G., The effect of pressure on diffusion in aqueous and alcoholic salt solution, *J. Chem. Phys.* **21**, 597 (1953).
44. Daune, M., Freund, L., and Scheibling, G., A new method for the study of Brownian translation diffusion, *J. chim. phys.* **54**, 924 (1957).
44a. Davies, J. T., and Wiggil, J. B., Diffusion accross the oil/water interface, *Proc. Roy. Soc.* A **255**, 277 (1960).
45. Dean, R. B., A new apparatus for measuring diffusion in solutions, *J. Am. Chem. Soc.* **71**, 3127 (1947).
46. Delahay, P., and Fike, C. T., Adsorption kinetics with diffusion control. The plane and the expanding sphere, *J. Am. Chem. Soc.* **80**, 2628 (1958).
47. Doane, E. P., and Drickamer, H. G., The effect of pressure on diffusion in the system CCl_4-SnI_4, *J. Chem. Phys.* **21**, 1359 (1953).
48. Dole, M., Relation between the Onsager and measurable diffusion coefficients in three-component systems, *J. Chem. Phys.* **25**, 1082 (1956).
49. Dunlop, P. J., Further studies of the diffusion of mixed solutes with the Gouy diffusiometer, *J. Am. Chem. Soc.* **77**, 2994 (1955). (Glycolamide-sucrose; glycine-glycolamide.)
50. Dunlop, P. J., and Gosting, L. J., Interacting flows in liquid diffusion: expressions for the solute concentration curves in free diffusion, and their use in interpreting Gouy diffusiometer data for aqueous three-component systems, *J. Am. Chem. Soc.* **77**, 5238 (1955).
51. Dunlop, P. J., The concentration dependence of the diffusion coefficient of raffinose in dilute aqueous solution at 25° C, *J. Phys. Chem.* **60**, 1464 (1956).
52. Dunlop, P. J., A study of interacting flows in diffusion of the system raffinose-KCl-H_2O at 25°C, *J. Phys. Chem.* **61**, 994 (1957).
53. Dunlop, P. J., Interacting flows in diffusion of the system raffinose-urea-water, *J. Phys. Chem.* **61**, 1619 (1957).
54. Dunlop, P. J., and Gosting, L. J., Use of diffusion and thermodynamic data to test the Onsager reciprocal relation for isothermal diffusion in the system NaCl-KCl-H_2O at 25°C, *J. Phys. Chem.* **63**, 86 (1959).
54a. Dux, J. P., and Steigman, J., Tracer diffusion coefficients of strontium ion in aqueous polystyrenesulfonic acid solutions, *J. Phys. Chem.* **63**, 269 (1959).
54b. Edwards, O. W., and Huffman, E. O., Diffusion of aqueous solutions of phosphoric acid at 25°C, *J. Phys. Chem.* **63**, 1830 (1959).
55. Ewing, C. T., Grand, J. A., and Miller, R. R., Viscosity in the sodium-potassium system, *J. Am. Chem. Soc.* **73**, 1168 (1951).
56. Fishman, E., Self-diffusion in liquid n-pentane and n-heptane, *J. Phys. Chem.* **59**, 469 (1955).
56a. Franck, E. U., and Jost, W., Transport phenomena in fluid mixtures, *Z. Elektrochem.* **62**, 1054 (1958).
57. Freise, V., Diffusion-caused convection, *Angew. Chem.* **69**, 679 (1957).
58. Freise, V., Convection current caused by diffusion, *J. chim. phys.* **54**, 879 (1957).
59. Fujita, H., Effects of a concentration dependence of the sedimentation coefficient in velocity ultracentrifugation, *J. Chem. Phys.* **24**, 1084 (1956).

60. Fujii, T., and Thomas, H. C., Self-diffusion of sodium ion in agar gel, *J. Phys. Chem.* **62,** 1966 (1958).

60a. Fujieta, H., Evalution of diffusion coefficients from sedimentation velocity measurements, *J. Phys. Chem.* **63,** 242 (1959).

61. Glaser, G., Diffusion of water vapor through plexiglass, *Angew. Chem.* **70,** 440 (1958).

62. Gosting, L. J., and Morris, M. S., Diffusion studies on dilute aqueous sucrose solutions at 1 and 25°C with the Gouy interference method, *J. Am. Chem. Soc.* **71,** 1998 (1949).

63. Gosting, L. J., and Akeley, D. F., A study of the diffusion of urea in water at 25°C with the Gouy interference method, *J. Am. Chem. Soc.* **74,** 2058 (1952).

64. Gosting, L. J., and Onsager, L., A general theory for the Gouy diffusion method, *J. Am. Chem. Soc.* **74,** 6066 (1952).

65. Gosting, L. J., and Fujita, H., Interpretation of data for concentration-dependent free diffusion in two-component systems, *J. Am. Chem. Soc.* **79,** 1359 (1957). (Formal series solution of the second Fick equation with concentration-dependent diffusion coefficient for one-dimensional free diffusion in two-component systems, making use of the method of successive approximations.)

66. Griest, E. M., Webb, W., and Schiessler, R. W., Effect of pressure on viscosity of higher hydrocarbons and their mixtures, *J. Chem. Phys.* **29,** 711 (1958).

67. Grunberg, L., and Nissen, A. H., The energies of vaporisation, viscosity and the structure of liquids, *Trans. Faraday Soc.* **45,** 125 (1949).

68. Grunberg, L., and Nissen, A. H., Viscosity of highly compressed fluids, *Ind. Eng. Chem.* **42,** 885 (1950).

69. Grunberg, L., The viscosity of regular solutions, *Trans. Faraday Soc.* **50,** 1293 (1954).

70. Grüttner, B., Jander, G., and Bertram, I., Determination of diffusion coefficients in solution, *Z. anorg. Chem.* **287,** 186 (1956).

71. Hammond, B. R., and Stokes, R. H., Diffusion in binary liquid mixtures, *Trans. Faraday Soc.* **49,** 890 (1953).

72. Hammond, B. R., and Stokes, R. H., The diffusion of carbon tetrachloride in some organic solvents at 25°C, *Trans. Faraday Soc.* **51,** 1641 (1955).

73. Hammond, B. R., and Stokes, R. H., Diffusion in binary liquid mixtures, *Trans. Faraday Soc.* **52,** 781 (1956).

73a. Hardt, A. P., Anderson, D. K., Rathbun, R., Mar, B. W., and Bable, A. L., Self diffusion in liquids. II. Comparison between mutual and self-diffusion coefficients, *J. Physic. Chem.* **63,** 2059 (1959).

74. Harned, H. S., Some recent experimental studies of diffusion in liquid systems, *Discussions Faraday Soc.* **24,** 7 — 16 (1957).

75. Harned, H. S., and Shropshire, J. A., The diffusion and activity coefficient of sodium nitrate in dilute aqueous solutions at 25°C, *J. Am. Chem. Soc.* **80,** 2618 (1958).

76. Harned, H. S., and Shropshire, J. A., The activity coefficients of alkali metal nitrates and perchlorates in dilute aqueous solutions at 25°C from diffusion coefficients, *J. Am. Chem. Soc.* **80,** 2967 (1958).

77. Harned, H. S., and Shropshire, J. A., The diffusion coefficient at 25°C of potassium chloride at low concentrations in 0.25 molar aqueous sucrose solutions, *J. Am. Chem. Soc.* **80,** 5652 (1958).

77a. Harned, H. S., and Shropshire, J. A., The diffusion coefficient at 25° of potassium chloride at low concentrations in 0.75 molar aqueous sucrose solutions, *J. Am. Chem. Soc.* **82**, 799 (1960).

78. Haycock, E. W., Alder, B. J., and Hildebrand, J. H., The diffusion of iodine in carbon tetrachloride under pressure, *J. Chem. Phys.* **21**, 1601 (1953).

79. Heiks, J. R., and Orban, E., Liquid viscosities at elevated temperatures and pressures: viscosity of benzene from 90° to its critical temperature, *J. Phys. Chem.* **60**, 1025 (1956).

80. Helfferich, F., and Plesset, H. S., Ion exchange kinetics. A nonlinear diffusion problem, *J. Chem. Phys.* **28**, 418 (1958).

81. Hellund, E. J., Temperature dependence of the viscosity of liquids, *J. Chem. Phys.* **24**, 1173 (1956).

82. Herzfeld, K. F., Bulk viscosity and sheer viscosity in fluids according to the theory of irreversible processes, *J. Chem. Phys.* **28**, 595—600 (1958).

83. Hirai, N., and Eyring, H., Bulk viscosity of liquids, *J. Appl. Phys.* **29**, 810 to 816 (1958). (A mechanism for bulk viscosity is proposed from the standpoint of the hole theory of liquids and the rate process theory.)

84. Hoffman, R. E., The self-diffusion of liquid mercury, *J. Chem. Phys.* **20**, 1567 (1952). (Measurements by the capillary technique.

85. Holmes, F. H., and Smith, P. J., The sedimentation and diffusion of cellulose acetate in acetone, *Trans. Faraday Soc.* **53**, 67 (1957).

86. Innes, K. K., Temperature dependence of viscosity of liquids, *J. Phys. Chem.* **60**, 817 (1956).

87. Innes, K. K., and Albright, L. F., Effect of temperature and solute volume on liquid diffusion coefficients, *Ind. Eng. Chem.* **49**, 1793 (1957).

87a. Irani, R. R., and Adamson, A. W., Transport processes in binary liquid systems, *J. Physical. Chem.* **64**, 199 (1960).

88. Jobling, A., and Lawrence, A. S. C., Viscosities of some lower aliphatic alcohols at constant volume, *J. Chem. Phys.* **20**, 1296 (1952).

89. Johnson, E. F., Molecular transport properties of fluids, *Ind. Eng. Chem.* **45**, 902 (1953).

90. Johnson, P. A., and Babb, A. L., Self-diffusion in liquids. I. Concentration dependence in ideal and non-ideal binary solutions, *J. Phys. Chem.* **60**, 14 (1956).

91. Kegeles, G., and Gosting, L. J., The theory of an interference method for the study of diffusion, *J. Am. Chem. Soc.* **69**, 2516 (1947).

91a. Kelly, F. J., and Stokes, R. H., Diffusion coefficients and densities for the systems carbon tetrachloride—m-xylene and carbon tetrachloride—mesitylene at 25° C, *Trans. Faraday Soc.* **55**, 388 (1959).

92. King, T. B., Diffusion in liquid silicates, *Angew. Chem.* **70**, 603 (1958).

93. Koeller, R. C., and Drickamer, H. G., The effect of pressure in self-diffusion in carbon disulfide, *J. Chem. Phys.* **21**, 267 (1953).

94. Koeller, R. C., and Drickammer, H. G., The effect of pressure on diffusion in CS_2 organic mixtures, *J. Chem. Phys.* **21**, 575 (1953).

95. Kuss, E., and Stuart, H. A., Specific viscosity of solutions of flat molecules, *Z. Naturforsch.* **3a**, 204 (1948).

96. Kraus, G., On the calculation of integral diffusion coefficients from free diffusion experiments, *J. Chem. Phys.* **20**, 200 (1952).

97. Lamm, O., The dynamics of the diffusion of fluids in relation to the choice of components, *J. Phys. Chem.* **59**, 1149 (1955).

98. Lauwerier, H. A., Diffusion from a source in a skew velocity field, *Appl. Sci. Research* **4**, 153—156 (1954). (A fluid flows with a nonuniform velocity $v_0 [1 + ay]$ in the x-direction of an x, y plane. The origin is a source of constant strength. For the boundary condition $c = 0$ at $y = -1/a$ the diffusion equation can be solved in an explicit form. A slightly skewed normal distribution function is obtained.)

99. Leech, J. W., Melting and diffusion, *Nature* **181**, 319 (1958).

100. Levenspiel, O., and Smith, W. K., Notes on the diffusion-type model for the longitudinal mixing of fluids in flow, *Chem. Eng. Sci.* **6**, 227 (1957).

101. Li, J. C. M., and Chang, P., Self-diffusion coefficient and viscosity in liquids, *J. Chem. Phys.* **23**, 518 (1955).

102. Li, J. C. M., Self-diffusion coefficient and viscosity in liquids, *J. Chem. Phys.* **23**, 518 (1955). Erratum: *J. Chem. Phys.* **29**, 1421 (1958).

103. Litowitz, T. A., Temperature dependence of the viscosity of associated liquids, *J. Chem. Phys.* **20**, 1088 (1952).

104. Lodding, A., Self-diffusion in liquid indium metal, *Z. Naturforsch.* **11 a**, 200 (1956).

105. Longsworth, L. G., Experimental tests of an interference method for the study of diffusion, *J. Am. Chem. Soc.* **69**, 2510 (1947).

106. Longsworth, L. G., Diffusion measurements at 25° of aqueous solution of amino acids, peptides and sugars, *J. Am. Chem. Soc.* **75**, 5705 (1953).

107. Longsworth, L. G., Exchange diffusion of ions of similar mobility, *J. Phys. Chem.* **61**, 244 (1957).

108. Longuet-Higgins, H. C., and Pople, J. A., Transport properties of a dense fluid of hard spheres, *J. Chem. Phys.* **25**, 884 (1956).

109. Lyons, M. S., and Thomas, J. V., Diffusion studies on dilute aqueous glycine solutions at 1 and 25°C with the Gouy interference method, *J. Am. Chem. Soc.* **72**, 4506 (1950).

110. Lyons, P. L., and Sandquist, C. L., A study of the diffusion of n-butyl alcohol in water using the Gouy interference method, *J. Am. Chem. Soc.* **75**, 3896 (1953).

110a. McCall, D. W., Douglass, D. C., and Anderson, E. W., Self-diffusion in liquids: Paraffin hydrocarbons, *Phys. Fluids* **2**, 87 (1959). (The pressure dependence of the self-diffusion coefficients of several normal paraffin hydrocarbons and the isomers of hexane have been determined. In addition, the temperature dependence of self-diffusion coefficients has been measured for the isomers of hexane. The volumes of activation are about 10—20% of the molar volumes in all cases. Diffusion coefficients computed from a semiempirical modification of an equation derived by Longuet—Higgins and Pople are compared with the experimental results.)

110b. McCall, D. M., Douglas, D. C., and Anderson, E. W., Diffusion in liquids, *J. Chem. Phys.* **31**, 1555 (1959).

111. McKenzie, J. D., and Hillig, W. B., Self-diffusion of liquids at the freezing point, *J. Chem. Phys.* **28**, 1259 (1958).

112. McKenzie, J. D., *J. Chem. Phys.* **28**, 1037 (1958).

113. McLaughlin, E., Viscosity and self-diffusion in liquids, *Trans. Faraday Soc.* **55**, 29 (1959). (Modified rate theory applied to hole model of liquids.)

114. Mason, D. M., Petker, I., and Vango, S. P., Viscosity and density of the nitric acid-nitrogen dioxide-water system, *J. Phys. Chem.* **59**, 511 (1955).

115. Meyer, R. E., and Nachtrieb, N. H., Self-diffusion in sodium near the melting point, *J. Chem. Phys.* **23**, 405, 1851 (1955). (Self-diffusion of

liquid sodium in the temperature range 98° to 226°C [capillary technique]; D = 1.10 · 10⁻³ exp [−2430/RT].)

116. Miller, D. G., The validity of Onsager's reciprocal relations in ternary diffusion, *J. Am. Chem. Soc.* **62**, 767 (1958).

117. Mills, R., The self-diffusion of chloride ion in aqueous alkali chloride solutions at 25°, *J. Phys. Chem.* **61**, 1631 (1957).

117a. Mills, R., Tracer diffusion of sodium and rubidium ions in aqueous alkali chloride solutions at 25°C, *J. Phys. Chem.* **63**, 1873 (1959).

118. Morgan, D. W., and Kitchener, J. A., Solutions in liquid iron; 3. diffusion of cobalt and carbon, *Trans. Faraday Soc.* **50**, 51 (1954).

118a. Mori, H., Statistical-mechanical theory of transport in fluids, *Phys. Rev.* **112**, 1829 (1958).

119. Mysels, K. J., Electrodiffusion: a fluctuation method for measuring reaction rates, *J. Chem. Phys.* **24**, 371 (1956).

120. Nachtrieb, N. H., Transport properties in pure liquid metals, liquid metals and solidification, pp. 49—55. *Am. Soc. Metals* (1958).

121. Nachtrieb, N. H., and Petit, J., Self-diffusion in liquid mercury, *J. Chem. Phys.* **24**, 746 (1956). (At atmospheric pressure D = 8.5 · 10⁻⁵ exp [−1005/RT] cm.² sec.⁻¹ from 0° to 98°. At 30° for pressures up to 8366 kg. cm.⁻², log₁₀ D = − 4.7889−9.637 · 10⁻⁶ P [kg. cm.⁻²]. Activation volume = 0.59 cm.³.)

122. Nachtrieb, N. H., and Petit, J., Self-diffusion in liquid gallium, *J. Chem. Phys.* **24**, 1027 (1956). (D = 1.07 · 10⁻⁴ exp [−1122/RT] cm.² sec.⁻¹. At 30°C log₁₀ D = − 4.7793−9.529 · 10⁻⁶ P [kg. · cm.⁻²]. Activation volume 0.55 cm.³ Stokes-Einstein radius agrees with ionic radius of Ga⁺³.)

123. Noller, H., and Hässler, A., Influence of diffusion in ion exchange catalysis, *Z. physik. Chem. (Frankfurt)* [N.S.] **11**, 267 (1957).

124. Noyes, R. M., Models relating molecular reactivity and diffusion in liquids, *J. Am. Chem. Soc.* **78**, 5486 (1956).

125. Ogston, A. G., Methods of describing unidimensional diffusion in binary liquid systems, *Trans. Faraday Soc.* **50**, 1303 (1954).

126. Olson, R. L., and Walton, J. S., Diffusion coefficients of organic liquids in solution, *Ind. Eng. Chem.* **43**, 703 (1951). (Water solutions [acetic acid, methyl alcohol, ethyl alcohol, n-propyl alcohol, isobutyl alcohol, isoamyl alcohol, formic acid, acetamide, phenol, allyl alcohol, glycerol]; Allyl alcohol—methyl alcohol, phenol—methyl alcohol, propionic acid—methyl alcohol, acetic acid—benzene, isoamyl alcohol—benzene, propyl alcohol—benzene, water—isoamyl alcohol, methyl alcohol—isoamyl alcohol, benzene—isoamyl alcohol.)

127. Opfell, J. B., and Sage, B. H., Relations in material transport, *Ind. Eng. Chem.* **47**, 918 (1955).

128. Othmer, D. F., and Thakar, M. S., Correlating diffusion coefficients in liquids, *Ind. Eng. Chem.* **45**, 589 (1953).

129. Ottar, B., Kinetic theory of self-diffusion in liquids, *J. chim. phys.* **54**, 856 (1957).

130. Paoletti, A., and Vicentini, M., Some examples of turbulent diffusion in liquid metals, *Phys. Fluids* **1**, 453 (1958).

131. Pantehenkov, G. M., Investigation of diffusion in liquids by a microdiffraction method, and certain problems of the theory, *J. chim. phys.* **54**, 931 (1957).

131a. Parker, R. A., and Wasik, S. P., Diffusion coefficients of dodecyl-trimethylammonium chloride in aqueous solution at 23°C, *J. Phys. Chem.* **63**,

1921 (1959). Diffusion coefficient $8.3 \cdot 10^{-6}$ cm.^{2} sec.$^{-1}$ when $c = 0.01$ g/ 100 ml. (misprint in author's summary !) while above critical micelle concentration $D = 2.2 \cdot 10^{-6}$, for $c = 0.57$ g./100 ml.

132. Partington, J. R., Hudson, R. F., and Bagnall, K. W., Self-diffusion of a series of aliphatic alcohols, *J. chim. phys.* **55**, 77 (1958).

133. Peter, S., Viscosity and self-diffusion of liquids, *Z. Naturforsch.* **9**, 98 (1954).

134. Peter, S., and Weinert, M., Diffusivity of hydrogen in hydrocarbons of elevated pressures, *Z. physik. Chem. (Frankfurt)* [N.S.] **9**, 49 (1956). (Improved form of multi-layer method.)

135. Petit, J., and Nachtrieb, N. H., Self-diffusion in liquid gallium, *J. Chem. Phys.* **24**, 1027 (1956).

136. Pontius, R. B., Kaplan, M. L., and Husney, R. M., The effect of buffer and electrolyte on the diffusion of an acid dye in gelatin, *J. Phys. Chem.* **60**, 9 (1956).

137. Pottie, R. F., Hamill, W. H., and Williams, R. R., Jr., Diffusion and hot radical kinetics in the photolysis of methyl iodide in cyclohexane, *J. Am. Chem. Soc.* **80**, 4224 (1958).

138. Powell, R. E., and Eyring, H., The properties of liquid sulfur, *J. Am. Chem. Soc.* **65**, 648 (1943).

139. Reamer, H. H., Opfell, J. B., and Sage, B. H., Diffusion coefficients in hydrocarbon systems. Methane-decane-methane in liquid phase, *Ind. Eng. Chem.* **48**, 275 (1956).

140. Reamer, H. H., Duffy, C. H., and Sage, B. H., Diffusion coefficients in hydrocarbon systems. Methane-pentane-methane in liquid phase, *Ind. Eng. Chem.* **48**, 282−284 (1956). (Fick diffusion coefficients for CH_4 in the liquid phase of the CH_4-pentane system at pressures up to 1700 lb./sq. in. in the temperature interval 40° to 280°F.)

141. Reamer, H. H., Duffy, C. H., and Sage, B. H., Diffusion coefficients in hydrocarbon systems. Methane-white oil-methane in liquid phase, *Ind. Eng. Chem.* **48**, 285−288 (1956). (Diffusion coefficients of CH_4 in the liquid phase of mixtures of CH_4 and a relatively heavy white oil at pressure up to 4500 lb./sq. in. in the temperature interval 40° to 340°F.)

142. Record, B. R., and Wallis, R. G., Study of diffusion of polyglutamine acid in solution of sodium halides, *J. chim. phys.* **55**, 110 (1958).

142a. Rice, St. A., and Kirkwood, J. G., On an approximate theory of transport in dense media, *J. Chem. Phys.* **31**, 901 (1959).

143. Riley, J. F., and Lyons, P. A., Intensity measurements applied to Gouy diffusiometry, *J. Am. Chem. Soc.* **77**, 261 (1955).

144. Robertson, E. R., Diffusion control in the polymerizations of methyl methacrylate and styrene, *Trans. Faraday Soc.* **52**, 426 (1956).

145. Rossi, C., Bianchi, E., and Rossi, A., Diffusion measurements in benzene, *J. chim. phys.* **55**, 97 (1958).

146. Rossi, C., Bianchi, E., and Rossi, A., Diffusion measurements of the molecules in water, *J. chim. phys.* **55**, 91 (1958).

147. Sanderson, R. T., Viscosity-temperature characteristics of hydrocarbons, *Ind. Eng. Chem.* **41**, 368 (1949).

148. Sandquist, C. L., and Lyons, P. A., Diffusion coefficients for the system biphenyl in benzene, *J. Am. Chem. Soc.* **76**, 4641 (1954).

149. Sata, N., and Okuyama, H., Study of the diffusion of surface active agents, *J. chim. phys.* **55**, 125 (1958).

150. Saxton, R. L., and Drickamer, H. G., Diffusion in liquid sulfur, *J. Chem. Phys.* **21**, 1362 (1953). (Measurements between 120 and 320°C by means of S^{35}. Pronounced change of temperature dependence in transition region.)

151. Scheibel, E. G., Liquid diffusivities, *Ind. Eng. Chem.* **46**, 2007 (1954).
152. Schlögl, R., and Stein, B., Experimental determination of the detour factor for diffusion in gels, *Z. physik. Chem. (Frankfurt)* [N.S.] **13**, 111 (1957).
153. Schulz, G. V., On the relations between diffusion coefficient and rate constant of bimolecular reactions in solutions, *Z. physik. Chem. (Frankfurt)* [N.S.] **8**, 284 (1956).
154. Scott, E. J., Tung, L. H., and Drickamer, H. G., Diffusion through an interface, *J. Chem. Phys.* **19**, 1075 (1951). (Diffusion equation solved for the case of two cells of finite length with an interface between the cells. The effect of an interfacial resistance to mass transfer has been considered.)
155. Shukla, R. P., and Bhatnagar, R. P., A note on viscosity of mixtures. II. Liquid-liquid ternary mixtures, *J. Phys. Chem.* **60**, 809 (1956).
156. Simpson, J. H., and Carr, H. Y., Diffusion and nuclear spin relaxation in water, *Phys. Rev.* **111**, 1201 (1958).
157. Spiers, J. A., Antigen-antibody reactions in gel single diffusion theoretical considerations, *Trans. Faraday Soc.* **54**, 287 (1958).
158. Stamm, A. J., Diffusion of water into uncoated cellophane. I. From rates of water vapor adsorption and liquid water adsorption, *J. Phys. Chem.* **60**, 76 (1956).
159. Stamm, A. J., Diffusion of water into uncoated cellophane. II. From steady-state diffusion measurements, *J. phys. Chem.* **60**, 83 (1956).
160. Stokes, R. H., Integral diffusion coefficients of potassium chloride solutions for calibration of diaphragm cells, *J. Am. Chem. Soc.* **73**, 3527 (1951).
161. Stokes, R. H., Woolf, L. A., and Mills, R. R., Tracer diffusion of iodide ion in aqueous alkali chloride solutions at 25°, *J. Phys. Chem.* **61**, 1634 (1957).
162. Stokes, R. H., and Woolf, L. A., Determination of diffusion coefficients of tracer ions by chemical analysis, *J. chim. phys.* **54**, 906 (1957).
163. Swalin, R. A., Correlation between frequency factor and activation energy for solute diffusion, *J. Appl. Phys.* **27**, 554 (1956).
164. Tannhauser, D. S., Concerning a systematic error in measuring diffusion constants, *J. Appl. Phys.* **27**, 662 (1956).
164a. Thomaes, G., and van Itterbeck, J., Application of the principle of corresponding states to the viscosity and diffusion of pure liquids and mixtures, *Molecular Physics* **2**, 372 (1959).
165. Tollert, H., Investigation of the flow diffusion effect, *Z. Elektrochem.* **60**, 1024 (1956).
166. Tonnelat, J., and Blain, F., Optical method for measuring diffusion coefficient with a vertical porous diaphragm, *J. chim. phys.* **54**, 920 (1957).
167. Trevoy, D. J., and Drickamer, H. G., Diffusion in binary liquid hydrocarbon mixtures, *J. Chem. Phys.* **17**, 1117 (1949). (Diffusion coefficients for binary mixtures of paraffin hydrocarbons and for mixtures of paraffin hydrocarbons with benzene.)
168. Tung, L. H., and Drickamer, H. G., Diffusion through an interface-binary system *J. Chem. Phys.* **20**, 6 (1952). (Diffusion between saturated layers in the system SO_2-n-heptane, using S^{35} tagged SO_2. Resistance in the interface is significant compared with the resistance to ordinary diffusion.)
169. Tung, L. H., and Drickamer, H. G., Diffusion through an interface-ternary system, *J. Chem. Phys.* **20**, 10 (1952). (Diffusion measurements at

22°C and at 40°C in the system phenol-H_2SO_4-water, using S^{35} tagged H_2SO_4. Measurements indicate a significant resistance in the interface at both temperatures.)

170. Tyrrell, H. J., The calculation of diffusion coefficients and Soret coefficients from optical measurements on pure Soret effect cells, *Trans. Faraday Soc.* **52**, 940 (1956).

171. Van Deemter, J. J., Zuiderweg, F. J., and Klinkenberg, A., Longitudinal diffusion and resistance to mass transfer as causes of nonideality in chromatography, *Chem. Eng. Sci.* **5**, 271 (1956).

172. van Hook, A., and Russel, H. D., The diffusivities of concentrated sucrose solutions, *J. Am. Chem. Soc.* **67**, 370 (1945).

173. Vitagliano, V., and Lyons, P. A., Diffusion coefficients for aqueous solutions of sodium chloride and barium chloride, *J. Am. Chem. Soc.* **78**, 1549 (1956).

174. Vitagliano, V., and Lyons, P. A., Diffusion in aqueous acetic acid solutions, *J. Am. Chem. Soc.* **78**, 4538 (1956).

175. Wagner, M. L., and Scherapa, H. A., Gouy diffusion studies of bovine serum albumin, *J. Phys. Chem.* **60**, 1066 (1956).

176. Waldmann, L., A stationary method for measuring diffusion coefficients, *Z. Naturforsch.* **5 a**, 322 (1950).

177. Wang, J. H., Self-diffusion and structure of liquid water. I. Measurement of self-diffusion of liquid water with deuterium as tracer, *J. Am. Chem. Soc.* **73**, 510 (1951).

178. Wang, J. H., Self-diffusion and structure of liquid water. II. Measurement of self-diffusion of liquid water with O^{18} as tracer, *J. Am. Chem. Soc.* **73**, 4181 (1951).

179. Wang, J. H., Tracer-diffusion in liquids. I. Diffusion of tracer amount of sodium ion in aqueous potassium chloride solution, *J. Am. Chem. Soc.* **74**, 1182 (1952).

180. Wang, J. H., Robinson, C. V., and Edelman, I. S., Self-diffusion and structure of liquid water. III. Measurement of the self-diffusion of liquid water with ^2H, ^3H, and ^{18}O as tracers, *J. Am. Chem. Soc.* **75**, 466 (1953).

181. Watts, H., Alder, B. J., and Hildebrand, J. H., Self-diffusion of carbon tetrachloride, isobars and isochores, *J. Chem. Phys.* **23**, 659 (1955).

182. Weir, F. E., and Dole, M., Diffusion in sugar solutions. IV. the Onsager diffusion coefficient for glucose diffusing in sucrose solutions, *J. Am. Chem. Soc.* **80**, 302 (1958).

183. Wernick, J. H., Determination of diffusivities in liquid metals by means of temperature-gradient zone melting, *J. Chem. Phys.* **25**, 47 (1956) (Diffusivities for Ge-Al, Ge-Au, Si-Al, fall in the 10^{-5} cm.^{2}/sec. range at temperatures of 530°C to 700°C.)

184. White, J. R., Diffusion coefficients of fatty acids and monobasic phosphoric acids in n-decane, *J. Chem. Phys.* **23**, 2247 (1955).

185. Williamson, B., and La Mer, V. K., The kinetics of activation-diffusion controlled reactions in solutions. The temperature dependence of the quenching of fluorescence, *J. Am. Chem. Soc.* **70**, 717 (1948).

187. Wunderly, C., Diffusion of proteins through a wedge-shaped agar gel, *Nature*, **182**, 1087 (1958).

188. Yang, L., Validity of Nernst-Einstein and Stokes-Einstein relationships in molten $NaNO_2$, *J. Chem. Phys.* **27**, 601 (1957).

189. Yang, L., Kado, S., and Derge, G., Diffusion in molten sulfides, *Angew. Chem.* **70**, 603 (1958).

THERMAL DIFFUSION

(Supplementary to Chapter XII, pages 489-532 in this volume)

For thermal diffusion in liquids, Drickamer and co-workers (73) successfully improved older attempts by Wirtz and Hiby [ref. (181), Chapter XII] for the calculation of the Soret coefficient. They tested their expression with a number of systems, (cf. Table A 12.1) which with a few exceptions, leads to remarkable agreement.

TABLE A 12.1
Observed and calculated thermal diffusion ratios*.

System	$T°C$	α_{obs}	α_{calc}
Sn-Bi	295	0.10	−0.15
Sn-Cd	295	0.35	0.325
Sn-Zn	375	4.10	4.14
Sn-Pb	295	1.90	1.09
Sn-Pb	450	0.83	0.46
Sn-Ga	295	0.18	0.12
Sn-Hg	295	−0.51	−0.54
Bi-Pb	295	1.13	0.64

* Taken from Winter and Drickamer (73).

REFERENCES

Book: Grew, K. E., Ibbs, T. L.: Thermal diffusion in Gases, Cambridge University Press, 1952.

General Bibliography

For additional papers concerned with thermal diffusion in gases see Reference list of appendix Chapter X "Diffusion in Gases".

1. Agar, J. N., Thermal diffusion and thermoelectric effects in solutions of electrolytes, *Revs. Pure and Appl. Chem. (Australia)* **8**, 1, 32 (1958).
1a. Agar, J. N., and Turner, J. C. R., Thermal diffusion in solutions of electrolytes, *Proc. Roy. Soc. (London)* A **255**, 307 (1960).
2. Alexander, K. F., Theory of thermal diffusion in liquids. I. The connection between kinetic and phenomenological theory of the transport-phenomena in continuous systems, *Z. physik. Chem. (Leipzig)* **203**, 181 (1954).
3. Alexander, K. F., Theory of thermal diffusion in liquids. II. Diffusion and thermal diffusion in binary liquid mixtures, *Z. physik. Chem. (Leipzig)* **203**, 223 (1954).
4. Alexander, K. F., and Dreyer, R., Separation of chlorine isotopes by liquid phase thermal diffusion, *Z. Naturforsch.* **10a**, 1034 (1955).
5. Becker, E. W., Thermal separation of gases at high pressures, *Z. Naturforsch.* **5a**, 457 (1950).
6. Becker, E. W., Effect of pressure on thermal diffusion in gases, *J. Chem. Phys.* **19**, 131 (1951).

7. Caskey, F. E., and Drickamer, H. G., Thermal diffusion in isotopic mixtures in the critical region, *J. Chem. Phys.* **21**, 153 (1953).

8. Chapman, J., and Tyrrell, H. J. V., Thermal diffusion potentials in non-isothermal systems. Part. 5. Measurements in the presence of a concentration gradient, *Trans. Faraday Soc.* **52**, 1218 (1956).

9. Clusius, K., and Bühler, H. H., Reactions with nitrogen[15]. XVI. Formation of nitrate in the oxidation of ammonia with hypobromite, *Helv. Chim. Acta* **37**, 3261 (1954).

10. Clusius, K., and Bühler, H. H., Separation tube. XIII. Preparation of the heavy carbon isotope C^{13} in pure state, *Z. Naturforsch.* **9 a**, 775 (1954).

11. Clusius, K., Bühler, H. H., Hürzeler, H., and Schumacher, E., XVI. Preparation of the isotope xenon-136, *Z. Naturforsch.* **10 a**, 809 (1955).

12. Clusius, K., and Hostettler, H. U., Behavior of sulfur dioxide in a thermal diffusion column, *Z. Naturforsch.* **12 a**, 83 (1957).

13. Clusius, K., and Huber, M., The separation tube. XIV. The separation swing. Thermodiffusion factors in the system CO_2-H_2, *Z. Naturforsch.* **10 a**, 230 (1955).

14. Clusius, K., and Huber, M., The separation tube. XV. The reversal of the thermal diffusion effect in mixtures of neon isotopes with ordinary and deuterated ammonia, *Z. Naturforsch.* **10 a**, 556 (1955).

15. Clusius, K., Huber, M., Hürzeler, H., and Schumacher, E., Separation tube. XVII. Preparation of rare isotope neon-21 of 99.6% purity, *Z. Naturforsch.* **11 a**, 702 (1956).

16. Clusius, K., Huber, M., Hürzeler, H., and Schumacher, E., Preparation of the rare isotope neon-21, *J. Chem. Phys.* **24**, 167 (1956).

17. Clusius, K., and Schumacher, E., Separation tube. XII. Preparation of pure argon[36] and enrichment of argon[38] to 90% with an auxiliary gas, *Helv. Chim. Acta* **36**, 969—984 (1953).

18. Clusius, K., Schumacher, E., Hürzeler, H., and Hostettler, H. U., XVIII. Preparation of pure rare isotopes argon-36 and argon-38, *Z. Naturforsch.* **11 a**, 709 (1956).

19. Corbett, J. W., and Watson, W. W., Thermal diffusion in krypton and argon, *J. Chem. Phys.* **25**, 385 (1956).

20. Danby, C. J., Lambert, J. D., and Mitchell, C. M., Separation of hydrocarbon isomers by thermal diffusion, *Nature* **177**, 1225 (1956).

21. Darken, L. S., and Oriani, R. A., Thermal Diffusion in solid alloys, *Acta Met.* **2**, 841 (1954).

22. Dickel, G., Busen, K. H., and Steiner, W., Transport-measurements in the separation tube, *Z. physik. Chem. (Frankfurt)* [N.S.] **17**, 1—10 (1958).

23. Dougherty, E. L., Jr., and Drickamer, H. G., A theory of thermal diffusion liquids, *J. Chem. Phys.* **23**, 295 (1955).

24. Dougherty, E. L., Jr., and Drickamer, H. G., Thermal diffusion and molecular motion in liquids, *J. Phys. Chem.* **59**, 443 (1955).

25. Drickamer, H. G., Mellow, E. E., and Tung, L. H., A modification of the theory of the thermal diffusion column, *J. Chem. Phys.* **18**, 945 (1950).

26. Emery, A. H., Jr., and Drickamer, H. G., Thermal diffusion in polymer solutions, *J. Chem. Phys.* **23**, 2252 (1955).

27. Emery, A. H., Jr., and Drickamer, H. G., Erratum: Thermal diffusion in polymer solutions, *J. Chem. Phys.* **24**, 620 (1956).

28. Giller, E. B., Duffield, R. B., and Drickamer, H. G., Thermal diffusion in the critical region. II, *J. Chem. Phys.* **18**, 1027 (1950).

29. Gillespie, L. J., and Breck, S., Thermal diffusion in ternary liquid mixtures, particularly aequeous solutions containing ferrous chloride, *J. Chem. Phys.* **9**, 370 (1941).

30. de Groot, S. R., On the thermodynamic theory of diffusion. Supplement VII, XVI., *Intern. Congr. Pure and Appl. Chem.*, (Paris) 18.—24. 7. (1957).

31. Grove, G. R., Foster, K. W., and Vallee, R. E., Gaseous thermal diffusion, *Phys. Rev.* **99**, 340 (1955).

32. Hirota, K., and Kobayashi, Y., Drickamer's modification of the theory of the thermal diffusion column, *J. Chem. Phys.* **21**, 246—249 (1953).

33. Hirota, K., and Kobayashi, Y, Continuous separation of gases by thermal diffusion. III. Separation under medium pressure, *J. Chem. Soc. Japan, Pure Chem. Sect.* **74**, 604 (1953).

34. van Itterbeck, A., and de Rop, W., Measurements of the velocity of sound in air under pressures up to 20 atmospheres combined with thermal diffusion, *Appl. Sci. Research* **6 A**, 21—28 (1956).

35. van Itterbeck, A., and de Rop, W., Measurements on thermal diffusion in hydrogen-nitrogen mixtures as a function of pressure, Proc. Joint Conf. on Thermodynam. Transport. Prop. of Fluids, London, July, 1957. (Pub. by *Inst. Mech. Engrs., London*, 1958).

36. Jeener, J., and Thomaes, G., On thermal diffusion in the liquid phase, *J. Chem. Phys.* **22**, 566 (1954).

37. John, H. F., and Bent, H. E., Separation of organic solutions by thermal diffusion, *J. Phys. Chem.* **60**, 1524 (1956).

38. Karger, W., Theory of the Soret effect in mixed electrolyte solutions, *Z. physik. Chem. (Frankfurt)* [N.S.] **5**, 233 (1955).

39. Korsching, H., A direct determination of thermal-diffusion coefficients in liquids, *Z. Naturforsch.* **10 a**, 242 (1955).

40. Langhammer, G., Pfennig, H., and Quitzsch, K., Thermal diffusion of macro-molecules in solution, *Z. Elektrochem.* **62**, 458 (1958).

41. Langhammer, G., and Quitzsch, K., Thermal diffusion in ternary mixtures containing one macromolecular component, *Z. physik. Chem. (Leipzig)* **208**, 131 (1958).

42. Lonsdale, H. K., and Mason, E. A., Thermal diffusion and the approach to the steady state in H_2-CO_2 and He-CO_2, *J. Phys. Chem.* **61**, 1544 (1957).

43. Moran, T. I., and Watson, W. W., Thermal diffusion factors for the noble gases, *Phys. Rev.* **109**, 1184 (1958).

44. Moran, T. I., and Watson, W. W., Thermal diffusion factors from column operation, *Phys. Rev.* **111**, 380 (1958).

45. Naylor, R. W., and Backer, O., Enrichment calculations in gaseous diffusion: large separation factor, *A. I. Ch. E. Journal* **1**, 95 (1955).

46. Pierce, N. C., Duffield, R. B., and Drickamer, H. G., Thermal diffusion in the critical region. I, *J. Chem. Phys.* **18**, 950 (1950).

47. Powers, J. E., The determination of the thermal diffusion constant in a batch thermo-gravitational column without reservoirs, Proc. Joint Conf. on Thermodynam. Transport. Prop. of Fluids, London, July, 1957. (Pub. by *Inst. Mech. Engrs., London*, 1958.)

48. Ramser, J. H., Theory of thermal diffusion under linear fluid shear, *Ind. Eng. Chem.* **49**, 155 (1957).

49. Raw. C. J. G., and Kyle, E., Thermal diffusion in hydrogen + boron trifluoride mixtures, *Trans. Faraday Soc.* **52**, 1216 (1956).

50. Rutherford, W. M., and Drickamer, H. G., Theory of thermal diffusion in liquids and the use of pressure to investigate the theory, *J. Chem. Phys.* **22**, 1157 (1954).

51. Rutherford, W. M., and Drickamer, H. G., The effect of pressure on thermal diffusion in n-paraffin hydrocarbon-CS_2 mixtures, *J. Chem. Phys.* **22**, 1284 (1954).

52. Rutherford, W. M., Dougherty, E. L., and Drickamer, H. G., Thermal diffusion in binary mixtures of CS_2 and hexane isomers, *J. Chem. Phys.* **22**, 1289 (1954).

53. Saxena, S. C., and Srivastava, B. N., Second approximation to the thermal-diffusion factor on the Lennard-Jones 12:6 model, *J. Chem. Phys.* **23**, 1571 (1955).

54. Saxena, S. C., and Mason, E. A., Higher approximations for the transport properties of binary gas mixtures. III. Isotopic thermal diffusion, *J. Chem. Phys.* **28**, 623 (1958).

54a. Saxena, S. C., and Mason, E. A., Thermal diffusion and the approach to the steady state in gases: II, *Molecular Physics* **2**, 379 (1959).

55. Saxena, S. C., Thermal diffusion of gas mixtures and determination of force constants, *Indian J. Phys.* **29**, 131 (1955).

55a. Saxena, S. C., and Watson, W. W., Isotope separation by a hot-wire thermal diffusion column, *Phys. Fluids* **3**, 105 (1960).

56. Saxton, R. E., Dougherty, E. L., and Drickamer, H. G., Thermal diffusion in binary liquid mixtures of molecules of simple symmetry, *J. Chem. Phys.* **22**, 1166 (1954).

57. Saxton, R. L., and Drickamer, H. G., Thermal diffusion in mixtures of tetrachlorethane with normal paraffin hydrocarbons, *J. Chem. Phys.* **22**, 1287 (1954).

58. Schumacher, E., Separation tube. X. Theory of the quantitative separation of gas mixtures, *Helv. Chim. Acta* **36**, 949 (1953).

59. Schumacher, E., and Clusius, K., Separation tube. *XI.* Quantitative separation of polycomponent mixtures with an auxiliary gas (separation of krypton and xenon with silicon tetrafluoride), *Helv. Chim. Acta* **36**, 961 (1953).

60. Seelbach, C. W., and Quackenbush, F. W., Thermal diffusion fractionation of industrial fat and oil derivates, *Ind. Eng. Chem.* **50**, 353 (1958).

61. Srivastava, B. N., and Madan, M. P., Thermal diffusion of gas mixtures and forces between unlike molecules, *Proc. Phys. Soc. (London)* **66 A**, 278 (1953).

62. Srivastava, B. N., and Saxena, S. C., Generalized relations for the thermal diffusion factor of inert gas mixtures with one invariable constituent, *Physica* **22**, 253 (1956).

63. Srivastava, B. N., and Srivastava, K. P., Force constants for unlike molecules on exp-six model from thermal diffusion, *Physica* **23**, 103 (1957).

64. Sullivan, L. J., Ruppel, T. C., and Willingham, C. B., Packed thermal diffusion columns, *Ind. Eng. Chem.* **49**, 110 (1957).

65. Thomaes, G., Thermal diffusion near the critical solution point, *J. Chem. Phys.* **25**, 32 (1956).

66. Thomas, W. J., and Watkins, S. B., The separation of common gases by thermal diffusion, *Chem. Eng. Sci.* **5**, 34 (1956).

67. Thomas, W. J., and Watkins, S. B., The separation of multicomponent mixtures of common gases by thermal diffusion, *Chem. Eng. Sci.* **6**, 26 (1957).

68. Thompson, C. J., Coleman, H. J., Ward, C. C., and Rale, H. T., Separation of organic sulfur compounds by means of thermal diffusion in the liquid phase, *Anal. Chem.* **29,** 1601 (1957).

69. Trevoy, D. J., and Drickamer, H. G., Thermal diffusion in binary liquid hydrocarbon mixtures, *J. Chem. Phys.* **17,** 1120 (1949).

70. Tichacek, L. J., Kmak, W. S., and Drickamer, H. G., Thermal diffusion in liquids; the effect of non-ideality and association, *J. Phys. Chem.* **60,** 660 (1956).

71. Tichacek, L. J., and Drickamer, H. G., Thermal diffusion near the critical solution temperature, *J. Phys. Chem.* **60,** 820 (1956).

72. Walther, J. E., and Drickamer, H. G., Thermal diffusion in dense gases, *J. Phys. Chem.* **62,** 421 (1958).

73. Winter, F. R., and Drickamer, H. G., Thermal diffusion in liquid metals, *J. Phys. Chem.* **59,** 1229 (1955).

74. White, J. R., and Fellows, A. T., Thermal diffusion efficiency and separation of liquid petroleum fractions, *Ind. Eng. Chem.* **49,** 1409 (1957).

75. Whitaker, S., and Pigford, R. C., Thermal diffusion in liquids, *Ind. Eng. Chem.* **50,** 1026 (1958).

APPENDIX — AUTHOR INDEX

Numbers in italics refer to the page on which the reference is listed. Numbers in parentheses are the reference numbers.